SECOND OPINION
An Introduction to Health Sociology

SECOND OPINION
An Introduction to Health Sociology

SECOND CANADIAN EDITION

Edited by *John Germov* | *Jennie Hornosty*

OXFORD
UNIVERSITY PRESS

OXFORD
UNIVERSITY PRESS

Oxford University Press is a department of the University of Oxford. It furthers the
University's objective of excellence in research, scholarship, and education by publishing worldwide.
Oxford is a registered trade mark of Oxford University Press in the UK and in certain other countries.

Published in Canada by
Oxford University Press
8 Sampson Mews, Suite 204, Don Mills, Ontario M3C 0H5 Canada

www.oupcanada.com

Library and Archives Canada Cataloguing in Publication

Second opinion : an introduction to health sociology / edited by John Germov, Jennie Hornosty.
— Second Canadian edition.

Includes bibliographical references and index.
ISBN 978-0-19-901813-0 (paperback)

1. Social medicine—Canada—Textbooks. 2. Health—Social aspects—Canada—Textbooks.
I. Germov, John, editor II. Hornosty, Jennie Mary, 1944–, editor

RA418.3.C3S43 2016   306.4'610971   C2016-901549-1

Cover image: Fanatic Studio/Getty Images; iStock.com/Larry Rains.

Oxford University Press is committed to our environment. This book is printed on
Forest Stewardship Council® certified paper and comes from responsible sources.

Printed and bound in the United States of America

1 2 3 4 — 20 19 18 17

For my wonderful sons,
Jason Hornosty and Justin Hornosty,
with love—
and hope for a peaceful and more equitable world.

Contents

Preface to the Second Canadian Edition

This thoroughly revised Canadian edition of *Second Opinion: An Introduction to Health Sociology* introduces readers to the sociology of health and illness through an accessible yet authoritative overview of key debates, research findings, and theories, with a particular emphasis on Canadian perspectives. Current Canadian material in the form of examples, research, and statistical information is integrated throughout the book. Critical approaches to health-related issues and a focus on social determinants of health as well as the contributions of Canadian researchers in this area are distinctive features of the book. A second unifying theme is a concern with explaining health inequalities; in this regard, the text examines the role of both structure and agency in creating and maintaining societal arrangements. Because health sociology is a complex and diverse area, rather than attempting to cover the entire field, the topics included in the book were chosen to reflect contemporary health-related issues that should be of special interest to Canadian students in the twenty-first century. A clear and straightforward writing style and special pedagogic features make the book student-friendly.

A growing number of scholars in the area of the sociology of health have examined the impact of various structural inequalities on the health outcomes of individuals. Research on the social determinants of health, such as income inequality, education, "race," environment, gender, Aboriginal status, and poverty, and the intersectionality of determinants, describes how such factors influence mortality and morbidity rates as well as the distribution and experience of illness within society. In addition to looking at these social determinants of health, Canadian researchers are looking at how economic and political inequalities—both within the country and on a global scale—affect health policy and the delivery of health services. A critical political economy approach situates health and illness within a historical context as well as examines how dominant values and ideologies influence decisions around health priorities at both a formal and informal level. These macro and structural perspectives have influenced my approach in putting together this second edition. At the same time, I have not ignored important contributions of the social constructionist tradition.

Each chapter in the book has seen revisions, some more substantial than others. In Chapters 2 and 3, for example, there is additional discussion of intersectionality and critical race theory. Chapter 4 still focuses on social class as a major determinant of health outcomes, but the intersectionality with other social determinants is explored in more detail. Chapter 6 on racialization and ethno-cultural diversity interrogates more critically notions of "race" and racialization. Chapter 7 further contextualizes Aboriginal peoples' health within the legacy of colonialism and the recent report of the Truth and Reconciliation Commission. Greater attention is given to the medicalization of men's health in Chapter 9; and the social construction of "normalcy" is addressed in the discussion of disability in Chapter 10. All the chapters were reviewed to incorporate the latest available data and reflect current debates and developments. Government cutbacks introduced by the previous federal Conservative government and changes to certain agencies meant that relevant comparable data were sometimes not available; for example, the cancellation of the *Health Policy Research Bulletin*, the elimination of Statistics Canada's mandatory long-form Census, and the closing of the Health Council of Canada that produced annual Progress Reports on health care and health-care delivery are just three examples that left gaps. While the new federal Liberal government is thankfully bringing back Statistics Canada's long-form census, the missing data cannot be recaptured; however, going forward, more reliable information should be available. It remains to be seen whether this government will also make other changes that would lead to more readily accessible and reliable health information.

As with the first edition, the key elements I incorporate in the book are a critical analytical focus, strong Canadian content, and an integrated approach including a discussion of contemporary theories and methodologies. Unlike some academics who purport neutrality, I reject the idea that our work can ever be value-free. The approaches we take or do not take, the questions we ask or do not ask, and the theories we choose to emphasize or ignore reflect our basic values and assumptions about how the world works. At the same time, as teachers we have a responsibility to present other perspectives and approaches, especially in books written for a student audience. It is my belief that this book successfully presents both my and my co-writers' values and assumptions as well as those of other perspectives. In some chapters, my personal views will be quite apparent: for example, I passionately believe that equal access to health care is an unalienable right and that one of the biggest challenges we face today as Canadians is the threatened erosion of our system of Medicare. However, this does not presume that all students will share or should share this view.

Structure and Content of the Book

Second Opinion assumes no prior knowledge of sociology and is intended for undergraduate students. The text is structured to provide a solid foundation in the sociology of health and illness and to map out the key dimensions of the social model of health, including the social determinants of health. As such, the book is divided into the following parts:

- Introduction: Health Sociology and the Social Model of Health
- Part 1: The Social Production and Distribution of Health and Illness
- Part 2: The Social Construction of Health and Illness
- Part 3: The Social Organization of Health Care: Politics, Values, and Professions
- Conclusion

The introduction provides the foundation for understanding sociological contributions to studying health and illness. Chapter 1 explains the development of the social model of health, reviews critiques of the biomedical model, and introduces students to "the sociological imagination" as a way to think critically about health issues. Chapters 2 and 3 specifically address some of the main theoretical perspectives and methodological approaches in health sociology. In Part 1, The Social Production and Distribution of Health and Illness, the focus is on health inequalities and the social determinants of health and their intersectionality with other determinants. Issues of class, gender, "race" and ethnicity, Aboriginal status, and the environment are the subject of separate chapters. Part 2, The Social Construction of Health and Illness, covers the debates about changing conceptions of health and illness; this section looks at the medicalization of society, the ways in which disabilities and chronic illnesses are constructed, and at issues around aging, death, and dying. The five chapters in Part 3, The Social Organization of Health Care: Politics, Values, and Professions, examine different aspects of the social organization of health care and health-care delivery, including, in Chapter 12, the dominant influence of the medical profession on other health professions and on health-care delivery. Chapter 13, on Canada's health-care experience, situates Medicare's development in a historical context. The role and values of the pharmaceutical industry and its interactions with Health Canada is the subject of Chapter 14, while Chapters 15 and 16, respectively, explore the current problems faced by the nursing profession and reasons for the growth of complementary and alternative medicines today. The conclusion provides a summary of major themes in the book, outlines some future trends in health sociology, and suggests ways students can use their critical thinking skills.

Overview of Key Features

Pedagogic features, an important aspect of the book, are found in each chapter and provide students with important learning tools. New to this edition, the visual program has increased to include photos as well as more figures and tables. These are important features for visual learners, and they provide visual interest for all students. In addition, all chapters and pedagogic features that were part of the first Canadian edition have been revised and updated. These features include the following:

- A **summary chart** that summarizes the social determinants of health at the beginning of the book.
- A **chapter overview** appears at the beginning of each chapter and includes a series of questions and a short summary of the chapter to encourage a questioning and reflective approach to the topic.
- **Key terms and concepts** are highlighted in bold in the text and defined in separate margin notes.
- A **summary of main points** appears at the end of each chapter to help students identify the important issues covered in the chapter.
- **Sociological reflection exercises** include self-directed or class-based exercises that help students apply their learning and highlight the relevance of sociological analysis.
- **Discussion questions** allow students to revisit key themes and ideas raised throughout the chapter.
- **Further investigation questions** help students to prepare for examinations and other assignments.
- **Further reading** lists some key books to allow students to research topics of particular interest.
- **Recommended chapter-specific web resources** allow students to explore different subject areas further.

Acknowledgements

It seemed not long after the first Canadian edition of Second Opinion was published that Suzanne Clark, Seniors Acquisitions editor of Oxford University Press, approached me about doing a second edition. Thank you for your confidence, Suzanne, and for getting the ball rolling. In writing this second edition I have been especially fortunate to work with Amy Gordon, as developmental editor. Amy, you've been fantastic to work with! I am most appreciative of your editorial advice, encouragement, enthusiasm, and patience, and I've learned a great deal. Karri Yano was my diligent copy editor. Thanks, Karri, for all your work. As well, thank you to Michelle Welsh and others at Oxford University Press who assisted with the final stages of the publication process.

I would like to acknowledge and give special thanks to my three Canadian contributors for their revisions to their respective chapters: Zelda Abramson, Associate Professor in Sociology at Acadia University; Patricia Armstrong, Distinguished Research Professor of Sociology at York University; and Joel Lexchin, MD, Professor in the School of Health Policy and Management at York University. As before, it's been great working with you. Thanks also to the anonymous reviewers who provided helpful suggestions and feedback at different stages of this process. Thank you as well to the Australian contributors for giving me the opportunity to work with their material. However, I alone bear responsibility for the Canadian content.

Writing would be a lonely endeavour were it not for the support of close friends and family. Katy, Francesca, Debbie & George, Charlene, Allan, Jon lifted my spirits through emails and phone conversations even though we no longer live in the same city; thanks for listening to my concerns, my feelings, regaling me with stories, and providing words of support. Luda, thanks for our newly-found and warm friendship. Especially, I also want to acknowledge and thank Susan and John, my long-time dear friends who have always been there for me.

Most important, I want to express my appreciation for and to and thank my family. I am most fortunate to have two wonderful children, Jason Hornosty and Justin Hornosty, who, during this process as always, have been supportive, loving, and encouraging. In a strange way, it is for them that I decided to do this book. I am also fortunate to have wonderful stepchildren: Michael Richardson, his partner, Meaghan Charlebois, and son, Liam; and Rebecca Richardson, her partner, Phil Allen, and daughters, Gemma and Mika. As well, I want to acknowledge my late partner, C. James (Jim) Richardson, who played such an important role in my academic life and with whom I first developed a course on the sociology of health and illness. And I want to remember my brother, Roy Hornosty, also a sociologist and a source of inspiration, who passed away some years ago. Also I want to acknowledge my former colleague and dear friend, Vanda Rideout, who recently passed away.

INTRODUCTION
Health Sociology and the Social Model of Health

The health of the people is really the foundation upon which all their happiness and all their powers as a state depend.

—Benjamin Disraeli

We live in a health-obsessed age: we are bombarded daily with messages from health authorities and professionals, fitness gurus, and various social and mainstream media advising us to "do this" and "not do that." The central message is that it is our individual responsibility to eat well, exercise, and live a healthy lifestyle. Yet amid this torrent of information, we hear very little about the social origins of disease or our societal responsibility to address the living and working conditions that impact our health. This is where a *sociological second opinion* can help.

It is often wise to get a second opinion. We seek second opinions about a whole range of things, but why do we need a second opinion about health and illness? What could sociology have to offer? And what is sociology, anyway? This book sets out to answer these questions and show the relevance of sociology to the study of health and illness. We all have a basic idea of what a medical opinion entails, even if we do not always fully understand that opinion. A sociology of health and illness offers a different perspective—a second opinion—by focusing on the social determinants that make us well or unwell.

At the heart of health sociology is a belief that many health problems have social origins. Health sociology thus asks us to look beyond medical opinions and individual cures to the way society is organized. When individuals suffer ill health and require health care, some of the causes and cures can lie in the social context in which people live and work. We can say, in fact, that health, illness, and the health-care system are by-products of the way a society is organized. This book shows you how the social, cultural, economic, and political features of society affect an individual's chance of health and illness.

This introductory part of the book provides an overview of health sociology: what it is, its major theoretical perspectives, and the types of health research it draws upon. Specifically, the Introduction consists of three chapters:

- Chapter 1 introduces the social model and the social determinants of health, and highlights the limitations of biomedical approaches. It also explains what is distinctive about a sociological perspective and how this perspective helps us analyze and understand health problems.
- Chapter 2 explores the main theoretical perspectives used in health sociology.
- Chapter 3 outlines methodological approaches and some key issues and debates sociologists encounter when researching health.

CHAPTER 1
Imagining Health Problems as Social Issues

John Germov & Jennie Hornosty

Since 2006, Parliament Hill has hosted free lunchtime yoga sessions to promote health and fitness. Is this an activity that all Ottawa residents can enjoy? Who might miss out? What social conditions are barriers to making healthy lifestyle choices?

Overview

- What social patterns of health and illness exist?
- What is the social model of health and how does it differ from the medical model?
- What are the social determinants of health?
- What is sociology and how can it be used to understand health and illness?

This chapter introduces the sociological perspective and demonstrates how this perspective is used to understand a wide range of health issues. While conventional approaches to health and illness focus on the biology and behaviour of individuals, health sociology focuses on the social determinants of health and illness, such as income, education, food security, the environment, employment, and working conditions. Health sociologists look for social patterns of illness, such as the variation in health status between such groups as women and men, the poor and the wealthy, immigrants and native-born, or the Aboriginal and non-Aboriginal populations. They seek social rather than biological or psychological explanations to explain why some groups of people get sicker and die sooner than others. Throughout this chapter, we will see examples of how health and illness can be analyzed sociologically using a social model of health that views health problems as social issues.

Introduction: The Social Context of Health and Illness

If we are ill, we tend to seek medical opinions and treatments to make us well. When we think of health and illness, we often conjure up images of doctors in white coats and of high-tech hospitals. Our personal experience of illness means that we tend to view it in an individualistic way—as a product of bad luck, poor lifestyle, or genetic fate. As individuals, we all want quick and effective cures when we are unwell, and thus we turn to medicine for help. Yet this is only part of the story.

Health and illness are also social experiences. For example, even the highly individualized and very personal act of suicide occurs within a social context. In 2011, of 3728 suicide-related deaths in Canada 75 per cent were male, with the highest rates occurring in the 45–49 and 50–54 age groups (Statistics Canada, CANSIM, table 102-0551). In fact, the social patterning of suicide was first highlighted in the late nineteenth century by the sociologist Émile Durkheim (1858–1917). While Durkheim acknowledged individual reasons for a person's committing suicide, he found that suicide rates varied between countries and between different social groups within a country.

The social context of health and illness is evident when we compare the life expectancy (LE) figures of various countries. Although there have been important gains in life expectancy over the last two decades, the benefits have been unevenly distributed (Usdin, 2007).

As we all know, LE in the least developed countries (UN classification) is significantly lower than that in industrially developed and comparatively wealthy countries, such as Canada, Australia, and the US. For example, the average LE at birth of people living in the least developed countries of the world in 2012 was 62 years with the African regions registering the lowest LE at 58 years. This is 20 to 25 years less than the life expectancy for developed countries, such as Canada, which has an average LE of 82 years (WHO, 2014). As Table 1.1 shows, LE varies among developed countries as well as between developed and developing countries.[1] Therefore, the living conditions of the country in which you live can have a significant influence on your chances of enjoying a long and healthy life. Table 1.1 also shows figures for health-adjusted life expectancy (HALE), which represents the number of years people can expect to live without chronic illness or disability; the figure for Canada is 71 and 73 for men and women, respectively.

By international standards, Canada ranks near the top of the LE and HALE scales, slightly below Australia and Japan. However, this is not due to any biological advantage in the Canadian gene pool but is, rather, a reflection of our distinctive living and working conditions. We can make such a case for two basic reasons. First, LE can change in a short period of time and, in fact, did increase for most countries during the twentieth century. For example, LE in Canada has increased by more than 20 years since 1920, which is too short a timeframe for any genetic improvement to occur in a given population (Statistics Canada, 2010a). Second, data compiled over decades of immigration show that the health of immigrants comes to reflect that of their host country over time, rather than their country of origin. The longer immigrants live in their new country, the more their health mirrors that of the local population (Beiser, 2005; Marmot, 1999; Newbold & Danforth, 2003; Veenstra, 2009b). This tendency has been referred to as the "healthy immigrant effect."

While the average Canadian LE figure is comparatively high, it is still important to distinguish between different social groups within Canada. Life expectancy figures are crude indicators of population health and actually mask significant health inequalities among social groups within a country. Those living in the poorest neighbourhoods (lowest quintile) have a life expectancy that is between 2.3 and 4.7 years less than those in the highest income quintile. In Canada, those in the lowest socio-economic group have the highest rates of illness and premature death, use preventive services less, and have higher rates of illness-related behaviours such as smoking (McIntosh et al., 2009; Raphael, 2009b, c).

As well, both Aboriginal Canadian men and women have an LE that is five to fourteen years less than the national average (Raphael, 2012a). Suicide rates among First Nations youth are five to seven times higher than for non-Aboriginal youth, while suicide rates for Inuit youth are among the highest in the world, at 11 times the national average (Health Canada, 2005c). Suicide rates among Canadian non-Aboriginal populations (16.3 per 100,000 males of all ages) are significantly lower than rates in Aboriginal populations (56.3 per 100,000 males) (Suicide in Canada, 2013, available at www.med.uottawa.ca/sim/data/Suicide_e.htm).

A further example of the social context of health and illness is seen when we consider global differences in maternal and neonatal mortality rates. According to the WHO, one

---

1. We recognize that these are problematic terms but are the ones most frequently found in the literature. Other terms used to make the same distinction are those of "global South" and "global North" or "low income" versus "high income."

Table 1.1 Life Expectancy and Health-Adjusted Life Expectancy at Birth

| Country | Life Expectancy (LE) 2012 | | Health-Adjusted Life Expectancy (HALE) 2012 | |
	Men	Women	Men	Women
Canada	80	84	71	73
Aboriginal Canadians Status First Nations 2001*	70.4	75.5	N/A	N/A
Afghanistan	58	61	49	49
Australia	81	85	71	74
China	74	77	67	69
Cuba	76	81	65	69
Denmark	78	82	69	72
France	79	85	69	74
Germany	78	83	70	73
India	64	68	56	58
Iraq	66	74	58	63
Italy	80	85	71	74
Japan	80	87	72	77
Nigeria	53	55	46	49
Sweden	80	84	71	73
United Kingdom	79	83	70	72
US	76	81	68	71

*Note: There is not more recent data for Aboriginal Canadians available.

Source: Adapted from data found at (1) WHO *World Health Statistics* 2014; (2) WHO Global Health Observatory (GHO) data ; (3) Statistics Canada, 2012.

indicator of health inequity worldwide is maternal mortality. In 2013, there were an estimated 289,000 maternal deaths globally (WHO, 2014). Although there has been a decline, developing countries continue to account for 99 per cent of such deaths annually (WHO, 2011). The **lifetime risk of maternal death** varies significantly by country. For example, in 2013 the lifetime risk of maternal death was 1 in 49 in Afghanistan; 1 in 5200 in Canada; 1 in 13,600 in Sweden; and 1 in 1800 in the US (World Bank, 2013).

The impact of health inequality begins in at birth. Despite substantial progress in reducing the under-five mortality rate globally, the inequities between high-income and low-income countries remain large. As seen in Figure 1.1 the under-five mortality rate in low-income countries in 2012 was more than 13 times the average rate in high-income countries (WHO, 2014, pp. 13–14). There is no natural cause for these differences; rather they reflect the differences in social disadvantage that different peoples experience.

Lifetime risk of maternal death
The probability that a 15-year-old female will die eventually from a maternal cause assuming that current levels of fertility and mortality (including maternal mortality) do not change in the future.

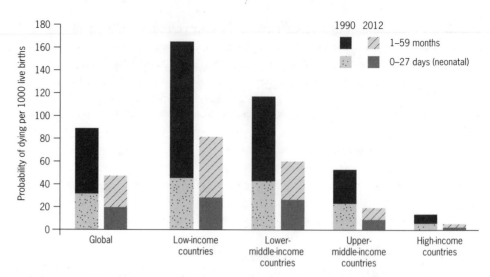

Figure 1.1 Differences between Low-Income and High-Income Countries in Neonatal and Infant Mortality Rates, 1990 and 2012

Note: Each bar indicates the total under-five mortality rate as the sum of the neonatal mortality rate (0–27 days; lighter-shaded bars) plus the combined mortality rate for infants aged 1–11 months and children aged 1–4 years (darker-shaded bars).

Source: WHO. (2014). *World health statistics.* p. 14, http://apps.who.int/iris/bitstream/10665/112738/1/9789240692671_eng.pdf.

Health sociology concerns the study of such social patterns of health and illness. It provides a second opinion to the conventional medical view of illness, derived from biological and psychological explanations by exploring the social context of health and illness—the social, economic, cultural, and political features of society that influence why some groups of people get sicker and die sooner than others. To find answers to why such health inequalities exist, we need to look beyond the individual and investigate the social origins of illness. To help us do that we need to develop our "sociological imagination."

Introducing the Sociological Imagination: A Template for Doing Sociological Analysis

What is distinctive about the sociological perspective? In what ways does it uncover the social structure that we often take for granted? How is sociological analysis done? The American sociologist C. Wright Mills (1916–1962) answered such questions by using the expression **sociological imagination** to describe the distinctive feature of the sociological perspective (see Box 1.1 for more on C. Wright Mills's life). The sociological imagination is "a quality of mind that seems most dramatically to promise an understanding of the intimate realities of ourselves in connection with larger social realities" (Mills, 1959, p. 15). According to Mills, the essential aspect of thinking sociologically, or seeing the world through a sociological imagination, is making a link between "private troubles" and "public issues."

sociological imagination
A term coined by C.W. Mills to describe the sociological approach to analyzing issues. We see the world through a sociological imagination, or think sociologically, when we make a link between personal troubles and public issues.

As individuals, we may experience personal troubles without realizing they are shared by other people as well. If certain problems are shared by groups of people, they may have a common cause and be best dealt with through some form of social or collective action. In the late 1960s, the phrase "the personal is political" became popular in the women's liberation movement. The phrase encapsulates the sociological imagination by linking women's personal experiences to wider social and political issues. For example, issues of sexism, discrimination, domestic violence, and access to child care and contraception were traditionally regarded as "personal troubles" and often considered taboo topics not fit for public discussion, leaving many women to suffer individually in silence. However, these personal problems were, and continue to be, shared by many women and can only be addressed through public debate and social reforms, such as pay equity, sexual harassment and sex discrimination legislation, and employment equity legislation. As Mills (1959,

Box 1.1 C. Wright Mills (1916–1962): "The Promise" of *The Sociological Imagination*

The Sociological Imagination, first published in 1959 and translated into 17 languages, was named as the second most popular book of the twentieth century by members of the International Sociological Association (Brewer, 2004). It is in the first chapter, "The Promise," that Mills lays out what he means by "the sociological imagination" as the necessary tool to understand how people's lives are shaped by circumstances or structural forces, in particular time and space, beyond their control; that is, to show the link between private troubles of people and the broader public issues. This has become a core concept in the sociological perspective.

C. Wright Mills was born in Waco, Texas, in 1916 and died at the age of 45 of a heart attack. He received his PhD in Sociology from Wisconsin University and spent the bulk of his career at Columbia University in New York. During this relatively short life, he produced 10 major works, many of them considered sociology classics. He was an outspoken critic both of the discipline and American society. Although an outsider to the profession, he influenced generations of radical sociologists and public intellectuals, and today there are numerous awards in his name. Todd Gitlin (2000), in the "Afterword" to the fortieth anniversary of *The Sociological Imagination*, referred to Mills as "a bundle of paradoxes." Gitlin writes,

He was a radical disabused of radical traditions, a sociologist disgruntled with the course of sociology, an intellectual frequently skeptical of intellectuals, a defender of popular action as well as a craftsman . . . one of the few contemporaries whose intelligence, verve, passion, scope—and contradictions—seemed alert to most of the main moral and political traps of his time . . . a best-selling sociologist who decided to write pamphlets, a populist who scrambled to find what was salvageable within the Marxist tradition, a loner committed to politics . . . yet hell-bent on finding, or forging, the leverage with which to transform America root and branch. (p. 229)

p. 226) states, "many personal troubles cannot be solved merely as troubles, but must be understood in terms of public issues—public issues must be revealed by relating them to personal troubles." Similarly, to understand the prevalence of cancer today, we need to look beyond individual experiences to get at the root causes.

The sociological imagination can be viewed as consisting of four interrelated parts (Willis, 2004):

1. Historical factors: how the past influences the present.
2. Cultural factors: how our culture impacts on our lives.
3. Structural factors: how particular forms of social organization shape our lives.
4. Critical factors: how we can improve on what exists.

This four-part sociological imagination template is an effective way to understand how to think and analyze in a sociological way. Figure 1.2 represents the sociological imagination template as a diagram that is easy to remember. Anytime you want to sociologically analyze a topic, simply picture this diagram in your mind.

Sociological analysis involves applying these four aspects to the issues or problems under investigation. For example, a sociological analysis of why manual labourers have a shorter life expectancy would examine how and why the work done by manual labourers affects their health, by investigating the following:

1. Historical factors: such as how practices in the past influence present work structures and ethics so as to make manual workplaces dangerous.
2. Cultural factors: such as the cultural value of individual responsibility and belief systems.
3. Structural factors: such as the way work is organized, the role of managerial authority, the rights of workers, and the role of the state.
4. Critical factors: such as alternatives to the status quo (increasing the effectiveness of occupational health and safety legislation, for instance).

Similarly, to understand the poor health outcomes among our Aboriginal peoples, we need to look at factors such as the history of colonialism, the impact of residential schools,

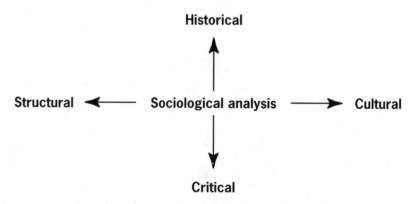

Figure 1.2 The Sociological Imagination Template

poverty and inequality, issues of self-government, and ways to incorporate the voices and perspectives of Aboriginal peoples.

By using the four parts of the sociological imagination template, you begin to "do" sociological analysis. It is worth highlighting at this point that the template simplifies the process of sociological analysis. When analyzing particular topics, it is more than likely that you will find that the parts overlap with one another, making them less clear-cut than the template implies. It is also probable that for some topics, parts of the template will be more relevant and prominent than others—this is to be expected. The benefit of the template is that it serves as a reminder of the sorts of issues and questions a budding sociologist should be asking.

Is Society to Blame? Introducing the Structure–Agency Debate

As individuals we are brought up to believe that we control our own destinies, especially our health: It is simply up to individuals to "do what they wanna do and be what they wanna be." However, this belief ignores the considerable influence of society. Sociology makes us aware that, individually, we cannot ignore the social conditions that influence our lives. We are social animals and are very much the product of our environment, from the way we dress to the way we interact with one another. We are all influenced by the **social structure**, such as our cultural customs and our **social institutions**. The idea of social structure serves to remind us of the social or human-created aspects of life, in contrast to purely random events or products of nature (Lopez & Scott, 2000). In other words, the social structure is a product of human action and interaction.

Understanding the structure of society enables us to examine the social influences on our personal behaviour and our interactions with others. Yet, to what extent are we products of society? How much **agency** do we have over our lives? Are we solely responsible for our actions or is society to blame? These questions represent a key debate in sociology, often referred to as the **structure–agency debate**. There is no simple resolution to this debate, but it is helpful to view structure and agency as interdependent—that is, humans shape and are simultaneously shaped by society. In this sense, structure and agency are not either/or propositions in the form of a choice between constraint and freedom but are part of the interdependent processes of social life. Therefore, the social structure should not automatically be viewed in a negative way—that is, as only serving to constrain human freedom—since in many ways the social structure enables us to live by providing health care, welfare, education, and work. As Mills maintained, an individual "contributes, however minutely, to the shaping of this society and to the course of its history, even as he is made by society and by its historical push and shove" (1959, p. 6). Mills was clearly a product of the "historical push and shove" of his social structure, as he uses the masculine *he* to refer to both men and women—a usage now seen as dated and sexist.

One way to think about the interdependence of structure and agency is to think of society as having a skeleton (social structure) that links its parts together. The "social skeleton" in Figure 1.3 shows the basic features of our social structure and is a way of conceptualizing how our society is organized. For example, the type of economy we have has influenced our culture and our political system. Different social groups form as a result of how social institutions are structured. Social classes emerge from the economic system: culture, laws, and education influence male and female roles, and attitudes toward people

social structure
The recurring patterns of social interaction through which people are related to each other, such as social institutions and social groups.

social institutions
Formal structures within society—such as health care, government, education, religion, and the media—that are organized to address identified social needs.

agency
The ability of people, individually and collectively, to influence their own lives and the society in which they live.

structure–agency debate
A key debate in sociology over the extent to which human behaviour is determined by social structure.

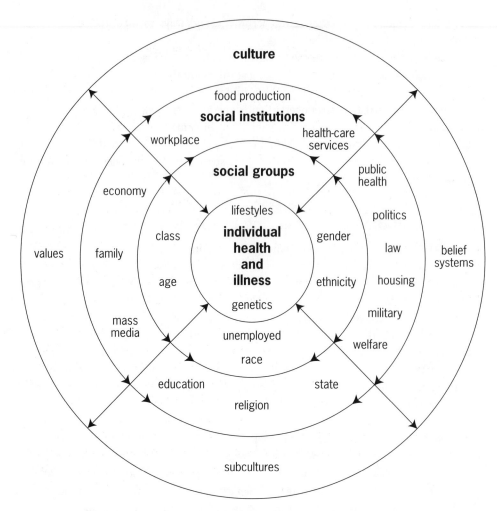

Figure 1.3 The Social Skeleton: Health, Illness, and Structure–Agency

whose appearance may vary from the majority or who act differently from the majority (e.g., gay/lesbian and transgender peoples, Indigenous peoples, and members of ethnic groups). The two-way arrows indicate that the various parts of the social skeleton are interrelated, and also that we exercise agency in our daily lives by which we can influence the way society is structured. Although customs and traditions dictate expected modes of behaviour, as individuals we have the scope to consciously participate in what we do. We can make choices about whether simply to act or to modify or change our roles.

To paraphrase Karl Marx, people make history but not necessarily under the conditions of their choosing. Although we are born into a world not of our making and in countless ways our actions and thoughts are shaped by our social environment, we are not simply "puppets on strings." Humans are sentient beings—that is, we are self-aware and thus have the capacity to think and act individually and collectively to change the society into which we are born. Structure and agency may be in tension, but they are interdependent—that is, one cannot exist without the other. Sociology is the study of the relationship between the individual and society; it examines how "we create society at the same time as we are created by it" (Giddens, 1986, p. 11).

The History of the Social Origins of Illness: Social Medicine and Public Health

Recognition of the social origins of health and illness can be traced to the mid-nineteenth century with the development of "social medicine" (coined by Jules Guérin in 1848) or what more commonly became known as **public health** (sometimes referred to as social health, community medicine, or preventive medicine). At this time, infectious diseases, such as cholera, typhus, smallpox, diphtheria, and tuberculosis, were major killers for which there were no cures and little understanding of how they were transmitted. During the 1800s, a number of people, such as Louis-René Villermé (1782–1863), Rudolf Virchow (1821–1902), John Snow (1813–1858), Edwin Chadwick (1800–1890), and Friedrich Engels (1820–1895), established clear links between infectious diseases and poverty (Porter, 1997; Rosen, 1972).

Engels, Karl Marx's collaborator and patron, in *The Condition of the Working Class in England* (1958/1845), made a strong case for the links between disease and poor living and working conditions as an outcome of capitalist exploitation. He used the case of "black lung," a preventable lung disease among miners, to make the point that

> the illness does not occur in those mines which are adequately ventilated. Many examples could be given of miners who moved from well-ventilated to badly venti-lated mines and caught the disease. It is solely due to the colliery owners' greed for profit that this illness exists at all. If the coal owners would pay to have ventilation shafts installed the problem would not exist. (1958/1845, p. 281)

Engels also noted the differences in the death rates between labourers and profes-sionals, claiming that the squalid living conditions of the working **class** were primarily responsible for the disparity and that "filth and stagnant pools in the working class quar-ters of the great cities have the most deleterious effects upon the health of the inhabitants" (1958/1845, p. 110).

In 1854, a cholera epidemic took place in Soho, London. John Snow, a medical doctor, documented cases on a city map and investigated all of the 93 deaths that had occurred within a well-defined geographical area. After interviewing residents, he was able to estab-lish that people infected with cholera had sourced their water from the same public water pump in Broad Street. Snow came to the conclusion that the water from the pump was the source of cholera, and at his insistence the pump's handle was removed and the epidemic ceased (McLeod, 2000; Porter, 1997; Rosen, 1972; Snow, 1936/1855). This case is famous for being one of the earliest examples of the use of **epidemiology** to understand and pre-vent the spread of disease.

Virchow, often remembered in medical circles for his study of cellular biology, also made a clear case for the social basis of medicine, highlighting its preventive role when he claimed

> [m]edicine is a social science, and politics nothing but medicine on a grand scale . . . if medicine is really to accomplish its great task, it must intervene in political and social life. The improvement of medicine would eventually prolong human life, but improvement of social conditions could achieve this result even more rapidly and successfully. (Cited in Porter, 1997, p. 415; and Rosen, 1972, p. 39).

public health
Policies, programs, and services designed to keep citizens healthy and to improve the quality of life. The focus is on enhancing the health status and well-being of the general population rather than just looking at the health of individual persons.

class (or social class)
A position in a system of structured inequality based on the unequal distribution of power, wealth, income, and status. People who share a class position typically share similar life chances.

epidemiology/social epidemiology
The statistical study of patterns of disease in the population. Originally focused on epidemics, or infectious diseases, the field now covers non-infectious conditions, such as stroke and cancer. Social epidemiology is a subfield aligned with sociology that focuses on the social determinants of illness.

state
A collection of government and government-controlled institutions, including parliament (the government and opposition political parties), the public-sector bureaucracy, the judiciary, the military, and the police.

Virchow was a significant advocate for public health care and argued that the **state** should act to redistribute social resources, particularly to improve access to adequate nutrition. Therefore, social medicine and the public health movement grew from the recognition that the social environment played a significant role in the spread of disease (Porter, 1997; Rosen, 1972). In other words, the infectious diseases that afflicted individuals had social origins that necessitated social reforms to prevent their onset (see Rosen, 1972 and 1993, and Waitzkin, 2000, for informative histories of social medicine; Porter, 1997, for a very readable history of medicine in general; Bloom, 2002, for a history of medical sociology; and White, 2001).

In Britain, Edwin Chadwick was a key figure in the development of the first Public Health Act (1848) based on his "sanitary idea" that disease could be prevented through improved waste disposal and sewerage systems, particularly by removing cesspools of decomposing organic matter from densely populated areas, as well as through the introduction of high-pressure flushing sewers and food hygiene laws to protect against food adulteration.

The Social Origins of Health and Illness in Canada

Canadian health researchers have focused on the social origins of health and illness by examining how people's living conditions impact their health. These conditions are referred to as the **social determinants of health** (Raphael, 2009a, b). Contrary to the assumption that individuals have personal control over their living conditions, these factors are imposed upon individuals by the types of communities, housing situations, work settings, social service agencies, and educational institutions with which they interact (Mikkonen & Raphael, 2010). Such an approach is necessary to explain existing and pervasive health inequities in Canada today. Marc Lalonde's *A New Perspective on the Health of Canadians,* released in 1974, was the first official recognition by the government that social and economic factors play a role in an individual's health status. Similarly, the Ottawa Charter for Health Promotion (1986), which emerged from the First International Conference on Health Promotion held in Ottawa, signalled a new multi-level discourse around health promotion. It identifies the fundamental prerequisites for health as "peace, shelter, education, food, income, a stable eco-system, sustainable resources, social justice and equity" (Ottawa Charter for Health Promotion, 1986).

social determinants of health
Refers to the social and economic environments in which people live that determine their health, including housing, job security, food security, working conditions, education, income, social class, gender, Aboriginal status, and the social safety net. The quality of these determinants is a reflection of how society is organized and how it distributes its economic and social resources.

Although the Public Health Agency in Canada was established only in 2004, from Canada's beginning in 1867, Parliament had jurisdiction over certain aspects of health. The first Quarantine Act was adopted in 1872 and remained largely unchanged until the severe acute respiratory syndrome (SARS) outbreak in 2003. Today the social determinants of health approach has been taken up by various public health units in the country as well as by the Public Health Agency of Canada. In his first and subsequent reports, Dr Butler-Jones, Canada's first chief public health officer, makes clear that existing health inequities can only be explained by looking at the interaction of social and economic factors on individuals' health status and behaviours (Butler-Jones, 2008, 2012).

Despite the influence of social medicine and the success of public health measures in the 1800s, health care developed in an entirely different direction. The insights of social medicine were, in fact, cast aside for almost a century as the new science of biomedicine gained ascendancy.

The Rise of the Biomedical Model

In 1878, Louis Pasteur (1822–1896) developed the germ theory of disease, whereby illness is caused by germs infecting organs of the human body: this model of disease became the foundation of modern medicine. Robert Koch (1843–1910) refined this idea with the doctrine of **specific etiology** (meaning "specific cause of disease") through "Koch's postulates": a set of criteria for proving that specific bacteria caused a specific disease (Capra, 1982; Dubos, 1959). The central idea was that specific micro-organisms caused disease by entering the human body through air, water, food, and insect bites (Porter, 1997). This mono-causal model of disease, which came to be known as the medical or **biomedical model**, became the dominant medical paradigm by the early 1900s.

While early discoveries led to the identification of many infectious diseases, there were, however, few effective cures. One of the earliest applications of the scientific understanding of infectious disease was the promotion of hygiene and sterilization procedures, particularly in surgical practice, to prevent infection through the transmission of bacteria (Capra, 1982). Until the early 1900s, it had been common practice to operate on patients without a concern for hygiene or the proper cleaning and sterilization of equipment, resulting in high rates of post-operative infection and death following surgery.

The biomedical model is based on the assumption that each disease or ailment has a specific cause that physically affects the human body in a uniform and predictable way, meaning that universal cures for people are theoretically possible. It involves a mechanical view of the body as a machine made up of interrelated parts, such as the skeleton and circulatory system. The role of the doctor is akin to a body mechanic, identifying and repairing the broken parts (Armstrong & Armstrong, 2003, pp. 12–45). Throughout the twentieth century, medical research, training, and practice increasingly focused on attempts to identify and eliminate specific diseases in individuals, and thus moved away from the perspective of social medicine and its focus on the social origins of disease (Najman, 1980).

Before the development of medical science, quasi-religious views of health and illness were dominant, whereby illness was connected with sin, penance, and evil spirits: the body and soul were conceived as a sacred entity beyond the power of human intervention. Therefore, the "body as machine" metaphor represented a significant turning-point away from religious notions toward a secular view of the human body. The influence of scientific discoveries, particularly through autopsies that linked diseased organs with symptoms before death, as well as Pasteur's germ theory, eventually led people to endorse a belief in the separation of body and soul. In philosophical circles, this view came to be known as mind/body dualism and was sometimes referred to as **Cartesian dualism**, after the philosopher René Descartes (1590–1650). Descartes, famous for the saying "I think, therefore I am," suggested that although the mind and body interacted with one another, they were separate entities. Therefore, the brain was part of the physical body, whereas the mind (the basis of individuality) existed in the spiritual realm and was apparent evidence of a god-given soul. Such a distinction provided the philosophical justification for secular interventions on the physical body in the form of medical therapies. Since the body was merely a vessel for the immortal soul or spirit, medicine could rightly practise on the body while religion could focus on the soul (Capra, 1982; Porter, 1997). The assumption of mind/body dualism underpinned the biomedical model, whereby disease was seen as located in the physical body, and thus the mind, or mental state of a person, was considered unimportant.

specific etiology
The idea that there is a specific cause or origin for each specific disease.

biomedicine/biomedical model
The conventional approach to medicine in Western societies, based on the diagnosis and explanation of illness as a malfunction of the body's biological mechanisms. This approach underpins most health professions and health services, which focus on treating individuals, and generally ignores the social origins of illness and its prevention.

Cartesian dualism
Also called mind/body dualism and named after the philosopher Descartes, it refers to a belief that the mind and body are separate entities. This assumption underpins medical approaches that view disease in physical terms and thus ignore the psychological and subjective aspects of illness.

The Limits of the Biomedical Model

While the biomedical model represented a significant advance in understanding disease and resulted in beneficial treatments, it has come under significant criticism from both within medicine and across a range of social and behavioural disciplines, such as sociology and psychology. The major criticism is that the biomedical model underestimates the complexity of health and illness, particularly by neglecting social, economic, and psychological factors (Armstrong & Armstrong, 2003). Features of the biomedical model that are subject to criticism can be grouped under the following terms and phrases:

- the fallacy of specific etiology
- objectification and medical scientism
- **reductionism** and **biological determinism**
- **victim blaming**

reductionism
The belief that all illnesses can be explained and treated by reducing them to biological and pathological factors.

biological determinism
An unproven belief that individual and group behaviour and social status are an inevitable result of biology.

victim blaming
The process whereby social inequality is explained in terms of individuals being solely responsible for what happens to them in relation to the choices they make and their assumed psychological, cultural, and/or biological inferiority.

The Fallacy of Specific Etiology

The idea of a specific cause for a specific disease, referred to as specific etiology, applies only to a limited range of infectious diseases (Armstrong & Armstrong, 2003). As early as the 1950s, René Dubos (1959, p. 102) argued that "most disease states are the indirect outcome of a constellation of circumstances rather than the direct result of single determinant factors." Furthermore, Dubos noted that not all people exposed to an infectious disease contracted it. For example, we may all come into contact with someone suffering from a contagious condition like the flu, but only a few of us will get sick. Therefore, disease causation is more complex than the biomedical model implies and is likely to involve multiple factors, such as physical condition, nutrition, and stress, which affect an individual's susceptibility to illness (Dubos, 1959).

Objectification and Medical Scientism

The biomedical model, underpinned by mind/body dualism and a focus on repairing the "broken" parts of the machine-like body, can lead to the objectification of patients. Since disease is viewed only in physical terms as something that can be objectively observed, treating "it" takes primacy over all other considerations, and patients may become objectified as "diseased bodies" or "cases" rather than treated as unique individuals with particular needs. This form of criticism often underpins claims of doctors' poor interpersonal and communication skills. Such a situation is also related to what Fritjov Capra (1982) calls "medical scientism"—that is, a reverence for scientific methods of measurement and observation as the most superior form of knowledge about understanding and treating disease. Therefore, patients' thoughts, feelings, and subjective experiences of illness are considered "unscientific" and are mostly dismissed.

Reductionism and Biological Determinism

A further criticism of the biomedical model is its reductionism and its mechanical conception of the body (Armstrong & Armstrong, 2003). The development of medical science has led to an increasing focus on smaller and smaller features of human biology for the cause and cure of disease—from organs to cells to molecules and most recently to genes. By reducing its focus on disease to the biological, cellular, and genetic levels, medicine has ignored or downplayed the social and psychological aspects of illness. In concentrating on the pathology within an individual body, patients and their suffering are divorced from their social environment, and the disease is treated as if it occurred in a social vacuum. Not only does this marginalize the importance of social support networks, it also ignores the role played by social factors, such as poverty, poor working conditions, racism, and discrimination, in affecting an individual's physical and mental health.

A related outcome of reductionism has been an ever-growing number of medical specialties, such as cardiology (heart specialty) and nephrology (kidney specialty) based on the assumption that each body part and function can be treated almost in isolation from the others. Such an approach has fuelled the search for "magic bullet" cures, resulting in huge expenditures on medical drugs, technology, and surgery. This approach has also led to a curative and interventionist bias in medical care, often at the expense of prevention and non-medical alternatives.

Reductionism can also lead to biological determinism: a form of social Darwinism that assumes people's biology causes or determines their inferior social, economic, and health status. Biological determinism underpins most elitist, racist, and sexist beliefs. For example, some people argue that the poor are poor because they are born lazy and stupid. Such views have often been used to justify slavery and exploitation of people of colour, of women, of children, and of workers in general; biological determinism is a convenient "explanation" that doesn't interrupt the status quo, particularly when those at the top of the social ladder espouse such views. When people argue that social or health inequalities are biologically determined, the implication is that little can or should be done to change those inequalities. Although such beliefs have no scientific validity, they have not vanished from our society and are the basis of so-called common-sense views of the world.

Victim Blaming

A final criticism of the biomedical model is its tendency toward victim blaming through the individualization of health problems (Ryan, 1971) because it locates the cause and cure of disease as solely within the individual. As Capra states, "[i]nstead of asking why an illness occurs, and trying to remove the conditions that lead to it, medical researchers try to understand the biological mechanisms through which the disease operates, so that they can then interfere with them" (1982, p. 150). Therefore, the individual body becomes the focus of intervention, and health and illness become primarily viewed as an individual responsibility. A preoccupation with treating the individual has the potential to legitimate a victim-blaming approach to illness, either in the form of genetic fatalism (your poor health is the result of poor genetics) or as an outcome of poor **lifestyle choices**. By ignoring the social context of health and illness and locating primary responsibility for illness within the individual, there is little acknowledgement of social responsibility—that is, the need to ensure healthy living and working environments.

Our critique of the biomedical model has necessarily been a generalization and does not imply that all doctors work from within the confines of this model. In fact, many of the criticisms of the model have come from those within the medical profession itself. Of interest is a recent research report by the Canadian Medical Association (CMA) on the role of physicians in achieving health equity that encourages doctors to engage differently with patients so as to address the social determinants of health. The report concludes that

lifestyle choices
The decisions people make that are likely to impact their health, such as diet, exercise, smoking, alcohol, or drug-use. The term implies that people are solely responsible for choosing and changing their lifestyle.

"Socio-economic factors play a larger role in creating (or damaging) health than either biological factors or the health care system" (Canadian Medical Association, 2013, p. 16). While it is now widely accepted that the causes of illness are multifactorial, it is still, however, fair to claim that the biomedical model remains the dominant influence on medical training and practice.

Rediscovering the Social Origins of Health and Illness

In the 1960s, Thomas McKeown (1979, 1988), a doctor and epidemiologist, was one of the earliest authors to expose the exaggerated role of medical treatment in improving population health. McKeown argued that the medical profession and governments had overestimated the influence of medical discoveries on improvements in life expectancy during the twentieth century. McKeown (1976, 1979) found that mortality (death) from most infectious diseases had declined *before* the development of effective medical treatments, meaning that improvements in life expectancy were not substantially due to medical intervention. Estimates reported by McKinlay and McKinlay (1977) are that only 10–15 per cent of increased longevity since 1990 is the result of improved health care. Raphael (2009b, p. 8) writes that in Canada dramatic declines in mortality had already happened by the time vaccines for major diseases, such as measles and polio, and treatments for scarlet fever, typhoid, and diphtheria appeared. The same general trend occurred in Great Britain, Australia, and the United States.

McKeown (1979) suggests that the major reasons for the increase in life expectancy were not due to medical treatments but, rather, to rising living standards, particularly improved nutrition, which increased people's resistance to infectious disease. While McKeown's work highlighted the importance of social, non-medical interventions for improving population health, Simon Szreter (1988) provides a more complex argument. He suggests that rather than the "'invisible' hand of rising living standards" (p. 37) it was the state's redistribution of economic resources that increased life expectancy through improved working conditions and a range of public health measures, such as improved public housing, food regulation, education, and sanitation reforms. Canadian researchers such as Armstrong and Armstrong (2003), Bryant (Bryant et al., 2010a), Coburn (2001), Raphael (2009b, 2012b), and others make the same argument.

While it is impossible to determine the exact contribution of public health measures, rising living standards, and medicine to improving population health, the significance of McKeown's work and subsequent findings, as well as research focusing on the social determinants of health, has been to highlight the importance of addressing the social origins of health and illness. As McKeown (1979) states, "there is need for a shift in the balance of effort, in recognition that improvement in health is likely to come in future— from modification of the conditions which lead to disease, rather than from intervention in the mechanism of disease after it has occurred" (p. 198). It is important to note that McKeown himself was not anti-medicine but wanted to reform medical practice so that it focused on prevention of what he saw were the new threats to health: personal behaviour, as evidenced through smoking, alcohol consumption, drug use, diet, and lack of exercise. Therefore, he still viewed health care in individualistic terms, by focusing preventive efforts at the level of modifying the behaviour of individuals. Others who focus more on structural factors have argued that it is organization of society and how a society distributes its material resources that significantly determine the health of individuals and populations (Chernomas & Hudson, 2013; Raphael, 2006, 2009a).

Lifestyle and Risk: From Risk-Taking to Risk-Imposing Factors

Since McKeown's work, there has been considerable growth in preventive efforts aimed at individuals, particularly in the form of identifying **risk factors**. While the notion of "lifestyle diseases" or "diseases of affluence" is a clear indication of the social origins of health and illness, many preventive efforts, in the form of **health promotion**, have tried to reform the individual rather than pursue wider social reform (ignoring the fact that diseases of affluence affect the least affluent much more). By solely targeting risk-taking individuals, there is a tendency to blame the victim by ignoring the social determinants that give rise to risk-taking in the first place, such as stressful work environments, the marketing efforts of corporations, and peer group pressure. Individuals are told to control stress, for example, by exercising more, getting more sleep, and eating healthier foods. Such an approach assumes that individuals can control all the factors that determine their health. Medical researchers and public health workers frequently emphasize the importance of traditional risk factors, such as cholesterol, diet, and physical activity, in decreasing a person's risk of heart disease and stroke.

In comparison to social determinants, however, these are relatively poor predictors (Raphael, 2009b, c, 2012b). More importantly, as Michael Marmot (1999, p. 1) incisively puts it, there is a need to understand the "causes of the causes." In other words, rather than just focusing on risk-taking individuals, there is also a need to address "risk-imposing factors" and "illness-generating social conditions" (Ratcliffe et al., 1984; Waitzkin, 1983)—the social, cultural, economic, and political features of society that create unhealthy products, habits, and lifestyles. Socio-demographic factors, such as unemployment rate, Aboriginal status, minority status, income, poverty, and education, are in fact better predictors of health status (Raphael, 2006, 2009a, 2012a).

There is no denying the significant role medicine has played in the treatment of illness, particularly in trauma medicine, palliative care, and general surgery, as well as in the prevention of illness through immunization. The primary expertise of doctors lies in fighting disease and treating individuals once they are ill. As we have seen, however, this is only part of the story. The reductionist focus of the biomedical model on individual pathology obscures the social origins of illness. The World Health Organization (WHO) effectively acknowledged this limitation of the model in 1946, when it included in its constitution the now-famous holistic definition of *health* as "a state of complete physical, mental and social well-being and not merely the absence of disease or infirmity" (WHO, 1946). This often-quoted definition implies that a range of biological, psychological, and social factors determine health. Furthermore, health is conceptualized as "not merely the absence of disease" but, rather, in the positive sense of "well-being." While this definition has been criticized for its utopian and vague notion of "complete well-being," it is of symbolic importance because it highlights the need for a broader approach to health than the biomedical model alone can deliver.

risk factors
Conditions that are thought to increase an individual's susceptibility to illness or disease, such as abuse of alcohol, poor diet, or smoking.

health promotion
Any combination of education and related organizational, economic, and political interventions designed to promote individual behavioural and environmental changes conducive to good health, including legislation, community development, and advocacy.

biopsychosocial model
An extension of the biomedical model, it is a multifactorial model of illness that takes into account the biological, psychological, and social factors implicated in a patient's condition. As with the biomedical model, it focuses on the individual patient for diagnosis, explanation, and treatment.

ecological model
Derived from the field of human ecology, and when applied to public health, it suggests that an understanding of health determinants must consider the interaction of social, economic, geographic, and environmental factors.

social model of health
Focuses on social determinants of health, such as the social production, distribution, and construction of health and illness, and the social organization of health care. It directs attention to the prevention of illness through community participation, political action, and social reforms that address living and working conditions.

The widespread recognition of the biomedical model's limitations, from those within and outside the medical profession, has led to the development of a variety of multifactorial models, such as the **biopsychosocial model** (Cooper et al., 1996; Engel, 1977, 1980), the web of causation (MacMahon & Pugh, 1970), and the **ecological model** (Hancock, 1985). While these models represent a significant advance over the biomedical model in acknowledging the multiple determinants of health, to greater and lesser degrees they remain focused on health interventions aimed at the individual, particularly through life-style/behaviour modification and health education. An explicitly **social model of health** that focuses on people's living conditions is necessary to substantially highlight the social determinants of illness and to propose health interventions at the population and community level (Ashton & Seymour, 1988; Baum, 2002; Chernomas & Hudson, 2013; Raphael, 2003, 2006, 2009a, 2012c; Waitzkin, 1983; WHO, 2011).

Holmes, Greene, and Stonington (2014) argue that there are benefits to reconceptualizing global health in terms of global social medicine. A social model of health, or what they term "social medicine," provides the "critical analytic and methodological tools to elucidate who gets sick, why and what we can do about it" (p. 476). Global health research and practice must seriously consider the social and political aspects of health to understand the fundamental causes of disease and to deliver appropriate global health interventions. As an example, they point to the work of V.K. Nguyen (2010), who described how the first waves of HIV treatment programs in West Africa were weakened by a focus on drug therapy that excluded wider social contexts. Recognizing that patients on therapy had nutritional needs (given the extensive poverty in the region), the aid organizations provided them with food. This, however, had the unintentional consequence of creating an incentive for patients to continue their risky behaviour, once infected, in order to receive food aid for their families. The program only became successful when it was recognized that poverty reduction for the entire community was required.

A Sociological Second Opinion: The Social Model of Health

The "social model of health," generally referred to in Canada as the social determinants of health approach, focuses attention on the societal level of health determinants and health intervention. It is consistent with the new public health paradigm, which combines traditional health promotion that focuses on individual behaviour with health measures designed to mitigate the effects of social inequality. The social model approach is drawn primarily from the field of health sociology, and has been used as a general umbrella term to refer to approaches that focus on the social determinants of health and illness (see Broom, 1991; Gillespie & Gerhardt, 1995; Mikkonen & Raphael, 2010; Raphael, 2006, 2009a). As Dorothy Broom (1991) states, "the social model locates people in social contexts, conceptualises the physical environment as socially organised, and understands ill health as a process of interaction between people and their environments" (p. 52). It is one of the aims of this book to map out the social model in more detail through a **political economy** lens to explain the underlying societal factors that give rise to the social determinants of health people experience. Table 1.2 contrasts the key features of the biomedical

political economy
An approach that emphasizes the links between people's health and the political, economic, and ideological conditions of a society.

model with the social model, focusing on the various social determinants of health, to highlight the different focus, assumptions, benefits, and limitations of each model. It is important to emphasize that focusing on material conditions does not deny the existence of biological or psychological aspects of disease that manifest in individuals, or deny the

Table 1.2 Comparison of Biomedical and Social Models of Health: Key Characteristics

	Biomedical Model	**Social Model**
Focus	• Individual focus: acute treatment of ill individuals • Clinical services, health education, immunization	• Societal focus: living and working conditions that affect health • Public health infrastructure, legislation, social services, community action, equity, access issues
Assumptions	• Health and illness are objective biological states • Individual responsibility for health	• Health and illness are social constructions • Social responsibility for health
Key indicators of illness	• Individual pathology • Hereditary factors, sex, age • Risk-taking factors	• Social inequality • Social groups: class, gender, "race," ethnicity, age, occupation, unemployment • Risk-imposing/illness-inducing factors
Causes of illness	• Gene defects and micro-organisms (viruses, bacteria) • Trauma (accidents) • Risk-taking behaviour/lifestyle	• Political/economic factors: distribution of wealth, income, power, poverty, level of social services • Employment factors: employment and educational opportunities, stressful and dangerous work • Cultural factors (values, traditions), prejudice, discrimination (racism, sexism, homophobia)
Intervention	• Cure individuals via surgery and pharmaceuticals • Behaviour modification (non-smoking, exercise, diet) • Health education and immunization	• Public policy • State intervention to alleviate health and social inequities/inequalities • Community participation, advocacy and political lobbying
Goals	• Cure disease, limit disability, and reduce risk factors to prevent disease in individuals	• Prevention of illness and reduction of health inequities to aim for an equality of health outcomes • Find root causes of illness
Benefits	• Addresses disease and disability of individuals • Prevention of disease through immunization	• Addresses the social determinants of health and illness • Highlights the need for preventive measures that often lie outside the scope of the health system
Criticisms	• Disease focus leads to lack of preventive efforts • Reductionist: ignores the complexity of health/illness • Fails to take into account social origins of health/illness • Medical opinions can reinforce victim blaming	• Utopian goal of equality leads to unfeasible prescriptions for social change • Over-emphasis on the harmful side effects of medical approaches • Proposed solutions can be complex and difficult to implement in the short term • Sociological opinions can underestimate individual responsibility and psychological factors

need for medical treatment. Instead, this focus highlights that health and illness occur in a social context and that effective health interventions, particularly preventive efforts, need to move beyond the medical treatment of individuals. Exposing the social origins of illness necessarily implies that a greater balance between individual and social interventions is required, since the vast majority of health funding continues to be directed toward medical intervention. Therefore, the social model is not intended to replace the biomedical model but, rather, to coexist alongside it.

The social model assumes health is a social responsibility by examining the social determinants of individuals' health status and health-related behaviour. While the biomedical model concentrates on treating disease and risk-taking among individuals, the social model focuses on societal factors that are risk-imposing or illness-inducing (for example, toxic pollution, stressful work, food insecurity, discrimination, racism), and in particular highlights the health inequalities suffered by different social groups based on class, **gender**, **ethnicity**, **"race,"** occupation, and so on. What should be clear from the comparison offered in Table 1.2 is that health issues have a number of dimensions. Furthermore, it is important to note that these societal factors are not uni-dimensional, but rather are multi-faceted and intersect in complex ways to affect the health and well-being of individuals (Hankivsky et al., 2011). For example, to understand and address the multi-dimensional nature of health inequality in vulnerable and marginalized populations, such as Indigenous peoples or immigrants, one needs to explain how categories such as gender, ethnicity, socio-economic status, sexual orientation, and age "interact with and affect one another to produce differentially lived social inequalities among people" (de Leeuw & Greenwood, 2011, p. 55).

The social model approach logically implies that any attempts to improve the overall health of the community need to address overall living and working conditions, such as poverty, food security, employment opportunities, housing, issues of racism, workplace health and safety, social services, and cultural differences. The social model gives equal priority to the prevention of illness along with the treatment of illness and aims to alleviate health inequalities and inequities. Such issues necessitate state interventions and community participation—including social services and public policies (such as pollution controls, workplace safety, guaranteed living wage)—which lie outside the strict confines of the health system or individuals' control. The social model helps us explain why different groups of people within Canada as well as people living in different parts of the world have such different health outcomes. A critical political economy approach goes a step further in that it considers how forces such as globalization and neo-liberalism affect the way societies are organized. Such an approach can help challenge people's current perception and beliefs and encourage them to think critically about how things could be different (Coburn, 2006). The social model makes it clear that many of the causes of sickness lie outside the strict confines of the health system or individuals' control.

> These inequities in health, avoidable health inequalities, arise because of the circumstances in which people grow, live, work, and age, and the systems put in place to deal with illness. The conditions in which people live and die are, in turn, shaped by political, social, and economic forces. (WHO, Commission on the Social Determinants of Health, 2008)

gender
This term refers to the socially constructed categories of feminine and masculine (the cultural values that dictate how men and women should behave), as opposed to the categories of biological sex (female or male).

ethnicity
Sociologically, the term refers to a shared cultural background, which is a characteristic of all groups in society. As a policy term, it is used to identify immigrants who share a culture that is markedly different from that of Anglo-Canadians. In practice, it often refers only to immigrants from non-English-speaking backgrounds (NESB migrants).

"race"
A term without scientific basis that uses skin colour and facial features to describe allegedly biologically distinct groups of humans. It is a social construction that is used to categorize groups of people and usually implies assumed (and unproven) intellectual superiority or inferiority.

The Three Main Dimensions of the Social Model of Health

The social model arose as a critique of the limitations and misapplications of the bio-medical model, such as its inability to effectively explain and address health inequalities experienced by various social groups (for example, Indigenous peoples, those living in poverty, immigrants, rural Canadians, etc.). Sociological research and theorizing that underpins the social model of health is comprised of three main dimensions or themes, which are reflected in the structure of this book:

1. The Societal Production and Distribution of Health and Illness

This dimension of the social model highlights that many illnesses are socially produced; that is, they are an outcome of people's material and living conditions. For example, ill-nesses arising from environmental contaminants, substandard housing, food insecurity, or unhealthy/unsafe workplaces are beyond an individual's control and therefore need to be addressed through legislation and appropriate policies at a societal level. Furthermore, there is an unequal distribution of wealth and income in society, and both are important determinants of health. For example, those in the lower socio-economic quintiles suffer higher rates of morbidity and mortality. As well, income is a determinant of other experi-ences, such as education, food security, employment, and quality of early life (Raphael, 2009b, p. 9). A focus, therefore, on the social production and distribution of health exam-ines the role that living and working conditions can play in causing and alleviating illness.

2. The Social Construction of Health and Illness

This dimension refers to how definitions of health and illness can vary among cultures and change over time—what is considered a disease in one culture or time period may be considered normal and healthy elsewhere and at other times. For example, homosex-uality was once considered a psychiatric disorder despite the lack of scientific evidence of pathology. It is no longer medically defined as a disorder. This is an example of how cul-tural beliefs, social practices, and social institutions shape or construct the ways in which health and illness are understood and experienced. Notions of health and illness are not necessarily objective facts or static states, but can be **social constructions** that reflect the culture, politics, and morality of a particular society at a given point in time.

social constructions
The socially created characteristics of human life based on the idea that people actively construct reality, meaning it is neither natural nor inevitable. Therefore, notions of normality/abnormality, right/wrong, and health/illness are subjective human creations that should not be taken as a given or universal.

3. The Social Organization of Health Care

This dimension of the social model concerns the way a particular society organizes, funds, and utilizes its health services. A central focus of study has been the dominant role of the medical profession, which has significantly shaped health policy and funding to benefit its own interests, largely to the detriment of nurses and to allied and alternative health prac-titioners. Unequal relationships between the health professions can prevent the efficient use of health resources and the optimal delivery of health care to patients. The state also plays a central role in shaping health-care delivery through public policy. For example, neo-liberal government policies put emphasis on the market and the private sector as the source of economic wealth and growth. This results in cutbacks in social programs and a growing gap between the rich and poor. In the health sector these policies mean a decrease in public expenditures for health, privatization of health services, and dismantling of pub-lic health infrastructure (Navarro, 2008, p. 153).

Conclusion

A common accusation made of sociology is that it is just common sense dressed up in unnecessary jargon. The subject matter of sociology is familiar, and as members of society it is easy to think we should all be experts on the subject. It is this familiarity that breeds suspicion and sometimes contempt. All disciplines have specialist concepts to help classify their subject matter, and sociology is no different. Sociological concepts, such as those you have been introduced to in this chapter, are used to impose a sense of intellectual order on the complexities of social life; they are a form of academic shorthand to summarize a complex idea in a word or phrase.

As this chapter has shown, to understand the complexity of health and illness we need to move beyond biomedical approaches and incorporate a social model of health. Sociology enables us to understand the links between our individual experiences and the social context in which we live, work, and play. With a sociological imagination, seeing health problems as social issues can be a healthy way of opening up debate on a range of topics previously unimagined.

Summary

- Much of health sociology has arisen as a critique of the dominance of the medical profession and its biomedical model.
- Health sociology examines social patterns of health and illness, particularly various forms of health inequality, and seeks to explain them by examining the influence of society. When groups of people experience similar health problems, there are likely to be social origins that require social action to address them.
- Health sociology challenges individualistic and biological explanations of health and illness through a social model of health that involves three key dimensions: the social production and distribution of health, the social construction of health, and the social organization of health care.
- The social model (generally referred to in Canada as the social determinants of health approach) concerns itself with searching for the root causes of health inequalities.
- The social model helps us make sense of differences in morbidity and mortality between groups within a society as well as differences among societies.
- The sociological imagination, or sociological analysis, involves four interrelated features—historical, cultural, structural, and critical—that can be applied to understand health problems as social issues.

Key Terms

agency

biological determinism

biomedicine/biomedical
  model

biopsychosocial model

Cartesian dualism

class (or social class)

ecological model

epidemiology/social
  epidemiology

ethnicity

gender

health promotion	reductionism	social model of health
lifestyle choices/factors	risk factors	social structure
lifetime risk of maternal death	social construction/ constructionism	sociological imagination
political economy	social determinants of health	specific etiology
public health		state
"race"	social institutions	structure–agency debate
		victim blaming

Sociological Reflection: A Sociological Autobiography

Apply the four parts of the sociological imagination template to explain the person you have become. In other words, write a short sociological autobiography by briefly noting the various things that have influenced you directly or indirectly in terms of your beliefs, interests, and behaviour.

- Historical factors: how has your family background or key past events and experiences shaped the person you are?
- Cultural factors: what roles have cultural background, traditions, and belief systems played in forming your opinions and influencing your behaviour?
- Structural factors: how have various social institutions influenced you?
- Critical factors: have your values and opinions about what you consider important changed over time? Why or why not?

Repeat the sociological reflection, but this time apply the sociological imagination template to a health problem of interest to you. Briefly note any key points that come to mind under the four parts of the template. What insights can you derive by adopting a sociological imagination?

Discussion Questions

1. How can illness have social origins? Refer to the social skeleton in Figure 1.3 and give examples in your answer.
2. What are the advantages and limitations of the biomedical model?
3. What have been some of the consequences of the dominance of biomedical explanations for our understanding of health and illness?
4. Why did the insights of social medicine/public health approaches have such a limited influence over the development of modern medicine?
5. What are the three key dimensions of the social model of health? Provide examples of each in your answer. What are the advantages and limitations of the model?
6. In 1946, the WHO defined health as a state of complete physical, mental, and social well-being and not merely the absence of disease or infirmity. Why might some groups regard this definition as radical and utopian? Who might these groups be? What do you think of the definition?

Further Investigation

1. "The influence of the biomedical model is waning—the future belongs to public health." Discuss.
2. "Illness is simply a matter of bad luck, bad judgment, or bad genetics." Critically analyze this statement by applying a sociological imagination to explore the social origins of illness.

Further Reading

Armstrong, P., Armstrong, H., & Coburn, D. (Eds.). (2001). *Unhealthy times: Political economy perspectives on health and care in Canada*. Don Mills, ON: Oxford University Press.

Bryant, T. (2009). *An introduction to health policy*. Toronto, ON: Canadian Scholars' Press Inc.

Bryant, T., Raphael, D., & Rioux, M. (2010). *Staying alive: Critical perspectives on health, illness and health care* (2nd ed.). Toronto, ON: Canadian Scholars' Press Inc.

Chappell, N., & Penning, M. (2009). *Understanding health, health care, and health policy in Canada*. Don Mills, ON: Oxford University Press.

Chernomas, R., & Hudson, I. (2013). *To Live and die in America: Class, power, health and healthcare*. Halifax & Winnipeg: Fernwood Press.

Coburn, D., D'Arcy, C., & Torrance, G. (Eds.). (1998). *Health and Canadian society: Sociological perspectives* (3rd ed.). Toronto, ON: University of Toronto Press.

Commission on the Social Determinants of Health (CSDH). (2008). *Closing the gap in a generation: Health equity through action on the social determinants of health*. Final Report. Geneva: World Health Organization.

Conrad, P. (Ed.). (2005). *The sociology of health & illness: Critical perspectives* (7th ed.). New York, NY: Worth Publishers.

Hankivsky, O. (Ed.). (2011). *Health inequities in Canada: Intersectional frameworks and practices*. Vancouver: UBC Press.

Marmot, M., & Wilkinson, R.G. (Eds.). (2006). *Social determinants of health* (2nd ed.). Oxford, UK: Oxford University Press.

Navarro, V. (1976). *Medicine under capitalism*. New York, NY: Prodist.

Panitch, L., & Leys, C. (Eds). (2009). *Morbid symptoms: Health under capitalism*. Socialist Register 2010. London: Merlin Press.

Raphael, D. (Ed.). (2009). *Social determinants of health* (2nd ed.). Toronto, ON: Canadian Scholars' Press Inc.

Raphael, D. (Ed.). (2012). *Tackling health inequalities: Lessons from international experiences*. Toronto: Canadian Scholars' Press Inc.

Usdin, S. (2007). *The no-nonsense guide to world health*. Toronto, ON: Between the Lines.

Waitzkin, H. (2000). *The second sickness: Contradictions of capitalist health care* (2nd ed.). Lanham, MD: Rowman & Littlefield.

Web Resources

Canadian Centre for Policy Alternatives
   (CCPA)
www.policyalternatives.ca

Canadian Community Health Survey,
   2013, Annual Component (CCHS)
*www23.statcan.gc.ca/imdb/p2SV
   .pl?Function=getSurvey&SDDS=3226*

Canadian Institutes for Health Information
   (CIHI): Health Indicators, 2013
*https://secure.cihi.ca/free_products/
   HI2013_Jan30_EN.pdf*

Canadian Policy Research Networks (CPRN)
www.cprn.org

Canadian Public Health Association
www.cpha.ca

Centre for Social Justice
www.socialjustice.org

American Sociological Association (ASA):
   Medical Sociology Section
www2.asanet.org/medicalsociology/

Public Health Agency of Canada
www.phac-aspc.gc.ca/index-eng.php

Statistics Canada: Health Reports
*www.statcan.gc.ca/ads-annonces/82-003-x/
   index-eng.htm*

World Health Organization (WHO): Social
   Determinants of Health
www.who.int/social_determinants/en/

CHAPTER 2
Theorizing Health: Major Theoretical Perspectives in Health Sociology

John Germov & Jennie Hornosty

Is this woman sick because she has a poor immune system? Or is she sick because she is exposed to viruses and bacteria on the daily two-hour transit commute she must make because she doesn't earn enough money to afford an apartment in the city? Does her lengthy commute prevent her from getting a good night's sleep? How might other social circumstances affect her health?

Overview

- What is sociological theory?
- Why is sociological theory necessary?
- What are the main theoretical approaches in health sociology?

This chapter provides an overview of some of the main theoretical perspectives and approaches in health sociology: functionalism, Marxism, Weberianism, symbolic interactionism, feminism, post-structuralism/postmodernism, and human rights and anti-racist frameworks. In drawing out the key features, assumptions, and concepts of these different perspectives, this chapter aims to provide an appreciation of what sociological theory is and why it is important. Differences between theoretical perspectives and the different questions addressed by these perspectives are discussed. The chapter ends with a caution against confusing perspectives with specific theories.

Introduction: What Is Theory and Why Do We Need It?

A theory is an explanation of how things work and why things happen. Theories allow us to make sense of our world—they provide answers to the "how" and "why" questions of life—by showing the way certain facts are connected to one another. We often think of theory as somehow divorced from reality, but we actually make use of theories every day of our lives. For example, when some people suggest that violence in video games or in the lyrics of popular music may lead to increased acts of violence in the wider community, they are espousing a theory of why things happen. Such explanations generally reflect people's fundamental beliefs and values.

People frequently express everyday theories on the differences between women and men, rich and poor, Black and white, heterosexuals and homosexuals, to name but a few. Such theories can influence how people relate to one another, how tolerant they are of others, and whether they support social policies and laws aimed at addressing various forms of discrimination and inequality. So, rightly or wrongly, people have opinions or theories about how and why social life is the way it is. Such everyday theories or opinions are generally based on unacknowledged prejudices or assumptions and lack reliable supporting evidence.

Perhaps because of our familiarity with the subject matter of sociology—the study of social life and human behaviour—it is not unusual to be a little skeptical of sociological theories. While many of us do not understand the theories of chemistry and physics, we tend to accept them because of their practical applications to such things as medicines and technologies. Sociological theories (or social theories for short), on the other hand, appear at first glance to be impractical and seem to complicate a world we already know much about (Craib, 1992). What sets sociological theories apart from everyday opinions is that they attempt to explain social life by presenting a logical, detailed, and coherent account derived from systematically researched evidence.

Theoretical Perspectives in Health Sociology: An Overview

The Answer to the Great Question . . . Of life, the Universe and Everything . . . Is . . . Forty-two.

—Douglas Adams, *The Hitchhiker's Guide to the Galaxy*

As the above quote implies, the search for a "theory of everything" is likely to be a futile task. Even if we could construct a theory that explained every imaginable social problem, public issue, or human action, its complexity would likely be so great as to make it unusable. A theory attempts to simplify reality and generalize its common and related features relevant to the topic at hand. The sheer variety of social life and the diversity of human behaviour mean that there is no single sociological "theory of everything." As Fritjov Capra (1982) puts it, "[a]ll scientific theories are approximations to the true nature of reality . . . each theory is valid for a certain range of phenomena. Beyond this . . . new theories have to be found to replace the old one, or, rather, to extend it by improving the approximation" (p. 93).

As you read the chapters of this book and consult the wider literature, you will quickly become aware that there are many different and sometimes opposing social theories on a topic. Over the years, many social theories have been developed and advocated by sociologists, making it frustrating for those new to sociology to steer a course through the maze of theories that exist. One way to navigate through this theory maze is to start by grouping theories into the following theoretical perspectives and frameworks:

- structural functionalism
- Marxism
- Weberianism
- symbolic interactionism
- post-structuralism/postmodernism
- feminism
- human rights and anti-racist approaches

Theoretical perspectives are a form of shorthand to group similar theories of society together. Within each perspective there exist many individual theories developed by different writers, but they all tend to share the core features of the particular perspective. Any attempt to group theories in this way necessarily involves simplification by focusing on the similarities within the one perspective, at the expense of the differences between specific theories. For example, many Marxist theorists today would disagree with some of Karl Marx's ideas, but they would nonetheless still share the core assumptions and principles of a Marxist perspective.

A key distinction between perspectives is the purpose or the questions they address. For example, some authors are concerned with explaining social order, others with explaining social inequality, and others with understanding and promoting social change. While these concerns often overlap, they have caused considerable debate among sociologists about the appropriate uses of sociological knowledge. Some perspectives, such as functionalism, attempt to understand society as it currently exists and assert that they do not take part in advocating how social life ought to be. Other perspectives seek to use sociological knowledge to promote social change. For example, Marxist, feminist, and anti-racist perspectives propose alternatives to present social arrangements to overcome social and economic inequalities.

Another distinction between theoretical perspectives is the level of analysis in relation to the **structure–agency debate**. Whereas we can imagine that the natural world exists without our presence, it is difficult to imagine that a society could exist without humans (Giddens, 1997). Humans collectively "make" society through their daily social interactions and through the social institutions they create, support, reproduce, and reform. It is this interplay between **social structure** and human **agency** that sociologists seek to understand. Despite this common goal, sociologists continue to disagree over the extent to which individuals shape or are shaped by the social structure.

Sociological perspectives can be depicted broadly along a structure–agency continuum, with structuralist approaches at one end and agency approaches at the other. Structuralist approaches assume that social structures, such as the economic and political system, play a significant role in shaping individual and group behaviour—that is, basic societal structures are a determining factor in how you think, feel, and act, as well as in your chances of health, wealth, and happiness. Agency approaches, on the other hand, tend to focus on micro factors: they see society as the product of individuals' acting socially or collectively to make the society in which they live. Agency perspectives focus on small-scale aspects of social interaction—such as that which occurs between health professionals and patients—or the meanings people give to their experiences. Functionalism and Marxism tend to focus more on societal structures, whereas Weberianism, symbolic interactionism, and postmodernism are more focused on the role of agency. Those working within a feminist perspective generally draw on either symbolic interactionism or structural approaches. For our purposes, it is important to realize that most sociological theories fall somewhere between these two poles—indeed, many contemporary social theories attempt to integrate structure and agency. Few authors writing within any of the perspectives completely deny the roles that social structure or human agency play in any given social situation; nevertheless, these perspectives reflect different starting points for analysis and guide one's research questions.

structure–agency debate
A key debate in sociology over the extent to which human behaviour is determined by social structure.

social structure
The recurring patterns of social interaction through which people are related to each other, such as social institutions and social groups.

agency
The ability of people, individually and collectively, to influence their own lives and the society in which they live.

Key Features of Major Theoretical Perspectives

Table 2.1 summarizes the key features of the major theoretical perspectives in health sociology and how, "at a glance," they apply to health issues. The remainder of the chapter provides greater detail on each perspective.

Structural Functionalism

Émile Durkheim (1858–1917), Talcott Parsons (1902–1979), and Robert Merton (1910–2003) are the key theorists of structural functionalism, more commonly referred to simply as functionalism. Once the dominant theoretical paradigm in the United States, this perspective studies the way social structures function to maintain social order and stability. Functionalism focuses on large-scale social processes and is based on the assumption that a society is a system of integrated parts, each of which has certain needs (or **functional prerequisites**) that must be fulfilled for social order to be maintained. Hence, functionalists study various parts of society to understand how they interrelate and function to promote social stability.

Functionalism is sometimes referred to as "consensus theory" because of its concentration on how social order is reached and maintained in society. In viewing society as a social system of related parts, functionalism has been particularly influential in organizational studies and public-policy analysis, where it is often referred to as "systems theory." For example, it is not uncommon to find descriptions of the health system as consisting of inputs, outputs, processes, and roles.

While such an approach can be useful for describing the basic operation of the health system, it neglects the influence of political, economic, and ideological interests, all of which make the health system less consensual, ordered, or systematic than a functionalist perspective would depict. Critics of functionalism also highlight its conservative tendencies (due to its focus on social stability and consensus) and hence its difficulties in accounting for social conflict and social change (Ritzer, 1996). Since the 1980s, some theorists, such as Jeffrey Alexander (1947–), have attempted to address many of these criticisms through the development of the perspective of "neo-functionalism" (see Alexander, 1985, 1998).

The functionalist analysis of health care has been primarily influenced by the work of Talcott Parsons (1951a), who viewed the health of individuals as a necessary condition of a stable and ordered society. He conceptualized illness as a form of **deviance**—that is, he viewed it as stopping people from performing various social roles, such as paid work and caring for children, which were essential to the functioning of society. In Parsons's terms, "health is intimately involved in the functional pre-requisites of the social system . . . too low a general level of health, too high an incidence of illness, is dysfunctional . . . because illness incapacitates the effective performance of social roles" (1951b, p. 430). For Parsons, illness disrupts the normal functioning of society; it was important that the sick are encouraged to seek expert help so that they return to health and can perform their social roles. The pathway to health was achieved through the **sick role**—that is, the social expectations that dictate how an individual sick person is meant to act and be treated.

According to Parsons, the sick role involves a series of rights and responsibilities. Once sick, individuals have the right to be exempted from their normal social roles, such as those of parent, employee, or student. This exemption from performing their duties is legitimated by medical diagnosis and treatment. For example, students regularly have to provide medical certificates to support their case for missing an exam or not submitting work on time. A further right of the sick person is not to be held responsible for the illness. Since illness is generally beyond individuals' control, they should be able to rely on others to care for them while they are ill.

However, the sick also have certain responsibilities. For example, they are expected to seek medical assistance and comply with the recommended treatment. Moreover, they

functional prerequisites
A debated concept based on the assumption that all societies require certain functions to be performed for them to survive and maintain social order. Also known as functional imperatives.

deviance
Behaviour or activities that violate social expectations about what is normal.

sick role
A concept used by Talcott Parsons to describe the social expectations of how sick people are expected to act and of how they are meant to be treated.

Table 2.1   Main Theoretical Perspectives in Health Sociology

Theoretical Perspective	Key Theorists	Key Concepts	Focus of Analysis	Health Example
Structural Functionalism	Émile Durkheim Talcott Parsons Robert Merton	• Value consensus • Sick role • Society as comprising interrelated parts	• Structuralist focus: shows how various parts of society function to maintain social order	• The sick role (social expectations of how doctors and patients should behave) exposes the management of illness as a social experience
Marxism (and Critical Political Economy Approach)	Karl Marx Friedrich Engels Vicente Navarro Pat and Hugh Armstrong David Coburn Howard Waitzkin	• Class conflict • Capitalism • Medical-industrial complex • Commodification of health care • Social inequality	• Structuralist focus: shows how the unequal distribution of scarce resources in a capitalist society is based on class division and highlights who benefits and who is disadvantaged	• Analyzes the links between class and health status, and between class, medical power, and profit-maximization • Concerned with social inequalities in health • Looks at role of the state in health care
Weberianism	Max Weber George Ritzer Bryan Turner	• Bureaucracy • Ideal type • Rationalization • McDonaldization • Verstehen	• Combines a primary focus on agency, with structuralist tendencies • Looks at how the increasing regulation of social life takes place and how this may stifle human creativity • Considers forms of social inequality and conflict	• Examines how health professionals are increasingly subject to regulation and managerial control, producing greater efficiency and uniformity in health-care delivery, but potentially decreasing the effectiveness of patient care
Symbolic Interactionism	George H. Mead Erving Goffman Anselm Strauss Herbert Blumer	• The self • Labelling theory • Stigma • Total institutions • Negotiated order	• Agency focused: emphasizes how individual and small-group interaction construct social meaning in everyday settings to reproduce and change social patterns of behaviour	• Uncovers how and why certain forms of behaviour are treated as deviance, exposing the stigma, negative consequences, and biased treatment of social groups whose behaviour is deemed abnormal (e.g., homosexuality) • Looks at the meaning of illness for individuals
Feminism	Dorothy Smith Patricia Hill Collins bell hooks Ann Oakley Meg Luxton Arlie Hochschild	• Patriarchy • Gender • Sexual division of labour • The double day • Intersectionality	• Consists of a range of strands that are either structuralist or agency focused • Concerned with gender inequalities; seeks to explain and change the unequal position of women in society	• Exposes sexism, racism, biological determinism, and gender inequality in health research, theory, and treatment • Critique of the medicalization of women's lives • Emphasizes intersectionality
Post-structuralism/ Postmodernism	Michel Foucault Jacques Derrida Judith Butler Deborah Lupton	• Discourse • Panopticon • Surveillance • Performativity	• Agency focused: critiques theories based on universal truths and structuralist assumptions • Concentrates on subjectivity, diversity, and fragmentation	• Examines how certain discourses of normality and panoptic effects serve to discipline and control various social groups

are obliged to recover and then resume their normal social duties. Alexander Segall, a Canadian health sociologist, proposes a revision of the sick role to reflect the fact that everyday self-care behaviours include health maintenance activities as well as managing one's illness. He argues that there should be a separation of the informal sick role from the formal patient role and that there is a need to recognize that one can enter and exit the sick role without seeking medical assistance (Segall, 1997, as cited in Segall & Chappell, 2000).

The sick role concept directs attention to the social nature of the illness experience and focuses attention on the doctor–patient relationship. However, the concept's importance also lies in the many critiques it has inspired as a result of its limited application to chronic, terminal, and permanently disabling conditions, as well as in its uncritical acceptance of the role of the medical profession and its neglect of the limitations of the **biomedical model**. Critics point out that one's ability to take on the sick role is shaped by such factors as ethnicity, class, age, occupation, and gender. Under neo-liberalism (characteristic of Canada and other Western societies), the imperative of health is individualized. Cuts to health care and social programs and increased privatization also limit people's ability to take on the sick role. Although doctors remain the legitimators of sickness, not all individuals have the necessary "doctor–patient relationship" required for the completion of medical forms and referrals to legitimate their situation in times of crisis, as Mack (2014) learned from her experience after a bicycle accident in Vancouver. Despite injuries sustained in the accident that resulted in numerous physical limitations for a period of time, she experienced difficulties getting the necessary validation to access the "sick role," as she did not have a family doctor.

biomedical model
The conventional approach to medicine in Western societies, based on the diagnosis and explanation of illness as a malfunction of the body's biological mechanisms. This approach underpins most health professions and health services, which focus on treating individuals, and generally ignores the social origins of illness and its prevention.

Marxism

The term *Marxism* refers to a wide body of theory and political policies based on the writings of Karl Marx (1818–1883) and Friedrich Engels (1820–1895). Marx was a philosopher, economist, and sociologist (see Box 2.1 for more on Marx's life). He was also politically active, and since his death his writings have not only inspired many sociologists but have also laid the foundations for numerous political and social justice movements around the world. Marxism, sometimes referred to as "conflict theory" or "materialism," asserts that society is dominated by a fundamental conflict of interest between two social **classes**—the bourgeoisie (the capitalist class) and the proletariat (the working class)—that comprise the economic system of **capitalism**. The capitalist class expands its control by exploiting the labour power of the working class (Marx, 1967/1867, 1970/1845). Some "conflict theorists," such as Randall Collins (1975) and Ralf Dahrendorf (1959), while acknowledging a debt to Marx, no longer consider themselves Marxists, and have incorporated other forms of social conflict, found in organizational settings and social movements, into their theory.

class (or social class)
A position in a system of structured inequality based on the unequal distribution of power, wealth, income, and status. People who share a class position typically share similar life chances.

capitalism
An economic and social system based on the private accumulation of wealth.

The influence and contribution of Marxism in sociology is widespread, but the perspective's core concern remains class analysis, especially its emphasis on class struggle as the defining feature of social life and the catalyst of social change (toward its goal of changing the social relations of production). Although Marxist analysis has a structural focus, Marx argued that it is conscious human action (*praxis*) that changes society. For Marx, human beings are products of their society yet are capable of transforming their social conditions (Marx, 1964/1844, 1970/1845). This relationship between structure and agency is a dialectic. People make history but they do so under circumstances directly found, given, and transmitted from the past, not those of their own choosing (Marx, 1959/1869). Many working within the Marxist tradition are activists who are committed to fighting for social justice. For others, Marxism is an emotionally charged term because of its negative association with **socialism** and **communism**, both concepts that have been distorted by the media and by some conservative academics.

Much of Marx's theory has been reinterpreted and modified and is now often referred to as neo-Marxism. Critical theory is one such neo-Marxist approach, in which a diverse group of theorists, such as Herbert Marcuse, Jürgen Habermas, Douglas Kellner, and Max Horkheimer, emphasize the importance of mass culture in comparison with the economy and merge psychoanalysis with Marxism (Ritzer, 1996). A critical political economy perspective which focuses on social inequality is another approach inspired by the works of Marx (Bourgeault, 2006). The emphasis is on how material conditions, and the way society is organized, directly and indirectly affect individuals and communities.

A Marxist perspective on health and illness is reflected in the contemporary writings of Pat and Hugh Armstrong (2003); David Coburn (2000, 2001); Howard Waitzkin (1983, 2000); Vicente Navarro (1976, 1986, 2004, 2008); Dennis Raphael (2006, 2009) and Bob Connell (1988). A primary focus is on the impact of working and living conditions in capitalist society and how these contribute to illness, as well as on the role of the medical profession. In particular, Marxist perspectives have highlighted that the exploitation of workers and the pursuit of profit inherent in the structure of capitalism can create dangerous work environments and poor living conditions, resulting in higher mortality and morbidity rates among the working class.

Marxist analyses of health care also look at the professional power of doctors that serve class interests by placing profit maximization above access to optimal health care. Navarro, Armstrong and Armstrong, and Waitzkin have been strong critics of the medical profession's individualistic focus and its continued reliance on the biomedical model. By locating the cause and treatment of illness in individuals and ignoring what Waitzkin (1983, 2000) calls "illness-generating social conditions," the medical profession is viewed as performing an ideological function by masking the real causes of illness and thereby supporting the capitalist system. According to Navarro (1986, p. 35), in capitalist societies the influence of work on health "is of paramount importance" since workers "have no control over their work and, thus, over their lives, including their health." Canadian researchers Pat and Hugh Armstrong (2003) have examined how the drive for profits in the health-care sector leads to management strategies that intensify work by nurses and create additional stress on them. David Coburn (2001) shows the effect of neo-liberal policies on exacerbating socially determined health inequalities, while Joel Lexchin (2001, 2010) explains how the pharmaceutical industry's profit motive can lead to negative health outcomes for patients. Toba Bryant (2009) looks at the impact of economic globalization on health policy and health-care provision in Canada.

Australian sociologists Evan Willis (1989a, b) and Bob Connell (1988) have highlighted the profit-orientation and entrepreneurial ethos of the medical profession and its tendency to align itself with upper-class interests. This was evidenced in Canada where two previous presidents of the Canadian Medical Association were supportive of more for-profit health care in Canada. Two historical doctors' strikes in the country also illustrate the self-interested orientation of the medical profession. Furthermore, fee-for-service, self-regulation, and the suppression of competition from other health

socialism/communism
Socialism is a political ideology with numerous variations but generally refers to the creation of societies in which private property and wealth accumulation are replaced by state ownership and distribution of economic resources. *Communism* represents a vision of society based on communal ownership of resources, co-operation, and altruism to the extent that social inequality and the state no longer exist. Both terms are often used interchangeably.

practitioners (Coburn, Torrance, & Kaufert, 1983; Torrance, 1998) are indicative of medicine's alignment with "the economic and ideological patterns of capitalism" (Connell, 1988, p. 214). According to Connell, this has resulted in a commonality of lifestyles and interests between doctors and the upper class so that "doctors as a group . . . have particular political and economic interests they do not share with most of their patients: interests in maintaining a sharp division of labour in health care, in a substantial amount of public ignorance about health, and in seeing that self-help arrangements for health care remain marginal or ineffective" (p. 214).

A further area of interest for Marxist critics has been the entry of large profit-oriented corporations, including pharmaceutical companies, into the health sector, often referred to as the **medical-industrial complex**, a term originally coined by Navarro and colleagues in 1967 (Navarro, 1998). The medical-industrial complex highlights the **commodification of health care**, whereby health is increasingly viewed as a commodity from which profit can be made, the pursuit of which may clash with the health needs of individuals and of the wider community. Connell (1988), among others, cautions against the vast growth and influence of profit-oriented medical enterprises, such as drug companies, pathology and radiology clinics, private health insurance companies, private nursing homes, and private hospitals. While Canadians have universal access to public health care through Medicare, some groups seek to undermine the system despite its overwhelming public support (Romanow, 2002). Joel Lexchin (2001, 2006, 2010b; Lexchin & Wiktorowicz, 2009) has written extensively about the growing cost of medications, profit strategies utilized by pharmaceutical companies, and the Canadian government's willingness to turn regulatory decisions over to drug manufactures.

medical-industrial complex
The growth of profit-oriented medical companies and industries, whereby one company may own a chain of health services, such as hospitals, clinics, and radiology and pathology services.

commodification of health care
Treating health care as a commodity to be bought and sold in the pursuit of profit maximization.

Political Economy Approach

political economy
Focuses on how political, economic, and ideological factors influence the distribution of power and other resources in a society, which in turn shapes individual experience and state policies.

A **political economy** approach to health and health care characterizes much of the critical work being done in Canada. In Canada, the political economy tradition goes back to the 1920s and 1930s and the writings of Harold Innis and the staples theory (1999/1930), which showed how staples, such as lumber, fish, and fur, shaped the economic and political structure of Canada. The more recent writings in Canadian political economy have been very much influenced by Marxism and take a critical materialist perspective that challenges the dominant beliefs about how society is structured and raises questions about how things could be different. Scholars such as Leo Panitch (1977; Gindin & Panitch, 2013) and Wallace Clement (1975) have looked at the interlinkages between economic, ideological, and political forces; feminists in that tradition, such as Pat Armstrong (Armstrong & Armstrong, 2010b) and Meg Luxton (1987; Braedley & Luxton, 2010), introduced a tradition of feminist political economy that paid attention to women's work in the home and to gender relations. William Carroll (2004) has used a political economy perspective to consider the role of transnational forces, such as globalization and neo-liberalism, in shaping corporate power in Canada. According to Armstrong, Armstrong, and Coburn (2001),

> Political economists grapple with the tensions between structure and agency, between ideas and material conditions, between class and gender, class and race, and between the tendency to separate aspects of these for the purposes of analysis and the need to unite them in order to understand the whole. (p. ix)

Box 2.1 Karl Marx (1818–1883): Intellectual and Revolutionary

History does *nothing*, it "possesses *no* immense wealth," it "wages *no* battles." It is *man*, real, living man [sic] who does all that . . . history is *nothing but* the activity of man pursuing his aims.

—Marx and Engels, *The Holy Family* (1845)

Karl Marx was born in Trier, a city in Prussia. He was educated at the University of Bonn and later at the University of Berlin, where he studied philosophy, law, history, and English and Italian languages. In addition to writing numerous books and pamphlets with his lifelong collaborator, Friedrich Engels, he was active in various political movements, including the First International and the Communist League. After being exiled from France for his radical activities and writings, he moved to London

Cornell University Library

The philosophers have only interpreted the world, in various ways; the point, however, is to change it. —Karl Marx, *Theses on Feuerbach* (March 1845)

with his wife, Jenny, where he lived out his life and did much of his research into and writings on the workings of the capitalist system.

It has been argued that few individuals in history have equaled his influence in the political sphere as well as the academic. Berlin (1963, p. 1) writes, "No thinker in the nineteenth century has had so direct, deliberate and powerful an influence upon mankind [sic] as Karl Marx." Singer (1980) compares his impact to that of Jesus or Muhammad, which has inspired political and economic revolutions around the world. Intellectually, "Marx's ideas brought about modern sociology, transformed the study of history, and profoundly affected philosophy, literature and the arts" (p. 1). His contributions to sociology include a theory of alienation, a theory of the state, social class, ideology, and praxis, and an understanding of the relationship between structure and agency. However, many who consider themselves Marxists have quite different interpretations of what Marx "really" meant. His work influenced what became known as conflict theory in the US, and the development of the Frankfurt School. In Canadian sociology, critical political economy and Marxist-feminism both owe a debt to Marx. It should also be noted that seldom has one individual engendered such hostility, especially in the United States. Today there is a revived interest in Marx's ideas. While some may disagree, many would argue that Marx is as relevant today, if not more so, than in the past.

In the area of health, political economy provides a unique contribution in that it focuses on the links between health and the economic, political, and social lives of people in different regions and societies. Political economy asks questions such as the following:

- Why do some people have better health than others?
- Why do some countries have a publicly supported universal Medicare system while others have for-profit health care?
- Why are there inequalities in access to health care?
- Why do social inequalities exist? (Coburn, 2010, p. 65)

As well, a critical political economy approach to health is materialist—that is, greater explanatory emphasis is placed on how society is organized and on the way people live rather than on the ideas they produce. Such analysis is illustrated in works by Canadian scholars such as David Coburn (2000, 2001, 2010); Dennis Raphael (2006, 2009b, c); Joel Lexchin (2001, 2006, 2010b; Lexchin & Wiktorowicz, 2009); Robert Chernmous and Ian Hudson (2013); and Pat and Hugh Armstrong (2001, 2003). In addition, Navarro and Muntaner's edited collection *Political and Economic Determinants of Population Health and Well-Being* (2004) and Panitch and Leys's collection *Morbid Symptoms: Health under Capitalism* (2009) provide excellent overviews of the current relationship between social inequalities and health worldwide. In another example of this type of analysis, all the contributors to *Unhealthy Times: Political Economy Perspectives on Health and Care in Canada* (2001), edited by Pat Armstrong, Hugh Armstrong, and David Coburn, use a critical political economy approach to view different facets of our health-care system. For example, Peggy McDonough (pp. 195–222) examines how workers' health is affected by global pressures on labour markets to downsize and increase the use of casual labour. Paul Williams et al. (A.P. Williams et al., 2001, pp. 7–30) look at how current pressures of neo-liberalism and globalization are trying to reduce government's role in health-care services in favour of the private sector.

Weberianism

Max Weber (1864–1920) (pronounced *vay-ber*)[1] ranks along with Marx as one of the most influential theorists in sociology. Weber (1968/1921) like Marx produced a theory of society that acknowledges the way in which people both shape and are shaped by the social structure. Weber's writings are extensive, but his major contributions concern his concept of social action, his notion of **verstehen**, his analysis of bureaucracy, and his account of power and social inequality through the concepts of class, status, and party. Like Marx, Weber viewed class as important and believed that social conflict was a defining characteristic of increasingly complex societies. Unlike Marx, rather than two basic classes, Weber also considered the middle classes as important, which he saw as consisting of those occupational groups with qualifications and skills that provided them with market advantages (higher wages, prestige, and better working conditions) over those in manual occupations. Not only did the diversity of social classes provide the basis for various forms

verstehen
Refers to a process of interpretative and empathetic understanding.

---

1. I would like to acknowledge a debt to Bessant and Watts (2002) for their insights in conveying the pronunciations of author surnames.

of collective action to protect and expand group interests, thereby laying the basis for social conflict, Weber suggested that in addition to class inequality, status groups and parties were also a source of group formation and social inequality.

Status groups reflect cultural and sometimes legally conferred privileges, social respect, and honour. They are usually based on membership in specific professional, ethnic, and religious groups, and members tend to share common interests and lifestyles. Status group membership is often restricted through what Weber termed a process of **social closure**. While class and social status tend to be closely related, they need not be. Moreover, other groups, or "parties" in Weber's terms, could also serve as the basis for collective interests and social inequality. "Parties" refer to groups attempting to wield power and include political parties, associations such as unions and professional bodies, as well as various interest/pressure groups.

Another strand of Weber's work concerned the process of **rationalization**, which he considered the overarching trend in society, epitomized by the growth of bureaucracy. Weber (1968/1921) predicted the "future belongs to bureaucratisation" (p. 1401) and described an **ideal type** bureaucratic organization as having a highly specialized and hierarchical division of labour bounded by formal rules and regulations (see Weber 1968/1921, pp. 221–3). For Weber, bureaucracies were an effective response to social complexity and democracy by attempting to eliminate fraud, mismanagement, and inefficiency through conformity to standardized procedures. Despite what he saw as the significant benefits of bureaucracy, he feared that social life would be so governed by objective and informal rules that people would become entrapped by an "iron cage" of regulations that would limit their creativity and individuality.

Weberian analyses of health tend to focus on health professions and the health bureaucracy. Prominent theorists include Robert Alford (1975), Magali Sarfati Larson (1977), Anne Witz (1992), Bryan Turner (1987), and George Ritzer (1993). Alford's classic work on barriers to reform in health care argues that health policy and the delivery of health care are a compromise between three main vested interest groups: professional monopolists (doctors), corporate rationalizers (public and private health sector managers), and equal health-care advocates (various patient rights groups). Like many Weberians, he acknowledges that some groups (such as doctors) are clearly dominant and exercise more power, but also maintains that other groups can and do exert influence. Ritzer updates Weber's idea of rationalization and suggests that the fast-food industry (rather than bureaucracy) represents an intensified model of rationalization, which he terms **McDonaldization**. For example, medical practice is increasingly subject to regulations and performance indicators so that health care becomes predictable and uniform (just like a fast-food restaurant). Armstrong and Armstrong's (2003) work from a political economy perspective also illustrates the rationalization of health-care delivery (nursing work) and the implementation of quality assurance techniques and cost-saving measures as a consequence of neo-liberalism. Ritzer's argument extends Weber's concept of the "iron cage," whereby the introduction of performance indicators that are motivated by cost factors alone may make health professionals more consistent in their treatment but may also dehumanize interaction with patients and lessen the flexibility and quality of care provided. In their study of nurses in Halifax, Beagan and Ells (2009) found that new managerial practices undermined nurses' professional values and reduced the quality of care. Nurses felt caught between their ethic of care and the institutions' demand for quantification.

social closure
A term first used by Max Weber to describe the way that power is exercised to exclude outsiders from the privileges of social membership (in social classes, professions, or status groups).

rationalization
The standardization of social life through rules and regulations. See *McDonaldization*.

ideal type
A concept originally developed by Max Weber to refer to the abstract or pure features of any social phenomenon.

McDonaldization
A term coined by George Ritzer to expand Weber's notion of rationalization; defined as the standardization of social life by rules and regulations, such as increased monitoring and evaluation of individual performance, akin to the uniformity and control measures used by fast-food chains. These principles are now applied to other sectors, both locally and globally.

Symbolic Interactionism

Symbolic interactionism is considered by many to have its roots in Weber's ideas. It is associated with key theorists, such as George Herbert Mead (1863–1931), Charles Cooley (1864–1929), Howard Becker (1928–), Erving Goffman (1922–1982), Anselm Strauss (1916–1996), and Herbert Blumer (1900–1987), who coined the term in 1937. The perspective arose as a reaction against structuralist approaches such as structural functionalism, which tends to view humans as simply responding to external influences. Instead, symbolic interactionists focus on agency and how people construct, interpret, and give meaning to their behaviour through interaction with others. The core philosophical assumption is that humans create reality through their actions and the meanings they give to them. Therefore, society is the cumulative effect of human action, interaction, and interpretation, and these are more significant than social structures—hence the focus of the perspective. Symbolic interactionism has a number of strands, such as ethnomethodology (see Garfinkel, 1967) and phenomenology (see Berger & Luckmann, 1967; Schutz, 1972/1933). Its emphasis on the **social construction** of reality has influenced many other perspectives, such as cultural studies and postmodernism (Ritzer, 1996).

Symbolic interactionism provides a theoretical bridge between sociology and psychology by concentrating on small-scale social interaction and how this impacts an individual's identity or image (often referred to as "the self" or "self-concept"). Cooley's (1964/1906) term "the looking-glass self" encapsulates this approach, whereby the reactions of others influence the way we see ourselves and thus how we in turn behave. For example, if people regularly tell you that you are attractive and intelligent, this reaction can influence what you believe and how you behave.

Symbolic interactionism emphasizes that health and illness are perceived subjectively and are social constructions that change over time and vary between cultures. Therefore, what is considered an illness is socially defined and passes through a social lens that reflects the culture, politics, and morality of a particular society at a particular point in time. An important contribution of social constructionism is its critique of **medicalization**, especially as embodied in psychiatry. Such a viewpoint has been used to great effect by interactionist theorists to expose many medical practices and opinions that are based on social (or moral) rather than biological factors. Many interaction studies have also focused on patients' subjective experience of illness, interactions between patients and health professionals, interactions among health professionals (especially between doctors and nurses) and the experience of health-care providers. For example, Schneider and Conrad's work on epilepsy (1983) looks at the meaning of having a chronic illness from the perspective of those who live with it. How does it affect their everyday lives and the lives of those around them? Gareth Williams (2000) looks at how people's beliefs about the cause of their rheumatoid arthritis need to be understood as part of a large narrative process that they construct. Becker (1963) argues that deviance is created through social interaction when certain behaviours or groups of people are labelled as deviant by social institutions, such as the police, the courts, and mental health authorities. According to Becker, "deviance is not a quality of the act a person commits, but rather a consequence of the application by others of rules and sanctions to an offender. The deviant is one to whom that label has successfully been applied; deviant behaviour is behaviour that people so label" (p. 9).

Labelling theory examines the effect that being labelled deviant has for the individual concerned. Such an approach draws attention to how and why certain behaviours and

social construction/ constructionism
Refers to the socially created characteristics of human life based on the idea that people actively construct reality, meaning it is neither "natural" nor inevitable. Therefore, notions of normality/ abnormality, right/wrong, and health/illness are subjective human creations that should not be taken as a given or taken for granted.

medicalization
The process by which non-medical problems become defined and treated as medical issues, usually in terms of illnesses, disorders, or syndromes.

labelling theory
Focuses on the effect that social institutions and professions (such as the police, the courts, and psychiatry) have in labelling (defining and socially constructing) behaviours and activities as deviant.

groups of people are labelled deviant. Moreover, labelling theory exposes the way that medicine (especially psychiatry) could be used as an instrument of **social control** to constrain the actions of so-called difficult social groups (see Roach Anleu, 1999; Szasz, 2007).

Canadian-born sociologist Erving Goffman (1961, 1963) examined **stigma** and focused attention on what he termed **total institutions**, such as asylums. According to Goffman, a person becomes stigmatized when they possess an attribute that negatively affects social interaction. He identified three forms of stigma: physical deformity, individual characteristics (mental disorder), and "tribal" factors (based on "race," ethnicity, and religion). In his terms, these resulted in tainted or "spoiled identities," whereby social interaction was affected by negative traits associated with the particular stigma. For example, people may react to someone with a physical disability through outright discrimination or may treat that person as if he or she were also mentally incompetent. A person diagnosed as having suffered from schizophrenia may be treated as (and often called) a "schizophrenic," as if it was the sole characteristic of who he or she was. In such cases, the stereotype associated with the condition overrides the actual personality, actions, and achievements of the individual concerned. A person with HIV/AIDS is similarly stigmatized.

Goffman's (1961) analysis of institutionalization (the incarceration of people for some form of treatment or sanction) focused on the experience from the perspective of the "inmates." His observations of the interaction between inmates and institutional staff reflected the overt and covert forms of power relationships imbued in what he termed the "total institution." While such institutions served to impose highly regimented and authoritarian forms of conformity on inmates, often to the detriment of their personal and health needs, they also resulted in a hidden "underlife" through which people kept a sense of their individual identity by resisting or undermining authority in secret ways (see also Scheff, 1966). Goffman's insights on the negative affects of institutionalization have had a wide social impact, which can be seen in fictional works such as the film *One Flew Over the Cuckoo's Nest*. Excellent discussions of deviance can be found in Sharyn Roach Anleu's (1999) *Deviance, Conformity and Control* and Peter Conrad and John Schneider's (1992) *Deviance and Medicalization: From Badness to Sickness*.

Post-structuralism and Postmodernism

The terms *post-structuralism* and *postmodernism*[2] are often used interchangeably (Ritzer, 1997) even though distinctions can be made between the two. For our purposes we will focus on their similarities and treat them as one (and for simplicity only use the term *postmodernism*). Postmodernism arose in the 1980s and reflects a diverse range of social theories from many academic disciplines, making it difficult to categorize or treat systematically. However, to greater or lesser degrees, most social theorists who fall under the umbrella of postmodernism share the following key assumptions:

- The rejection of universal truths about the world, instead suggesting that reality is a social construction. Therefore, all theoretical perspectives (whether they be in the natural, health, or social sciences) reflect the vested interests of one group or

social control
Mechanisms that aim to induce conformity, or at least to manage or minimize deviant behaviour.

stigma
A physical or social trait, such as a disability or a criminal record, that results in negative social reactions, such as discrimination and exclusion.

total institutions
A term used by Erving Goffman to refer to institutions, such as prisons and asylums, in which life is highly regulated and subjected to authoritarian control to induce conformity.

---

2. The use of either term usually reflects a particular author's preference; however, some writers who are considered postmodern theorists dispute the validity of the term or any attempt to generalize postmodernism. The spelling of the terms also varies slightly, with some authors preferring to use a hyphen: *post-modernism*.

another and thus all knowledge is merely a claim to truth, reflecting the subjectivity of those involved.

- The rejection of grand theories or **meta-narratives** (or **meta-analysis**): postmodernists dispute the existence or importance of unifying trends and structural determinants such as functional prerequisites, class conflict, patriarchy, or rationalisation.
- Since no perspective is neutral and there are no universal structural determinants of social life, postmodernists focus on how truth claims about the world are socially constructed. Thus, there is no single reality or ultimate truth, only versions or interpretations of what is "real," "true," "normal," "right," or "wrong." Such a perspective supports tolerance of diversity, but can imply that "almost anything goes."

meta-narratives (or **meta-analysis**)
The "big picture" analysis that frames and organizes observations and research on a particular topic.

In sociology, the work of Michel Foucault (1926–1984) has had the most influence, especially his historical work on asylums, prisons, and hospitals, which uncovered how knowledge and power are used to regulate and control various social groups. Foucault's (1979) conceptualization of the panopticon as a metaphor for his theory of surveillance and social control has been a key legacy of his work. The panopticon ("all-seeing place") was developed by Jeremy Bentham in the eighteenth century as an architectural design for a prison, consisting of a central observation tower surrounded by circles of cells so that every cell could be observed simultaneously. According to Foucault,

> All that is needed, then, is to place a supervisor in a central tower and to shut up in each cell a madman, a patient, a condemned man, a worker, or a schoolboy . . . [resulting in] a state of consciousness and permanent visibility that assures the automatic functioning of power . . . in short, that the inmates should be caught up in a power situation of which they themselves are the bearers. (1979, pp. 200–1)

Therefore, control could be maintained by the assumption of being constantly under surveillance so that individuals subjected to the disciplinary gaze were "totally seen without ever seeing, whilst the agents of discipline see everything, without ever being seen" (Foucault, 1979, p. 202). Bourgeault (2006, p. 49) writes that Foucault's work on how medical knowledge and discourse have been used to control the body through systems of surveillance in the supposed broader interest of society is a critical insight. For example, the wide promotion of the thin ideal of female beauty in Western societies results in panoptic effects whereby many women perceive themselves to be under constant body surveillance and undergo numerous disciplined activities in an attempt to conform to the pressure to be thin. Lupton (2012) examines how new mobile computer technologies in medicine and social media applications are used to target health messages at individuals, thus extending the temporal nature of health surveillance. These technologies construct the individual "as both an object of surveillance and persuasion and as a responsible citizen who is willing and able to act on the health imperatives . . . and to present their body/self as open to continual measurement and assessment" (p. 229).

Feminism

Feminist perspectives in sociology first arose in the 1960s and were primarily aimed at addressing the neglect of gender issues and the blatant sexism of traditional sociological theories, exposing that most mainstream sociology was in fact "male-stream" (Smith, 1974, 1987; Sydie, 1987). Feminists pointed out that some approaches perpetuated sexist assumptions about the role of women in society, such as Parsons's view of women as performing "expressive roles" in society, fulfilling the "function" of providing emotional care and support of men and families. Other perspectives, such as traditional Marxist theories of class and symbolic interactionists excluded the study of women. Women's experiences as workers, caregivers, partners, or victims of abuse were rarely studied or theorized about. Hence, early feminist perspectives addressed the question "What about the women?" and focused on social inequality between women and men. They argued that differences between women and men were socially constructed, not natural, and that the world is gendered such that women and men have fundamentally different experiences and access to power. This essentialist construction of women has been criticized for its failure to recognize the diversity of different women's realities, such as those shaped by "race," class, gender identity, etc.

One of the most eminent feminist theorists is Canadian sociologist Dorothy Smith (1926–), who made the important distinction between a sociology *of* women and a sociology *for* women. In *The Everyday World as Problematic: A Feminist Sociology* (1987), Smith outlines the differences between men's standpoint and women's. According to Smith, men's standpoint is linked to the **relations of ruling** but has been represented as universal. However, "the fulcrum of a sociology for women is the standpoint of the subject. A sociology for women preserves the presence of subjects as knowers and actors. It does not transform subjects into the objects of study . . ." (p. 105). A sociology for women begins with the actualities of their everyday worlds and "offers an understanding of how those worlds are organized and determined by social relations immanent in and extending beyond them" (p. 106). Smith's **institutional ethnography** (IE) approach is a way to examine the link between people's everyday experiences and the relations of ruling that coordinate and shape those lives as a means to help people understand how and why things happen (1987, 1993): "Rather than taking up issues and problems as they have been defined by the discipline [sociology], the aim is to explicate the actual social processes and practices organizing people's everyday experience from a standpoint in the everyday world" (1987, p. 151). Smith developed the approach initially in a feminist context as a method that could produce a "sociology for women"; however, she sees this approach as having much wider applications (see Box 2.2 for more on Dorothy Smith). Canadian researchers such as Janet Rankin and Marie Campbell (2006, 2009) have used institutional ethnography to examine the Canadian health-care system and the work of nurses. Christina Sinding (2010) employed institutional ethnography to explore health-care disparities in the context of her study on cancer care in Ontario.

Feminism is a diverse social and intellectual movement that addresses many issues from a range of academic disciplines. Some prominent theorists include Sandra Harding (1991), Dorothy Smith (1987/1974, 1987, 1993), Patricia Hill Collins (2000), bell hooks (1984), Shulamith Firestone (1979/1970), Judith Butler (1990), Carol Gilligan (1993), and Catharine MacKinnon (1989). Today there are many "feminisms" which defy easy categorization. Some distinguish between three "waves" of feminism: first wave, second wave, and third wave. Others group feminism according to "schools of thought," typically into four groups: liberal feminism; radical feminism; socialist and Marxist feminism; and post-structuralist/postmodern feminism.[3] Increasingly important perspectives are those of Black/anti-racist and Indigenous feminisms.

relations of ruling
A concept used by Dorothy Smith to refer to a complex of organized practices, including government, law, bureaucracy, professional organizations, educational institutions and discourses in texts, and objectified social relations with their gender subtext, that coordinate and organize the lives of individuals. In this mode of ruling, the particular actualities of people's everyday lives are abstracted and objectified into standardized forms of knowledge that in turn regulate, guide, and control their lives (Smith, 1987).

institutional ethnography (IE)
A feminist research strategy associated with Dorothy Smith combining theory and method. It begins from the standpoint of people in the actualities of their everyday world to show how people's social relations are organized by forces outside of them.

---

3. Other variants of feminism include ecofeminism, cultural feminism, psychoanalytic feminism, maternal feminism, transfeminism, Third World feminism, etc.

Box 2.2 Dorothy Smith (b. 1926): Canadian Feminist Sociologist

> Being excluded, as women have been, from the making of ideology, of knowledge, and of culture means that our experience, our interests, our ways of knowing the world have not been represented in the organization of our ruling nor in the systematically developed knowledge that has entered into it.
>
> —Dorothy Smith, *A Peculiar Eclipsing: Women's Exclusion from Man's Culture* (1978)

Dorothy Smith, renowned Canadian Feminist scholar, laid the foundations for a critical feminist sociology by outlining the importance of including the everyday, lived experiences of women in sociological analysis.

Dorothy Smith, a leading Canadian feminist sociologist, was educated in London, England, and Berkeley, California. She taught at the University of British Columbia, the Ontario Institute for Studies in Education (OISE), now the department of Sociology and Equity Studies in Education at the University of Toronto, and as an adjunct professor of Sociology at the University of Victoria. The author of many influential books and articles, she has received numerous prestigious awards in sociology both in Canada and internationally. She was a pioneer in challenging the exclusion of women's experiences and knowledge and laid the foundation of an emergent feminist sociology. However, her theorizing was a means to reclaim the voices of all disenfranchised groups, including those marginalized by race and class. It is said of her book, *The Everyday World as Problematic*, that it "single-handedly reshaped the social sciences" (www.peoplesworld.org/feminist-and-marxist-dorothy-smith-receives-lifetime-sociology-award). Dorothy Smith is, however, much more than just a scholar. Elaine Coburn (2010) summarizes her many contributions best in the following way.

> Dorothy Smith is a world-renowned Marxist feminist scholar and activist and a formidable intellect. Her decades of scholarly and activist contributions combine a lively sociological imagination with unfailing rigour, inspiring and challenging academics, professionals and "ordinary" women and men to consider how social relationships and power are organized in everyday life." (p. 9)

For an excellent interview with Dorothy Smith, see William Carroll, "You Are Here" in *Socialist Studies*, 6(2) (Fall 2010), 9–37.

Earlier feminist perspectives stressed the importance of **patriarchy**. Feminists argued that the social structure is patriarchal, with social institutions, such as the legal, health, and education systems, as well as the wider culture reflecting sexist values and supporting the privilege of men. They highlighted that gender is a social construction and identified gender-role **socialization** and sex discrimination as keys to understanding inequality between the sexes.

Black feminists, however, like Patricia Collins and bell hooks and Indigenous feminists such as Patricia Monture (Suzack et al., 2010) have criticized much of feminism for its failure to recognize other forms of oppression. They argue that cultural patterns of oppressions, such as colonialism, race, class, ethnicity, and sexual orientation, are interrelated and bound together. Collins (2000a) used a paradigm of intersections as shaped by race, class, gender, and sexuality to understand Black American women's experiences. Canadian anti-racist feminists have also challenged mainstream feminist theorizing about the common experience of women and the essentialist notions of gender, and are developing a more inclusive feminist theory that examines the interconnections between race, class, and gender (Man, 2012, p. 236). The concept of **intersectionality** is crucial as a means of understanding the intersecting nature of oppression.

> All women may currently occupy the position "woman" . . . but they do not occupy it in the same way. Women of colour in a white ruled society face different obstacles than do white women, and they may share more important problems with men of colour than with their white "sisters" . . . Consolidating all women into a falsely unified "woman" has helped mask the operations of power that actually divide women's interests as much as unite them. (Poovey, 1988, p. 59)

In other words, privileging "sisterhood," based on idealized universal assumptions of common female experiences, values, and perceptions ignores the very real material differences of power and privilege in society.

Intersectionality theory, which has its roots in US Black feminist scholarship, problematizes the view that inequities can be explained by unitary categories of social position, such as sex or race. Rather, this perspective asserts that there are multiple social processes that intersect in complex multi-factorial ways to create processes of oppression. Black feminist Patricia Collins (2000a, p. 18) explains that "intersectionality refers to particular forms of intersecting oppression, for example, intersections of race and gender, or of sexuality and nation. Intersectional paradigms remind

Patricia Hill Collins has made significant contributions to sociology. In her most famous work, *Black Feminist Thought*, she articulated how intersections of race, class, and gender mutually construct one another in an "interlocking oppression."

patriarchy
A system of power through which males dominate households. It is used more broadly by feminists to refer to society's domination by patriarchal power, which functions to subordinate women and children.

socialization
The process of learning the culture of a society (its language and customs), which shows us how to behave and communicate.

intersectionality
A term coined by American critical race scholar, Kimberlé Chrenshaw in 1989 to examine how race and sex/gender were mutually constituted for African-American women. The idea that one needs to examine how various biological, cultural, and social categories interact on multiple (and often simultaneous) levels that lead to oppression and inequality.

us that oppression cannot be reduced to one fundamental type, and that oppressions work together in producing injustice." In other words, rather than examining race, class, gender, and nation as separate systems of oppression, "the construct of intersectionality references how these systems mutually construct one another" (Collins, 2000b, p. 47). Collins (1993) reminds us that we need to move away from dichotomous thinking and additive analyses of oppression to get at the interlocking dimension of oppression and the barriers created by it. Similarly, Mohawk scholar Patricia Monture (2012, p. 199) explains that intersectionality is not just a combination of discriminations that operate on an individual simultaneously but rather the intersection produces a distinct and unique experience. Focusing on health disparities, Canadian scholars Dhamoon and Hankivsky (2011) stress that

> Intersectionality is concerned with simultaneous intersections between aspects of social difference and identity (as related to meanings of race, ethnicity, indigeneity, gender, class, sexuality, geography, age disability/ability, migration status, religion) and forms of systemic oppression . . . that are complex and interdependent. (p. 16)

An intersectional approach in health research theorizes that "an individual's experience, and their health are not simply the sum of their parts" (Bauer, 2014, p. 11). In the case of Aboriginal women, for example, their gender is constituted and their health affected by cultural meanings and processes found in Indigenous culture as well as their experiences of colonialism. See Hankivsky (ed.) (2011) for excellent examples of intersectionality in health research.

Feminist perspectives on health care have underpinned the women's health movement and have drawn attention to how patriarchy has shaped the ideas and practices of medicine and how gender is a factor in every aspect of illness. Today there is growing attention to how various forms of oppression intersect to influence the health of different groups of people (Hankivsky, 2011; McGibbon & McPherson, 2011). "Feminist intersectionality theory provides a comprehensive foundation for interrogating the multiple ways that the [social determinants of health] shape women's health across the lifespan" (McGibbon & McPherson, 2011, p. 63). Some other topics that feminists have addressed are the following:

sexual division of labour
Refers to the nature of work performed as a result of gender roles. The stereotype is that of the male breadwinner and the female homemaker.

emotional labour
Refers to the use of feelings by employees as part of their paid work. In health care, a key part of nursing work is caring for patients, often by providing emotional support.

- The medicalization of women's bodies and women's lives (Berenson et al., 2009); the medicalization of menopause and childbirth (Ehrenreich & English, 1973; McCrea, 1983); unwarranted and sometimes harmful interventions in the management of pregnancy, childbirth, contraception, reproductive technology, and gynecological disorders (Annandale & Clarke, 1996; Kaufert & Gilbert, 1987; McCrea, 1983; Oakley, 1980; Riessman, 1983; Walters, 1992, 1994).
- The **sexual division of labour** in health care, particularly the historical role of women healers; the subordination of female-dominated professions, such as nursing; the performance of **emotional labour** and the predicament of female health-care providers; the role of women as informal carers outside the health system; and the effect of the increasing entry of women into the medical professions (Armstrong et al., 2008; Armstrong & Braedley, 2013; Ehrenreich & English, 1973, 1974, 1979; Hothschild, 1979; Kirk, 1994).

- Sexism and **biological determinism** in health care, particularly medical research and treatment, according to which much health research has been conducted on men and extrapolated to women, and how women's specific health concerns have been under-researched or falsely assumed to be the result of their menstrual cycles—that is, women as "helpless victims of their hormones" (Barrett & Roberts, 1978; Findlay & Miller, 2002; Mitchinson, 1993; Walters, 1994).
- The issues of sexuality, rape, and domestic violence as key health issues requiring the need for appropriate health policies and specialized training of health workers (Browne et al., 2011; Ford-Gilboe et al., 2006, 2009; Varcoe, 2009; Wuest et al., 2007).
- Body image and eating disorders (Bartky, 1998; Bordo, 1993; Berenson et al., 2009; Williams & Germov, 2004; Wolf, 1991).

biological determinism
An unproven belief that individual and group behaviour and social status is an inevitable result of biology.

Today feminist perspectives and concerns are a central feature of sociology and health sociology in particular. Feminism has exposed the sexism of medical approaches and facilitated increasing attention on women's health rights in terms of health research, funding, and the provision of appropriate services (see Annandale, 2004, for a review of feminist theories applied to health). For example, the Canadian Institutes for Health Research (CIHR), a health-research funding agency with a focus on translating research findings into practice, requires funding applicants to show how they will address issues of gender and sex (Sharman & Johnson, 2012).

Human Rights and Anti-Racism Perspectives

Human Rights

Using human rights is a means to making equitable health outcomes a social imperative.

—Marcia Rioux (2010, p. 97)

The 1948 Universal Declaration of Human Rights recognizes the right of everyone to the highest attainable standard of physical and mental health. It mandates countries to create conditions that provide healthy and safe working conditions, social security, adequate access to food, clothing, and housing, and other underlying determinants of health (Schrecker et al., 2010). Human rights principles and standards provide a powerful moral argument to address health inequities in global health (Robinson, 2007). Human rights principles provide the impetus behind global approaches to health equity such as articulated in the WHO Commission on the Social Determinants of Health (CSDH, 2008) and the more recent World Conference on Social Determinants of Health (WHO, 2011). Similarly, a human rights perspective underscores societal and governmental responsibilities in countries such as Canada to design health systems and implement health policies that are consistent with human rights requirements, and to promote the well-being of all peoples, particularly for those most disadvantaged (Chapman, 2014).

A human rights approach, while not a theory, provides a framework for developing health programs and policies using human rights principles as the basis for design, implementation, and evaluation. Such an approach focuses on addressing health inequities at the local and global level. This approach suggests that the right to health must be understood in connection with other inalienable human rights: non-discrimination and equality, including women's reproductive rights; political and civil rights; economic, social, and cultural rights, including the right to an adequate standard of living, to education, and to cultural freedom; and the right of nations to development and economic autonomy (Rioux, 2010, pp. 97–9). A human rights approach interrogates health and health care from the perspective of social justice; it underscores the fact that poor health status is related to the exclusion and loss of human rights: "The movement toward defining health as a human right requires a social injustice-based analysis of the relationships among health and social policy decisions, health and social service expenditures, population health outcomes, and the social determinants of health" (McGibbon, 2009, p. 319). McGibbon stresses the need for an intersectionality framework that recognizes that health and access to health care is influenced by an intersection of identities (gender, race, ethnicity, sexual orientation, [dis]ability, age) and social determinants of health, such as class, early childhood development, employment, education, as well as individuals' geographical location.

Anti-Racism

> Race is more than a theoretical concept. It is also an idea that governs social relations. . . . The concept of race is used to establish advantage and privilege, as well as disadvantage and injury.
>
> —George Sefa Dei (1999, pp. 24–5)

A growing number of scholars are recognizing that the structure and experiences of "race" and racism are critical for understanding the health experiences of racialized groups. Canadian anti-racist scholar George Sefa Dei (1999, pp. 17–35) points out that "race" is a socio-political construction by which dominant groups can exercise power and control over those defined as "other." Galabuzi (2009, pp. 252–79) reminds us that racialized groups encounter processes of marginalization in many spheres of life and that the experience of racism is a primary source of stress and hypertension in racialized communities. Critical race theory is an emerging transdisciplinary methodology grounded in race equity and social justice principles. Critical race theory scholars argue that eliminating racism is central to achieving health equity. They examine the ways in which structural racism influences both health and the production of knowledge about populations, health, and health disparities (Ford & Airhihenbuwa, 2010a, p. s31). Anti-racist researchers, for example, have documented the various ways in which social determinants of health and institutionalized racism in the health-care system negatively impact the health status of racialized peoples. Sefa Dei argues that anti-racism praxis requires recognizing the saliency of "race" and racial oppression in people's lives. See Chapters 6 and 7 for a further discussion of "race" and racism.

Conclusion

Despite the differences among the theoretical perspectives discussed here, the distinctions among specific social theories produced by individual authors are likely to be less clear-cut. While sociologists generally align themselves with particular perspectives, they tend to be in less disagreement than the differences between perspectives might imply. This is partly because sociologists attempt to incorporate the insights of a range of perspectives into their specific social theory.

While the existence of so many perspectives can be challenging, new theories and perspectives are likely to continue to emerge. Sociological theories change over time as society itself changes and new knowledge, ideas, and capabilities emerge. This is as true of natural sciences as it is of the social sciences. In response to social change and the development of new insights, theories are regularly modified, reinterpreted, and even rejected.

The theoretical perspectives presented in this chapter are more complex than can be discussed here. Furthermore, no attempt has been made to evaluate the theoretical perspectives. Rather, the aim has been to convey a basic understanding of some of the main assumptions, concepts, and approaches to explain the differences between perspectives and the insights they offer.

At this point, it is important to sound a note of caution about the use and critique of sociological theories. When attempting to evaluate how well a specific social theory fits the evidence, there is a danger of making the mistake of critiquing the general perspective to which the theory belongs, rather than assessing the insights of the specific theory itself. This is not an argument to ignore the various limitations of theoretical perspectives but, rather, a warning against falling into the trap of dismissing a theory because of the perspective with which it is associated. A much healthier approach is to adopt a position of theoretical pluralism—that is, to accept that many theories have something to offer even though you may have a preference for a certain theoretical perspective. Since different theoretical perspectives address different levels of analysis and different issues, these perspectives should be viewed as potentially complementary rather than automatically oppositional (Turner & Samson, 1995). It is up to you to judge how well a particular theory fits the researched evidence based on your reading and experience.

Summary

- Sociologists seek to interpret their findings by offering a "how" and/or "why" explanation—a theory—for what they seek to understand.
- There is often disagreement over which "how" and "why" explanations, or social theories, best explain certain aspects of social life.
- One way to understand the range of social theories that exist is to group them into main theoretical perspectives: functionalism, Marxism, Weberianism, symbolic interactionism, feminism, and post-structuralism/postmodernism.
- Human rights and anti-racist perspectives complement other theories.
- Differences between the theoretical perspectives are based on a range of philosophical assumptions and levels of focus, which direct attention to particular aspects of social life and how they should be investigated.
- The use of theoretical perspectives oversimplifies reality. Sociologists may adopt different theoretical positions according to the topic under study or may incorporate the insights of other perspectives into their own social theory.

- It is important to be aware of the underlying assumptions and limitations of theoretical perspectives. A specific social theory should always be evaluated on its own merit.

Key Terms

agency	intersectionality	sick role
biological determinism	labelling theory	socialization
biomedical model	McDonaldization	social closure
capitalism	medical-industrial complex	social construction/
class	medicalization	constructionism
commodification of	meta-analysis/	social control
health care	meta-narratives	social structure
deviance	patriarchy	socialism/communism
emotional labour	political economy	stigma
functional prerequisites	rationalization	structure–agency debate
ideal type	relations of ruling	total institutions
institutional ethnography (IE)	sexual division of labour	verstehen

Sociological Reflection: What's Your Theory?

Sociological theories can help us to understand how and why certain health problems exist. As this chapter has shown, most theories can be grouped into different theoretical perspectives:

- functionalism
- Marxism
- political economy
- Weberianism
- symbolic interactionism
- feminism
- post-structuralism/postmodernism
- human rights and anti-racist approaches

Which theoretical perspective do you prefer? Why? Identify some of the key insights into understanding health and illness that your preferred perspective provides.

Discussion Questions

1. Why is theory necessary? Provide examples in your answer.
2. What are some of the limitations of adopting one theoretical perspective and ignoring others? Provide examples in your answer.
3. Which perspectives focus attention on health inequality and how do they contribute to our understanding of health and illness?
4. What insights into health issues and health care have feminist perspectives provided?

5. In what ways do intersectionality perspectives increase our understanding of the complexity of health issues?

Further Investigation

1. Choose two of the perspectives discussed in this chapter and examine the similarities and differences in their approach to studying health and illness.
2. "The sick role is no longer applicable to the experience of illness and health care in a postmodern world." Discuss.
3. Compare Marxist and symbolic interactionist perspectives on a health issue of your choice.

Further Reading

Health Sociology Texts

Armstrong, P., Armstrong, H., & Coburn, D. (Eds.). (2001). *Unhealthy times: Political economy perspectives on health and care in Canada.* Toronto, ON: Oxford University Press.

Bolaria, S., & Dickinson, H. (Eds.). (2009). *Health, illness & health care in Canada* (4th ed.). Toronto, ON: Nelson Education Ltd.

Bryant, T., Raphael, D., & Rioux, M. (Eds.). (2010). *Staying alive: Critical perspectives on health, illness and health care* (2nd ed.). Toronto, ON: Canadian Scholars' Press Inc.

Chappell, N., & Penning, M. (2009). *Understanding health, health care and health policy in Canada.* Toronto, ON: Oxford University Press.

Coburn, D., d'Arcy, C., & Torrance, G. (Eds.). (1998). *Health and Canadian society: Sociological perspectives* (3rd ed.). Toronto, ON: University of Toronto Press.

Conrad, P. (Ed.). (2005). *The sociology of health and illness: Critical perspectives* (7th ed.). New York, NY: Worth Publishers.

Hankivsky, Olena (Ed.). (2011). *Health inequities in Canada: Intersectional frameworks and practices.* Vancouver: UBC Press.

Lorber, J., & Moore, L. (2002). *Gender and the social construction of illness* (2nd ed.). New York, NY: AltaMira Press.

Navarro, V. (1986). *Crisis, health & medicine: A social critique.* London, UK: Tavistock.

Panitch, L., & Leys, C. (2009). *Morbid symptoms: Health under capitalism.* Socialist Register 2010. London: Merlin Press.

Raphael, D. (Ed.). (2009). *Social determinants of health: Canadian perspectives* (2nd ed.). Toronto, ON: Canadian Scholars' Press.

Raphael, D. (Ed.). (2012). *Tackling health inequalities: Lessons from international experiences.* Toronto, ON: Canadian Scholars' Press, Inc.

General Social Theory Books

Garner, R., & Hancock, B.H. (2014). *Social theory: Continuity and confrontation: A reader* (3rd ed.). Toronto, ON: University of Toronto Press, Higher Education Division.

Jagger, A. (1983). *Feminist politics and human nature.* New Jersey: Rowman & Allanheld.

Ritzer, G., & Stepnisky, J. (2013). *Sociological theory* (9th ed.). New York, NY: McGraw-Hill.

Seidman, S. (2013). *Contested knowledge: Social theory today* (5th ed.). Malden, MA: Wiley-Blackwell.

Smith, D. (1987). *The everyday world as problematic: A feminist sociology.* Toronto, ON: University of Toronto Press.

Smith, D. (1990). *The conceptual practices of power: A feminist sociology of knowledge.* Toronto, ON: University of Toronto Press.

Sydie, R.A. (1994). *Natural women, cultured men: A feminist perspective on sociological theory.* Vancouver, BC: UBC Press.

Tong, R.P. (2009). *Feminist thought: A more comprehensive introduction* (3rd ed.). Philadelphia, PA: Westview Press.

Weedon, C. (1997). *Feminist practice and poststructuralist theory* (2nd ed.). Cambridge, MA: Blackwell.

Web Resources

Feminist.com
www.feminist.com/resources/links/ links_health.html

American Sociological Association: Medical Sociology
www2.asanet.org/medicalsociology/

Canadian Women's Health Network
www.cwhn.ca

Feminist Theory Website: Feminism in Canada
www.cddc.vt.edu/feminism/can.html

Sociosite: General theory
www.sociosite.net/topics/theory.php

Health related
www.sociosite.net/topics/health.php

Social Theory and Health
www.palgrave-journals.com/sth

CHAPTER 3
Researching Health: Methodological Traditions and Innovations

Jennie Hornosty & Douglas Ezzy

Participatory action research, such as FoodARC depicted above, involves working with individuals, community organizations, government, and university-based researchers in order to collaboratively design, implement, and evaluate a research project.

FoodARC Research Centre

Overview

- What are the major approaches to researching health and illness?
- What are the limitations of the major research methods used in biomedical studies, such as evidence-based medicine, randomized control trials, and epidemiology?
- In what way do health sociologists address some of these limitations through qualitative approaches to the study of health and illness?
- What are some recent innovations in qualitative methods?

Health research includes a number of different methodologies. In this chapter, we examine quantitative and qualitative methodologies and the limitations of the dominant research methods used in biomedical studies of health and illness, which tend to emphasize individualistic approaches to health. In contrast, epidemiological and qualitative methodologies informed by a sociological perspective recommend health policy responses that are more focused on social, cultural, and public-health factors. Sociological research in the study of health and illness today is becoming more diverse with new methodologies. Intersectionality theory and critical race theory inform some of the recent health research, especially by researchers using a qualitative methodology.

Introduction: Different Approaches for Researching Health Issues

As noted in the previous chapter there are a variety of theoretical perspectives in sociology that guide research in the areas of health and illness. Each perspective has certain basic assumptions that guide the methodology, questions, and focus of research. For example, scholars within a Marxist or political economy perspective often use historical and comparative data to look at macro issues; they ask questions about the structure of inequality and its impact on health and the health-care system. Researchers working in the symbolic interaction tradition, on the other hand, will focus on micro issues, such as people's experiences of illness and the meanings they attach to those experiences. Feminist sociologists research both macro and micro issues. In each case, their primary concern is women's experience and the impact on women's health; the aim of the research often is to empower women.

Broadly speaking, research methods can be categorized as either quantitative or qualitative, although many researchers use a combination of the two, or what is referred to as "mixed methods." Although the field of health sociology publishes its own journals and increasingly contributes to health-policy debates, many of the **research methods** are still profoundly shaped by biomedical research. This is reflected by its dominance in the field of "scientific" research, which covers nearly all aspects of health and illness. And although biomedical research methods, such as **randomized control trials (RCTs)**, are not part of

research methods
Procedures used by researchers to collect and investigate data.

randomized control trials (RCTs)
A biomedical research procedure used to evaluate the effectiveness of particular medications and therapeutic interventions. *Random* refers to the equal chance of participants being in the experimental or control group (the group to which nothing is done and is used for comparison); *trial* refers to the experimental nature of the method.

health sociology's research methods, it is essential that health sociologists understand their logic and the consequences of the theoretical and political baggage those research methods carry with them.

The first part of this chapter discusses positivist **quantitative research**, such as randomized control trials, evidence-based medicine (EBM), and the more public-health-oriented epidemiological research methods. The second part provides an overview of traditional **qualitative research**, and discusses some of the recent innovations in qualitative methods, pointing to the value of experimentation in methodologies. It should be remembered that there are fundamental differences between quantitative and qualitative approaches, in terms of research design, the methods of data collection, the types of questions asked, and the analysis of the information gathered.

quantitative research
Research that focuses on the collection of statistical data.

qualitative research
Research that focuses on the meanings and interpretations of the participants.

Quantitative Research and the Positivist Tradition

Quantitative approaches and **positivist research methodologies** attempt to study the world through standardized procedures, uninfluenced by politics, subjectivity, or culture. These methodologies, including randomized control trials and epidemiological surveys, are thought to be very powerful methods for examining the efficacy of various treatments and identifying the risk factors associated with particular diseases. They have been used by government bodies such as Health Canada as a basis for health reform and determining health policy. However, positivist methodologies are not useful for examining meanings, interpretations, and the experience of illness. In many government agencies and funding bodies, positivist research is typically considered to be more important than other forms of research and, as a consequence, the cultural and interpretative dimensions of social life are often inadequately researched and understood. Further, supporters of positivist methodologies pretend that politics do not influence the research process and, as a consequence, are often blind to the power of the particular interest groups that these research methodologies serve.

positivist research methodologies
Research methods that attempt to study people in the same way that physical scientists study the natural world—by focusing on quantifiable and directly observable events. Such research methods focus on the collection of statistical data.

Randomized Control Trials (RCTs)

Randomized control trials, considered by many as the "gold standard" of clinical evidence, can be a powerful way of demonstrating the efficacy of drugs and other biomedical interventions for diseases. An excellent example is a double-blind study conducted in four Canadian centres over three winter seasons to study the effectiveness of light therapy compared to antidepressants to treat seasonal affective disorder. Randomized patients were assigned to eight weeks of either a 10,000-lux light treatment and a placebo capsule or a 100-lux light treatment (a placebo light) and 20 mg of fluoxetine (an antidepressant). The researchers found no significant difference between light therapy and antidepressant medication (Lam et al., 2006). The trial was randomized in the sense that whether a person received light therapy or an antidepressant was decided randomly. Randomized trials prevent doctors, for example, from choosing to give the medication to people that they think may be more likely to benefit. The trial was controlled in the sense that a comparison group of people who did not receive the medication but who were drawn from the same social group were included in the trial. The benefit of the treatment or medication was then assessed by comparing the two groups; the only difference was whether they received light therapy or medication. RCTs are important because they allow cherished beliefs to be disproved. For example, the drug clofibrate was initially thought to be beneficial because it significantly reduced the level of cholesterol in the blood. It was used extensively to treat high cholesterol until an RCT demonstrated that, on the contrary, it increased mortality (Sackett, 1981). RCTs are often mistakenly viewed as the best way to demonstrate causal links between factors under investigation but these procedures privilege biomedical over social responses to illness.

RCTs are privileged because they are thought to be "objective" and "value free"; however, this is not necessarily the case. Richards (1988) provides an excellent account of the social and political nature of RCTs. She makes the strong claim that "[t]he randomised controlled clinical trial, no matter how tightly organized and evaluated, can neither guarantee objectivity nor definitively resolve disputes over contentious therapies or technologies" (p. 686). She provides a detailed analysis of the use of RCTs to test the efficacy of vitamin C as a cancer treatment, involving two rival medical clinics. According to Richards, the rival clinic which was funded to conduct the trials "made no attempt to evaluate the efficacy of vitamin C . . . and ignored or were unaware of the available information on the physicology of vitamin C which should have been taken into account in the design of their study" (p. 672). Her point is that the conduct of the published RCTs was clearly influenced by the theoretical and professional perspectives of the scientists involved.

Furthermore, she argues that the most telling criticism of the debate over vitamin C is that the clinic advocating the value of vitamin C was prevented from publishing further research and was not given the opportunity to comment on the existing studies already published. This demonstrates the myth of disinterested and open scientific discussion. Richards concludes, "If the orthodox claim of the inefficacy of vitamin C in cancer treatment prevails . . . it will *not* be as the result of agreement or consensus brought about by the disinterested application of impersonal rules of experimental procedure" (p. 672) (original emphasis). Rather it is the direct, or indirect, influence of big business with vested interests in maintaining control over expensive treatments and preventing the use of widely available, relatively inexpensive alternatives: "The institution of medicine has a great deal invested in the perpetuation of the myth of objective evaluation. It underpins the cognitive and social authority of its practitioners and legitimates powerful vested interests, not only in medicine, but in society at large" (p. 686).

David Healy (2003, 1997), a psychiatrist and once a consultant for such major pharmaceutical industries as Eli Lilly, Pharmacia, and Upjohn, also raises important questions about the objectivity of medical research. He points out that big pharmaceutical companies today fund much of the medical-scientific research. This raises important questions about conflict of interest in drug regulation and bias in the research process. Healey notes that there is often suppression of data on lethal side effects of drugs and that articles in prestigious medical journals are frequently written by ghost writers employed by pharmaceutical companies.

A criticism of one RCT does not, of course, demonstrate that all RCTs are unreliable. RCTs are a statistical tool to assess the relative effectiveness of intervention and the assessment of various treatments. Physicians and scientists use them, for example, to determine the efficacy of new types of medications. And, as in the previously mentioned study of seasonal affective disorder, RCTs can show that non-drug modalities can be as effective as drugs for certain health issues. However, the criticisms made of RCTs do demonstrate that political and theoretical interests are also inherent in the conduct of medical and health research. This is one of the central insights of the application of sociological theory to **biomedical** research methodology.

Evidence-Based Medicine (EBM)

Although contested, **evidence-based medicine** (EBM) is considered to be one of the most important social movements in public health and clinical medicine in recent years (Bell, 2012). The concept originated with a group of clinical epidemiologists at McMaster University in Hamilton, Ontario, in the early 1990s (Bell, 2012; Cohen et al., 2004). EBM is a tool used to evaluate health-care information that equates evidence with positivist research and clinical expertise. It is an extension of the privileging of RCTs, and proponents of EBM argue that clinical practice should be based on evidence from RCTs rather than on other forms of evidence that are thought to be potentially more biased and therefore less effective. Initially its focus was limited to clinical epidemiology and academic medicine; however, more recently it has been applied to other aspects of health-related activity, including complex behavioural interventions targeting whole communities (Bell, 2012, p. 314).

Critics have pointed out that both RCTs and EBM are not as universally applicable and objective as they are claimed to be. Both are infused with political and theoretical biases that are unavoidable. While they may be useful and rigorous within the parameters for which they are designed, they become problematic when researchers forget or ignore that they cannot be used to assess all aspects of health and illness, particularly those relating to social, cultural, and interpretative dimensions of illness (Bell, 2012; Cohen et al., 2004; May, 2012).

The underlying world view that privileges RCTs as the so-called gold standard against which all other methodologies must be assessed results in a failure to properly research or understand the dimensions of health and illness that cannot be studied utilizing RCTs. The definition of evidence is narrow (Cohen et al., 2004); the focus of RCTs and EBM is on the individual and is not context-specific. Social structural influences on health and social, economic, and cultural factors that profoundly shape the distribution of disease in contemporary society are not acknowledged. In other words, the social determinants of health or how the intersectionality of identities influences health and illness in populations is not factored in (McGibbon, 2009; Raphael, 2009b). "Potential differences in the effectiveness of interventions based on factors such as sex, social class, age and ethnicity are elided" (Bell, 2012, p. 316). As such, EBM and RCTs do not represent the radical paradigm shift that their advocates insist they do. This "one size fits all" orientation of EBM "aligns with the neoliberal restructuring of the welfare state and the rationalisation of healthcare services it has engendered" (Bell, 2012, p. 313). Both RCTs and EBM are an extension of the positivist, individualistic, politically driven model of science that has informed most of modern medical practice. Both treat people as a collection of bodily parts that can be quickly fixed, rather than using a more holistic approach that takes into account individuals' social, psychological, and physical needs (Armstrong & Armstrong, 2003).

Similarly, privileging RCTs and EBM implicitly devalues interpretive and other qualitative approaches to the experience of illness. The problematic nature of this somatic

biomedicine/biomedical model
The conventional approach to medicine in Western societies, based on the diagnosis and explanation of illness as a malfunction of the body's biological mechanisms. This approach underpins most health professions and health services, which focus on treating individuals, and generally ignores the social origins of illness and its prevention.

evidence-based medicine (EBM)
An approach to medicine that maintains that all clinical practice should be based on evidence from randomized control trials (RCTs) to ensure treatment effectiveness and efficacy.

fundamentalism is clearest in the treatment of so-called diseases such as depression and mental illness, where huge sums of money are expended on new drugs, but by comparison relatively little research has been conducted on the social and cultural dimensions of such illnesses. In the 1990s, there was a rapid increase in the use of psychotropic medications, including stimulants, for children and adolescents to treat attention deficit hyperactivity disorder (ADHD) (Conrad, 2007, pp. 126–7). Rather than focusing on the cultural and social factors that might explain the rise of ADHD, positivist- and RCT-inspired research would focus on the efficacy of various drug treatments or would search for the problem in an individual's biology (Reid et al., 1993).

Despite the many criticisms made of EBM health care, it continues to enjoy a high status among government agencies and various health-care organizations, including internationally. The real danger, according to Bell (2012), lies in its extraordinary power to influence national and international policy agendas:

> . . . there is a very real danger that such reviews will lead to the promotion of sexist, racist and classist interventions that are ineffective or actively harmful for certain segments of the population. . . there is also a larger danger that ethnocentric (especially Eurocentric or Americentric) interventions will be universalised as "best practice" for populations around the globe for which they are ill suited. (p. 319)

Social Epidemiology and Population Health/ Public Health Research

Epidemiological surveys that purport to be objective and value-neutral share many similarities with positivist science, and like EBM, claim to provide evidence-based data. Such surveys gather quantitative data, are typically very large, and generate statistically representative samples that can be used to generalize the findings to the general population. Conventional **epidemiology** examines the distribution of diseases and tries to identify the specific nature of the **risk factors** associated with the development of the disease that can then be targeted in both prevention and treatment of the disease (Daly et al., 1997). As discussed in Chapter 1, a classic example is the work of Dr John Snow, widely referred to as the "father of epidemiology," 150 years ago in England. Snow wanted to understand why so many people in London had become ill with cholera. Using statistical mapping methods, he found that the patterns of the disease could be linked with specific water supplies (Vachon, 2005).

Social epidemiology, which gained prominence in the mid-twentieth century, documents and analyzes inequalities in health at the societal level. A central question is who and what is responsible for population patterns of disease and well-being (Krieger, 2001). Its purpose is to provide a systematic and comprehensive study of relationships between health and a broad range of social determinants and factors, such as gender, race, class, Aboriginal status, etc. as well as social policies (Harper & Strumpf, 2012). Such research occupies a key place in public health policy both within Canada and international organizations such as WHO, and provides the basis to track health inequalities as well as structure interventions to mitigate these. For example, we know that HIV/AIDS is a global health issue that knows no boundaries. However, AIDS is unevenly distributed,

epidemiology
The statistical study of patterns of disease in the population. Originally focused on epidemics, or infectious diseases, it now covers non-infectious conditions, such as stroke and cancer. **Social epidemiology** is a subfield aligned with sociology that focuses on the social determinants of illness.

risk factors
Conditions that are thought to increase an individual's susceptibility to illness or disease, such as abuse of alcohol, poor diet, or smoking.

both within a country and among countries. According to the Public Health Agency of Canada (PHAC, 2011f) at the end of 2011 an estimated 71,300 people were living with HIV infection (including AIDS), representing an increase of 11.4 per cent from 2008. When the AIDS epidemic first came into public consciousness, prevention efforts were focused on the entire population. However, epidemiological research has demonstrated that men who have sex with men, injecting drug users, and those in prison are at a much higher risk than the general Canadian population (PHAC, 2008). Research also indicates that Aboriginal injection drug users in Vancouver are becoming infected with HIV at twice the rate of non-Aboriginal injection drug users (CIHR, 2006). Such findings illustrate the importance of prevention campaigns that target certain groups, making more effective use of resources. In the case of Aboriginal peoples, it is crucial that the planning and implementing of any public health strategy is carried out in partnership with the Aboriginal community.

Population health and public health researchers are among those who use quantitative methods of social epidemiology as the basis for their research. Different theories as to causes of health inequalities inform research in social epidemiology (Krieger, 2001). One such trend, informed by critical political economy, explicitly addresses economic and political determinants of health. Core questions include the impact of prioritizing capital accumulation, the impact of neo-liberal policies on dismantling the welfare state, or how social inequalities involving race, sexuality, gender, etc. play out within and across socio-economic positions. "The underlying hypothesis is that economic and political institutions and decisions that create, enforce, and perpetuate economic and social privilege and inequality are root—or 'fundamental'—causes of social inequalities in health" (Krieger, 2001, p. 670). Much of the current Canadian population health research operates from this basic assumption. For example, see the collection in Dennis Raphael (2009a), *Social Determinants of Health*. Using ecosocial theory is another approach in contemporary social epidemiology. This approach "embraces a social production of disease perspective while aiming to bring in a comparable rich biological and ecological analysis" (Krieger, 2001, p. 672). A key concept here is that of "embodiment," that is, how individuals biologically incorporate the material and social worlds in which they live.

A recent development in population health research methodology is to incorporate **intersectionality** theory (Bauer, 2014). Much of the documentation to date on health inequalities has focused on a single category of difference, such as "race" or sex, or has considered multiple social positions, but does not consider how such categories intersect to constitute health impacts. In such an approach, "the health status of Aboriginal women in Canada . . . would be assumed to be sufficiently understood through adding together the independent health impacts of being Aboriginal with those of being female." By contrast, an intersectional approach "assumes that an individual's experience, and their health, are not simply the sum of their parts . . . what it means to be a woman and what the health implications are, may be different for Aboriginal women versus non-Aboriginal women" (Bauer, 2014, p. 11). Incorporating intersectionality in population health research provides for a more precise identification of inequalities and helps to ensure that the results are more relevant to specific communities. A good example of intersectional quantitative research is that of Gerry Veenstra (2011). Using data from the Canadian Community Health Survey collected by Statistics Canada in 2003, Veenstra applied regression modelling to investigate health outcomes associated with intersections between race, gender, class, and sexual

intersectionality
A term coined by American critical race scholar Kimberlé Chrenshaw in 1989 to examine how race and sex/gender were mutually constituted for African-American women. The idea that one needs to examine how various biological, cultural, and social categories interact on multiple (and often simultaneous) levels that lead to oppression and inequality.

orientation. His research shows that each of the four axes of inequality intersected significantly with at least one other. "Multiple jeopardy," that is, inordinate amounts of disadvantage, pertained to poor homosexuals and (possibly) South Asian women who were at an unexpectedly high risk of fair/poor self-rated health (Veenstra, 2011, p. 10). Another Canadian example of intersectional analysis with quantitative research is the research by Karen Kobayashi and Steven Prus (2011) to study the intersection of age, gender, and visible minority status. They found that the healthy immigrant effect (see Chapter 6) applies to mid-life males, specifically for those who have migrated less than 10 years ago but the differences are not as consistent for women. "[T]he study findings underscore the necessity for policy makers to address the differential health care needs of immigrant adults by gender and age group" (p. 193).

Although useful as a basis for developing public health strategy, survey research privileges those aspects of social life that can be quantified and statistically measured. Quantitative research cannot uncover the social mechanisms that help us understand the reasons behind the observed correlations. Partly in response to the limitations of survey research, there has been a growing acceptance in recent years of qualitative research in social epidemiology (Muntaner & Gomez, 2003). Seen as a complement, it serves as a tool to find social mechanisms, such as racism or discrimination, that are not addressed in quantitative studies. And, qualitative information suggests different explanations than what may be conveyed through quantitative surveys (2003, p. 55). For example, there is an impressive array of survey and statistical data that demonstrate that, on virtually every health measure, the health of Aboriginal peoples in Canada is significantly worse than that of non-Aboriginal Canadians (Health Canada, 2012b). However, these data fail to examine "why" and "how" social-historical factors, such as colonization and racism, continue to play a role in Aboriginal peoples' daily lives to the detriment of their health. Qualitative methodologies, on the other hand, examine people's meanings and interpretations to help us understand the "why" and "how."

The Qualitative Tradition

The logic, theoretical framing, and practice of qualitative methods differ fundamentally from those of the statistical approach of the quantitative tradition. These differences are both the qualitative tradition's strength and its weakness. The strength lies in the qualitative method's ability to contextualize a situation and examine the meanings and interpretations of health-related issues that are inaccessible to traditional statistical methods. Its weakness is that positivist scientific methods and rhetoric still dominate in the spheres of policy-making, research funding, and the publishing of academic journals. Consequently, qualitative research and many aspects of life that are only brought to light using qualitative methods are frequently ignored and undervalued.

Qualitative methods differ from quantitative methods in two ways. First, qualitative researchers examine *meanings*. They explicitly examine how people interpret or make sense of their illness experience. While statistics reduce interpretations and evaluations to scales and numerical values, much of qualitative research is exploratory in nature. Qualitative researchers are interested in the stories, in the ways that people make sense, and in the way social interaction and culture change these meanings. Second, qualitative methods typically use a very different sampling strategy. Statistical studies generally use random sampling, which allows the researcher to generalize the findings to the population at large. The objective of qualitative sampling, however, is to reflect the diversity in a given population or to capture a targeted group to ensure specific experiences are represented, not to make statistical generalization. This is called **purposive sampling,** where the aim is to be able to describe the processes, meanings, and interpretations that lie behind the different aspects of people's experience.

Qualitative research aims to provide understanding of the meanings and details that shape why people do what they do. It allows researchers to identify interpretative processes to make sense of statistically observed relationships and provide a basis for possible interventions. For example, in Ezzy's qualitative study of mental health and unemployment, the focus was to understand why some people report feeling depressed after losing a job while other people report feeling much better about themselves (Ezzy, 2000b). Survey research had already established that about one-third of people who lose their job report feeling better, and two-thirds report feeling worse. A sample of unemployed people was not drawn randomly, that is, to ensure statistical representativeness, but purposively, to ensure that there were enough people to interview from both groups so that the processes that lead to depression or hope were clearly understood. That is to say, the sample was chosen purposively to ensure that the different types of meanings of unemployment were properly understood, rather than to ensure that they statistically represented the more general population of unemployed people.

Qualitative researchers also examine how individual meanings are shaped by people's cultural and social context. For example, "obesity"[1] is considered a major health concern today in Canada. It must be noted that this is a contested term and that Body Mass Index has been criticized as a tool because it does not differentiate between fat and muscle (it measures mass indiscriminately); as well, the cut-off points for what constitutes "obese" and "overweight" and "ideal weight" have changed over time. As well, it is not the best fit for all ethnicities. However, it remains the simplest and cheapest way to measure "obesity" fairly accurately and it is seen as a useful predictor of health issues related to weight. A recent Statistics Canada report cited by the CBC found that two-thirds of all Canadians were overweight, with 20 per cent "clinically obese" (CBC, 2011). In response, Canadians were admonished to make wiser food choices that are beneficial to maintaining a certain weight. However, what does being overweight mean, and does it have the same meaning for all Canadians? Using qualitative methodology, Ristovski-Slijepcevic et al. (2010) examined the social, cultural, and political contexts within which people make food choices and conceptualize issues of weight. Based on interviews with adult Black and white women and men living in Halifax, Nova Scotia, and in Vancouver, British Columbia, they found that although there was general acceptance of the discourse that weight gain is unhealthy, "there was much diversity in how such discourses were taken up, leading to complex combinations of body image and weight understandings based on gender, ethnic and regional background" (p. 326). For example, Black women were more likely than white women and all men to reject the general assumption that being thin is equated with healthiness. Their

purposive sampling
Refers to the selection of units of analysis to ensure that the processes involved are adequately studied, and where statistical representativeness is not required.

---

1. Although the term *obesity* is used extensively in much of public health research, the term is contested by many researchers who raise questions about the pathologization of natural body-weight, and point to the fact that calling people "obese" medicalizes human diversity. See Rothblum and Solovay (2009) for a discussion of these issues.

conception of healthy and unhealthy weight was in contrast to the medically defined standard. The authors concluded that interpretations of body image, weight, and health must be understood within the larger social, cultural, and political contexts in which people make choices.

Another example of how qualitative research can provide a more nuanced and comprehensive understanding in health research is evidenced by Boston's (1999) study of palliative care nurses in Canada. Nursing administrators had implemented a workload-measurement statistical system whereby all aspects of the nurses' work were quantified in an attempt to plan nursing requirements and to increase efficiency of services. Based on a qualitative study using 50 long interviews, Boston showed that this attempt to objectively quantify and systematize nurses' work failed to deal with the nature of nursing care required in a multicultural environment. The problem that Boston identified was not simply that the workload-measurement system had insufficient categories to cover the wide range of tasks that nurses consider part of their work. Rather, Boston argued that it is impossible to quantify many aspects of nursing practice that involve intuitive and personalized ways of dealing with patients in a culturally complex environment. In particular, dealing with patients from diverse cultural backgrounds requires taking time to learn, understand, and accommodate culturally distinct responses to terminal illness, diagnosis, and rituals associated with death and dying. These processes are extremely difficult to quantify. As a consequence, "that subjective 'inner' knowledge, which necessarily involves prioritizing cultural concerns, is left to 'fall between the cracks'" (p. 151). In short, statistical, categorical, and deductive methodologies for assessing and studying nursing practice miss many of the central tasks that nurses perform.

Evaluating the Quality of Qualitative Research

The criteria for what constitutes good research also significantly change between quantitative and qualitative methods. In survey research, studies are designed to be valid (to accurately reflect what is being studied) and reliable (or repeatable, and subsequently verifiable).

Surely, you might ask, qualitative research should also aim to be valid and reliable? However, the problem with these terms is that they ignore the way in which social life is a product of interpretative processes. Qualitative researchers tend to prefer to use the term **rigour** to avoid the positivist overtones of the terms *validity* and *reliability*. The aim of rigorous research is to closely scrutinize the meanings and interpretations of the people being studied (Lincoln, 1995). People's meanings change with time and depending on to whom they are talking. Qualitative methods try to explicitly engage with the fluidity of meanings and interpretations rather than avoiding them. Often this requires examining the social context in which an illness or behaviour occurs.

rigour
A term used by qualitative researchers to describe trustworthy research that carefully scrutinizes and describes the meanings and interpretations given by participants.

For example, Hornosty and Doherty's research on family violence in farm and rural communities found that meanings of family violence and people's willingness to report family violence are influenced by the values, environments, and familial relationships characteristic of rural communities (2003, 2004). In their interviews with abused women in rural New Brunswick, Hornosty and Doherty found that structural and cultural factors—such as geographic and social isolation, the lack of anonymity and confidentiality, patriarchal attitudes, community values, and rural identity—were barriers to rural women's both naming and reporting abuse. Farm women, they found, had additional barriers, such as concerns with the survival of the family farm and their attachment to farm animals. Their research shows that programs designed to address the needs of abused women must be sensitive to social and cultural locations to be effective.

Making sense of the data involves using inductive strategies that are sensitive to the social context in which behaviour occurs. In according authenticity to women's experiences in their everyday lives, the researchers gave voice to those whose views have historically been marginalized. In other words, an aim of qualitative research is to examine the contexts in which meanings and interpretations are constructed. Unlike quantitative studies that are concerned more with issues of frequency and distribution, the goal of qualitative studies is to grasp the subjective aspects of social life. Meaning and the interpretative process are integral to qualitative methods, and rigorous research explicitly engages with the interpretative process.

Analysis and Reporting of Qualitative Research

For qualitative research the structure of analysis and the nature of research reports are quite different to statistical studies. The analysis process does not aim to follow prescribed procedures to produce objective results, although good procedure is important. Rather, qualitative analysis methodologies, such as thematic analysis (Kellehear, 1993), **grounded theory** (Strauss & Corbin, 1990; Glaser & Strauss, 2012), narrative analysis (Riessman, 1993), and cultural studies (Alasuutari, 1995), all aim to analyze data by interpreting them. The process of interpretation can be described, but it cannot be systematized. This difference is clearest in the computer packages developed to assist qualitative data analysis. These computer packages, for example NVivo, do not analyze the qualitative data for the researcher; rather, they assist the analysis through sophisticated search, coding, and filing mechanisms (Rice & Ezzy, 1999). It is impossible to automate the process of qualitative data analysis, as can be done with statistics, because the process of interpretation and understanding is central to the analytic process. Since the heart of qualitative research is in the detail, research reports are difficult to produce as short summaries. This kind of research reporting typically requires long quotations and careful explanation of cultural and social context.

> **grounded theory**
> Usually associated with qualitative methods, it refers to any social theory that is derived from (or grounded in) empirical research of social phenomena.

Grounded theory is widely used in qualitative health research, and is the most-often cited methodology in qualitative studies in medicine (Sbaraini et al., 2011). It emerged in the 1960s from Glaser and Strauss's research program on dying in hospitals and their attempt to generate a theory grounded in empirical data (Walker & Myrick, 2006). Rather than having theory guide the research in a deductive manner as typical of quantitative research, grounded theory uses an inductive approach; that is, researchers first gather data and then systematically develop a theory. The data analysis process—a complex, methodical, rigorous, and creative process—that the researcher engages in is key (Walker & Myrick, 2006). It is aptly described in the following way: "If you're a grounded theorist, you engage a 'zigzag' approach to research—jumping from the field to the drawing table, then back again—in an ever-changing process of fine-tuning your findings. Grounded theory is all about having an open mind and seeing where the data take you" (Institute for Work & Health, 2012, available at http://www.iwh.on.ca/wrmb/grounded-theory). Dastjerdi et al. (2012), for example, used grounded theory to explore and understand the processes by which Iranian immigrants learn to access health-care services in Canada. They describe in some detail the complexity and various steps involved in analyzing the data in order to "reflect the logic of a participant's experience in order to provide authenticity" (p. 4).

In qualitative research, the voice of the participants is privileged, rather than that of the researcher. The goal is to genuinely hear the voices of participants and understand their perspectives in terms of their lived reality. The interviews and focus group discussions with participants must be read and re-read, thus engaging in a process of imaginative participation. In this way, it is possible to discover new meanings and see relationships between social phenomena. Qualitative interviews are not events in which objective information is gathered from subjects. People do not have objective, unchanging stories of events that they carry around in their heads and that a qualitative researcher can simply gather like statistical measurements. Rather, people shape and change their stories, often unconsciously, to fit the particular interactive context. Interviews, then, are moments of the co-creation of narratives (Estroff, 1995). This explicit engagement with personal subjectivity and the interpretative process may sound far from scientific; however, the alternative is to pretend that you can avoid the interpretative process. Qualitative researchers argue that it is impossible to avoid the role of subjectivity in the research process; rather, researchers must make their values explicit. The aim is not to avoid subjectivity but to allow researchers to engage in a dialogue with the participants (Lincoln, 1995). To do so requires researchers to be honest about the influence of their own subjectivity on the research process.

Innovative Directions in Qualitative Research

Despite the continued privileged status of statistic-based methods, qualitative research is becoming increasingly popular in studies on health and medicine. A specialist journal, *Qualitative Health Research,* was established in 1991. And, there are now numerous specialist research conferences, nationally and internationally, for qualitative health research (Sbaraini et al., 2011). In response to positivist critiques of qualitative research as being "unscientific," some traditional qualitative researchers attempted to present their research in standard scientific format and distance themselves from their research, claiming neutrality and objectivity (Green, 1998). The problem with this attempt to make qualitative methods seem more scientific is that it devalues the central process that qualitative methods aim to examine—the process of interpretation. While qualitative methods can be moulded to fit this scientific world view, researchers are increasingly arguing that such an approach is deceptive and does not produce research that is as useful, insightful, and respectful (Denzin, 1997; Ezzy, 2001). Presently, qualitative researchers are pushing their methodology even further away from the theory and practice of the positivist tradition, using research such as **participatory action research** (PAR), which argues for a greater degree of engagement by participants in the research process (Reinharz, 1992). More recently, qualitative innovators have looked to intersectionality, which, as we saw earlier, acknowledges the multiplicity of people's social locations, and **critical race theory** (CRT) to more specifically take into account the influences of racism.

Participatory action research is increasingly used in health and public health research. It has been described in the health literature as "transformative, an empowering process whereby researchers and participants co-create knowledge while developing a sense of community, educating each other by negotiating meanings and raising consciousness"

participatory action research (PAR)
A more activist approach to research whereby researchers work with local communities, social groups, or individuals to empower the group or its representatives. Often involves participants in formulating the research questions.

critical race theory (CRT)
A theoretical framework that posits racialization as a key structuring mechanism in society. Focuses on how socially constructed racial and ethnic categories are used to order groups in a way that disenfranchises and oppresses people. Goal is to not only understand inequities but to develop strategies to eliminate them.

(MacDonald, 2012, p. 43). It differs from most other approaches in that "it is based on reflection, data collection, and action that aims to improve health and reduce health inequities through involving the people who, in turn, take actions to improve their own health" (Baum et al., 2006, p. 854). Simply explained, it is collaborative research that is conducted with and for people, rather than on them, in a manner that leads to social change. PAR recognizes persons being studied as equal partners or co-researchers at the various stages—design, execution, analysis, and dissemination—of the research process (Baum et al., 2006; MacDonald, 2012). See Hornosty and Doherty's (2004) research mentioned above. Researchers engaged in PAR work employ various methods for data collection associated with qualitative research, including interviews, focus groups, and participant observation. But, some researchers may include quantitative methods such as surveys to gather supplemental information. PAR has been central to research in a number of areas including education, community development, feminist research and family violence research, as well as health.

PAR has increasingly been used in Indigenous health research, both nationally and internationally, and has the strong potential to decolonize the effects traditional Western research has had on Indigenous people (Baum et al., 2006). In its guidelines for health research involving Aboriginal peoples, the Canadian Institute for Health Research (CIHR) states that communities should be given the option of a participatory research approach (McHugh & Kowalski, 2009). Researchers in British Columbia used a fusion of Indigenous methodologies with PAR in partnership with an urban Aboriginal community in the Okanagan to undertake a case study on the social and health-service delivery systems Aboriginal people encounter. Evans et al. (2009) suggest such a fusion is a "particularly effective way of transforming Indigenous peoples from the objects of inquiry to its authors" (p. 893). McHugh and Kowalski (2009) developed a PAR project with young Aboriginal women in Saskatoon, Saskatchewan, to develop initiatives for action at the individual, provincial, and national levels to promote positive body-image experiences. While acknowledging that PAR is particularly useful for research with Indigenous peoples, McHugh and Kowalski explain that building relationships and engaging in the research process is not straightforward. In their paper, they describe some of the methodological challenges they encountered in the process.

PAR has frequently been used in mental health research and in response to survivor's movements' demands, such as the disability rights movement and the mental health-service–user survivor movement, for a voice in planning appropriate treatment and services (Baum et al., 2006; Davidson et al., 2010; Schneider, 2012). For example, Barbara Schneider of the University of Calgary used PAR with a group of people diagnosed with schizophrenia in two of the "Hearing (our) Voices" projects to investigate interactions with their medical professionals and to look at the issue of housing for people diagnosed with schizophrenia (Schneider, 2012). Based on her experience, Schneider concludes that her projects

> demonstrate the potential of participatory research to draw on the strengths and abilities of people diagnosed with schizophrenia. . . to offer significant insights into their own situations and experiences, to identify the kinds of treatment and support that will enable them to rebuild their lives, to contribute to the production of knowledge about schizophrenia, and to advocate for change in how people diagnosed with schizophrenia are treated. (p. 161)

She further suggests that PAR has the potential to promote health equity and social justice through its inclusion of marginalized people as equal participants and contributors to society.

Recently, researchers at York University and the University of Toronto have combined PAR with technology: Flicker et al. (2008) describe the e-PAR model that they developed to engage youth in community health promotion and to promote empowerment. Their model draws on participatory research approaches that acknowledge that local communities often have the knowledge crucial for addressing their own social problems. The unique contribution of this model is the use of technology as a means of empowerment. At the crux of this model is the belief that youth can play active roles as change agents to transform the world. As Flicker et al. argue, we live in a digital age and young people especially are actively engaged with social media. "The e-PAR Model defines technology as 'youth media' . . . incorporating a wide range of communication tools (e.g. the Internet, photography, video and music production software) that promote community development . . . civic engagement and social activism" (p. 288). The model was implemented in seven different projects with youth between the ages of 11 and 24. Based on those experiences, the authors conclude that the e-PAR model has the potential to transform approaches to adolescent health. The model has received recognition from bodies such as UNESCO and is currently being applied in a variety of international contexts including Kenya, Vietnam, Egypt, Israel, and Palestine.

In 2009, the International Collaboration for Participatory Health Research (ICPHR) was created to consolidate existing knowledge about the use of participatory research approaches worldwide to address health issues. According to the organization's "Position Paper," a goal of ICPHR is to enhance the role of participatory health research (PHR) in "intervention design and decision-making on health issues and thus to provide a means for people most affected by health problems to influence how these problems are addressed in society" (ICPHR, 2013, p. 3). The expectation is that PHR will be integrated in policy-making to address issues of health inequality in disadvantaged communities.

In her edited collection, *Health Inequities in Canada: Intersectional Frameworks and Practices* (2011), Olena Hankivsky speaks of "the transformational promise of intersectionality as a research paradigm for improving the understanding of and response to diversity in health and illness . . ." (Hankivsky et al., p. 1). Although intersectionality has been applied in population health, health services, and even some basic science research, it has not yet, according to Hankivsky, been successful in transforming mainstream health research and policy. Yet, she argues, an intersectional framework is essential when studying such a complex and multi-dimensional phenomenon as health. As we noted earlier, intersectionality is a research paradigm based on a key assumption that people have multiple social identities or positions that interact at multiple levels to affect health and well-being. It "emphasizes the ways in which differences work through one another to produce something unique and distinct from any single form of difference standing alone" (Hankivsky et al., 2011, p. 13). No one social identity is considered more important than another. So for example, in the case of a middle-class Black gay man, it is not class, then race, then sexual orientation, then gender, or vice-versa. Rather it is the intersection of these social identities in a given society at a given time that constitutes one's being. Whereas more traditional research, for example, may compare the health status of say Black men with white men, intersectional research guards against treating members of a single social group as the same and assuming they share the same experience. That is, it resists the essentializing of any social categories (Hankivsky et al., 2010). An intersectionality paradigm can be incorporated into numerous methodologies, including participatory action research, a social determinants approach, narrative-based studies, Indigenous philosophies, feminist-based research, political economy approaches, and interview and survey analysis. "[T]he important point is that there is no single ideal way to undertake intersectionality work; in fact, different kinds of complementary research are essential" (Hankivsky, 2011, p. 27).

De Leeuw and Greenwood (2011), for example, merge intersectionality with explorations about the social determinants of Indigenous people's health in Canada. They consider how "colonial constructions of indigenous identity lead to significant divides between indigenous peoples and into differential abilities to access health care or support services. . ." (p. 54). In their research, Lee and Sum (2011) used participatory action research and photovoice, "a methodology that employs photos, narratives, stories and discussions to assist research participants in describing and reflecting on their experiences" (p. 147) to understand health and well-being from the perspectives of racialized young women who live transnational lives, that is, women who have moved across numerous borders and cultural worlds prior to their arrival in Canada. "The stories and photos that co-researchers generated help reveal how macro-social structures such as nation, culture, and borders, among others, have diverse, generative, layered, co-constitutive, and interactive effects on the personal intimate aspects of their everyday lives" (p. 162). The women's definitions of health were multi-layered and do not fit neatly into Western biomedical definitions.

The preceding examples of intersectional research illustrate clearly why many dimensions of social location and difference must be taken into account in developing future research and health policy. Racial disparities in health outcomes have been well documented, and racism is understood as a social determinant of health in Canada (Galabuzi, 2009; Nestel, 2012). As well, a growing number of researchers have suggested that any study of the pathways to health inequities must incorporate a specific focus on "race" (Nestel, 2012, p. 8). Critical race theory provides the field of public health a new paradigm for investigating the root causes of health disparities (Ford & Airhihenbuwa, 2010a).

CRT seeks to uncover how racialization contributes to the problem at hand. Researchers employing critical race theory and methodology embrace the anti-essentialism of intersectionality but centre on "race" and racism as a starting point. "The emphasis on the disruption of racism and negative racialized relations, the centering of 'race' in the problematizing of social relations, underpinned by a social justice agenda and the transformation of negative social relations are fundamental to the identity of CRT methodologies" (Hylton, 2012, p. 28). In other words, CRT shifts the discourse from the majority group's perspective to that of the marginalized group (Ford & Airhihenbuwa, 2010a). The challenge, however, to CRT researchers is how to privilege "race" without losing sight of the complexities of the intersection of "race" with other constructed identities and forms of oppression. Ford and Airhihenbuwa (2010b) have developed a new methodology, the Public Health Critical Race praxis (PHCR), to assist public health researchers with using CRT to conduct health equity research. The PHCR schematic they've developed provides a road-map that indicates the order of how to proceed during the research process (including how to take a "race conscious orientation"), the main areas of focus at each phase, and the principles on which to draw (see Figure 3.1). Ford and Airhihenbuwa (2010b) suggest that PHCR advances the goals of public health in important ways: it improves the conceptualization and measurement of racism's effects on health; it makes health disparities central to issues of racial equity; it provides critical tools for conducting empirical research; and it assists in developing appropriate interventions (p. 1397).

Participatory action research, intersectionality, and critical race theory are important developments in the qualitative tradition in health research. However, it could be argued that these innovative approaches still follow a typical social science model for doing research. Some qualitative innovators, influenced by the postmodernist challenge to positivism, have experimented with other ways of doing research, exploring new writing styles and making the researcher the subject of the research. By suggesting that many ways of knowing and inquiry are legitimate, postmodernism made it possible for researchers to reconceive the objectives and forms of social science inquiry (Ellis et al., 2011; Wall, 2006). **Autoethnography** is one such method, whereby the researcher draws on her or his personal experience in a reflexive manner to understand a societal phenomenon. It is, as the

autoethnography
An ethnography that focuses on the experience of the researcher.

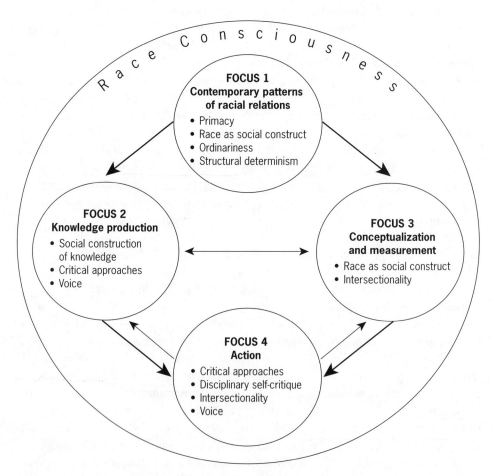

Figure 3.1 Public Health Critical Race Praxis (PHCR) Model and Process
Race consciousness, the four focuses and ten affiliated principles.

Source: Ford, C., and Airhihenbuwa, C. (2010b). The public health critical race methodology: Praxis for antiracism research. *Social Science & Medicine, 71,* p. 1391, with permission of Elsevier.

name implies, an **ethnographic** study that focuses on the experience of the researcher: "Autoethnography blurs distinctions between social science and literature, the personal and the social, the individual and culture, self and other, and researcher and subject" (Ellis, 1998, p. 49). In contrast to traditional scientific approaches that stress objectivity, autoethnography "accommodates subjectivity, emotionality, and the researcher's influence on research" (Ellis et al., 2011, n.p.).

Ellis (1995, 1998) provides a detailed study of loss and illness through her autoethnographic account of her 10-year relationship with her dying partner. Her autoethnography, *Final Negotiations*, is a story-like account that at times feels like a popular autobiography but that also demonstrates the influence of a careful social science approach to observation, analysis, and recording of experience. Ellis says that the aim of writing about her intimate experiences grew out of her frustration with traditional methodologies and reports that failed to engage with the detail of daily experiences of those living with chronic illness. There is no one correct way of doing autoethnography. It varies widely, "from the highly introspective, through more familiar approaches connected to qualitative research, to somewhat experimental literary methods" (Wall, 2006, p. 6). Ferrari and Drew (2005) constructed their autoethnography jointly to make sense of Ferrari's experience of dementia. See Box 3.1 for an excerpt from their book.

Ellis et al. (2011) write that autoethnographic research can "sensitize readers to issues of identity politics, to experiences shrouded in silence, and to forms of representation that deepen our capacity to empathize with people different from us" (n.p.). It opens up a wider lens on the world. For other examples, see Kim Foster's (Foster et al., 2005)

ethnography
A research method that is based on direct observation of a particular social group's social life and culture—of what people actually do.

Box 3.1   Excerpts from *Different Minds* (2005)

By Dr Leo Ferrari and Lorna Drew, Fredericton, NB

By sharing experiences of our uninvited encounter with Dr Alzheimer's disease we can break through the barriers of silence and loneliness. Let us speak out proudly and loudly about it—even laugh and realize that we too have our contributions to make to the rich tapestry of human life!

> The metaphor that I like is that my life is like a fog. I've lived by the sea, and I always loved the mistiness of it. You can sit on a boat and see the shore—and sometimes you can't. If I don't write down what I did yesterday, it'll be gone. But I can still see the distant shores. I can remember my childhood vividly, but I can't remember the last few days.
>
> —Leo Ferrari

> Stories heal, and making narrative sense of a life lived with Alzheimer's disease gives me both the perspective to stand outside events (and sometimes laugh) and the feeling that I have some sort of mastery over an illness whose symptoms more often than not play havoc with what used to be an ordinary life.
>
> —Lorna Drew

autoethnographic journey as a psychiatric mental health nurse, where she documented and reflected on her experiences of being an adult child of a mother with schizophrenia. This approach provided a new perspective that enhanced her ability to understand and empathize with her patients. This self-conscious orientation, she concludes, is particularly helpful for mental health practice. Dr Marina Malthouse (2011) provides a powerful narrative of a daughter's journey and the shifting nature of her relationships with her mother and her Alzheimer's dementia. She discusses how and why her relationship with her mother's behaviour shifted from one of frustration to acceptance and compassion.

Autoethnography has been criticized for being insufficiently rigorous, theoretical, and analytical, and for being too aesthetic, emotional, and therapeutic (Ellis et al., 2011). Some argue that autoethnography is literature, not social research. Others point out that there is considerable value in experimenting with a variety of methodologies, analytic procedures, and writing styles in order to better understand social life and to respond to the epistemological and methodological issues raised by the postmodernists (Richardson, 1994).

Conclusion

The methodology one chooses is shaped by the amount of existing knowledge about a topic, one's theoretical perspective, the nature of one's research question, the purpose of one's study, and the intended audience. Today, an increasing number of researchers are using a combination of quantitative and qualitative methodologies, often referred to as mixed methods research, to address a particular research problem. Despite some authors' claims and assumptions to the contrary, no research methodology is objective or inherently superior to another. Each type of research method reflects particular philosophical, political, and theoretical interests that can influence the collection of data and their interpretation. This means that the privileging of biomedical research methods tends to benefit the political interests of those involved in biomedical professions and industries. The privileging of qualitative research gives voice to those who are frequently marginalized from mainstream culture. This chapter advocates a balanced approach and highlights the contributions of social epidemiology and traditional and innovative qualitative methodologies to health research.

Summary

- Health research includes a number of different methodologies. Each methodology has its place and provides important and useful information about different aspects of contemporary experiences of health and illness.
- No research methodology is inherently objective. Each reflects particular political and theoretical interests.
- Some methodologies, such as RCTs, are often considered more important than others and, as a consequence, our contemporary understandings of health tend to emphasize biomedical and individualistic responses.

- In contrast, social epidemiology and qualitative methodologies informed by socio-logical theory are more focused on social, cultural, and public-health factors.
- Social epidemiology provides a systematic and comprehensive study of rela-tionships between health and a broad range of social determinants and factors, such as gender, race, class, Aboriginal status, etc., as well as social policies, and occupies a key place in public-health policy.
- Qualitative methodologies focus on interpretation and how individual meanings are shaped by people's cultural and social context. The voice of participants is privileged.
- Qualitative research is becoming increasingly popular in health research.
- New innovations in qualitative research include participatory action research, intersectionality perspectives, critical race methodology, and autoethnography.

Key Terms

autoethnography

biomedicine/biomedical model

critical race theory

epidemiology/social epidemiology

ethnography

evidence-based medicine (EBM)

grounded theory

intersectionality

participatory action research

positivist research methodologies

purposive sampling

qualitative research

quantitative research

randomized control trials (RCTs)

research methods

risk factors

rigour

Sociological Reflection: The Methods Made Me Do It

Identify three advantages and disadvantages of quantitative and qualitative research methods when studying health issues. Think of a health issue that is important to you. What methodology would be most appropriate to use to do research on that issue? Explain why you chose the particular method you did.

Discussion Questions

1. What are the implications for public health of the privileging of randomized control trials (RCTs) and evidence-based medicine (EBM)?
2. Identify two health issues that can be addressed by social epidemiological research, and two that cannot.
3. In what ways do innovative approaches in qualitative research discussed in this chapter strengthen the qualitative tradition?
4. What are the fundamental differences between quantitative and qualitative approaches to research in health and well-being?
5. Why do qualitative researchers place such importance on examining "meanings" and "interpretation"?
6. Why are positivist approaches so frequently used in health research?

Further Investigation

1. Find a recent journal article that reports a randomized control trial for the treatment of HIV/AIDS, cancer, or tuberculosis. Find another journal article that discusses the same health issue but from a critical perspective that focuses on the role of social and economic factors that shape the distribution of the disease. Compare and contrast these two articles. What different conclusions can you make from these two articles about the particular health issue you chose?
2. Why is it important to study meanings and culture in order to understand health in contemporary society? Draw on at least three published qualitative studies of a health issue to illustrate your argument.

Further Reading

Bryman, A., & Teevan, J. (2005). *Social research methods: Canadian edition*. Toronto, ON: Oxford University Press.

Denzin, N. (1997). *Interpretive ethnography*. London, UK: Sage.

Ford, C., and Airhihenbuwa, C. (2010). The public health critical race methodology: Praxis for antiracism research. *Social Science & Medicine, 71*, 1390–8.

Hankivsky, O. (Ed.). (2011). *Health inequities in Canada: Intersectional frameworks and practices*. Vancouver: UBC Press.

Reinharz, S. (1992). *Feminist methods in social research*. New York: Oxford University Press.

Rice, P., & Ezzy, D. (1999). *Qualitative research methods: A health focus*. Melbourne: Oxford University Press.

Web Resources

Community-based Research Canada
www.communityresearchcanada.ca

International Institute for Qualitative Methodology
www.uofaweb.ualberta.ca/iiqm/

International Collaboration for Participatory Health Research
www.icphr.org

International Consortium for the Advancement of Academic Publication (ICAAP): Free Resources for Program Evaluation and Social Research Methods
http://gsociology.icaap.org/methods

Sage Publications: Research Methods
www.sagepub.com/research-methods.sp

SocioSite: Research Methodology and Statistics
www.sociosite.net/topics/research.php

PART 1
The Social Production and Distribution of Health and Illness

All animals are equal but some animals are more equal than others.

—George Orwell, *Animal Farm*

The chapters in Part 1 concern the first dimension of the social model of health first introduced in Chapter 1: the social production and distribution of health. Most people generally assume that health and illness are simply undisputed facts, that medicine is best equipped to deal with health problems, and that illness is a matter of bad luck, fate, or individual responsibility. Health sociology debunks the myth that illnesses are solely the fault or responsibility of the individual. While health problems are experienced by individuals, they also have wider social determinants. Social determinants alert us to how social and economic environments in which people live and the distribution of societal resources can impact on people's health.

The chapters in this part focus on five social determinants of health and their intersections with other determinants to explain health inequalities in Canada: class, gender, "race"/ethnicity, Aboriginal status, and environment. The fact that there are significant social patterns in the distribution of health and illness—in which some groups of people suffer much higher rates of illness and premature death than others—implies not only that health inequalities have social origins but also that the removal of such inequalities requires social action and structural reform.

Part 1 is divided into five chapters:

- Chapter 4 examines the links between class and related social determinants of health and health inequalities.
- Chapter 5 focuses on women's health and explains why gender is an important determinant of health and illness.
- Chapter 6 explores the links between racialization and health; it also looks at issues related to immigrant health.
- Chapter 7 examines the reasons for the poor health status of Aboriginal Canadians: First Nations, Inuit, and Métis peoples.
- Chapter 8 considers the role of our environment in the production of health and illness.

CHAPTER 4
Class, Health Inequality, and Social Justice

Jennie Hornosty & John Germov

Vancouver pedestrians ignore a homeless man begging on the street. How does Canada's universal health-care policy try to address the social inequality of homelessness? In what ways does it overlook this population? How does social inequality impact peoples' health?

Overview

- What is class and how does it help to explain health inequalities in Canada?
- What are the major social determinants of health?
- How do these social determinants impact health?
- What can be done to address class-based health inequalities?

There is a significant amount of research that shows the connection between class and health. People with less income and wealth have higher rates of death and illness than wealthier people do. This chapter discusses the concept of class, provides up-to-date evidence of class-based health inequality in Canada, and examines different explanations of health inequality. Classes arise from the social structure; therefore, class-based health inequality needs to be addressed primarily through structural changes to the economy, to the workplace, and to the community, guided by public policies based on social justice.

Introduction: Why Class Matters

We all have some basic notion of **class** and class difference. We see such differences every day—between low-priced and expensive cars, fast-food and fine-dining restaurants, public and private schools, and downtown ghetto areas and exclusive suburbs. Debates over the importance of class focus on the extent to which class determines your **life chances**—that is, your chances of social mobility, of gaining an education, and of getting a certain type of job. While most people acknowledge the existence of class, few recognize that social class is one of the strongest inequality-based determinants of health in Canada (Veenstra, 2009b, p. 362). Despite access to free public health services through **Medicare**, the most disadvantaged people in Canada still die younger and have the highest rates of illness and disability. As the evidence presented in this chapter will show, class is a significant basis of health inequality in Canada. Yet what, exactly, is class?

Defining *Class*

Popular notions of class tend to focus on lifestyle differences, such as cars and fashion, as social markers of status. While consumption patterns may indicate class membership in a general sense, they shed little light on how class differences are generated in the first place. Sociological analyses of class tend to focus on the underlying factors that actually produce and reproduce class differences. The different theoretical perspectives that sociologists use (as discussed in Chapter 2) have resulted in continuing debate over appropriate definitions and theories of class (see Goldthorpe, 1996; Grabb, 2007; Wright, 1997).

class (or social class)
A position in a system of structured inequality based on the unequal distribution of power, wealth, income, and status. People who share a class position typically share similar life chances.

life chances
Derived from Max Weber, the term refers to people's opportunity to realize their lifestyle choices, which are often assumed to differ according to their social class.

Medicare
Canada's universal health-care program funded and administered by federal, provincial, and territorial governments.

Most discussions of social class are rooted in Marxian and Weberian approaches. For Marx, classes are a product of social relations and are defined by one's relationship to the means of production. Marx spoke of two major classes—the bourgeoisie (those who owned the means of production) and the proletariat (those who sold their labour power). However, he also described another class, the petite bourgeoisie (such as independent and small business owners), whom he expected would disappear with more advanced forms of capitalism. Weber shared Marx's belief that economic inequalities, that is, class, were central in explaining an individual's life chances; however, he refined Marx's notion of class relations to include hierarchies of prestige and political inequalities. Weber referred to these structures of inequality as class, status, and party. There is ongoing debate about the precise meaning of *class* today and how best to measure it. In fact, there are many models of class.

Canadian sociologist Edward Grabb (2009, pp. 3–7) points out that one ongoing debate is whether *class* refers simply to those who share similar economic circumstances or whether *class* should be used only when referring to a group of people who share both an economic category and a sense of common membership or purpose—what Marx referred to as "class consciousness." Grabb suggests that the different perspectives on class cannot be incorporated into a single definition. According to him, classes exist primarily as categories of people who do not necessarily share a sense of group membership. However, classes are not merely equivalent to strata or ranked statistical aggregates determined by variables such as income, education, or occupation. Class divisions involve more fundamental and uniform cleavages and are generally defined as economically based entities; they "exist as structural entities because certain enforceable rights or opportunities—such as the right to own and to exclude others from owning productive property—define them and distinguish them from each other" (p. 3). Both relations of domination and exploitation and the distribution of material benefits (e.g., income) are ways of delineating classes. However, there is no agreement about how many classes actually exist in modern societies. Nevertheless, Grabb goes on to argue that although Canada is complex and internally diverse, this country does have a class structure that consists of three basic elements. The first is the dominant class of large-scale owners of productive property (what Marx referred to as the capitalist class); the second is the subordinate class of workers who live by selling their labour power to the owning class (the proletariat); the third middle group or class is more heterogeneous, consisting of educated professional, technical, or administrative personnel, small-scale business owners, and various salaried employees or wage earners with credentials, training, or skills.

According to those working within a Marxist tradition, a relational understanding of social class is necessary where the primary organizing principle is material oppression. McMullin writes that material oppression occurs when the material welfare of one group depends on the material deprivations of another, which entails being excluded from access to productive forces (2010, p. 37). Like Grabb, McMullin suggests that in Canada there are three broad classes that can be distinguished on the basis of ownership of the means of production and occupation. Members of the upper class own the means of production and/or control the labour process; included in this group are company presidents and CEOs. The middle class includes workers who have more control over the work process than those in the working class; this group includes those in middle-management positions, professionals, and the self-employed. Those in the working class—the third class—have little control over the work process; they are excluded from access to productive forces and are in an oppressive relationship with their employers (McMullin, 2010).

To add to the confusion as to the precise meaning of *class*, some scholars use the term interchangeably with that of *socio-economic status* (SES). SES is somewhat equivalent to what Grabb refers to as "strata." SES is determined by ranking people, usually according to income, education, and occupation levels, and grouping them into corresponding high, medium, and low SES groups. Categorizing people into SES groups is a relatively straightforward process, and this is why much of the **empirical** evidence of class inequality tends to be based on SES. However, SES is a descriptive classification system and offers little insight into how and why such inequality exists, effectively ignoring such questions by transforming "the lived reality of class . . . to an abstraction for the purpose of statistical treatment" (Connell, 1977, p. 33). Nevertheless, class inequality in society is often described in terms of comparisons between strata, usually using income or wealth, as a basis of stratification. As we shall see, many studies on inequality in health use these as proxies for social class.

empirical
Describes observations or research that is based on evidence drawn from experience. Empirical observations or research are therefore distinguished from something based only on theoretical knowledge or on some other kind of abstract thinking process.

Class Inequality in Canada

Canadians tend to underestimate the amount of class inequality in our society. Although Canadians like to think of themselves as being a middle-class nation, the reality is that the gap between the rich and the poor in Canada continues to increase. While the poor become poorer, the rich become richer (Andersen & McIvor, 2013; Conference Board of Canada, 2011; Macdonald, 2014; Osberg, 2006). In 2004, for example, the average earnings of the richest 10 per cent of families in Canada were 82 times more than that earned by the poorest 10 per cent (Yalnizyan, 2007). In its 2011 report, the Conference Board of Canada raised concern that Canada has been unable to reverse the rise in income inequality, which has increased over the last 20 years. The Board went on to note that such inequality could undermine social cohesion, ranking it twelfth out of 17 peer countries. Using tax file data, Armine Yalnizyan (2010) calculated that between 1982 and 2007, "the share of all income going to the richest 1% almost doubled . . . rising from 7.9% to 13.8%. . . . By 2007 . . . the richest 1% claimed a bigger piece of the income pie than at any time since 1941" (p. 12). And, she went on to show that "between the mid-1970s and 2007 the share of income accruing to the richest 0.01% Canadians *more than quintupled*" (p. 13). Canada is not unique in this regard. While income inequality has followed different patterns across OECD countries, beginning with the late 1980s, income inequality has become more widespread. "The latest trends in the 2000s showed a widening gap between rich and poor not only in some of the already high-inequality countries like Israel and the United States, but also—for the first time—in traditionally low-inequality countries, such as Germany, Denmark, and Sweden and other Nordic countries . . ." (OECD, 2011a, p. 24).

While Canada has experienced relative affluence since the Depression years, this has not uniformly been the experience for all Canadians. Between the 1950s and the 1970s, Canadians enjoyed rising incomes and general economic prosperity. However, by the early 1980s family earnings began to stagnate despite the increasing number of women who entered the labour force (Urmetzer & Guppy, 2009, p. 83). Then, in the 1990s incomes for those at the very top began to increase dramatically. For example, "by 2007, the richest

0.1% of Canadians held 5.5% of total income in Canada, more than double their share in the early 1980's" (Yalnizyan, 2010, p. 12). Much of the rise in inequality that occurred can be attributed to cuts in government social spending, a change in tax structure that favoured the rich, deregulation, declines in unionization rates and a decline in large-scale well-paying manufacturing jobs (Anderson & McIvor, 2013, p. 1; Krugman, 2009, cited in Conference Board of Canada, 2011).

Inequality in Income Distribution

One frequently used indicator of class inequality is income distribution. A common way to measure inequality in income distribution is to divide the population into fifths or quintiles (each representing 20 per cent of the population) and then compare the share of total income that each group received. Data show that in 2011, the highest quintile got 47.2 per cent of all income earned in Canada. By comparison the lowest quintile received only 4.1 per cent of all income (Statistics Canada, CANSIM Table 202-0701). A comparison of income distribution at different points in time shows that the highest quintile received the biggest increase since 1976 (from 43.0 per cent to 47.2 per cent) while the portion of income going to the lowest quintile has decreased (from 4.2 per cent to 4.1 per cent). In fact, as shown in Table 4.1 all but the highest quintile saw their percentage of before tax income decline.

One way for governments to redistribute income so as to increase equality is through taxation and transfer payments, such as unemployment insurance, social assistance, and pensions. An examination of income distribution after taxation and transfers shows that the proportion each quintile received was altered somewhat. In 2011, the lowest quintile received 4.8 per cent of income after taxes while the highest quintile received 44.3 per cent. This suggests that transfer payments have some equalizing effect as they raise the income of those at the bottom, if only minimally (Curry-Stevens, 2009; Sharpe, 2011). However, the ongoing assault on social programs and the progressive dismantling of the welfare state by the former Harper Conservative government (2006–15) significantly eroded the effect of such transfers (Andersen & McIvor, 2013; Curry-Stevens, 2009; Osberg, 2008; Yalnizyan, 2010). It remains to be seen whether the recently elected Liberal government will reverse the previous cuts. The previous New Brunswick government was planning to

Table 4.1 Percentage of Total Before-Tax Income Going to Family and Unattached Individuals by Quintile, 1976–2011

	1976	1981	1991	2001	2005	2011
Lowest quintile	4.2	4.6	4.5	4.1	4.1	4.1
Second quintile	10.6	11.0	10.0	9.7	9.6	9.6
Middle quintile	17.4	17.7	16.4	15.6	15.6	15.3
Fourth quintile	24.7	25.1	24.7	23.7	23.9	23.8
Highest quintile	43.0	41.6	44.4	46.9	46.9	47.2

Source: Adapted from Statistics Canada. Table 202-0701. Market, total and after-tax income, by economic family type and income quintiles, 2011 constant dollars. *CANSIM* Available at www5.statcan.gc.ca/cansim/a26?lang=eng&id=2020701

bring in a flat-tax structure, which would significantly reduce corporate taxes and income taxes for those in the highest income bracket. While those in the lower brackets would also pay less tax, this would not benefit them to the degree that it would those who are wealthier. More importantly, a lower tax base would inevitably mean cuts to social programs, most of which provide benefits to those in the lowest income bracket. Such measures would further exacerbate the gap between the top and lowest quintiles.

Inequality in Wealth

Another important measure of economic inequality is that of wealth (or net worth), which refers to an individual's value of all assets minus any debts at a given point in time. Assets include bank deposits, investment certificates, pension plans, stocks, shares, bonds, mutual funds, owner-occupied dwellings, real estate, and equipment. Included in debts are mortgages, credit-card balances, and various types of loans. In Canada, as in other countries, wealth is generally more unequally distributed than income. Because wealth represents one's total worth, it is argued that wealth distribution is a more accurate picture of inequality in a society.

Wealth inequality in Canada continues to be high. In his analysis of Statistics Canada's 2012 wealth survey, David Macdonald (2014) shows that the top 20 per cent of families own almost 70 per cent of net wealth. The greatest dollar gains in wealth went to the highest quintile, whereas the poorest 20 per cent remain in a net debt position, owing more than they own. "The level of wealth inequality in Canada has reached such extremes that in 2012 . . . the 86 wealthiest Canadian-resident individuals (and families) held the same amount of wealth as the poorest 11.4 million Canadians combined" (p. 5). Table 4.2 shows the degree of wealth inequality since 1999. Although there is a slight decrease in the proportion of wealth that went to the highest quintile from 1999 to 2012, the poorest 40 per cent of Canadian families also lost ground in terms of wealth. Whereas the two highest quintiles saw increases of about 80 per cent in median net worth, the lowest quintile saw a decrease of 15 per cent. The lowest quintile had a median net worth of 1,100 compared to almost $1.4 million for those in the highest quintile. As illustrated in the following infographic,

Table 4.2 Distribution of Wealth (Net Worth) among Families and Unattached Individuals, Canada, 1999, 2005, and 2012

	1999	2005	2012	Median net worth (2012) Dollars	Median net worth 1999–2012 % Change
Bottom quintile	–0.1	–0.1	–0.1	1,100	–15.4
Second quintile	2.6	2.3	2.2	56,100	41.7
Middle quintile	8.8	8.4	9.0	245,000	78.8
Fourth quintile	20.1	20.2	21.5	575,500	83.6
Top quintile	68.6	69.2	67.4	1,380,000	80.7

Source: Statistics Canada. (2014). Table 3: Distribution and median net worth by quintile in *Survey of Financial Security, 2012. The Daily*, February 3, 2014. Available at www.statcan.gc.ca/daily-quotidien/140225/t140225b003-eng.htm.

Canada's wealth gap is illustrated in the infographic above, providing context for the amount of wealth held by the wealthiest 86 Canadians.

however, the concentration of wealth is even greater for those at the very top who increase their substantial wealth through the building and trading of assets that is facilitated by legal tax loopholes (Macdonald, 2014).

Inequality in Economic Power

Research on power and class in Canada shows that economic power is still highly concentrated among a small group of powerful and interconnected corporations. In the past, many of these companies were owned or controlled by a few established families who formed the economic elite—including the Irvings, the McCains, the Westons, and more recently the Stronachs and the Aspers (Grabb & Hwang, 2009). According to Bill Carroll (2009, p. 30), companies in Canada with assets greater than $25 million or annual revenue greater than $100 million claim 79.4 per cent of all business assets.

Among *Forbes* magazine's 2014 list of the world's 1645 billionaires, there were 32 Canadians (www.forbes.com/billionaires/list/#tab:overall). *Canadian Business* provides a list of the 100 wealthiest Canadians in 2014 based on their net worth in 2013. In the top four were

- David Thomson, who controls a media empire including major shares in the *Globe & Mail* newspaper, ranked 24th in the world; in 2014, with a net worth of $26.1 billion, the Thomson family was the richest in Canada.

- Galen Weston, the Loblaw's grocery chain magnate, ranked 134th in the world, second in Canada; his net worth was $10.4 billion.
- The Irving family of New Brunswick, who made their fortune off oil and related industries, were the third richest in Canada in 2014, with a net worth of $7.8 billion.
- Ted Rogers, Jr, the president and CEO of Rogers Communications Inc., had a net worth of $7.6 billion, making him the fourth richest Canadian. (*Canadian Business,* 2014. www.canadianbusiness.com/lists-and-rankings/rich-100-the-full-2014-ranking/)

How are those in the economic elite affected by financial crises? In 2008, Canadians, as others, were hit by a worldwide economic recession and thousands of workers were thrown out of work; however, this did not impact negatively on Canada's 100 highest paid CEOs. Of note is that there were only three women among the list. By 2013, the average pay of the highest paid 100 CEOs was 171 times more than the pay of the average worker. Put another way, these CEOs earned a year's worth of minimum wage work by 1:11 p.m. on January 2. Their average compensation was $7.96 million compared to total average Canadian income of $46,634 (Mackenzie, 2014). Not all of this income comes just from salary, however; a significant amount comes from share, stock options, and pension entitlements, which further increases CEOs' accumulation of wealth.

Debates about the upper class concern not only its wealth but also its influence—on whether it acts as a **ruling class**. While few theorists would argue that the upper class rules in a direct way, there is also little disputing that through their companies, members of the upper class can affect investment, employment, and the stock market. In this way, their economic power provides them with significant political influence. The upper class may not pull the strings directly, but its members share similar interests. For example, they may pressure governments to adopt policies of low taxation and deregulation to aid the pursuit of profit maximization; such policies tend to benefit the already well-off. However, such a situation is not beyond change; no natural law of profit and wealth operates here. Class inequality is an outcome of the **social structure** and, as recent history teaches us, the structure of a society can be subject to social change—social policies and taxation rates can work to either consolidate or redistribute wealth (see Andersen & McIvor, 2013; Carroll, 2009, 1984; Grabb, 2009). Class inequality affects us all; however, it needs to be remembered that the degree of income and wealth inequality captured by using quintiles masks the inequality within quintiles. Women, for example, on average earn less than men; racialized people, immigrants, and Aboriginal peoples often face discrimination in the labour force, as do peoples with disabilities.

On the other side of the economic coin, poverty rates in Canada have fluctuated over the years; however, poverty remains a significant problem. In 2007, 2.9 million Canadians (9.2 per cent of the population) lived in poverty (National Council of Welfare, 2009). In 2009, nearly one in ten Canadians was living in poverty. In 2011, according to data from Statistics Canada, this figure dropped slightly to 8.8 per cent (nearly three million Canadians) (Statistics Canada, 2013e). Racialized Canadians, Aboriginal peoples, people with disabilities, females, and children are those most likely to be among the poor. For example, nearly one-quarter (23.5 per cent) of people with disabilities and 17.3 per cent of off-reserve Aboriginal people were poor. The poverty rate for racialized Canadians is double that of their non-racialized counterparts (National Council of Welfare, 2012). For Indigenous children, the poverty rate is 40 per cent compared to 15 per cent for all other children (Macdonald & Wilson, 2013).

ruling class
A disputed term used to highlight the point that the upper class in society has political power as a result of its economic wealth. The term is often used interchangeably with *upper class*.

social structure
The recurring patterns of social interaction through which people are related to each other, such as social institutions and social groups.

One indication of the extent of poverty is the growing use of food banks. Food insecurity—that is, inadequate or insecure access to food due to financial constraints—is a significant social and public health problem in Canada. Nearly 13 per cent of Canadian households (4 million individuals, including 1.15 million children) experienced some level of food insecurity (Tarasuk et al., 2013). The situation is especially acute in the three territories. **Food security** is a social determinant of health. Children in food-insecure households are more likely to suffer from depression and asthma. Adults in food-insecure households have poorer physical and mental health and higher rates of chronic illnesses (Tarasuk et al., 2013). In March 2013, 833,098 Canadians used a food bank at least once: over one-third of users were children. This is 23 per cent higher than in 2008, before the economic recession began (Food Banks Canada, 2013). Another indication of poverty is the number of homeless people. It is estimated that in Canada at least 200,000 people are homeless in a given year; on any given night at least 30,000 experience homeless (Gaetz et al., 2013). In addition, it is estimated that as many as 50,000 Canadians on any given night are what is termed "hidden homeless"—that is, those who couch surf temporarily, staying with friends or relatives because they have nowhere else to live (Gaetz et al., 2013). Although individual experiences of poverty and homelessness have always existed, "homelessness as a social 'problem' has emerged only in the last two decades. Changes in our economy and housing market, as well as significant shifts in policies addressing poverty, have contributed to the homelessness crisis across the country" (Gaetz et al., 2013, p. 14). Social assistance, the Canada Child Tax Benefit, free drug coverage, and the availability of food banks ameliorate some of the worst excesses of poverty, but these do nothing to change the growing gap between the rich and the poor.

A decade of policies influenced by **neo-liberalism** and **economic rationalism**—during which financial and labour markets were deregulated, government spending was cut, and taxation was lowered—has revealed the **trickle-down theory** to be without substance. Proponents of trickle-down theory oppose state intervention in economic matters and argue that the best way to stimulate the economy is to provide tax breaks to corporations in the belief that this will result in more jobs being created with higher wages for the average worker. The assumption is that economic growth flows from the top to the bottom. This is the opposite of Keynesian economic theory, which urges active government intervention in the marketplace and public policies that promote full employment and price stability as the best way to stimulate economic growth. Keynesian economics is associated with the establishment of the welfare state, in which the government assumes primary responsibility for the welfare of its citizens in such matters as education, health care, employment, and social security. Neo-liberals contend that the welfare state interferes with economic growth and the virtues of a market economy. The result is a reduction in social expenditures in areas like the environment, health, social assistance, and social insurance programs, including unemployment insurance—that is, those measures that are important in reducing inequalities. In recent years, Canadians have seen a substantial erosion of a number of these social safety nets (Osberg, 2009, 2006; Whittington, 2013).

Inequality in Health

Canada is considered one of the wealthiest countries in the world and, generally speaking, Canadians are a privileged and healthy people. But health inequality, like social inequality, is a reality in Canada. Health Canada, according to its official website, is committed

food security
A state that "exists when all people, at all times, have physical and economic access to sufficient, safe and nutritious food to meet their dietary needs and food preferences for an active and healthy life" (Agriculture and Agri-Food Canada, 1998).

neo-liberalism
Economic policies and ideology that advocate a free market for the production and distribution of resources, an enhanced role for the private sector, and a reduction of government involvement in the economy.

economic rationalism
Term used to describe a political philosophy based on small-government and market-oriented policies, such as deregulation, privatization, reduced government spending, and lower taxation.

trickle-down theory
The theory that everyone benefits by allowing the upper class to prosper relatively unfettered. If wealthy capitalists are allowed and encouraged to maximize their profits, it is believed that this increased wealth will eventually "trickle down" to the workers.

to improving the health of all of Canadians, and a goal of Canadian health policy is to reduce or eliminate socio-economic inequalities in health (Wilkins, Tjepkema, Mustard, & Choini're, 2008). However, if we accept that we should aim to live in a society that has equality of health outcomes—that is, there are no health inequalities based on group membership, such as class—then by current standards there is considerable room for improvement. Studies of morbidity (illness) and mortality (death) have consistently shown that the poor have the highest rates of illness and the shortest life expectancy (Wilkins, Tjepkema, Mustard, & Choini're, 2008; Tjepkema et al., 2013).

As Chapter 1 discussed, health inequality was a key focus of early **public health** efforts in the 1800s, particularly through the work of Friedrich Engels, Edwin Chadwick, and Rudolph Virchow (Engels, 1958/1845; Porter, 1997; Rosen, 1993). Despite these early efforts, it was not until 1980 and the publication of *Inequalities in Health* (Department of Health and Social Security, 1980) in the United Kingdom, commonly referred to as the Black Report after its chairman Sir Douglas Black, that interest in health inequality was renewed (see Marmot, 2004; Townsend et al., 1992; Whitehead, 1998; Wilkinson, 1996). In Canada, the 1974 Lalonde report, *A New Perspective on the Health of Canadians*, and the 1986 Epp report, *Achieving Health for All: A Framework for Health Promotion*, both signalled the government's recognition that social and economic conditions had a part to play in health outcomes. Subsequently, Canadian researchers identified income and its distribution as one of the key social determinants of health (see Health Canada, 2002c; Mikkonen & Raphael, 2010; Raphael, 2009a, 2012b).

Are widening inequalities making Canadians less healthy? The unequivocal answer is "yes." Research in Canada and other countries has consistently found that social inequalities in society, no matter what measure is used, lead to inequalities in health (Health Canada, 1999c; Raphael, 2009a). Although the overall standard of health in Canada has improved, this high standard of health has not been shared equally by all sectors. Socio-economic status, living conditions, working conditions, Aboriginal status, the environment, and gender all have a bearing on the health status of individuals. Health status also varies across and within Canadian cities, provinces, and territories. For example, in 2009, life expectancies ranged from a high of 81.7 years in British Columbia to a low of 75.1 years in the territories, the lowest of which is Nunavut at 71 years (HRSDC, Health-life Expectancy at Birth; Nunavut News, 2013). Socio-economic factors are key influences in the health of populations; a wealth of international evidence has shown that there is a clear relationship between socio-economic status and health (Navarro, 2004, 2009; Navarro & Muntaner, 2004; Marmot et al., 1997; Marmot & Wilkinson, 2006).

Income is also a good predictor of mortality from a range of diseases (Auger & Alix, 2009; Raphael, 2009b; Statistics Canada, 1999; Wilkins et al., 2002). Canadians who live in the poorest neighbourhoods are more likely to die from cardiovascular disease, cancer, diabetes, and respiratory diseases than other Canadians. A review of Canada's census metropolitan areas (CMAs) found that life expectancy is highest in CMAs with the highest average household income, the highest proportion of post-secondary graduates, and the largest share of the population comprising immigrants (Senzilct, 2007). As Raphael (2009b) has argued, income is a determinant of health in itself but it also is a marker of other social determinants, such as education, working conditions, employment, food security, and quality of housing. A higher income also means greater choices and more control over one's life. According to the Second Report on the Health of Canadians (Health Canada, 1999c), low-income Canadians are more likely to die earlier and suffer more

public health/public health infrastructure
Public policies and infrastructure to prevent the onset and transmission of disease among the population with a particular focus on sanitation and hygiene, such as clean air, water, and immunization. *Public health infrastructure* refers specifically to the buildings, installations, and equipment necessary to ensure healthy living conditions for the population.

illnesses than those with higher incomes, regardless of age, sex, race, and place of residence. Susan Crompton (2000) found that despite the introduction of universal health care in Canada just over 40 years ago, low-incomes earners have lower life expectancies and higher rates of morbidity. This disparity exists even though low-income Canadians use health-care services more frequently.

Poor health, however, is not simply concentrated among those in the lowest quintile; rather, there is a social gradient that runs right across the population. Health status declines as one's socio-economic status declines (Health Canada, 1999c; Marmot et al., 1991). The Whitehall studies in England in the 1960s (see Marmot et al., 1991, 1999) first found a "social gradient" in the mortality rate of British civil servants, whereby life expectancy increased for each employment level up to the top of the public-service hierarchy. The social gradient of health was evident along the whole occupational hierarchy, suggesting that health inequality affected not only those at the bottom but also the relatively well-paid white-collar workers. The researchers also found that **risk factors**, such as smoking, drinking alcohol, and not exercising, accounted for only a small percentage of the social gradient and could not explain the health inequality between the occupational grades of the civil servants in the studies (Marmot et al., 1997, 1999; Marmot, 2000).

risk factors
Conditions that are thought to increase an individual's susceptibility to illness or disease, such as abuse of alcohol, poor diet, or smoking.

Subsequent research has shown that a gradient in health status from low to middle to highest income quintile can be observed on nearly all measures of mortality and morbidity. For example, Greenberg and Normandin (2011) show that life expectancy in higher income neighbourhoods was higher than that in lower income quintiles, with poor males being especially disadvantaged. As can be seen in Figure 4.1, the gap between the lowest and highest income groups for men was 4.7 years and 2.3 years for women. A similar difference in infant mortality rates exists between neighbourhoods with the highest and

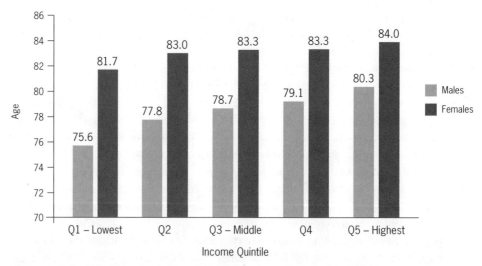

Figure 4.1 Life Expectancy at Birth, by Sex, Neighbourhood Income Quintiles, 2005–2007.

Source: Greenberg, L., & Normandin, C. (2011). Chart 5, Life Expectancy at Birth, by sex, Neighbourhood Income Quintiles, 2005–2007. *Disparities in life expectancy at birth.* Component of Statistics Canada Catalogue no. 82-624-X. Health at a Glance. www.statcan .gc.ca/pub/82-624-x/2011001/article/11427-eng.htm

lowest incomes (Butler-Jones, 2008). Twenty-two per cent of total potential years of life lost (PYLL) prior to age 75 among Canadians can be attributed to income differences (Raphael, 2001). A comparison of health-adjusted life expectancy (HALE) across income groups shows that at birth women in the highest income groups have a HALE that is 3.2 years higher than women in the lowest group. Similarly, men in the highest income group have a HALE 4.7 years higher than men in the lowest group (Health Canada, 2006a). A comparison of health disparities (such as rate of heart attacks and self-injury) by neighbourhood income quintile found a significant difference between the most affluent quintile and the poorest of 26 per cent (CIHI, 2013). Those in the lowest income quintile have more than double the chance of having two or more chronic conditions (PHAC, 2011e). In other words, Canadians in higher income groups live longer and have healthier lives than those in lower income groups.

In a nationally representative population-based cohort study in Canada, Wilkins, Tjepkema, Mustard, and Choini're (2008) found that regardless of whether status was measured by education, occupation, or income, people of higher socio-economic status had lower mortality rates than those of lower socio-economic status.

> The lowest mortality rates were among the university-educated, the employed, those in professional and managerial occupations, and those in top-income brackets. The highest mortality rates were among people with less than secondary graduation, those who were unemployed or not in the labour force, those in unskilled jobs, and those in the lowest income brackets. (Wilkins, Tjepkema, Mustard, & Choini're, 2008, p. 38)

They found a clear gradient with the greatest difference between those in the bottom two quintiles. However, it must be acknowledged that other factors such as Aboriginal status and racialization intersect with income and other socio-economic variables in ways that further disadvantage members of certain groups. Both women and men with Aboriginal origins had higher mortality rates than persons with no Aboriginal ancestry (Wilkins, Tjepkema, Mustard, & Choini're, 2008) and infant mortality rates among Aboriginal peoples is higher than the general population (Butler-Jones, 2008).

Various explanations are advanced for the strong relationship between income inequalities and health. These include the following:

1. Material/structural pathways. That is, income inequities lead to other material inequities, such as inadequate nutrition or poor housing, which may lead to health disparities.
2. Behavioural/cultural pathways. That is, health disparities may be the result of different behaviours or lifestyles among different socio-economic groups, such as smoking or drinking.
3. Psychosocial pathways. Stress associated with living at the bottom of the social hierarchy may lead to disease or related health outcomes (Gupta & Ross, 2007, pp. 27–8).

While individual income is clearly a factor in health status, some have suggested that the distribution of income in society is an equally, if not more, important determinant of health. In *Unhealthy Societies*, Richard Wilkinson (1996) presents empirical evidence to support a thesis that societies with lower levels of income inequality have the highest life expectancy. His argument is that once a country reaches a certain amount of wealth, determined by **gross domestic product** (GDP) per capita (per head of population), and undergoes the "epidemiologic transition" from infectious disease to chronic disease as the major cause of mortality, increases in national wealth have little impact on population health. Raphael (2001) notes that studies show that as economic inequality increased in Great Britain, the most affluent in Britain had higher death rates among adult men and infants than the least well off in Sweden, even though the British had higher absolute incomes.

Wilkinson argues that it is not the total wealth of a society that is important but, rather, the distribution of that wealth—the more egalitarian a society is, the better the life expectancy and hence the less likelihood of health inequality. In *The Spirit Level: Why Equality is Better for Everyone,* Wilkinson and Pickett (2010) examine hundreds of peer-reviewed studies and data from 23 rich countries to support the earlier thesis that more equal societies improve health for everyone. Using measures such as homicides, teenage pregnancies, obesity, mental well-being, life expectancy, infant mortality, and stress, they show that more unequal societies are less healthy. "Even when you compare groups of people with the same income, you find that those in more unequal societies do worse than those on the same income in more equal societies" (p. 192). A comparison of mortality rates between counties in more equal American states with those in less equal states, for example, found that at all levels of income, death rates were lower in the 25 more equal states, even after controlling for other variables (pp. 179–80). Wilkinson's earlier work spawned a significant literature debating the merits of his study and its conclusions. While some studies have supported his findings (see Raphael, 2001) others have cast doubt on the accuracy and strength of his claims. For example, in a significant study by Ken Judge and colleagues (1998), statistical associations between income inequality and population health were found to be small, posing "a serious challenge to those who believe that the relationship is a very powerful one" (Judge et al., 1998, p. 578). Considerable debate also exists around Wilkinson and Pickett's *The Spirit Level.* Critics have questioned their use and interpretation of data, accused them of exaggerating correlations and questioned their conclusions (Simic, 2012). See also Wilkinson and Pickett (2010, pp. 273–98).

The Social Determinants of Health

In Canada, as throughout the world, substantial gains have been made in improving health outcomes, but these have not been shared equally by all. For example, racialized persons, those with less education, Aboriginal peoples, and the homeless are at greater risk of having poor health. As seen above, class (i.e. income and wealth) is an important predictor of whether we are healthy or become ill. Research suggests that health inequities cannot be explained by a biomedical approach to health and illness. The **social determinants of health** approach grew out of researchers' attempts to find social mechanisms to explain why different groups of people experienced different degrees of illness. It has been a focus of much significant research at the global level and within Canada. The term is relatively new, although the concept can be linked back to early work of Rudolf Virchow and Friedrich Engels and other pioneers of social medicine.

> Social justice is a matter of life and death . . . inequities in health . . . arise because of the circumstances in which people grow, live, work and age, and the systems put in place to deal with illness. The conditions in which people live and die are, in turn, shaped by political, social and economic forces. (Commission on the Social Determinants of Health, 2008)

Dennis Raphael, the Canadian researcher most associated with the concept, defines the social determinants of health as the economic and social conditions that shape the health of individuals and communities. They are, Raphael (2009b) argues, the primary determinants of whether individuals stay healthy or become ill. Such an approach focuses on how society is organized and how it distributes its economic and social resources as predictors of health and illness. In other words, social determinants of health deal with two key issues: societal factors (e.g., income, education, employment) and societal forces (economic, social, and political) that influence the quality of societal factors that shape health (Raphael, 2009b).

Marc Lalonde's 1974 report signalled Canada's first government recognition that good health was influenced by a number of factors, including a person's social and economic environment. In 1986, then minister of health Jake Epp tabled a government framework for health promotion that highlighted the need for government to reduce income-related health inequities. The Ottawa Charter for Health Promotion, which developed from the First International Conference on Health Promotion in Ottawa in 1986, more explicitly identified the prerequisites of health as peace, shelter, education, food, income, a stable ecosystem, sustainable resources, social justice, and equity (Ottawa Charter for Health Promotion, 1986). These prerequisites, Raphael points out, are all concerned with structural aspects of society rather than with individual behaviours, as is the focus in medical and behavioural approaches. Concerned about what he considered shortcomings in the social determinants of health field, Raphael and others expanded the inclusion of social determinants to reflect more accurately the Canadian reality. The 12 determinants that emerged from the Social Determinants of Health Across the Life-Span conference at York University, 2002, have been further expanded to the 14 indicated in Box 4.1.

These have become the basis for critical materialist approaches to health inequality among Canadian researchers.

Box 4.1 Social Determinants of Health

Aboriginal status	gender
disability	housing
early life	income and income distribution
education	race
employment and working conditions	social exclusion
food insecurity	social safety net
health services	unemployment and job security

Each of these social determinants of health has been shown to have strong effects upon the health of Canadians. Their effects are actually much stronger than the ones associated with behaviours such as diet, physical activity, and even tobacco and excessive alcohol use.

Source: Adapted from Mikkonen J., & Raphael D. (2010). *Social determinants of health: The Canadian facts*, p. 9. Available at www.thecanadianfacts.org/The_Canadian_Facts.pdf.

Social determinants are not discrete variables; rather they are an interrelated set of factors. The scenario in Box 4.2 illustrates the mechanism and pathways by which socio-economic factors influence health. From a materialist perspective, the story in Box 4.2 also shows how individual behaviour, such as play, is structured by the material conditions of a person's life. Researchers working from an intersectionality perspective remind us that social determinants also intersect differently with different peoples' social locations. For example, the pathways through which material conditions operate, while similar, would be different if Jason was Jill or an Aboriginal child or a child of a single parent.

Research has shown that early childhood experiences help set a trajectory for later life: they are powerful predictors of adult physical and mental heath, such as coping skills, resistance to health problems, and overall well-being (Friendly, 2009). However, children's health is integrally related to the health and well-being of their families and the social and economic resources available to them. The fact, as we saw earlier, that a significant percentage of Canadian families live in poverty and experience food insecurity means that large numbers of children experience various forms of material and social deprivation (Raphael, 2014). Early childhood education and quality child-care programs have been identified as an important way of enhancing childhood development and promoting equity (Friendly, 2009). Yet, "Canada is one of the lowest spenders on supports and benefits of early child development" (Raphael, 2014, p. 226).

Income, education, and employment are inextricably linked; a good education is necessary to obtain a secure, well-paying job. These factors in turn determine the neighbourhood in which a person lives, the quality of housing, access to higher education, the ability

---

Box 4.2 But Why?

Why is Jason in the hospital?
Because he has a bad infection in his leg.
But why does he have an infection?
Because he has a cut on his leg and it got infected.
But why does he have a cut on his leg?
Because he was playing in the junk yard next to his apartment building and there was some sharp, jagged steel there that he fell on.
But why was he playing in a junk yard?
Because his neighbourhood is kind of run down. A lot of kids play there and there is no one to supervise them.
But why does he live in that neighbourhood?
Because his parents can't afford a nicer place to live.
But why can't his parents afford a nicer place to live?
Because his Dad is unemployed and his Mom is sick.
But why is his Dad unemployed?
Because he doesn't have much education and he can't find a job.
But why . . . ?

Source: Health Canada. (1999). What makes Canadians healthy or unhealthy? *Toward a Healthy Future, Second Report on the Health of Canadians*, p. vii.

to purchase nutritious food, leisure activities, and the quality of early childhood health—all of which influence physical, emotional, and psychological well-being. Employment and working conditions are important social determinants in that they are related to wealth and financial security, but also the working environment has an impact on physical and mental health. Certain occupations expose workers to hazardous materials. See Chapter 8 for examples. Unemployment and low income can lead to financial and life stress, which can have health consequences such as high blood pressure and heart disease (Butler-Jones, 2008). The 2007–8 economic downturn saw hundreds of thousands of Canadians lose their jobs, many of these in the higher paying manufacturing sector. Especially hard hit have been youth (those aged between 15 and 24) who are more likely to be employed in precarious, low-wage, no-benefits jobs. Even those with post-secondary degrees are over-represented in the part-time and non-permanent workforce (Foster, 2012). Studies have shown an association between unemployment and increased heart disease, suicide, and a variety of physical and mental health disorders, including depression, anxiety, disturbed sleep, and reduced decision-making ability (Canadian Public Health Association, 1996; Institute for Work & Health, 2009). Job insecurity is exacerbated by rapid changes in the labour market, workplace transformations such as downsizing and workers' "low level of confidence in the adequacy of the social safety net" in Canada today (Tompa et al., 2009, p. 93). Studies show that temporary and contract workers are more stressed and less healthy overall. Downsizing has been linked to more workplace fatalities and accidents (Tompa et al., 2009). In 2010, 27 per cent of Canadian workers described their day-to-day lives as highly stressful and another 46 per cent said that they were "a bit" stressed. Sixty-two per cent of those who said they were highly stressed identified work as their main source of stress (Crompton, 2011). Stress at work is associated with a host of mental health issues and, according to Thorpe and Chénier (2011), accounts for 78 per cent of short-term disability claims and 67 per cent of long-term disability claims in Canada.

Food insecurity and poverty go hand in hand. Living in poverty often means lack of food, poor housing, cold houses, isolation and lack of opportunity, worry, and despair (Frank, 2013). We are constantly told that to stay healthy, we should eat healthy and nutritious foods, including large quantities of fresh vegetables and fruits, although many Canadians cannot afford to do so. The major reason for food insecurity is inadequate income: "the risk of food insecurity escalates as the adequacy of household income declines" (Tarasuk, 2009, p. 209). The work of Lesley Frank, a sociologist at Acadia University, gives a human face to the meaning of poverty and infant food insecurity (2013). Her examination of the intersections between household food insecurity of low-income mothers in Nova Scotia and infant feeding shows mothers making compromises on a regular basis. On the basis of qualitative interviews, Frank demonstrates how and why infant food security is related most importantly to the food security of the mother, and the socio-cultural relations, including government policies, which make that possible:

> Being income insecure led to active breastfeeding as a means to secure food for babies in the face of poverty, *and* it compromised breastfeeding success through fears of failed production due to the poor diet of mothers, which often lead to non-affordability of formula and the need to seek formula through non-traditional routes. . . . [E]xternal social factors at the root of income insecurity found expression in socio-cultural food practices, of which infant feeding and families' responses to living with the condition of food insecurity were both a part. (Frank, 2013, pp. 230–1)

A lack of resources, for whatever reason, affects the degree to which people can exercise control over their lives. The social safety net—itself a social determinant of health—refers to a range of government benefits, protections, and programs that help to increase economic security and lessen inequality. These include social assistance, disability, maternity and child care benefits, (un)employment insurance, health and social services, and retirement pensions. These protections can lessen some of the stress of being unemployed, becoming ill, or growing older and are important for the well-being of individuals and their families (Mikkonen & Raphael, 2010). A strong social safety net is crucial for the overall health of people. However, government cutbacks and changes to key social programs over the last decade have eroded Canada's safety net. Neo-liberal policies have led, as we saw earlier, to a growing gap between the rich and poor. Recent changes to the employment insurance system and cuts to various social programs leave more people vulnerable to economic insecurity. According to Bryant, Raphael, Schrecker, and Labonte (2010), since the 1980s, there has been a weakening in Canada's capacity to address health inequalities, in part due to "shifts in the political economy of the nation that has led to welfare state retrenchment and governmental withdrawal from assuring an equitable distribution of the social determinants of health across the population" (p. 2). Research on the social determinants of health suggests that unless these trends are reversed, the overall health of Canadians will not improve significantly. And some populations, including Aboriginal peoples, immigrant and racialized groups, and peoples with disabilities, will experience more disadvantage than others (discussed in more detail in later chapters).

Explaining Health Inequality

Explanations of health inequality can be roughly divided into two main categories: individualistic explanations and materialist/structural explanations. More recently, some researchers have looked at psychosocial factors, such as social cohesion. Individualistic perspectives focus on individual biomedical and behavioural risk factors as the primary contributors to poor health. Conversely, materialist/structural explanations are concerned with the role of social, economic, and political factors in determining the social distribution of health and illness.

Individual-Level Explanations

Three examples of individual explanations (first introduced in the Black Report [Department of Health and Social Security, 1980]) include

1. The artifact explanation suggests that links between class and health are artificial and are the result of statistical anomalies or the inability to accurately measure social phenomena. This viewpoint is easily disputed by the vast amount of evidence that has demonstrated that health inequality exists (see Raphael, 2009a; Wilkins, Tjepkema, Mustard, & Choini're, 2008).

2. **Social Darwinist** explanations suggest that social and health inequalities are due to biological inferiority. This viewpoint acknowledges the relationship between class and health but explains it by assuming that inequality is "natural" and thus

social Darwinism
The incorrect application of Charles Darwin's theory of animal evolution to explain social inequality by transferring his idea of "survival of the fittest" among animals to "explain" human inequality.

inevitable, meaning nothing can or should be done about it. Such a viewpoint has been effectively dismissed by social-science research, but Macintyre (1997) suggests there is a "soft" version (her term) of this explanation that is still commonly ascribed to and has some explanatory power. The soft version suggests that social selection can play a part, whereby poor health early in life results in poor educational performance and occupational achievement. The central idea here is that people's health disadvantage (for example, disability) causes social disadvantage, such as poverty. However, ignored in this approach is the fact that these health disadvantages are often the result of socio-structural factors.

3. Cultural/behavioural explanations focus on the individual to explain health inequality in the form of risk-taking or illness-related behaviour, such as smoking, drug use, excess alcohol consumption, and poor dietary intake, as the primary causes of ill health. Such accounts have rightly been criticized for their **victim blaming** and overly simplistic account of inequality.

A focus on changing the behaviour of individuals assumes they exist in a social vacuum and ignores the social context, social relations, and social processes that affect their lives. Individuals are blamed for their "failure to seize the opportunity or to work sufficiently hard within the current social structure"; any inadequacies and inequities within the current social structure are ignored (Travers, 1996, p. 551, cited in Raphael, 2009c, p. 21). Furthermore, there are illness-inducing factors that lie outside an individual's control, such as stressful work environments or the marketing efforts of corporations. The concept of the **risk society** (Beck, 1992) epitomizes the social basis of risk-imposing environments that impact people's health and influence health-related behaviours.

Therefore, a focus on the individual as the cause and cure of illness, particularly through behaviour modification (which has often been the prescription of much medical, **epidemiological**, and psychological research), will have limited success and also assumes that individuals have the time, resources, and motivation to change their lifestyle.

Materialist/Structural Explanations

Materialist/structural explanations concern the role of social, economic, and political factors in determining the social distribution of health and illness. The focus is on the distribution of economic and social resources. Materialist/structural explanations have been particularly addressed by Marxist and Weberian perspectives, which direct attention away from individualistic and victim-blaming accounts and toward the basic class structure of society. The value of class analysis is evident when examining the role of income inequality in understanding and addressing health inequality.

Using social determinants of health, such as income, employment, Aboriginal status, or gender, to examine the reasons for health inequalities illustrates a materialist or structural approach. The focus is on how society is organized. Material circumstances are related to health directly and indirectly via the social and work environments, which have an impact on psychological factors and health-related behaviour. To illustrate how societal decisions shape health and health status, Brunner and Marmot (2006, cited in Raphael, 2009c, pp. 22–3) provided a model that shows the influences of social structure on health via three pathways: material, psychosocial, and behavioural. Material factors

victim blaming
The process whereby social inequality is explained in terms of individuals being solely responsible for what happens to them in relation to the choices they make and their assumed psychological, cultural, and/or biological inferiority.

risk society
A term coined by Ulrich Beck (1992) to describe the centrality of risk calculations in people's lives in Western society, whereby the key social problems today are unanticipated hazards, such as the risks of pollution, food poisoning, and environmental degradation.

epidemiology/social epidemiology
The statistical study of patterns of disease in the population. Originally focused on epidemics, or infectious diseases, it now covers non-infectious conditions such as stroke and cancer. Social epidemiology is a subfield aligned with sociology that focuses on the social determinants of illness.

are the concrete living conditions that individuals find themselves in, for example, type of employment and income. These factors determine an individual's degree of political influence and social standing. Those in low-skilled jobs are near the bottom of the social hierarchy and in turn have little political influence, which can create psychological stress and feelings of hopelessness and despair. These feelings can lead to health-threatening behaviour, which leads to illness and poor health. In turn, these behavioural responses can lead to organ damage, negative early life experiences for children, feelings of exclusion, etc. These different pathways, according to Raphael, do not occur in a linear fashion but, rather, operate in a feedback loop (2009c, pp. 22–3).

Building on Brunner and Marmot's model, Raphael (2009c, pp. 23–36) specifies four additional specific pathways that mediate the social determinants of health and health status: materialist, neo-materialist, life-course, and social comparison models. He explains that from a materialist view, the three key mechanisms are (1) experience of material living; (2) experience of psychological stress; and (3) adoption of health-supporting or health-threatening behaviours. The first component, the quality of material life conditions, influences individual development, family life, and community environments. Poverty and wealth, for example, are associated with the likelihood of developing physical problems, such as chronic disease; developmental problems, such as impaired cognitive abilities; educational problems, including learning disabilities; and social problems, such as dysfunctional family life. The second component of this model focuses on the relationship between living conditions and life-threatening stress as explained by Brunner and Marmot (2006). The third component focuses on the relationship between stress, a consequence of poor material conditions, and various health-threatening behaviours. As Raphael notes, a number of Canadian studies have found that the unemployed, people with low income, and those with inadequate housing are less likely to be physically active and are more likely to consume excessive alcohol or to smoke. Chapter 7 addresses these pathways from the experiences of Aboriginal peoples in Canada.

Neo-materialist explanations share the basic premises with materialism as to the importance of material conditions in explaining health outcomes, but extend their analysis to looking at how these living conditions come about. That is, neo-materialist explanations look at how various societies allocate economic and social resources among their citizens. One explanation as to why Canadians generally enjoy better health than Americans as measured by infant mortality rates and life expectancy is that Canada has a more equitable distribution of income and wealth, as a result of its redistributive income policies. (A closer look at the health of Canadians is found in Chapter 13.) Materialist and neo-materialist explanations are favoured by Marxists and others working within a political economy perspective. Of concern is how to change the inequitable material conditions in which people find themselves. Such analysis is often situated within a **social justice** framework, and may include policy recommendations to eliminate social inequalities.

social justice
A belief system that gives high priority to the interests of the least advantaged.

Life-course approaches pay attention to how the various social determinants of health influence health across the lifespan and emphasize the accumulated effects of adverse social and economic conditions. Hertzman (2000a, cited in Raphael, 2009c) outlines three types of health effects that are relevant: latent effects, pathway effects, and cumulative effects. Latent effects are biological or developmental early life experiences, such as low birth weight, which can be good predictors of heart disease and adult-onset diabetes in later life. Similarly, early exposure to environmental toxins can lead to respiratory problems in adults. Pathway effects refer to experiences that set individuals onto trajectories that influence health and well-being over the lifespan. For example, living conditions influence children's reading ability, which can lead to lower educational achievements, which can result in poor employment opportunities, which results in lower income and a greater likelihood of illness and poor health. Cumulative effects refer to the accumulation of these various advantages or disadvantages over time.

Finally, explanations of health inequality based on the social comparison approach (similar to psychosocial explanations) focus on social distance and individuals' position in a social hierarchy as an explanation of health differences. The argument is that in unequal societies individuals compare their status and material conditions to that of others. Feelings of shame, worthlessness, and envy can lead individuals to participate in conspicuous consumption, to take on additional employment, or to adopt poor coping behaviours, such as smoking, alcohol consumption, or overeating—all of which lead to negative health outcomes. Inequalities create hierarchies that at the community level can weaken social cohesion, making individuals more distrusting of one other, and result in a deterioration of communal structures and social programs. See, for example, Wilkinson and Pickett (2010) for a discussion as to how the inequitable distribution of wealth leads to decreased social cohesion and its negative impact on health.

Psychosocial Explanations

A number of researchers more recently have pointed to psychosocial factors and the lack of **social cohesion** or **social capital** as the basis for the persistence of health inequality in developed countries. The psychosocial thesis is a neo-functionalist perspective that proposes that societies with greater income inequality have less social cohesion or social capital. The idea of social cohesion or social capital is a reworking of Émile Durkheim's (1984/1893; 1951/1897) concept of social solidarity. More recently, the concept of social capital has been advanced in the work of Pierre Bourdieu (1986), James Coleman (1988), and Robert Putnam (1993). Social capital refers to social relations and networks that exist among social groups and communities and that provide access to resources and opportunities for mutual benefit. Social capital depends on a high level of community participation, altruism, trust, and an expectation of reciprocity. It has been suggested that a lack of social capital or social cohesion explains why certain social groups adopt health-damaging behaviour, such as using alcohol or drugs. The assumption is that access to social capital will lead to improved health outcomes by lowering stress and by providing outlets for social interaction and opportunities for enhancing control over one's life through democratic participation in community life (Winter, 2000a, b). It is interesting to note that working-class examples of social capital, such as collective action through union involvement, are seldom taken into account as evidence of social cohesion by psychosocial proponents (Muntaner & Lynch, 1999).

Critics point out that not all groups in society have the same access to social capital. Differential access to social capital based on identities such as "race," class, and gender is a reality in Canadian society. Proponents of social capital also downplay the

social cohesion
A term used to refer to the social ties that are the basis for group behaviour and integration. See *social capital*.

social capital
A term used to refer to social relations, networks, norms, trust, and reciprocity between individuals that facilitate co-operation for mutual benefit.

possibility that it can have negative implications, whereby communities and membership of certain clubs and associations can be used for the social exclusion of others, such as ethnic minorities.

The preferred policy prescription of psychosocial approaches is to facilitate social cohesion (trust, reciprocity, co-operation, community participation) rather than advocate political and economic change, an exception being Wilkinson and Pickett's approach (2010). Class relations that create income inequality in the first place are downplayed (Coburn, 2000; Lynch, 2000; Muntaner & Lynch, 1999; Raphael, 2001). As David Coburn (2000) argues, there is an implicit assumption that wider reform, such as income redistribution to decrease inequality, is beyond reach. Instead, attention is focused on psychosocial factors at the level of the individual and the community in which an individual lives rather than on the wider structural factors, such as the social and economic policies which governments pursue that foster economic inequality. By marginalizing the role of public policy in both undermining and creating social capital, there is the potential to fall into the trap of a "community-level version of 'blaming the victim' " (Muntaner & Lynch, 1999, p. 59).

Conclusion

Class matters. The concept of social class is difficult to operationalize definitively in modern complex societies. Different theorists have different notions of how to define *class*. Nevertheless, the concept remains a useful one since it makes clear that the unequal distribution of wealth and power is embedded in the social structure. The importance of a class analysis becomes evident when we look at the distribution of mortality and morbidity within populations; the links between lower social class and poor health are no longer disputed. Income and wealth differences are often proxies of class used to explain the degree of class-based health inequalities. This social patterning of health inequalities makes clear that the different outcomes are not simply a matter of individual behaviour. Rather, individuals work and live in social contexts that create exposure to health-enhancing or health-damaging environments. Besides looking at class, researchers operating from a materialist or neo-materialist framework consider other social and political factors to better understand the root causes of differences in health status. The social determinants of health approach, which expands beyond class, provides a framework for explaining the different pathways through which economic, social, and political factors affect health status. Health determinants such as "race," gender, Aboriginal status, employment, food security, income, and education intersect and mutually reinforce one another in different and complex ways. All of which occurs within the context today of class inequality, neo-liberalism, and globalization. It is also important to make a distinction between health inequality and health inequity. Health inequality refers to the different health statuses associated with various social groups, for example in terms of class, gender, ethnicity, and indigeneity. Health inequity refers to whether such inequalities are unjust and avoidable. The concern is whether a society provides the conditions necessary for optimal health, such as adequate income, food, employment, social inclusion, for everyone equally.

Summary

- Following Marx and Weber, class refers generally to economic inequalities.
- Class inequality exists in Canada, with the gap between the rich and poor, as measured by income and wealth, increasing.
- Poverty remains a significant problem; large numbers of Canadians experience food insecurity.
- Research consistently provides evidence of class-based health inequalities. Rates of mortality and morbidity are higher among people in the lower class.
- There is evidence of a social gradient of health.
- Some argue that more egalitarian societies have better health outcomes for everyone.
- The social patterning of health inequality indicates that differences are not simply a matter of individual behaviour.
- The social determinants of health are the economic and social conditions that affect the health of individuals and social groups. Fourteen different social determinants have been identified as being important in Canada.
- The social determinants of health are not discrete variables, but intersect in complex ways. Researchers study the different pathways by which socio-economic factors influence health. Research shows that certain groups of people experience more disadvantage than others.
- There are two main types of explanations for health inequality: individualistic and materialist/structural.
- Individual-level explanations look at differences in behaviour for an explanation.
- Materialist/structural explanations look to how a society is organized and the role of social, economic, and political factors
- Psychosocial explanations—somewhat of a hybrid—look at social capital and social cohesion to explain health differences.

Key Terms

class (or social class)
economic rationalism
empirical
epidemiology/social
  epidemiology
food security
gross domestic product
  (GDP)
life chances

Medicare
neo-liberalism
public health/public
  health infrastructure
risk factors
risk society
ruling class
social capital
social cohesion

social Darwinism
social determinants
  of health
social justice
social structure
trickle-down theory
victim blaming

Sociological Reflection: Examining Social Determinants

Raphael (2009b, c, 2006) and others suggest that social determinants of health are important predictors of health outcomes. Which of the determinants mentioned do you consider most important, and why? Take one social determinant and, using an empirical example, explain the pathways through which it affects health.

Discussion Questions

1. What might be done to increase public awareness about the significance of the social determinants of health?
2. In what ways can class analysis shed light on why health inequality exists?
3. How might the collapse of oil prices in Alberta and Newfoundland affect the health of the people? Will certain groups of people be more affected than others?
4. How can we explain the persistence of health inequalities in Canada despite our system of universal health care?
5. Why is an intersectionality approach to health essential for an understanding of the existence of health inequalities?
6. Given that there are social patterns of health-related behaviour, to what extent are individuals responsible for their health?

Further Investigation

1. For a two-week period, analyze how your local newspaper covers health-related stories. Is there a particular bias in terms of how health issues are covered? If you were basing your understanding of the causes of health and illness on these media accounts, what conclusions about health would you come to?
2. Equal access to health care does not lead to equal health outcomes. Discuss.
3. Health education as a policy response to addressing health inequality individualizes the social origins of illness in a risk society. Discuss.

Further Reading

Armstrong, P., Armstrong, H., & Coburn, D. (Eds.). (2001). *Unhealthy times: Political economy perspectives on health and care.* Toronto, ON: Oxford University Press.

Butler-Jones, D. (2008). *Report on the state of public health in Canada: Addressing health inequalities.* Ottawa, ON: Public Health Agency of Canada.

Coburn, D. (2009). Inequality and health. In L. Panitch & C. Leys (Eds.), *Morbid symptoms: Health under capitalism.* London: Merlin Press.

Cockerham, W.C. (2013). *Social causes of health and disease* (2nd ed.). Cambridge: Polity Press.

Hankivsky, O. (Ed.). (2011). *Health inequities in Canada: Intersectional frameworks and practices.* Vancouver: UBC Press

Marmot, M., & Wilkinson, R.G. (Eds.). (2006). *Social determinants of health* (5th ed.). Oxford, UK: Oxford University Press.

Mikkonen, J., & Raphael, D. (2010). *Social determinants of health: The Canadian facts.* Toronto: York University School of Health Policy and Management. Available at www.thecanadianfacts.org/

Muntaner, C., Lynch, J., & Davey Smith, G. (2001). Social capital, disorganized communities and the third way: Understanding the retreat from structural inequalities in epidemiology and public health. *International Journal of Health Services, 31*(2), 213–37.

Navarro, V. (Ed.). (2007). *Neoliberalism, globalization and inequalities: Consequences for health and quality of life.* Amityville, NY: Baywood Publishing.

Raphael, D. (Ed.). (2009). *The social determinants of health* (2nd ed.). Toronto, ON: Canadian Scholars' Press.

Raphael, D. (Ed.). (2012). *Tackling health inequalities: Lessons from international experiences.* Toronto, ON: Canadian Scholars' Press.

Waitzkin, H. (2000). *The second sickness: Contradictions of capitalist health care* (2nd ed.). Lanham, MD: Rowman & Littlefield.

Wilkinson, R., & Pickett, K. (2010). *The spirit level: Why equality is better for everyone.* London: Penguin Books.

Web Resources

Canadian Centre for Policy Alternatives (CCPA)
www.policyalternatives.ca

Canadian Council on Social Development (CCSD)
www.ccsd.ca/

Canadian Public Health Association
http://www.cpha.ca/en/programs/policy.aspx

Centre for Social Justice (CSJ)
www.socialjustice.org

Food Banks Canada
http://www.foodbankscanada.ca

International Society for Equity in Health (ISEQH)
www.iseqh.org

Inequality.org
www.inequality.org

Povnet
www.povnet.org/site-map

Public Health Agency of Canada: Population Health Approach
www.phac-aspc.gc.ca/ph-sp/index-eng.php

Statistics Canada: Research Projects from the National Longitudinal Survey of Children and Youth (NLSCY)
http://www.statcan.gc.ca/rdc-cdr/proje_nlscy-elnej-eng.htm

UCL Institute of Health Equity
http://www.instituteofhealthequity.org/articles

Upstream
www.thinkupstream.net/about_upstream

World Health Organization (WHO): Social Determinants of Health
www.who.int/social_determinants/en/

CHAPTER 5
Women's Health in Context: Gender Issues

Pat Armstrong

Dr Carys Massarella is lead physician at the Quest Community Health Centre in St Catharines, one of the few transgender-care clinics in Canada. Canada's transgender community experiences significant difficulty accessing medical care. What might prevent a transgender Canadian from accessing health care?

Overview

- Why focus on women's health?
- Why explore differences among women?
- Why does context matter in health?

Women's bodies must be understood within a context characterized by inequities not only between women and men but also among women. This context—which includes the social and physical environments, employment, and income—structures inequities in ways that can be harmful to health and that are unequally harmful to women and men. Similarly, the way health services are organized and practised has unequal consequences for women as patients and as care providers, and can promote inequities among women. Personal health practices and educational achievement matter, as do coping skills and social networks—so, too, does genetic endowment. But until we address these structural and health inequities through public policy and educate both policy-makers and health practitioners about how gender matters, we cannot expect women or men to live lives that are as healthy as possible.

Introduction: Contextualizing Women's Health

This chapter is about women's health, broadly defined. Too often, women's health is reduced to a discussion of their reproductive organs. Indeed, women's health issues are understood as universal and are, therefore, universally interpreted, treated, and experienced. This chapter challenges those assumptions, locating women's health within global, national, regional, and local contexts and in what Dorothy Smith (1990) calls **relations of ruling**. Bodies are not irrelevant, but they can only be understood within specific locations, times, spaces, and relations. Those relations are highly gendered and characterized by inequalities. The focus here is on Canada and Canadian research, policies, and practices, with Canada understood within the larger context of global patterns and exchange. Although one country serves as a focus and a way of illustrating the importance of specific locations, many of the patterns can be found throughout the high-income countries.

Feminist political economy provides the theoretical frame for this chapter, although this approach is informed by a range of perspectives. Starting from this framework means emphasizing **context** and the inequities shaped by political and economic forces, including those related to **gender**. At the same time, most modernist and post-structuralist perspectives teach us to challenge the **dichotomies** that have often been part of political economy and to attend to discourses (Moss & Teghtsoonian, 2007) while other feminist approaches stress the intersection of gender and class with other social, sexual, and geographic locations (Hankivsky et al., 2011).

Because **bodies** have been the starting point for much of the literature on women's health, the chapter begins with an examination of the role women's bodies play in shaping

relations of ruling
Dorothy Smith's term for the way social processes are structured by the powerful in ways that shape our consciousness and our practices.

context
The social, political, physical, and economic environment.

gender
Most frequently understood as "a multidimensional social construct that is culturally based and historically specific, and thus constantly changing" (Johnson et al., 2009, p. 6), but this chapter challenges the possibility of separating gender from sex.

dichotomies
Distinctions made between two parts that are understood to be distinct and quite different.

bodies
Material constructs, usually talked about as physically separate from the environment but understood here as shaped by the environment.

their health. Because context matters in the very structure of bodies as well as in their treatment, the chapter then moves on to explore the contexts that shape women's health.

Nature and Nurture

There have long been debates in the social sciences about what is biologically determined and what is socially constructed, arguments often characterized as *nature* versus *nurture*. In briefly reviewing the issues in the debates, this section seeks to make three basic points. First, there are no simple dichotomies between the physical and the social or even between women and men. This first point leads to the second one: namely, that all health issues are women's issues while recognizing that there are significant differences among women and no clear boundaries among and within genders. Third, bodies still matter and there are broad similarities among women related to their bodies that must be taken into account even while acknowledging that there are a host of other factors that shape bodies in variable ways. Equally important, women frequently are treated as a group in ways that shape their opportunities.

Traditionally in the social sciences, *sex* is used to refer to bodies. Based on their review of the term's usage, Johnson et al. (2009) conclude that **sex** "is a multidimensional biological construct that encompasses anatomy, physiology, genes, and hormones, which together affect how we are labelled and treated in the world" (p. 5). *Gender*, on the other hand, is "a multidimensional social construct that is culturally based and historically specific, and thus constantly changing" (p. 6).

This notion of sex has helped us explore differences between women and men that go well beyond those linked to reproduction. So, for example, research by Abramson (2009, p. 54) has shown that women's "cardiovascular risk factors and symptoms differ from those of men," with "women more likely to experience vague pain or discomfort in the chest, neck, back or arms" (p. 53). Such evidence helps alert physicians and women to the possibility that symptoms in women may not follow what are thought to be the key indicators of a heart attack and thus avoid an untimely death. This evidence also emphasizes the importance of exploring the possibility that differences shape all aspects of bodies and not just those related to breasts, wombs, and hormones. However, it is important to note that Abramson talks about women being more likely to have these experiences and symptoms of heart attacks. She is not setting out a dichotomy, a clear line between women and men, but, rather, identifying patterns that are more common in women than in men. Part of the reason it is difficult to draw clear lines between women and men is that nurture shapes nature, creating biological differences among women as well as between women and men. As Fausto-Sterling (2005) concludes in the first of two articles that use research on bones to explore the impact of anatomies and physiology, the "sex-gender or nature-nurture accounts of difference fail to appreciate the degree to which culture is a partner in producing body systems commonly referred to as biology—something apart from the social" (p. 1516). Her later investigation of the relationship between race and bones leads her to argue that "race turns out to not be a useful variable per se" (2008, p. 682), either. She concludes that "nurture, culture, environment, geography, experience, and history—however we describe it—shape nature; nature influences how such shaping proceeds."

sex
Most frequently understood as "a multidimensional biological construct that encompasses anatomy, physiology, genes, and hormones, which together affect how we are labelled and treated in the world" (Johnson et al., 2009, p. 5). However, this chapter challenges the possibility of separating gender from sex.

In short, there is no simple dichotomy between sex and gender, between bodies and their social and physical environments. They are mutually constituted, with the result that there are significant physiological differences among women as well as differences in the way female bodies are interpreted and experienced. The same holds true for male bodies. Moreover, bodies are constantly changing in relation to environments. In addition, there is not even a simple genetic dichotomy that separates everyone into two sexes as controversy over who can play on female Olympic teams has shown (Simpson et al., 2000). "Therefore our common binary understanding of sex (male/female) is limiting and unrepresentative of the breadth and variety that exists with respect to human sexual characteristics" (Johnson et al., 2009, p. 5).

This understanding of sex and gender as binary also means that lesbian, gay, bisexual, transgender, and queer (LGBTQ) populations are excluded or made invisible in much of health research (Taylor et al., 2012). Similar to arguments about the nature/nurture dichotomy, debates about sexuality emphasize the importance of historical and social context along with the power relations that shape bodies and practices (Spade & Valentine, 2008). As Anna Travers (2015) explains, there is a growing body of Canadian research focused on sexual and gender minority women although we still have a long way to go before there is adequate research, let alone appropriate strategies to address the problems revealed. The issues for this population are complex, even when it comes to identifying who fits in to the category, but there is increasing evidence that sexual- and gender-minority women face particular forms of discrimination when they encounter the health-care system and particular health issues as a result of the discrimination they face in daily life. Ellen Taylor et al. (2012) emphasize the dangers of lumping together peoples with diverse sexualities and gender experiences. To adequately address how sexual orientation and gender identity intersect with other social locations and identities to affect the diverse health needs of members of LGBTQ communities would require a separate chapter.

Nevertheless gender, like sex, remains a useful concept. Just as sex draws our attention to the physiological and alerts us to differences embedded in bodies, gender reminds us that context matters and that some differences are primarily environmental. Indeed, we do not have language that allows us to easily capture this lack of dichotomy and must rely on the terms *male/female* to talk about physiological aspects of differences, and *masculine* and *feminine* to reference those differences associated more with the environment. Equally important, there are often strategic or analytical reasons for doing such dichotomizing, as the case of symptoms for heart attacks shows. We need to keep reminding ourselves, though, that these are neither fixed categories nor simply dichotomous ones.

What this means is that we cannot understand bodies outside their environments. But bodies still matter: only women menstruate, lactate, and gestate; only men can produce semen. Not all women do all of these things and not all men produce semen, but most women and most men have the potential to do so, respectively. Moreover, hormonal balances differ in most women and men, as do chromosomes. Indeed, researchers have claimed that every organ has the capacity to respond differently in women and men (Gesensway, 2001). However, these physiological differences are not only altered by environments; they are also interpreted by them. For example, the meaning of having babies or breasts varies significantly with place and time, is experienced differently, and has different consequences depending on our social, physical, and historical locations, and depending on other social relations, such as sexual ones.

Contexts and the Factors that Shape Health

social determinants of health
Refers to the social, economic, and physical factors that influence an individual's or a group's health. The term has become widely used in academic and policy circles to indicate that health is structured by more than health services, although the specific determinants on the list vary.

This leads us to examine the environments or contexts that shape women's bodies and their health. The Public Health Agency of Canada (PHAC) (2014b) recognizes 12 **social determinants of health**: income and social status; employment; education; social environments; physical environments; healthy child development; personal health practices and coping skills; health services; social support networks; biology and genetic endowment; gender; and culture.

There is a broad consensus that all these factors influence health, although not all governments include gender in their list and lists vary somewhat among governments. There are three interrelated problems, though, with the way these factors are often understood. First, these determinants are frequently seen as independent variables rather than as interconnected ones. Employment and income, for example, are inextricably intertwined. A second and related problem has to do with the profound **inequities** in power, not only among individuals but also among groups, that set the context for these factors—inequities that are not usually part of the discussion in the government's determinants of health literature. Finally, all of these factors are profoundly gendered.

inequities
A term used instead of *inequality* because it implies injustice and because it does not imply the objective of treating everyone the same, as is implied by *equality*. Equitable treatment or conditions require recognizing differences and addressing them in ways that are socially just.

Nevertheless, this list of determinants provides a useful frame for exploring women's health. At the same time, it is important to recognize the fundamental inequities that shape all aspects of health. In recognition of the interpenetration of these factors, what follows lumps several of them together and treats all of them as gendered.

Healthy Child Development

The shaping of our bodies and our health begins at least at conception, and so, too, do sex–gender divisions. According to the website for the Public Health Agency of Canada (2014b), "new evidence on the effects of early experiences on brain development, school readiness and health in later life has sparked a growing consensus about early child development as a powerful determinant of health in its own right" (p. 1). PHAC goes on to explain that the most important period of development is from conception to age six, which leads directly to questions about both conception and maternal health.

women's health movement
In Canada, included both formal and informal organizations of women that addressed issues ranging from birth control to poverty. The movement did not have a single voice or leader but, rather, encompassed a variety of groups and activities, collectively known as the women's health movement.

Until 1969, it was illegal to provide information on or to sell methods for birth control. Abortions were also illegal in Canada. All this changed in 1969, in large measure as a result of the **women's health movement** (Boscoe et al., 2004). Women today have much more choice in whether and when they get pregnant. By the time of the Public Health Agency's maternity experiences survey report in 2009b (p. 12), more than 90 per cent of women said they were happy or somewhat happy to find out they were pregnant. As McKay (2006) explains in his study of the significant decline in teen pregnancies since the laws were changed and services expanded, this trend "can be viewed as a fairly direct indicator of young women's increasing opportunities and capacity to control their sexual and reproductive health" (p. 157). This decline, he goes on to point out, cannot be primarily explained in terms of women seeking abortions, given that abortion rates have been declining since 1990. New services and better **education** are more important factors. There are, however, provincial and territorial variations in teen pregnancy rates that can be attributed at least in part to limited access to sexual and reproductive health services in rural and northern communities (Maticka-Tyndale et al., 2001, p. 29). Similarly, there are

education
Refers to formal schooling.

variations among adult women, with more limited access for those who are poor, home-less, or from Aboriginal communities.

Supports for pregnant mothers have also improved. Perhaps most importantly, women have won the right to paid maternity leave. Not all women benefit, however. According to the Public Health Agency study (2009b, p. 17), just over two-thirds of women received some maternity or parental benefits. Moreover, in the federal support scheme, the max-imum benefits are set at 55 per cent of income, with a firm upper limit that leaves the over-whelming majority of women without enough money to support themselves. Women with **disabilities** frequently fail to qualify for paid maternity leave because of their interrupted work patterns. Yet women with disabilities are particularly in need of support when they have young children (Pinto, 2009).

At the same time that more women are successfully using contraception, more women are seeking services that will help them get pregnant. Such fertility problems are not sim-ply about bodies but, rather, also reflect social factors, such as delaying pregnancy until women are established in paid jobs and long-term use of birth control pills. Women have only limited access to publicly funded fertility services in Canada, making money a factor in access. Women who do use fertility clinics for such assistance are more likely to have multiple births, which may mean health problems for both mother and child (Bissonnette et al., 2007; Tulandi et al., 2006).

Once a woman is pregnant, maternal health is obviously a critical concern for future child health as well as for the woman: "By international standards, Canada ranks among the best in the world in maternal and child health" (Sutherns, 2009, p. 19). One reason we do so well is that our public health system provides hospital and doctor services without charge and is of high quality, making them broadly accessible. But as this author goes on to explain, however, Canada has been moving down in the rankings, and both poor women and Aboriginal women have disturbing rates of maternal and infant mortality. Women in rural areas have more limited access and many poor women cannot take time off work to seek pre- or post-natal care. The closure of many rural hospitals in recent years has made care more difficult to find, and cutbacks in the number of hospital beds in urban areas has exacerbated the problem (Kornelsen, 2006), especially for immigrant women and for women who have difficulty communicating in English or French (Bierman et al., 2010). At the same time, family doctors are leaving obstetrics in part because of burnout and limited support, and they are in particularly short supply in rural and remote com-munities (CIHI, 2004).

Nevertheless, almost all women get **public care** even if it may be distant from the rela-tives and friends who can provide support. Nearly 60 per cent of women receive their care from an obstetrician, and another third see a family physician (Public Health Agency of Canada, 2009b, p. 12), with two-thirds of mothers attended by an obstetrician/gynecol-ogist at the birth. Although physicians have undoubtedly contributed to Canada's good record, the women's health movement has been critical of the high involvement of spe-cialists and the treatment of most births as an illness involving multiple medical inter-ventions. Their protests have helped change how doctors handle birth in hospitals, have influenced the decreased use of such practices as enemas and shaves, and have encouraged the attendance of partners at births. The women's health movement also worked success-fully to make midwifery not only legal but also publicly funded in a number of provinces. Women fought for midwifery because midwives approach pregnancy as a health rather

disabilities
The social model of disabilities understands physical and mental limitations as primarily the result of social conditions while the medical model understands these limitations as primarily the result of bodies.

public care
Refers to health care provided by health-care professionals in a public setting, such as a doctor's office or hospital. Public care is part of Canada's publicly funded, universal health-care insurance policy.

than an illness issue and because they provide continuous support from early on in the pregnancy to well after birth. However, the number of midwives is limited and only 7 per cent of mothers report having a midwife or nurse-practitioner as their care providers (Public Health Agency of Canada, 2009b, p. 12).

Although maternity-care services are important, they are not the only factor in maternal and child health. Exposures to environmental contaminants in our food, water, air, households, and paid workplaces can have negative consequences for a mother and the fetus she carries: "These harmful effects may emerge early as miscarriages, and may result in life-time deficits for the expected child such as lower IQs or learning disabilities" (Wordsworth & Armstrong, 2009, p. 26). Drugs, including prescribed medications, may have a negative impact on maternal health as well (Mintzes & Jureidini, 2009). Nutrition and appropriate housing are also critical for pregnant women, but many women neither can afford the kinds of food or shelter that good health requires nor have other resources, such as time, to ensure a healthy diet. Both are beyond the reach of the growing number of homeless women who are pregnant and give birth. Personal health practices also play a role. Smoking and drinking in particular have been implicated in poor health outcomes for the fetus, but here education campaigns may have had an effect. Only 1 in 10 women reported drinking alcohol during pregnancy, with the lowest rates among those with the lowest incomes. In contrast, women with lower levels of formal education and lower income were more likely than other women to smoke during pregnancy, although most do not and it is important to consider the particular stresses on their lives that can contribute to such practices (Public Health Agency of Canada, 2009c, p. 13). In addition, women may enter pregnancy in a state of health that complicates their pregnancy: "Specific biological conditions, such as obesity, hypertension, and pre-existing chronic conditions are linked to an increased maternal mortality rate" (The Source, 2009).

Men also contribute to the health of the mother and the fetus, although much less attention is paid to the male contribution. The health of the sperm matters, but we have only limited research on the factors that may make male sperm harmful. The male influence on pregnancy often goes beyond their sperm contribution, however. Spousal physical and sexual assault during and following pregnancy are far too common, as they are at other times. The Public Health Agency of Canada (2009c, p. 13) survey found that 1 in 10 women report being abused before pregnancy. While nearly half of them said the abuse decreased during pregnancy, 1 in 20 reported an increase in abuse during this time and 16 per cent said it increased after birth.

All these factors, both personal and structural, contribute to the health of the woman and the fetus she carries and thus to differences among women and their children. Most women report that they and their children are healthy after birth. However, women under age 20, women with low incomes, and women with low levels of formal education are less likely than other women to report that their babies are in excellent health (Public Health Agency of Canada, 2009c). For multiple structural reasons, Aboriginal women are the most likely to experience teen pregnancy and "generally speaking, early motherhood increases the vulnerability of a young First Nations woman who is already disadvantaged socio-economically by reason of her cultural background and gender" (Guimond & Robitaille, 2008, p. 50).

The kinds of support women receive after they have children have a profound impact on both mother and child, in part, because women still bear the primary responsibility for child care. In Canada, women who are recognized as landed immigrants or citizens are eligible to receive $100 a month per child under six years of age. While this amount does help, it is not enough to pay for child care or indeed for most of a baby's daily needs: "Currently, only 12% of preschool aged children in Canada can access regulated childcare spaces" (Angus, 2009, p. 1). Indeed, Canada lags far behind most high-income countries in terms of both the support for and availability of daycare services, ranking last among 25 industrialized countries (Angus, 2009). The only province that comes close to having a universal child-care program is Quebec. In 1997, the province introduced a $5-a-day child-care program and full-day kindergarten (now increased to $7 in 2013). Evidence suggests that this program, along with generous parental leave and affordable housing, has been the main factor in reducing poverty in that province by 40 per cent (Goar, 2009).

As Cleveland and Krashinsky (1998) show, "stimulating day care can have strong and lasting effects on child development" (p. 4). At the same time, they (Cleveland & Krashinsky, 2003) challenge the notion that the best care is always care by the mother and that all mothers can provide adequate care. Child care can also mean the family has a decent income while the children grow up, allowing mothers to return to paid work after childbirth. Based on her review of the literature, Waldfogel (2002) concludes that early supports not only "improve mother–child interaction" but also "raise maternal employment and education" and that this is especially the case for mothers with the least education (p. 531).

Children, fathers, and mothers may also benefit from father care (Kramer & Thompson, 2005). The Father Involvement Research Alliance (FIRA) (2010, p. 1) recognizes that women still do the bulk of child care even though men are doing more (2010, p. 6). And few men take paternity leave, in part, because in most cases the household cannot afford to lose the higher male income and, in part, because it is still difficult to gain acceptance for males to take time off from their paid jobs. However, FIRA cites a host of research to argue that the "provision of accessible, affordable, high-quality child care can facilitate the support, education and connection of both mothers and fathers" (p. 6).

There are two main points to this section on healthy child development. The first is to show that this factor overlaps with others, is highly gendered, and is influenced by relations of power. The second is to reveal some of the patterns for women as a group and for different groups of women. In sum, women's access to means for planning birth as well as to appropriate maternity care and child care are central to early child development. All these processes are shaped by women's location, relations, and resources. The following sections are similarly constructed, with similar purposes in mind for other factors.

Education and Social Status, Income and Employment

It is useful to consider education and social status, and income and employment together because they are so closely intertwined. Education can mean we develop knowledge and skills necessary for survival; it can be an indicator of social status. But perhaps most important, education can have a profound impact on what kind of job we get and what kind of income we earn. What follows, then, is a brief outline of how they are intertwined in ways that shape women's health.

If level of education is an independent factor determining health, then women should be healthier than men. The number of women graduating from university has been rising much more rapidly than the number of men. By the 1990s, the majority of undergraduate diplomas and certificates were granted to women. Although women formed the overwhelming majority in traditional female areas such as health professions, education, social sciences, humanities, and the arts, they now also account for almost half of those graduating with diplomas in agriculture, nearly a third of those in mathematics and physical sciences, and a quarter of those in engineering and applied sciences. Similarly, women accounted for the majority of full- and part-time community college students by the 1990s. At the other end of the education scale, men are more likely than women to have less than a Grade 9 education. Employed men are also less likely than employed women to have a post-secondary degree or diploma (Statistics Canada, 2006d, Chapter 4). According to 2006 census data (our last reliable data), 42 per cent of the men in the labour force did not have a degree or diploma while this was the case for 39 per cent of the women. Only in the case of post-graduate degrees do men form a significant majority of graduates and women are rapidly catching up. Yet, at the same time that women were passing men in terms of education levels, men's life expectancy was increasing somewhat faster than women's (Statistics Canada, 2013g, Table 20). Clearly, something more than education is involved in health.

While women as a group have been gaining on men in terms of education, there are significant differences among women's level of education. According to Statistics Canada (2013g, Table 11 & Table 3), Aboriginal women are the least likely to have advanced education and they have a lower life expectancy than other women. Women with activity limitations also have fewer educational credentials, although those between the ages of 25 and 54 are as likely as other women to have a college diploma (Statistics Canada, 2013g, Table 5). The women most likely to have university degrees are those who are foreign-born and those who identified themselves as visible minority (Statistics Canada, 2013g, Table 2 and Chart 6). But these higher levels of education do not guarantee the health of immigrant or racialized women. Although immigrants initially tend to be healthier than those already in Canada, their health gradually converges with that of long-term residents (Zhao, Xue, & Gilkinson, 2010). And the health of racialized women tends to be lower than that of other women in Canada (Agnew, 2009). Although education is important to health, the impact clearly varies and operates in unison with other factors, some of which themselves help explain the low levels of education.

One of those factors is income, along with parental level of education. More women than men live below the poverty line: "In Canada, the most vulnerable to poverty are Canadians from racialized communities, recent immigrants (many of whom are also from racialized communities), Aboriginal people, and persons with disabilities. . . . But in all the vulnerable groups, poverty rates for women are higher than those for men" (Townson, 2009, p. 5). Even when transfer payments and tax credits are taken into account, a quarter of the women in lone-parent families have incomes that keep them in poverty (Townson, 2009, p. 6). The causes are many. Welfare is worth less and less, and has become more and more difficult to get. Many men fail to make support payments after relationships dissolve, leaving many women who parent alone with little income. In addition, women are less likely than men to have employment-related pensions and as a result often must depend on Old Age Security in their senior years, a dependency that puts them in a low-income category. Women are also less likely than men to be eligible for unemployment insurance and frequently receive less money when they are deemed eligible. And poverty is hazardous to women's health. For example, poverty "is one of the primary forces that create conditions of HIV risk" and helps account for the fact that women now account for a growing number of those with HIV (Buhler, 2008, p. 2).

Not only women without jobs or without higher education are poor, however. Minimum wage in Canada does not lift people above the poverty line if they do not have full-time, full-year employment and access to affordable housing. Given that women account for the majority of those employed at minimum wage and those employed part-time or part-year, many women with paid work still live in poverty. The link between poverty and women's mental health has long been established (Belle, 1990), and poverty usually means poor housing and nutrition as well.

As a result of their successful struggles to gain access to both higher education and jobs, women have been able to enter the labour force in large numbers and even make it into jobs with better pay and conditions that take them above poverty levels. In spite of these gains, however, employed women still tend to make less than employed men. Furthermore, although education does make a difference to the wage gap, there is a wage gap even if men and women are matched for age and education as shown in Table 5.1. Lack of education hurts women more than it hurts men, while more education often does not translate into benefits for racialized and/or immigrant women. A 2014 study "that followed a group of men and women for two decades reports that over the study period, men who had obtained a bachelor's degree by 1991 had earned, on average, $732,000 more than those whose education ended at a high school diploma. For women, the difference between the two groups was $448,000" (Statistics Canada, 2014c). These wage differences reflect in part the segregation of the labour force into male and female jobs and in part the low value given to jobs done mainly by women—in other words discrimination.

Lower wages for women mean less social status as well as more limited access to the kinds of goods and services that can help women maintain their health. Indeed, lower wages frequently reflect discrimination, which itself can be harmful to women's health.

Table 5.1 Average Annual Earnings of Women and Men Employed Full-Year, Full-Time, by Educational Attainment, 2008

Level of Education	Women	Men	Earnings ratio
	Dollars		Percentage
Less than grade 9	20,800	40,400	51.5
Some secondary school	28,600	43,600	65.6
Graduated high school	35,400	50,300	70.4
Some post-secondary	36,400	50,100	72.6
Post-secondary certificate or diploma	41,100	57,700	71.2
University degree	62,800	91,800	68.3
Total	44,700	62,600	71.3

Source: Statistics Canada. (2011). Table 6.9: Average annual earnings of women and men employed full-year, full-time, by educational attainment, 2008. *Women in Canada: A gender-based statistical profile,* p. 149.

Furthermore, when women take on paid jobs, most still bear primary responsibility for household and care work. According to the 2006 Census (Pearce, 2014), 20 per cent of women compared to 8 per cent of men did 30 hours or more of unpaid work each week. As a result of the double shift at paid and unpaid work, women often experience time poverty (Turner & Grieco, 2000). This, too, can be harmful to women's health, adding to their levels of stress. Moreover, the prospect of taking on the double load can contribute to women delaying childbirth, which in turn may have other health consequences. For example, the higher rates of breast cancer among teachers have been "explained as a result of delayed childbirth among this occupational group" (Messing, 1998, p. 4). Women with paid jobs are, however, often more healthy than those without paid work, in part, because paid employment not only provides access to income and to social networks, it can also mean rewards from using their education and skills in a socially recognized way.

However, women's paid jobs are not without hazards of their own. As Messing (1998) explains in *One-Eyed Science*, research on workplace hazards has focused mainly on male work and has applied male standards even when women's work is examined. Women's jobs, especially those involving working in an office, teaching children, or caring for others, are too often assumed to be safe, without risks. Yet Messing convincingly demonstrates that women face a host of visible and invisible hazards at work that are only now being revealed, and many have yet to be recognized by workers' compensation boards that still reflect male standards. Health-care workers, for example, suffer from mental stress caused by "work overload, pressure at work, lack of participation in decision-making, poor social support, unsupportive leadership, lack of communication/feedback, staff shortages or unpredictable staffing, scheduling or long work hours and conflict between work and family demands" (Yassi & Hancock, 2005, p. 35). Chemical exposure at work can result in breast cancer (Brophy et al., 2012).

For women, lack of full-time employment or casual and temporary work can also increase stress, and so, too, can lack of control over their work, a problem that more women than men face in the labour force. The resulting stress can have both mental and physiological consequences, including increased blood pressure and stress hormone response (Fox et al., 1993; Theorell et al., 1993). Women's jobs also frequently involve physical risks, although such risks are often cumulative, appearing over a long period rather than resulting from a sudden, obvious injury. Messing's (1998) research on teachers, for instance, shows that women who work for years with young children commonly suffer from severe back problems resulting from their work.

In addition, violence, sexual harassment, and bullying are far too common, especially for women employed in jobs traditionally dominated by men. "The social costs of violence against women, including health care for victims, criminal justice, social services, and lost productivity, are estimated in the billions of dollars. The psychological impacts for victims and their family and friends cannot be measured in dollars" (Ontario Women's Justice Network, 2013). The hazards women face in their other job at home, caring for children, the elderly, and houses, tend to be particularly invisible, hidden in the household away from public scrutiny (Rosenberg, 1990). And women who are dependent on males for support may be especially vulnerable to violence at home that they may find more difficult to resist when they have no income of their own.

Although lesbians had higher levels of education and were more likely to be in the highest income quintile than either heterosexual women or men (Tjepkema, 2008, p. 57), they have poorer health outcomes than heterosexual women in Canada (Steele et al., 2009). This may be because they often face discrimination, harassment, bullying, and violence that can negatively affect health outcomes. Bisexual women and trans women are overrepresented among low-income Canadians, making them additionally vulnerable (Meyer, 2003).

In sum, more women have higher education and more have paid employment as well as higher incomes than in the past. For some, this has meant better health. But persistent inequality, not only in comparison to men but also among women, is harmful to the health of too many women. Higher education does not necessarily mean higher incomes nor does a white-collar job or staying at home necessarily mean safe work.

Health Services

Health services obviously have an impact on women's health, although they are not the only or even the main factor. It is not surprising, then, that "the women's health movement has focused on three main issues: the health-care delivery system, the development and analysis of the social determinants of health, and a commitment to increase the participation of women in all aspects of health care" (Boscoe et al., 2004, p. 8). These issues overlap and interpenetrate with the social determinants as important within heath services as they are outside them.

Women fought hard in the nineteenth century to gain access to medical schools and to maintain their place as midwives. While they did manage to enter medical schools before the turn of the century, quotas on female students were not lifted until the 1970s. Once women were able to compete for entry on the same basis as men, they began to flood into medical schools and now outnumber men. They were less successful in midwifery, and it is only now that the majority of Canadian jurisdictions have made midwifery legal and supported. The late nineteenth century was also the period when women fought to make nursing a respectable profession, but it was not until nurses organized in unions that they gained decent wages and working conditions (Armstrong & Silas, 2014). Nevertheless, nursing remains a female-dominated profession, with more than 9 out of 10 nurses women. Debates continue about women's natural caring capacities and whether this makes them more suitable than men to nursing (Nelson & Gordon, 2006). And issues still remain regarding access to employment in care, especially in relation to the recognition of foreign credentials. But health and social services now provide employment for nearly one in five women in the labour force (Armstrong et al., 2008).

Today, four out of five people employed in health services are women, and women take the major responsibility for unpaid personal care (Armstrong, Laxer, & Armstrong, 2010; Armstrong, 2013; Sinha, 2012). Although the health-care sector is heavily gendered, this does not necessarily mean that women run the show or that the system is responsive to women's needs. The women's movement has long been critical of the medical approach to care and of the way increasing aspects of women's lives have been defined as medical problems (Lorber, 2000; Moss & Dyck, 2003). Childbirth is one example of medicalization, as birth became increasingly treated as an illness to be medically managed rather than as a process often mainly requiring support. Mental health is another example where women were frequently defined as neurotic and treated with drugs when their main problem was the discrimination they faced in their daily lives or the attitudes of physicians (Smith &

David, 1975). Women fought to put women's health in women's hands and to educate both male and female providers, who had been trained in the old ways, about women's health from women's perspective. They have enjoyed some success in reducing medical interventions, but there are still high rates of Caesarean births, and drugs are still too often used in ways that are harmful to women's health (Rochon Ford & Saibil, 2010).

The women's health movement was not only concerned with the medical establishment's emphasis on surgery and drugs, and its attitudes toward women, but also with the dichotomy assumed between minds and bodies and between being sick and being well. The mind/body distinction contributed to the dismissal of many problems as simply being in women's heads. At the same time, the distinction between sickness and health left many of those with chronic health issues and those with disabilities not only without the kinds of support they required but also excluded (Smith & Hutchinson, 2004). Assumptions about heterosexuality were also pervasive, leaving lesbian and other women who do not fit into this box fighting for appropriate care (Travers, 2009). And approaches that focus only on bodies or minds, outside their environments, are inadequate in restoring or promoting health and ignore the interconnections among the determinants of health. A woman without housing, for example, cannot easily follow doctor's orders on wound care.

Although practices within care remain open to criticism, it is clear that women as a group have benefited significantly from access to quality health services. Men are more reluctant to seek health-care services than women, especially for depression or psychological problems (CIHR, 2014; Noone & Stephens, 2008), in part because of gender expectations. Gay men were more likely than heterosexual ones to have consulted a family physician, medical specialist, or nurse in the preceding 12 months (Tjepkema, 2008), perhaps because this community has worked to inform themselves about the use of health services. As noted earlier, the introduction of a **public health-care system** without fees has been particularly important to women because they use the system more for themselves, for their children, and for their parents and because it has meant more and better jobs for women. Women are less likely than men to have private health insurance or the money to pay for care in the absence of public care, thus cutbacks in public services are most likely to affect them. Women are also more likely than men to take their children to receive care (Women and Health Care Reform, 2008). As Bierman (2007) puts it, "women and men differ not only in patterns of illness and disease risk factors, but also in their social contexts. Consequently, they have different experiences with health care, including differences in access, quality and health outcomes" (p. 1520).

Moreover, medical advances have contributed to women's longevity and to women's quality of life. For example, women are more likely than men to suffer from the arthritis that ruins their hips and knees, so the methods for replacing hips and knees have been particularly important for them (Jackson et al., 2006).

However, women have not benefited equally from the health-care system. Immigrants and racialized women may find it difficult to access services because of language and cultural barriers that are too often combined with discriminatory practices (Bierman et al., 2010; Zazzera, 2007). Lesbian and bisexual women can encounter homophobic and heterosexist attitudes and practices on the part of health-care providers. This can result in their avoiding or delaying medical care and examinations (Dunn, 2006; Rainbow Health Ontario, 2011). Women with disabilities face not only physical and attitudinal barriers but financial and transportation ones as well (Ethno-Racial People with Disabilities Coalition

public health-care system
Refers to Canada's universal, publicly funded health-care system.

of Ontario and the Ontario Women's Health Network, 2008). They also feel they are "perceived as a great drain because as women with disabilities, they take too much time from an already strained system" (p. 4). Similarly, elderly women, who make up the majority of those living in residential care, often experience less than adequate care.

Moreover, reforms over the last couple of decades have also been detrimental to women's health in a number of ways (Armstrong et al., 2012). The move throughout the high-income countries to shorter patient stays in hospitals, to outpatient services, and to the closure of many long-term care facilities has meant a significant increase in women's unpaid care work (Duxbury, Higgins, & Shroeder, 2009). People are sent home quicker and sicker or not admitted at all, leaving the care primarily to women, even if they have paid jobs as well. It is the women with the least income who are the most likely to provide the unpaid care because they cannot afford to pay for supports (Guberman, 1999). Equally important, the patients who are sent home alone and without the necessary care are most likely to be women. The costs of care are also shifted in the process, given that the Canada Health Act—the federal legislation that sets out the principles on which public health-care services are based—only requires that hospital and doctor care be provided without fees. Women are disproportionately affected because they are less likely than men to have private health insurance or high enough incomes to cover payments. The resulting stress and physical demands can be harmful to women's health.

Within paid services, work has been transformed in ways that undermine the health of those employed in health care (Armstrong et al., 2008). The adoption of managerial practices taken from the for-profit sector has meant work speedup and loss of control for many of the women who provide paid care. According to Statistics Canada, those in health services are the most likely to be absent from work for illness or injury (Perspectives on Labour and Income, 2009, Table 4), and these rates have been rising along with reforms. Infection rates among patients have also been rising with part of the problem being the cutbacks in cleaning within care facilities, which is primarily done by women. The determinants of health approach tells us the work organization and clean environments are critical to health, but not enough attention is paid to these determinants within health services.

In sum, health services are largely care for women by women. Access to care improved dramatically with public health care, especially for poorer women, and so did women's health. However, the quality of care women receive remains an issue, and differences among women are if anything increasing as more care requires payment and as more work is sent home.

Personal Health Practices and Coping Skills; Social Support Networks; Social and Physical Environments

Undoubtedly, personal health practices along with coping skills and support networks are important to women's health. But these personal practices, coping skills, and support networks are shaped by context and culture—in other words, by the social and physical environments identified as other determinants of health. It is women who take primary responsibility for health promotion in the home and who are primarily held responsible for health promotion in the home: "Regardless of location, however, women tend to be the primary seekers of health information for their children and other family members, as well as for themselves" (Wathen & Harris, 2006, p. 1). And increasingly women are held responsible for their own care and health, as self-care is promoted at the same time as there are cutbacks in health services (Meadows, Thurston, & Berenson, 2001). Women have long been centrally involved in keeping their families healthy and engaged, but their capacity to do so may be limited or expanded by their environments as well as by their access to education and resources.

In short, the barriers to health promotion and self-care among women extend far beyond individual will. Take diabetes as an example. Diabetes has reached epidemic proportions and is particularly common among First Nations women, with rates four times higher than among non–First Nations women and two-and-a-half times higher than in First Nations men (Dyck et al., 2010, p. 1). Diabetes prevention and management is now largely the responsibility of the patient with the expectation that prescribed diet, exercise, monitoring, and injections will be carried out by the individual (Collins et al., 2009). Yet the development of diabetes is frequently beyond the control of these women: "What is clear is that the rapid appearance of type 2 diabetes particularly among First Nations people and other indigenous and developing populations has been precipitated by environmental rather than genetic factors" (p. 1). Once diagnosed, access to the kinds of food prescribed is beyond the reach of many First Nations women and so is the equipment required for easy monitoring.

Exercise provides another example. Fitness is increasingly stressed as important to health and self-care. However, research from 2009 shows that fitness levels among children and youth have declined since 1981 with more girls than boys needing improvement (Tremblay et al., 2010). Part of this decline can be attributed to more time with sedentary electronic equipment, but part can be attributed to the cutbacks in school physical fitness programs and after-school access to facilities or programs. The lack of exercise for fitness among adult women can be linked to their time-poverty and to their limited access to the kind of early learning that develops strategies for staying fit throughout life.

Social support can help promote self-care strategies and can help women cope with maintaining the health of their families. This support may be emotional or material; it may involve providing information or positive feedback. Women tend to provide material support more in terms of services such as caregiving than in terms of money. They are more frequently the ones who provide emotional support for their families and health information to their friends and relatives. Women also tend to have more extensive social networks than men, and such networks can contribute to everything from better mental health to lower rates of breast cancer (Fuhrer et al., 1999). Women are also active in their cultural communities, often providing the glue that keeps traditions and practices alive. However, providing support for others, without this being reciprocal, can undermine health. Equally important, social networks and cultural communities may exert pressures to conform or even express condemnation that may be harmful to health. A culture of violence within a community, for example, can be harmful to women. Moreover, many women lack significant social networks or the kinds of social supports that help them stay well and sustain them when they are not. But we need more research on these supports, their impact, and their differences. For instance, on the basis of their research on women with HIV/AIDS, Maggi and Daly (2006) conclude this:

> With the changing face of the HIV epidemic in Canada, we need to know more
> about what unique social and emotional supports women with HIV/AIDS need,

given their gendered life experiences, their multiple roles (e.g., mother, partner, caregiver, worker, community participant), and what resources they are able to access, given their life circumstances. (p. 1)

Developing and maintaining social networks are one means women use to cope. These are far from the only ones, however. Women usually learn multiple skills from each other to cover a range of situations from bleeding noses to thinning soup as a means of feeding large families on little money. Their strategies address not only their own illnesses and those of their families but also their environments. Research suggests that women are more likely than men to cope with pain by problem solving and by using affirmative statements (Unruh et al., 1999). Cohen (1991) has documented how women who come to Canada as live-in domestics cope with racism and exploitation by developing contacts outside these private households, by redefining the situation, and by using resources they find within the homes where they work. The women who take up this domestic work and leave their families behind are displaying a coping strategy in the very act of leaving their countries to find means of supporting their families back home. Acharya and Northcott (2007) talked to South Asian women immigrants to Canada who dealt with the pain of cultural shock and alienation by keeping busy. Homeless young women develop a variety of means of coping from camouflaging their bodies to exchanging sex for shelter as a way of coping with their lack of homes, while living on the street may itself be a way of coping with sexual assault at home (Oliver, 2010).

Not all women have had the opportunity to learn the kinds of coping strategies that are effective in particular situations, either because they have lacked teachers or because their skills were learned in another environment and do not work in their current one. And not all women have access to the kinds of resources that would help them cope. Some environments just make it too hard to cope. Workplaces that create the conditions of harassment and racism, for example, and that deny women the means to resist and support in altering these conditions can leave women without coping methods. Similarly, working conditions that speed up the work, make employment precarious, and allow workers little control, along with physical spaces or demands that strain the body, can slowly undermine health in spite of women's strategies. When another job at home is added to the load, women's health can collapse. Not all women have the capacity to cope in some areas, due to illness, injury, or disability, often combined with a lack of resources and barriers that are difficult to overcome.

In short, it is hard to address issues of health-promoting activities for women and for those they care for without also addressing issues of environments. Women tend to build strong social networks and social supports, but these can be disrupted or prevented by social and physical environments. As Paltiel (1997) summed it up more than a decade ago, "healthy public policy calls for action for reducing inequities, building supportive environments, and enhancing measures that favour coping and control" (p. 28).

Conclusion

This chapter argues for a focus on women's health for several reasons. First, for the most part women's health issues are different from those of men. Second, there are significant differences among women. Third, women's health is often neglected in research and policy. Women's health deserves to be studied on its own, not only in comparison to men, and research must recognize that all populations are gendered. Too much research and policy ignores gender, frequently assuming what is the case for certain men is also the case for everyone. It is the women's health movement and feminist researchers who have developed gender-based analysis methods, methods that are now being taken up and applied to men.

Such research is critical in recognizing issues for men and among men. Both notions of masculinity and men's work hours are factors limiting the extent to which they utilize health services, although they are more likely than women to have their heart attacks diagnosed and their bad knees treated (Jackson, Pederson, & Boscoe, 2009). They are also less likely than women to be prescribed treatment for depression (Ogrodniczuk & Oliffe, 2011). And men are more likely than women to successfully commit suicide or to die in workplace and other accidents (Statistics Canada, 2014e). However, it is always important to recognize that men as a group are more powerful than women as a group and research based on men is far more common.

This chapter also argues that bodies must be understood within a context characterized by critical inequities not only among women and men but also among women. As the World Health Organization (WHO) (2008) explains, "inequities in health, avoidable health inequalities, arise because of the circumstances in which people grow, live, work, and age, and the systems put in place to deal with illness. The conditions in which people live and die are, in turn, shaped by political, social, and economic forces" (p. 3). Those circumstances are profoundly shaped by the national political economy and by policies within nations. Such an argument leads to the focus on Canada, and the specific circumstances faced by women in Canada. At the same time, global forces also shape the context for women in Canada and how Canada acts internationally shapes the circumstances in which other women live. Increasingly, Canada has adopted neo-liberal policies at home and abroad, with an emphasis on market forces and personal responsibility for both health and care. Services focused on women and support for research on women have been dramatically cut. International programs supporting women have been significantly reduced; more women have been brought to Canada as temporary care workers to do low paid care work; and health services for refugees cancelled. The result is too often more work and less care for women, as well as greater inequities among women. As the WHO (2008) puts it, "social justice is a matter of life and death." We need to act now to put social justice back on the agenda.

Summary

- There is no simple dichotomy between sex and gender, or between bodies and their social and physical environments. They are mutually constituted, with the result that there are significant physiological differences among women as well as differences in the way female bodies are interpreted and experienced. Moreover, bodies are constantly changing in relation to environments.
- The determinants of health overlap, are highly gendered, are influenced by unequal relations of power, and are shaped by context.

- There are some patterns that can be identified for women as a group and for different groups of women. All these processes are shaped by the women's location, relations, and resources.
- There is little research on sexual and gender minority women, or how sexual orientation and gender identity intersect with other social locations so as to affect health needs.
- The health-care sector is highly gendered.
- All health issues are women's issues, and collective action on health issues can make a difference.
- Men are more reluctant than women to seek health-care services. Notions of masculinity and men's work hours are factors limiting the extent to which they utilize health services.

Key Terms

bodies	disabilities	public health-care system
context	education	relations of ruling
social determinants	gender	sex
of health	inequities	women's health
dichotomies	public care	movement

Sociological Reflection: On Women's Health

- Why is women's health a sociological issue?
- Can we understand women's health without sociology?
- What are the key components in a sociology of women's health?
- Does a feminist political economy approach help us understand women's health?

Discussion Questions

1. What difference can education make to women's health?
2. Is poverty a women's health issue?
3. Can we talk about women's health without talking about men?
4. Can we analyze the health of women as a group or should we focus exclusively on particular groups of women?
5. Can a women's health movement stay focused on health-services issues?
6. What happens to our understanding of women's health if we treat the determinants as independent variables?

Further Investigation

1. Are health-care reforms benefiting women as a group? Are they benefiting particular groups of women?
2. What are the conflicts, if any, between women as care providers and women as patients?

Further Reading

Abramson, B. (2009). Women and health: Taking the matter to heart. In P. Armstrong and J. Deadman (Eds.), *Women's health intersections of policy, research, and practice* (pp. 53–60). Toronto, ON: Women's Press.

Armstrong, P., Amaratunga, C., Bernier, J., Grant, K., Pederson, A., & Willson, K. (Eds.). (2002). *Exposing privatization: Women and health care reform.* Aurora, ON: Garamond.

Armstrong, P., Armstrong, H., & Scott-Dixon, K. (2009). *Critical to care: The invisible women in health services.* Toronto, ON: University of Toronto Press.

Armstrong, P., & Pederson, A. (2015). *Women's health: Intersections of research, policy and practice.* Toronto: Women's Press.

Johnson, J.L., Greaves, L., & Repta, R. (2009, 6 May). Better science with sex and gender: Facilitating the use of a sex and gender-based analysis in health research. *International Journal of Health Equity.*

Messing, K. (1998). *One-eyed science. Occupational health and women workers.* Philadelphia, PA: Temple University Press.

Moss, P., & Dyck, I. (2003). *Women, body and illness.* Oxford, UK: Roman and Littlefield.

Moss, P., & Teghtsoonian, K. (Eds.). (2007). *Contesting illness processes and practices.* Toronto, ON: University of Toronto Press.

Rochon Ford, A., & Saibil, D. (Eds.). (2010). *Push to prescribe. Women and Canadian drug policy.* Toronto, ON: Women's Press.

Rosenberg, H. (1990). The home is the workplace: Hazards, stress and pollutants in the household. In M. Luxton & H. Rosenberg (Eds.), *Through the kitchen window.* Toronto, ON: Garamond.

Smith, D. (1990). *Texts, facts, and femininity: Exploring the relations of ruling.* Toronto: University of Toronto Press.

Web Resources

British Columbia Centre of Excellence for Women's Health
www.bccewh.bc.ca

Canadian Centre for Policy Alternatives.
https://www.policyalternatives.ca/

Canadian Institutes of Health Research (CIHR)
www.cihr-irsc.gc.ca

Canadian Women's Health Network
www.cwhn.ca/en

National Network on Environments and Women's Health
www.nnewh.org

The Source: Women's Health Data Directory
www.womenshealthdata.ca/default_en.aspx

Statistics Canada
http://www.statcan.gc.ca/pub/89 -503-x/2010001/article/11543-eng .htm#a29

CHAPTER 6
Racialization, Ethno-Cultural Diversity, and Health

Jennie Hornosty

[H]ealth . . . takes place within specific contexts of history, political economy, and "race"/class/gender relations, and we cannot decontextualize our understanding and interpretation of health care encounters . . . [or] "neutralize social differences" . . .

—Tang and Browne (2008, p. 124)

How might racism, language barriers, cultural barriers, and discrimination affect a person's relationship with his or her doctor and experience of interacting with the health-care system in general? Do these factors influence when and how people access health care?

© iStock.com/Creativa Images

Overview

- What does the research evidence tell us about the health status of Canada's racialized peoples?
- How important is ethnicity (or culture) in determining health outcomes for Canada's ethnically diverse population?
- What are the intersections between racism, poverty, immigration, and health?

This chapter examines two social dimensions of health. It first looks at the issue of racism and the health status of Canada's racialized groups. Second, the chapter examines issues related to ethnicity and immigrant health more generally. It reviews patterns of immigration, the ethno-cultural diversity of Canada, and how these factors are related to health status and the use of health services. In this context, ethnicity is examined in terms of its implications for social location rather than as a purely cultural phenomenon. Research evidence is provided to support the argument that focusing on the intersection of social determinants, such as poverty, unemployment, racism, and social exclusion, is essential for understanding disparities in health outcomes. It is argued that the provision of health care in a racially and culturally diverse society requires structural changes, including changes in the structure of health-care services.

Introduction: Racialized Groups and Health Inequities

A large body of American research indicates that "health inequities among racial minorities are pronounced, persistent, and pervasive" (Gee & Ford, 2011, p. 115). Studies further show that individuals who report experiencing racism have greater rates of illness (Gee & Ford, 2011). Smedley (2012) points to studies that indicate a positive link between perceived race-based discrimination and higher blood pressure levels, hypertension, and cardiovascular, respiratory, and pain-related issues. Canadian evidence indicates that racialized group members have more unmet health needs than those from non-racialized groups (Hyman, 2009, p. 7). Earlier research, discussed by Pollock et al. (2012, p. 63), shows adverse health outcomes are associated with discrimination (including on the basis of "**race**"), which manifest in poor physical and mental health and risky lifestyle behaviours. Research on the health needs of Black women in Nova Scotia identified diabetes, cardiovascular disease, HIV/AIDS, and mental health as prominent concerns (cited in Hyman, 2009, p. 7).

"race"
A social construct without any scientific basis to describe allegedly biologically distinct groups.

Racism, Racialization, and Health

Nearly 20 per cent of Canadians identify as belonging to a "visible minority"; 3 in 10 were born here (Statistics Canada, 2013f). Projections, based on current immigration trends, suggest that by 2031, members of racialized groups will comprise approximately between 29 to 32 per cent of all Canadians (Statistics Canada, 2010c). Given that there is a growing body of research that links racism to poor health (De Maio & Kemp, 2010; Paradies, 2006), we need to understand how "race" and **racism** can have an impact on health outcomes and lead to health inequities. It is an accepted fact today that "race" is a social construct and does not have any basis in biology. The concept of "race," as referring to a range of immutable and distinct biological traits between groups of people, has been scientifically discredited (Nestel, 2012; Patychuk, 2011). However, we continue to group people on the basis of selective phenotypic characteristics and treat the resulting groupings as though they are naturally constituted (Li, 2008, p. 21, cited in Veenstra, 2009a, p. 538). Racism is a set of beliefs and practices that, regardless of intent, perpetuates the idea of race-based biological differences and the superiority of one racial group over another. Racism takes many forms: at the interpersonal level, at the institutional level, and at the structural level. Institutional racism is manifest in the unequal access to social, economic, and political systems that determine the distribution of society's resources due to racial characteristics (Galabuzi, 2004, cited in Hyman, 2009, p. 10). **Racialization** is the social process by which racial categories are constructed as real, different, and unequal in ways that have social, economic, and political consequences, such as **social exclusion** and marginalization (Galabuzi, 2001, 2009). In other words, racism and racialization are practices by which visually identifiable groups are subject to various forms of exclusion and discriminatory practices that can translate into health disparities. To date, there is little Canadian research that has explicitly examined the effects of racialization on health inequalities (Patychuk, 2011; Nestel, 2012).

As we saw in Chapter 4, social and economic conditions have a significant effect on health. In Canada, studies indicate that there continues to be major disparities in health determinants, such as income, employment, and poverty (Galabuzi, 2009, 2012; Levy et al., 2013; Block, 2010). Racialized Canadians are more likely to experience disproportionate levels of poverty, homelessness, inadequate housing, and discrimination (Access Alliance, 2005). They are three times more likely to live in poverty than other Canadians—19.8 per cent compared to 6.4 per cent (Galabuzi, 2012). Members of racialized groups are more likely to be unemployed or underemployed, to work in lower-skill jobs at low pay, and may have disproportional numbers of one-parent families (Ornstein, 2006). A recent report by the Canadian Centre for Policy Alternatives (Block, 2010), for example, demonstrates that racialized Ontarians (with the exception of those who identify as Japanese) are more likely to experience higher unemployment rates and earn less, even after controlling for age and education (see Figure 6.1).

Racialized group members in Toronto—Canada's most "ethno-racially" diverse city where almost half of the population identify as a member of a group that has been racialized—are more likely to live in neighbourhoods with higher poverty rates, limited employment opportunities, poor access to transportation, and fewer health and social services (Levy et al., 2013, p. 23). Such neighbourhoods are also vulnerable to environmental risks (Teelucksingh, 2007, p. 648). These structural inequalities have serious health implications (Auger & Alix, 2009; Galabuzi, 2009; Raphael, 2009c). Those who live in the poorest neighbourhoods are more likely to die from cardiovascular disease, cancer, diabetes, and respiratory diseases (cited in Access Alliance, 2005). Children from racialized groups make up 43 per cent of children living in poverty, even though they comprise only 23 per cent of children in Ontario (Access Alliance, 2005). They are more likely to

racism/racist
Racism refers to a set of false beliefs that one racial group is naturally superior to another group based on biological differences. It perpetuates notions of cultural superiority and inferiority and is one basis for social exclusion and discriminatory practices.

racialization
The social process by which racial categories are constructed as real, different, and unequal in ways that have social, economic, and political consequences.

social exclusion
A process whereby some groups in society are denied access to material and social resources, thereby excluding their full participation in society. It produces inequality in outcomes.

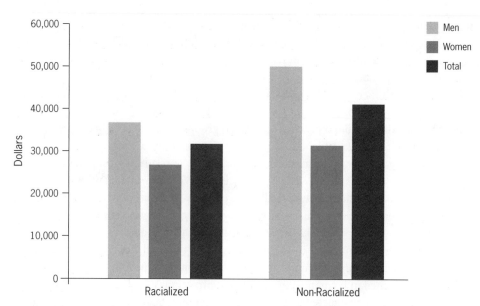

Figure 6.1 Average Employment Income, Ontario, 2005

Source: Adapted from Statistics Canada, *2006 Census of the Population.* Catalogue Number 97-563-XCB20006060.

have higher rates of depression, anxiety, and antisocial behaviours (Samaan, 2000, cited in Access Alliance, 2007). Childhood exposure to racial discrimination has been linked to poor child health and development (Priest et al., 2013).

These inequalities in material conditions are the result of social exclusion and affect the health and well-being of individuals and groups: "Groups experiencing some form of social exclusion tend to sustain higher health risks and lower health status" (Galabuzi, 2009, p. 252). Poor jobs and working conditions can result in more workplace injuries, harassment, and exposure to environmental hazards such as toxic substances. These groups are also subject to discrimination and racism, which are often at the root of social exclusion. Hyman (2009, p. 9) notes that a direct impact of racism on health behaviours includes resorting to high-risk health behaviours, such as substance abuse, self-harm, and other negative coping responses, as well as delays in seeking health care. Health-care providers may have a conscious or unconscious bias against members of racialized groups that can affect the care they provide (Levy et al., 2013, p. 25; Women's Health in Women's Hands Community Health Centre, 2003). Health care services are also pre-dominantly Eurocentric in values, world view, and practice that provide systemic challenges for people from racialized groups. Kafele (2004) further writes: "Racial profiling, racist assumptions, and stereotyping in psychiatry are often believed to be strong deter-mining factors in intake, assessment, and diagnosis and misdiagnosis" (pp. 2–3).

Racism has both a direct and indirect impact on health. Krieger (2011, p. 223) suggests that there are six pathways through which racism harms health, including economic and social deprivation and discrimination and other forms of socially inflicted trauma (cited in Nestel, 2012, p. 18). Experiences of racism can lead to depression, psychological distress, hypertension, and high blood pressure. Equally, racial inequities in major socio-economic determinants of health produce a cumulative structural disadvantage for members of racialized groups. The existing research suggests that an intersectional analysis is needed to fully appreciate how racism as a structural factor intersects with other dimensions of inequality, such as gender and class.

With the rise of genomic research, there is growing concern that gene mapping and gene research, according to "racially defined" groups, could increase scientific and societal racism (Zusevics, 2013; Patychuk, 2011). Despite proof that "race is arbitrary biological fiction," racial taxons (groupings) have been "medicalized," that is, given legitimacy through their use in medical literature and practice as acceptable descriptive labels that are integral to proper diagnosis and treatment of disease (Witzig, 1996, p. 675). This "racial profiling" of disease can lead to serious medical error, and also obscures the social and environmental conditions that give rise to diseases (Braun et al., 2007; Reardon, 2008; Witzig, 1996). Examining newspaper coverage of immigrant tuberculosis (TB) in Canada, Reitmanova and Gustafson (2012b) show that TB is presented in such a way that suggests the roots of the disease are located in "the racialized immigrant body" (p. 914). This suggests "the problem of immigrant TB in Canada can be solved by biomedical responses to the racialized body. The important links between TB and poverty, and the broader socioeconomic and political context in which immigrant health is embedded, were largely ignored . . ." (p. 918). There is a need, they suggest, to challenge models of infectious diseases that tend to racialize and medicalize the risks of infections in socio-economically disadvantaged populations (Reitmanova & Gustafson, 2012a).

Canada's Cultural Mosaic

The latest information on immigration and ethnocultural diversity compiled from the National Household Survey (NHS) 2011 indicates that there are now over 200 ethnic origins in Canada (Statistics Canada, 2013f). This is a dramatic contrast from the turn of the twentieth century, when the census recorded about 25 different **ethnic groups** in this country. It has been estimated that since 1990 Canada has received on average 200,000 **immigrants** per year (Statistics Canada, 2008c). It is not surprising, therefore, that there has been a growing interest in issues relating to the health and illness of Canada's ethnic groups and immigrant population. Understanding the health patterns and behaviour of the immigrant community is important since immigrants constitute a large proportion of the population (Pérez, 2002). Immigrants, especially those who are first generation, are sometimes viewed as people with problems because they do not fit neatly into the culture and structure of the Canadian health-care system. The challenge for health-care service providers is to address the needs of this ethnically diverse group of peoples whose understandings of health and illness may be different from those of the once-dominant Anglo majority.

Ethnic Diversity in Canada

Canada today is considered one of the most ethnically diverse countries in the world. Its development has been and continues to be shaped by different waves of immigrants.

ethnic group
A group of people who not only share an ethnic background but also interact with each other on the basis of their shared ethnicity.

immigrants
First-generation immigrants are those who were born outside of Canada. Second generation refers to those who are Canadian-born and have at least one parent who was born outside Canada. Third generation or more are the offspring of Canadian-born parents (Statistics Canada, 2003).

Canada accepts proportionately more immigrants and refugees than any other country (Pérez, 2002). In 2011, for example, just over one in five (20.6 per cent) of those living in Canada were foreign-born, the highest proportion in 75 years. A large proportion of them—17.2 per cent—are recent immigrants, having come to Canada between 1 January 2006 and 10 May 2011 (Statistics Canada, 2013f). Projections by Statistics Canada (2010c) indicate that by 2031 one in four Canadians could be foreign-born. This shift in the percentage of foreign-born persons is due to the fact that the foreign-born population is growing about four times faster than the rest of the population (p. 16).

The composition of immigrants has changed significantly over the years. At the beginning of the twentieth century, the majority of immigrants came from the United Kingdom or the United States. However, by the 1910s and 1920s there were increased numbers from European countries, such as Russia, Ukraine, Hungary, and Italy. Immigration from Asia was low, and there is evidence that Canada's immigration policy had racist undertones. For example, although Chinese immigrant workers had played an import role in the building of the TransCanada Railway, a so-called head tax was first imposed in 1885 as a way of regulating future Chinese immigration. This tax required every Chinese person entering Canada to pay a large sum of money, a policy that made it virtually impossible for Chinese men to bring brides or wives to Canada (Boyd & Vickers, 2009). In 1923, the federal Parliament passed the Chinese Immigration Act, also known as the Chinese Exclusion Act, which restricted virtually all immigration from China to Canada: only diplomats, children born in Canada, merchants, and students would be permitted. This act effectively stopped immigration to Canada between 1923 and 1947 (the year it was repealed).

In the 1920s, 1930s, and 1940s, there was increased immigration from European and Eastern European countries. However, when World War Two II declared, Canada prohibited immigration from countries with which Canada was at war. These barriers also meant that many Jewish refugees attempting to leave the chaos and persecution in Europe were turned away. Another example of racist policy in Canada was the war-related measures that forced Japanese Canadians who were living within a 100-mile area of British Columbia's coastline to relocate to detention-style internment camps, even though most were native-born or naturalized Canadians (Boyd & Vickers, 2009). Although the postwar era saw an immigration boom, immigration policies at the time basically precluded certain groups of people from coming to Canada. The Immigration Act of 1952 indicated national origin as a possible ground for exclusion. Admissible persons were those who were born or had citizenship in the United Kingdom, Australia, New Zealand, the Union of South Africa, the United States, and selected European countries (Boyd & Vickers, 2009).

A change came in 1967 when immigration regulations replaced national origin as a criterion with an assigned points system based on an applicant's age, education, language skills, and economic characteristics. The change also allowed immigrants to sponsor relatives to immigrate to Canada. In 1978, a new Immigration Act incorporated humanitarian grounds as a basis for admission. The most recent legislation, which became law in June 2002, the Immigration and Refugee Protection Act, retains the following three criteria for admission: labour market considerations, family reunification, or humanitarian grounds (Boyd & Vickers, 2009, p. 247).

Changes in immigration policies over the past century have shaped the ethno-cultural composition of Canada. The most dramatic difference in the face of Canada between the first two-thirds of the twentieth century and the Canada of today is the large proportion of immigrants from non-European countries. In 2011, the largest number of recent immigrants (those who came since 2006) were born in Asia (including the Middle East); they comprised 56.9 per cent of newcomers. By contrast, only 8.5 per cent of the foreign-born population who came to Canada prior to the 1970s were born in Asia. The situation was reversed in the case of European immigrants: of those who came to Canada during the 2006–11 period, only 13.7 per cent were born in Europe, whereas 78.3 per cent of immigrants who reported coming to Canada before 1971 were from Europe. In 2011, nearly one out of every five people identified themselves as being a member of the **visible minority** population: of those who arrived since 2006, 78 per cent were from racialized groups. The three largest racialized groups combined—South Asians, Chinese, and Blacks—accounted for 61.3 per cent of the visible minority population (Statistics Canada, 2013f). See Figure 6.2, which illustrates the major racialized groups in Canada in 2006 and projects these numbers to 2031 if current patterns of immigration continue.

The immigrant population is unevenly distributed throughout the country. According to the NHS 2011 (Statistics Canada, 2013f), immigrants, especially those who recently arrived in Canada, tend to settle in major urban centres. In 2011, Toronto, Vancouver, and Montreal accounted for nearly two-thirds (63.4 per cent) of the country's immigrant population and 62.5 per cent of those who had arrived since 2006. Similar to the residence pattern of other immigrants, the vast majority (95.2 per cent) of visible minorities lived in Ontario, British Columbia, Quebec, or Alberta. In 2011, more than half (52.3 per cent) made Ontario their home. However, it is British Columbia where the highest proportion of its population (27.3 per cent) belong to visible minorities, followed by Ontario with 25.9 per cent.

visible minorities
A term used by Statistics Canada and other government bodies "to refer to persons, other than Aboriginal peoples, who are non-Caucasian in race or non-white in colour," as defined by the Employment Equity Act.

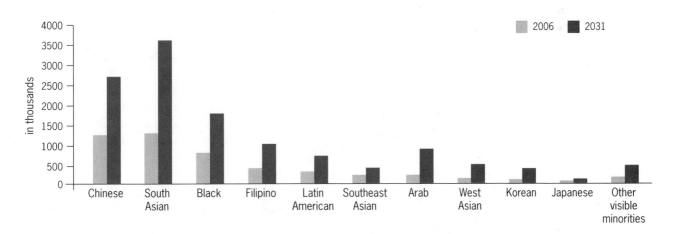

Figure 6.2 Visible Minority Groups in Canada in 2006 and a Projection for 2031

Source: Adapted from Minister of Industry. (2010). Table 4, Population by visible minority group and projection scenario, Canada, 2006 and 2031. *Projections of the Diversity of the Canadian Population; 2006 to 2031.* Available at www.statcan.gc.ca/pub/91-551-x/91-551-x2010001-eng.pdf, p. 23.

How Are Ethnicity and Health Related?

Two previous reports commissioned by Health Canada (Health Canada, 1999a; Hyman, 2001) identified some of the main findings in immigrant health research but also indicated that there are still many gaps in our understanding of how and why the health of more recent immigrants differs from that of the Canadian-born population. Much of the research on ethnicity and health tends to treat ethnic groups as a homogenous category; however, as we have suggested previously, an intersectional approach provides for a much better explanation of how one's social location is related to health experiences. The intersection of socio-economic factors, gender, country of birth, experiences of marginalization and racism, cultural understandings of health and illness, and language barriers are among the main factors that might explain ethnic differences in health outcomes.

The "Healthy Immigrant Effect"

One frequently asked question is whether the health of immigrants is different from those who were born in Canada. There is a belief among some Canadians that immigrants are not healthy and that they overutilize health-care services. Research, however, suggests that this is not the case. In fact, it has been well documented that when immigrants first arrive in Canada, they are in better health than native-born Canadians, and they also have lower mortality rates (Beiser, 2005; Hyman & Jackson, 2010; Newbold, 2005, 2009; Newbold & Danforth, 2003; Ng et al., 2005a, b). They are, moreover, less likely to have chronic conditions or disabilities and are more likely to rate their health as good, very good, or excellent. However, once they have lived in the country for a number of years, their health status declines and shows patterns that are similar to those of native-born Canadians or immigrants who have been in Canada for a period longer than 10 years. This health advantage that newly arrived immigrants appear to have is referred to as the **healthy immigrant effect**. Similar findings have been observed in Australia, the United States, and other Western European countries (Subedi & Rosenberg, 2014).

> **healthy immigrant effect**
> Refers to the finding that newly arrived immigrants appear to have a health advantage but after a period of time their health status tends to converge toward that of the host population.

With the exception of tuberculosis and some groups' susceptibility to diabetes and liver disease, recent immigrants appear to be less like likely to suffer from chronic illnesses and disability. They have a longer life expectancy and more years of life free from disability. However, studies have also shown that there is a gradient of worsening health, that is, that the health advantage new immigrants enjoy appears to deteriorate the longer they reside in the host country, sometimes as soon as 5 to 10 years after arrival (Ali et al., 2004; Newbold, 2009; Subedi & Rosenberg, 2014). Such generalizations, however, mask the considerable heterogeneity among immigrant groups (Ng & the LHAD research team, 2011). Comparing two cohorts of immigrants who arrived in Canada in the same time period, Subedi and Rosenberg (2014), for example, found "statistically significant differences in the socioeconomic characteristics and health outcomes of immigrants having less than 10 years of residency compared to those having more than 10 years in Canada" (p. 109). Using the information from the 2000–2001 Canadian Community Health Survey, Pérez (2002) found that the rate of chronic conditions among immigrants was significantly lower than that observed for the Canadian-born population (Ali et al., 2004). The pattern was similar for both men and women although women had a higher prevalence of chronic conditions than men. However, Pérez did not find a correlation between length of time in Canada and increased risk for specific chronic conditions when factors such as age, education, and household income were taken into account. Similarly, Karen Kobayashi et al. (2008) found that health advantages of certain ethno-cultural groups, such as the Chinese and South Asians, regardless of immigrant status, can best be attributed to differences in social, structural, and lifestyle environments. They conclude that "health differences between ethnic foreign-born and [Canadian-born persons who share the same ethnocultural origin] generally converge after controlling for sociodemographic, socioeconomic status (SES), and lifestyle factors" (p. 129). In their study of recent immigrants to Ontario, Creatore et al. (2010) found that the risk of diabetes among immigrants from South Asia was triple that of immigrants of Western European and North American origin. Their research suggests that beyond factors such as age and obesity,[1] risk for diabetes is not evenly distributed across ethnic groups, although the risk for diabetes increased the longer immigrants lived in Canada. Using longitudinal data collected over the period 1994–5 to 2002–3, Ng et al. (2005a) found that based on self-reports of health status, immigrants' health did deteriorate but that this deterioration applied only to immigrants from non-European origins, especially those who had arrived since the mid-1980s. Recent non-European immigrants were twice as likely as the Canadian-born population to report a deterioration in their health (see Figure 6.3). Edward Ng (2011) found that while age-standardized mortality rates (ASMRs) of immigrants were significantly lower than that of the Canadian-born population, there were variations among the immigrant groups depending on their country of origin. While for most groups, the ASMRs increased with the duration of residence in Canada, this was not the case for all groups and also varied by gender. The above research reminds us, while we can speak in general terms about a "healthy immigrant effect," it is especially important to not assume homogeneity among immigrant groups.

A couple of possible reasons have been given for the healthy immigrant effect. One explanation might be that the immigration process is such that it selects what are perceived as the best immigrants on the basis of education, language ability, job skills, and health, and screens out those people who have serious health problems (Ali et al., 2004; Hyman, 2001). Canada's Immigration and Refugee Protection Act states that an applicant should be rejected if he or she "is likely to be a danger to public health" or if it is expected that she or he would "cause excessive demand on health and social services" (cited in Beiser, 2005, p. s31). Another possible reason might be self-selection. That is, people who choose to emigrate are in better health and as a result are able and motivated to move, excluding those who are sick.

Decline in Immigrant Health Post-Immigration

So how might we explain the different findings that suggest immigrant health deteriorates after arrival? One possible explanation is that of "lifestyle" change; that is, the longer immigrants live in Canada, there is a greater likelihood that their lifestyle behaviours

---

1. I acknowledge that this term is contested by critical scholars for its stigmatizing effect, but it is the terminology used in the literature reviewed.

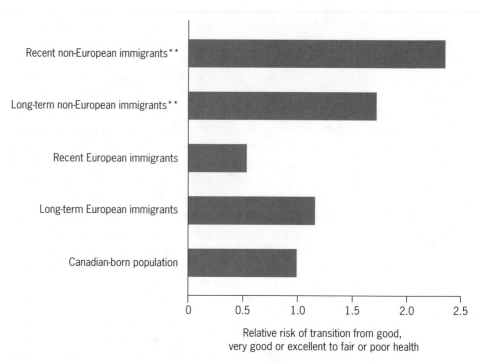

Figure 6.3 Comparison of Self-Reported Health Status for European Immigrants and Non-European Immigrants

**Significantly different from estimate for Canadian-born (p<0.01).

Source: Ng, et al. (2005). Dynamics of Immigrants' health in Canada: Evidence from the National Population Health Survey. In Statistics Canada, *Healthy today, healthy tomorrow? Findings from the National Population Health Survey.* Available from www.statcan.gc.ca/pub/82-618-m/2005002/pdf/4193621-eng.pdf

acculturation
A multidimensional process by which newcomers to a country take on the values and behaviours of their host country.

begin to more closely resemble the behaviours of Canadians in general, including poor health behaviours such as smoking, drinking, and poor dietary habits. This is believed to occur through a process of **acculturation** whereby the ideas, values, and behaviours of immigrants' place of origin are replaced by those in the new culture (Hyman, 2001). Pérez (2002) and Newbold (2009) among others question this assumption. Newbold (2009) writes, "the factors associated with declines in health tended to be dominated by sociodemographic effects, including age, gender, origin, and immigrant class" (p. 331). In a qualitative exploration of immigrant health, Dean and Wilson (2010) found that none of the immigrants with whom they spoke identified lifestyle change as a factor related to health status. Those who reported a worsening of health (a minority) attributed it to the stress associated with trying to settle in a new country, including difficulties in finding employment. Barriers to health-care services, including the lack of culturally appropriate health-care services, may also explain the causes of deteriorating health conditions for some new immigrants (Subedi & Rosenberg, 2014; Dean & Wilson, 2010). Age is another possible variable that might explain differences. Recent immigrants tend to be younger than the Canadian population as a whole. As a result they would experience fewer health problems, such as diabetes, obesity, cardiovascular and coronary disease, and respiratory problems, which tend to be disproportionately found among aging populations.

The social determinants of health have a significant influence on the health of immigrant groups. As immigrants begin the resettlement process, for example, they are more likely to experience stressors such as unemployment, poverty, social exclusion, limited social supports, and lack of access to services, all of which adversely affect health. Poor quality housing, for example, increases their likelihood of exposure to risk factors for various diseases and compromises their access to treatment (Beiser, 2005). Kobayashi and Prus (2012) note that markers of social inequality matter in assessing the health of immigrants. Using data from the Longitudinal Survey of Immigrants to Canada, De Maio and Kemp (2010) found that discrimination and inequality contributed significantly to a decline in self-reported health status of immigrants. They conclude that the social patterning behind the health transitions of immigrants signals the importance of the social determinants of health (p. 462). However, not all are at the same risk of transitioning to poorer health. The heterogeneity among immigrants highlights the need to examine critical intersections of age, gender, racialization, social class, immigration, and ethnicity (De Maio & Kemp, 2010; Hyman & Jackson, 2010; Kobayshi & Prus, 2012).

Refugees and Health

As a whole, **refugees** "tend to be a vulnerable population, in that they have not voluntarily chosen to leave their country of origin . . . may also be separated from other family members at the time of resettlement, be survivors of torture and have lost most of their material possessions, wealth, and status" (McKeary & Newbold, 2010, p. 525). They are more likely to experience socio-economic disadvantages, social exclusion, and the health problems associated with these disadvantages than other immigrant groups (Hyman, 2001). The number of refugees entering Canada in a given year varies. In 2012, 23,056 refugees and their families came to Canada, which is 26 per cent fewer than 2011 (AMSSA, 2013). It is argued that changes to Canada's Immigration and Refugee Protection Act in 2012 have made it more difficult for refugees to claim asylum in Canada (Canadian Council for Refugees, 2013; Wingrove, 2014). However, as of April 2016 the recently elected Liberal government has welcomed over 26,000 Syrian refugees to Canada. Refugees, many of whom are fleeing war, torture, and gender-based violence have greater health needs than other immigrants, particularly related to emotional and mental health, including post-traumatic stress disorder (Newbold, 2009; Hansson et al., 2012). Changes to the act by the previous Conservative government included cuts to health-care coverage for refugee claimants. On July 4, 2014, the federal court struck down the cuts as unconstitutional because they constitute "cruel and unusual" treatment that could jeopardize the health, safety, and lives of refugees (Canadian Council for Refugees, 2014; Black, 2014).

Since refugees arrive in Canada with few, if any, economic resources or lack the documentation and/or English language skills that are needed to find skilled employment, they are more likely to have very high rates of unemployment and welfare dependency compared with those born in Canada and with other immigrants. The refugee experience and the resettlement process is often traumatic; a loss of personal and cultural identity, depression, post-traumatic stress disorder, developmental problems in children, and family violence are commonly identified as health issues (Fowler, 1998). Refugees may come from countries, or have spent years in refugees camps, with sub-standard living conditions and inadequate or non-existent health services, which puts them "at increased risk from infectious diseases . . . viral hepatitis, parasitic diseases . . . dental disease, vitamin D and other nutritional deficiencies, and chronic diseases" (Biggs & Skull, 2003, p. 65). They are often without a

refugees
Individuals who flee their country of origin because of a fear of persecution for reasons of gender, sexual orientation, ethnicity, religion, political opinion, nationality, or membership in a particular social or racialized group.

network of friends or family, which can increase feelings of isolation and loneliness, which adds to the difficulty of finding the necessary health services and appropriate health care. They also experience more systemic barriers than other immigrants in accessing health care (McKeary & Newbold, 2010). Yet we need to remember that there is heterogeneity also among refugees groups in terms of their pre- and post-migration experiences. Based on a representative population of refugees in Alberta, 68 per cent of whom were from the former Yugoslavia, Maximova and Krahn (2010) found that those who had spent time in a refugee camp or who held professional jobs in their home country had a greater decline in mental health status. Economic hardship in Canada was associated with a decline in physical health. Using a qualitative approach to talk about the acculturation of former Yugoslavian refugees, Djuraskovic and Arthur (2009) conclude that for these refugees, acculturation and identity reconstruction is a fluid process connected to their subjective experiences.

Immigrant and Refugee Women and Health

There is limited research on the health status of immigrant and refugee women in Canada. However, studies do suggest that they are more likely to experience stress, anxiety, and depression (Ahmad et al., 2004; Meadows, Thurston, & Melton, 2001). Loss of familial and social networks, difficulties in accessing health services, and anxieties around meeting new gender role expectations compromised their mental health. Other research shows that immigrant women receive "less than optimal maternity care" and are at increased risk for post-partum depression (Higginbottom et al., 2014, p. 545). It has also been suggested that immigrant women may be more vulnerable to mental health problems due to previous trauma, the impact of discrimination, social isolation, as well as economic and social marginalization (Spitzer, 2005, p. s86). Refugee women in particular may have experienced multiple traumas, such as rape and other forms of gender-based violence, which can lead to major depression, including post-traumatic stress disorder (Hyman, 2001). Employment barriers, which stem from a lack of Canadian work experience or "appropriate" credentials, are additional sources of stress. Immigrant and refugee women are overrepresented in contingent employment and low-wage jobs, often have little or no job security, and experience unsafe work conditions, all of which impact negatively on health (Ontario Council of Agencies Serving Immigrants, 2005).

Family violence cuts across all social classes and ethnic groups; however, Brownridge and Halli (2002) found that immigrant women to Canada from developing countries experienced the highest prevalence of violence. Moreover, immigrant women are more likely to face special problems and have fewer alternatives to leave abusive relationships. A study of South Asian immigrant women in Toronto found that the main reasons women gave for delayed help-seeking from professionals were "social stigma, rigid gender roles, marriage obligations, expected silence, loss of social support after migration and limited knowledge about available resources and myths about partner abuse" (Ahmad et al., 2009, p. 613). Social stigma was related to concerns that their disclosure would lead to disrespect for the family and parents. They also spoke of the cultural assumptions that so-called real South Asian women would remain silent about their situation, would maintain their marital obligations, and would remain subordinate to their husbands. Many immigrant women are also isolated because of limited language skills, lack of support networks, and economic dependence on their spouses, and may be fearful that speaking out will lead to deportation. They turn for help only after experiencing pronounced mental and physical health problems (Ahmed et al., 2009).

The Social and Cultural Construction of Health and Illness

Health and *illness* are terms that we typically take for granted. We know what it means to be healthy, and we know when someone is ill. We tend to assume that these are objective facts: states of the body and the mind that can be measured against what is viewed as normal. Sociologists and anthropologists, however, have shown us that health and illness are **social constructions**; they are not objectively defined. Definitions of *health* and *illness*, and understandings of appropriate health care vary over time and across cultures.

Furthermore, in any society, some members have more power than others to define health and illness. Some people are the custodians of so-called legitimate medical knowledge, while other members of society, who do not have specialist knowledge, are encouraged to define health and illness in the same ways as those who are considered experts. In Canadian society, the dominant cultural model of health and illness is that of **biomedicine**, and the experts are health professionals, such as doctors.

Different cultures have different understandings of health and illness, and people within societies are differentially located with respect to access to expert knowledge in this area. Their understanding and experience could affect both their willingness to seek medical attention as well as their ability to access medical services. Cultural understandings and the structure of health care both play important parts in determining how health and illness are approached by different groups of people. One needs to remember that the dominant Anglo-Canadian view that scientifically based Western medicine is superior has also been influenced by culture.

Cultural Beliefs and Health

Cultural beliefs and values play an important role in an individual's understanding of health and illness. These beliefs influence how symptoms are recognized and to what they are attributed (Anderson et al., 2003). The Vietnamese, for example, believe that physical and emotional illness is caused by an imbalance in the forces of *am* and *duong* (similar to the Chinese yin and yang). One cause of mental illness is believed to be possession by ancestral spirits who have been offended and have become angry (Lien, 1992). Among Latin Americans, the word *susto* refers to illnesses associated with unexpected experiences of fright that produce symptoms such as loss of appetite, nervousness, and depression. In a classic study in the United States on the effects of culture on pain, Zborowski found that pain and the significance attributed to pain symptoms varied by culture and ethnicity (cited in Anderson et al., 2003, p. 69). Different ethnic groups may also have different expectations of what constitutes appropriate treatment, which will, in part, reflect different cultural understandings of the causes of health and illness. For example, many from former Yugoslavia believe in the value of medicinal mud baths and healing spas to treat ailments such as rheumatism, arthritis, and respiratory problems (Eastern European Communities, n.d.).

Cultural beliefs and experiences influence how symptoms are identified, attitudes toward health care and health-care–seeking behaviours, notions of appropriate treatment, use of health services, and willingness to report certain health problems. In their study of perceptions of health among a diverse group of immigrant women in Prince Edward

social construction/ constructionism
Refers to the socially created characteristics of human life based on the idea that people actively construct reality, meaning it is neither natural nor inevitable. Therefore, notions of health/illness are subjective human creations that should not be taken for granted.

biomedicine/biomedical model
The conventional approach to medicine in Western societies, based on the diagnosis and explanation of illness as a malfunction of the body's biological mechanisms. This approach underpins most health professions and health services, which focuses on treating individuals and generally ignores the social origins of illness and its prevention.

Island, MacKinnon and Howard (2010) found that the women saw a physician usually only in cases of serious illness. For routine illnesses they relied on traditional or herbal remedies. One woman described how in her country of origin one dealt with headaches in the following way: "When I have a headache, my mom go out in garden and just pick some leaves and put on my head" (MacKinnon & Howard, 2010, p. 202). Kirmayer et al. (2007) found that in comparison to anglophone and francophone Canadian-born, Vietnamese, Caribbean, and Filipino immigrants were significantly less likely to use primary-care mental-health services or to seek out specialty mental-health care. Instead they were more likely to seek sources of help in their community, including from religious leaders or traditional healers, or to rely on traditional or alternative medicine at home. But according to Kirmayer et al., the lower rates of mental-health–service use among the immigrant groups cannot be attributed simply to differences in levels of distress or to their use of alternative sources of help; rather, cultural factors may be involved. In some cultures, there is a great deal of stigma attached to mental-health problems; such problems are understood as personal ones that are best dealt with alone or through religious or community institutions. This is well illustrated by some of the women that MacKinnon and Howard interviewed (2010). One woman stated that

> It [mental health issue] is my problem, I would solve it. Best to fight that by yourself or with the help of family, friends or with herbal medicines. (p. 202)

Another woman explained it this way:

> . . . if we have problem, in our culture they say you only supposed to talk to family, like you shouldn't talk outside the family because you always want the family looks good. So, most . . . people is pretty shy to talk about their personal life, even [if] have problem. (p. 202)

Qualitative studies by Whitley et al. (2006) and Gurm et al. (2008) suggest that some immigrants may believe in the curative power of non-medical interventions, such as a religious deity, traditional folk medicine, or the power of spirituality in mediating health experiences and hence may be more hesitant to use biomedical health services. Other studies also point to cultural factors to explain differences in health experience, behaviour, and health status among ethnic groups. In a cross-cultural, comparative study of seven cultural groups in Canada, Kopec et al. (2001) found that there were substantial differences between the groups in their reporting of pain, emotional function, and cognitive function, which could not be explained by differences in socio-economic status and self-reported chronic conditions. They concluded that cultural factors, such as different conceptions of health and cultural differences in the meaning and reporting of illness, may play a significant role in explaining some of the observed differences. In another study that explored the intersections of ethnicity, gender, age, and immigrant status as determinants of the health status of Canadians, Karen Kobayashi (2003) found that there are significant differences in health status and health-care utilization among immigrant groups. She concluded that cultural characteristics along with socio-structural factors are salient predictors of population health. According to Kobayashi, the key emergent issue with regard to adults' health status is "the clash between the ethno-cultural values and beliefs of foreign-born . . . and the health care system" (p. 10).

Groups differ not only in terms of culture but also, and perhaps more importantly, in terms of their social location—that is, in terms of their location in the structure of social inequality. Racialized groups (whether born in Canada or not) and immigrant groups are not homogeneous, unified wholes that speak with one narrative voice. Moreover, culture is not static but changes over time (Este, 2007). New immigrants to Canada will likely retain some parts of their culture of origin, but over time they will begin to embrace certain aspects of Canadian culture, thus forging a new culture that will evolve, develop, and change over time (Kobayashi, 2003, p. 95).

How to Provide Culturally Competent Health Care

Access to health care is considered fundamental to good health (Butler-Jones, 2008). The challenge for health-care providers in an ethnically and culturally diverse and racialized country such as Canada is to ensure that health resources and services are equitable for all Canadians, regardless of cultural characteristics, including ethnic origin, immigrant status, or charter language ability (Kobayashi, 2003). It has been suggested that health disparities for racialized and ethnically diverse groups can be reduced in part by the provision of **culturally competent health care** (Anderson et al., 2003). *Cultural competency* has been defined as "the ability to conduct professional work in a way that is consistent with the expectations which members of distinctive cultures regard as appropriate among themselves" (cited in Este, 2007, p. 95).

culturally competent health care
Delivery of health-care services in a way that recognizes the cultural beliefs and needs of those they serve.

One aspect of culture competency is the ability to deliver health services in the language of those needing the care. Linguistic and communication barriers hinder equitable access to health care, especially for people who do not speak one of Canada's official languages fluently (Access Alliance, 2005; McKeary & Newbold, 2010). As can be seen in Figure 6.4, communication barriers could be a problem for a significant number of immigrant women.

In their study of first-generation immigrant groups in Montreal, Leduc and Proulx (2004) found that language and ethnic origin were two of the main criteria used in choosing health-care providers. Not being able to communicate their health needs or not fully understanding the instructions given to them added additional tension to new immigrant families who were already under considerable stress. Similarly, nearly all of the immigrant women in MacKinnon and Howard's study (2010) identified language as a major barrier affecting their health. The following comments made by the women illustrate this clearly:

"Language stresses out. Not being able to communicate."

"[Language] big problem, because you can't say anything you want to say."

"You want to talk to somebody, just to talk. Without language you can't, you feel frustrated." (p. 204)

Linguistic barriers also exist if trained professional interpreters are unavailable or if health information is not translated in multiple languages (Access Alliance, 2005). Clear

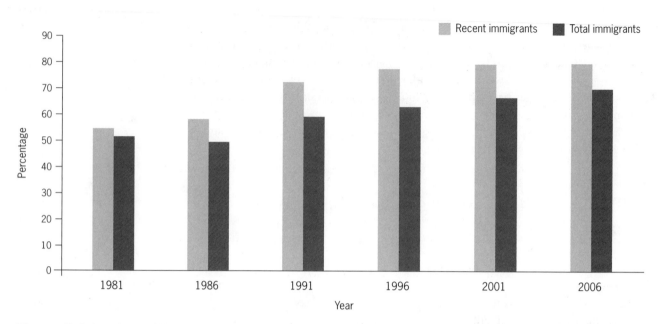

Figure 6.4 Immigrant Women Whose Mother Tongue Is Neither English Nor French, Canada, 1981 to 2006

Source: Chui, T. (2011). Chart 9.12, Immigrant Women Whose Mother Tongue Is Neither English nor French, Canada, 1981 to 2006. In Statistics Canada, *Women in Canada: A Gender-Based Statistical Report*, p. 265. Available at www.statcan.gc.ca/pub/89-503-x/89-503-x2010001-eng.pdf.

communication between patient and health-care worker is crucial in the delivery of quality health care (Bischoff et al., 2003). Interpreters are essential in order to make appropriate diagnoses and to comply with treatment regimes. For this to occur, however, it is necessary to employ professionally trained interpreters who "have a good grasp of medical technology" (National Health Strategy, 1993b, p. 82), but such people are not always available in clinical settings (Levy et al., 2013). If no interpreters were available, patients would rely on family and friends to interpret, which can compromise both their privacy and confidentiality (Higginbottom et al., 2014, p. 557). When immigrants lack the necessary language skills they find it difficult to schedule appointments, to describe their problems, or to understand verbal and written instructions, all of which compromise the quality of care. An inability to communicate also undermines the faith a patient has in the care received and decreases the likelihood of returning for further help (Anderson et al., 2003; Leduc & Proulx, 2004). Language difficulties and the need for interpretation services are considered one of the most significant barriers in accessing care (McKeary & Newbold, 2010, p. 529).

Culturally competent health care also requires that services provided are seen as culturally appropriate. Arabic women, for example, tend to have a strong cultural preference for antenatal care provided by women, but this is often unavailable (Bennett & Shearman, 1989). The gender of health professionals is also important for Sri Lankan, Filipina, and Vietnamese women, especially for gynecological services (Leduc & Proulx, 2004). Half of the immigrant women in MacKinnon and Howard's study similarly expressed preference for a female doctor, especially in situations where they had to remove their clothing. One woman stated it bluntly: "If there is no female doctor, I would not get a gynecological exam" (MacKinnon & Howard, 2010, p. 205). Cultural and communication barriers have also been identified as a reason that Pap-smear screening tests are underutilized by many immigrant and ethnic minority women in Canada (McDonald & Kennedy, 2007). Research has highlighted the need for hospitals to take account of different cultural practices in relation to childbirth and post-partum confinement (Allotey et al., 2001; Manderson & Mathews, 1981; Rice, 1994; Rice et al., 1994).

A Euro-centric orientation in services, cultural insensitivity, discrimination, and a lack of health-care providers from the same cultural background have been identified as significant barriers for ethnic groups (Access Alliance, 2005; Anderson et al., 2003; Hyman, 2001):

> They were coming from a completely different culture . . . They didn't understand my culture and it didn't seem like they made an effort to either. It was more just like, "Well, it shouldn't be that way" and it's almost like my own culture was being put down. (Women's Health in Women's Hands Community Health Centre, 2003, p. 28)

In some cases, perceptions that health professionals may not understand their culture or may be prejudiced against it had an impact on their use and selection of health-care services (Access Alliance, 2005; Egan & Gardner, 1999; Hyman, 2001; Women's Health in Women's Hands Community Health Centre, 2003). In a participatory action study with young "women of colour" in the Toronto area, the researchers found that one in five women reported that they had experienced racism when they had used the health-care system (Women's Health in Women's Hands Community Health Centre, 2003). One young woman described her experience this way:

> I guess it was racism. Just because, when someone tries to make themselves, you know, superior to you because of their culture and their ways, it is racism. So I mean, it didn't affect me greatly but the fact that it was there scared me. Because I mean, who knows what levels that could have been taken to. That's in their practice and who knows what they're preaching subconsciously to people. (p. 27)

Many of the young women in the Toronto study (Women's Health in Women's Hands Community Health Centre, 2003) reported having positive experiences with the health-care system and good relationships with their doctors. However, nearly one-third (29.6 per cent) reported having negative experiences; reasons for this included lack of trust and different views of appropriate care, poor communication between doctor and patient, language difficulties, cultural insensitivity, lack of knowledge of patients' culture, and discrimination (p. 25). Perceptions and experiences of racism and discrimination can discourage individuals from seeking health-care services or following advice. At the level of provider–patient interaction, discrimination can lead to misdiagnosis and misuse of interventions (Pollock et al., 2012, p. 75).

Poverty, transportation issues, shortage of services, and lack of child care have also been identified as barriers to access. Equity in health-care access requires more than the removal of financial barriers, although this is important. "Western health-care institutions and the medical system are premised on the 'universal' patient body, with very little recognition of the social context/identity of that body" (McKeary & Newbold, 2010, p. 532). The current health-care system is structured to meet the needs of its dominant population but can create barriers for those whose appearance, speech, behaviours, or values are different. Health equity and social justice require culturally appropriate care that acknowledges diversity and difference and is readily available in all areas and for all health services (Anderson et al., 2003; Fenta et al., 2007; Simich et al., 2005). But, what would a culturally competent health-care system look like? It has been suggested that it would include the following: a culturally diverse staff that reflects the communities served, professionally trained interpreters and translators, the acknowledgement of racism, the inclusion of anti-racist perspectives in organizational policy and staff training, training for health-care providers about the cultures of the people they serve, linguistically and culturally appropriate educational materials, and culturally specific health-care settings (Anderson et al., 2003; Patychuk, 2011; Pollock et al., 2012). But it is not enough to just focus on interactions between users and health-care providers at the interpersonal level; rather one must address "the role of systemic, institutional and organizational racism in shaping these encounters" (Allan & Smylie, 2015, p. 29). In addition, all services need to be examined from a gender lens as well as for their sensitivity to difference based on factors such as age, sexual orientation, and disability. Treating everyone exactly the same ignores structural inequalities, and therefore perpetuates inequity (Tang & Browne, 2008, p. 118). To fully achieve health equity, other social determinants of health must be addressed such as poverty, racism, unemployment, and social exclusion that are at the root of health disparities.

Conclusion

Although Canada is considered a multicultural society, social exclusion, racism, and socio-economic disparity remain a reality for racialized groups, immigrants, and refugees (Galabuzi, 2009; Hou et al., 2009; Ornstein, 2006). Research shows that racism is an important determinant of health; it "influences health including health behaviours, stress, material deprivation, and access to quality health care" (Hyman, 2009, p. 11). The review of research on the relationship between immigrant experience and health demonstrates that both cultural and structural factors can play a significant role in health outcomes and health-care experiences. Culturalist explanations of health recognize the importance of cultural differences in the meaning of health and illness among people of different ethnic backgrounds, as well as the effects of these in diagnosis and treatment. Structuralist (or materialist) explanations stress the significance of social location as a major factor in health outcomes. These explanations look at social inequality and social determinants of health as important predictors of health status. The challenge for the future in health-care delivery is to integrate these two approaches while recognizing that equity does not mean treating everyone the same. Increasingly, more researchers are doing this by focusing on the complex interrelationships between structural factors, ethnicity, racialization, and culture (Galabuzi, 2009, 2001; Kobayashi et al., 2008; Access Alliance, 2005; Patychuk, 2011).

Summary

- Racism operates at various levels and leads to negative health outcomes for members of racialized groups.
- Experiences of racism can lead to physical and emotional health problems.
- Racialized Canadians experience disproportionate levels of unemployment, poverty, inadequate housing, and discrimination.
- Canada's ethnic composition is changing, with increased numbers of immigrants coming from non-European countries.
- Most research suggests that recent immigrants tend to have longer life expectancy and lower levels of morbidity. This is referred to as the "healthy immigrant effect."
- There is considerable heterogeneity among immigrant people. Certain groups such as refugees, those from racialized backgrounds, and women tend to experience more socio-economic disadvantages and more health problems.
- Cultural beliefs, values, and practices can influence how health is understood, what are considered appropriate treatments, and the use of health-care services.
- Culturally competent health services are needed to ensure health resources and services are equitable for all groups. At a minimum, this would include having a culturally diverse staff that reflects the communities served and developing anti-racist policies and staff training to prevent discrimination.
- Health equity requires both acknowledging and respecting "difference" as well as structural changes that address social determinants of health.

Key Terms

acculturation

biomedicine/
  biomedical model

culturally competent
  health care

ethnic group

healthy immigrant effect

immigrants

"race"

racialized groups

racism/racist

refugees

social construction/
  constructionism

social exclusion

visible minority

Sociological Reflection: What's Your Ethnicity?

We often think of ethnicity as something that immigrants possess, noting how "they" are different from "us." Yet we all have an ethnic identity that reflects the culture in which we have been socialized. Being conscious of your own ethnicity can help you to understand cultural differences and avoid ethnocentrism (judging the beliefs and practices of different cultures from the perspective of one's own culture).

- How would you describe your ethnic background?
- What are some distinctive features of your ethnicity?
- Why might some people be labelled as ethnic in Canada and others not?
- In what ways might racism and ethnocentrism affect the quality, accessibility, and appropriateness of health-care delivery?

Discussion Questions

1. Choose one of the following groups: immigrant women, racialized immigrant groups, or refugees. In what ways would their health concerns be similar to and/or different from those of the Canadian-born population?
2. What kinds of barriers do members of racialized groups experience in obtaining health care?
3. How do challenges that confront immigrant women in finding health services differ from those confronting immigrant men?
4. In what ways does social exclusion lead to poor health?
5. What do you think is the best explanation for the "healthy immigrant effect"? Give reasons for your answer.
6. What do you think should be done to improve access and remove barriers to health-care services for immigrants generally?

Further Investigation

1. Critically assess the relative significance of pre-migration and post-migration factors on the health of immigrants in Canada. What patterns (if any) are apparent?
2. Choose any (one) racialized group and explore the intersections of social determinants of health and culture as these relate to the health outcomes for that group.
3. Find out the ethnic composition of the population in your area (if possible, you might also get an age and gender breakdown). What changes would you make to current services in your area in order to meet the needs of the whole community?

Further Reading

Access Alliance. (2005). *Racialized groups and health status: A literature review exploring poverty, housing, race-based discrimination and access to health care as determinants of health for racialized groups.* Available at http://accessalliance.ca/sites/accessalliance/files/documents/Literature%20Review_Racialized%20Groups%20and%20Health%20Status.pdf

Beiser, M. (2005, March/April). The health of immigrants and refugees in Canada. *Canadian Journal of Public Health, 96*, supplement 2, 30–44.

Galabuzi, G.E. (2005). *Canada's economic apartheid: The social exclusion of racialized groups in the new century.* Toronto, ON: Canadian Scholars' Press, Inc.

Health Canada. (2010). *Migration health: Health policy research bulletin.* Issue 17. December. Available at www.hc-sc.gc.ca/sr-sr/pubs/hpr-rpms/bull/2010-health-sante-migr/index-eng.php

Kobayashi, K., & Prus, S. (2012). Examining the gender, ethnicity, and age dimensions of the healthy immigrant effect: Factors in the development of equitable health policy. *International Journal for Equity in Health, 11*(8), 1–6.

Nestel, S. (2012). *Colour-coded health care: The impact of race and racism on Canadians'
health*. Toronto: Wellesley Institute. Available at: www.wellesleyinstitute.com

Ng, E., Wilkins, R., Gendron, F., & Berthelot, J-M. (2005). *Healthy today, healthy tomorrow?
Findings from the National Population Health Survey*. Ottawa, ON: Statistics Canada.

Reitmanova, S., & Gustafson, D. (2012). Exploring the mutual constitution of racializing and medicalizing discourses of immigrant Tuberculosis in the Canadian press.
Qualitative Health Research, 22(7), 911–20.

Simich, L., Beiser, M., Stewart, M., & Mwakarimba, E. (2005). Providing social support for immigrants and refugees in Canada: Challenges and directions. *Journal of
Immigrant Health, 7(4)*, 259–68.

Web Resources

Access Alliance, Multicultural Community
Health Centre
www.accessalliance.ca

Canadian Council for Refugees
www.ccrweb.ca

Canadian Race Relations Foundation
www.crr.ca

Canadian Research Institute for the
Advancement of Women
*www.criaw-icref.ca/
ImmigrantandRefugeeWomen*

Health Equity Council
www.healthequitycouncil.ca

Inclusive Cities Canada
*www.racialequitytools.org/resourcefiles/
inclusivecitiescanada.pdf*

LEGIT: Canadian Immigration for
Same-sex Partners
www.legit.ca

CHAPTER 7
Canada's Aboriginal People and Health: The Perpetuation of Inequalities

Jennie Hornosty

Colonization is recognized as a foundational determinant of Indigenous health globally, and the relationship between racism and colonization are inextricably intertwined. . . .

—Allan & Smylie, (2015, p. 6)

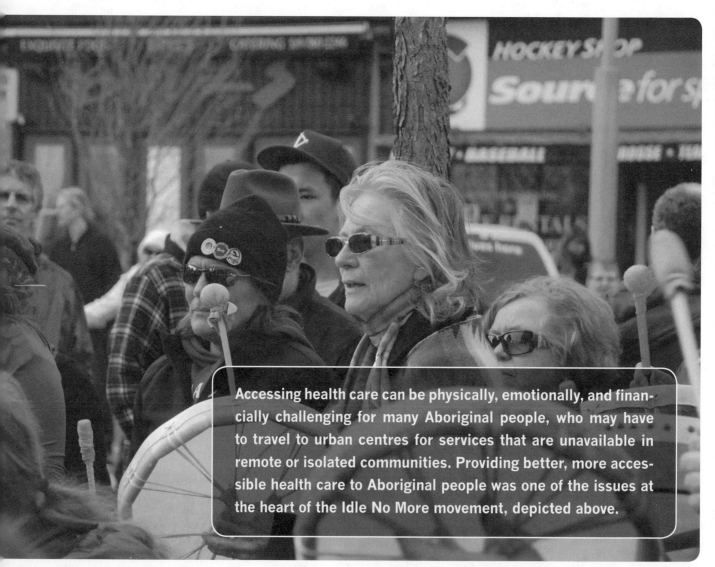

Accessing health care can be physically, emotionally, and financially challenging for many Aboriginal people, who may have to travel to urban centres for services that are unavailable in remote or isolated communities. Providing better, more accessible health care to Aboriginal people was one of the issues at the heart of the Idle No More movement, depicted above.

Overview

- Who are Aboriginal Canadians and what is their health status compared to non-Aboriginal Canadians?
- What are the key social health determinants of Aboriginal people's poor health?
- Why do these health inequities persist today?
- What are Aboriginal people's perspectives on health and well-being?

Canada has a publicly funded health-care system of which many Canadians understandably are proud. However, not all people have benefited equally. On virtually every indicator of health, the condition of Aboriginal people living in Canada is below that of non-Aboriginal Canadians. Aboriginal people have higher rates of mortality and morbidity and higher incidences of tuberculosis, alcoholism, and suicide than the rest of the population. They also are more likely to be unemployed, to live in poverty and substandard housing, and to have lower education attainment levels. This chapter explores possible explanations for these inequities and situates the existing inequality in a broader social and historical context of Aboriginal people's experiences of colonization, dispossession, racism, and marginalization from the dominant economy. As well, the chapter explores the health implications of these processes. Although efforts have been made to improve the health status of Aboriginal people, many structural inequalities remain.

Introduction: Who Are the Aboriginal Canadians?

In order to talk about the health status of Aboriginal peoples, we need to define the people of whom we are talking. **Aboriginal people** is a collective name for all the original inhabitants of North America and their descendants. The Canadian Constitution Act of 1982 recognizes three distinct groups of Aboriginal people: Indians (today commonly referred to as **First Nations**), **Métis**, and **Inuit**. Some use the terms *Indigenous* or **Indigenous people** interchangeably with *Aboriginal people* to collectively describe these three distinct groups. Each group has its own unique history, languages, spiritual beliefs, and cultural practices. The most recent data from the National Household Survey 2011 indicates that there were just over 1.4 million Canadians in 2011 who identified as belonging to one of the three groups of Aboriginal peoples, and they represent 4.3 per cent of the total Canadian population (Statistics Canada, 2013a).

Métis are persons of mixed Aboriginal and European ancestry who identify themselves as Métis. They account for 32.3 per cent of the overall Aboriginal population and speak a variety of First Nations languages. The Métis population is concentrated in western Canada and Ontario (84.9 per cent); nearly one-quarter (21.4 per cent) reside in Alberta (Statistics Canada, 2013a). Inuit are the smallest group of Aboriginal peoples, comprising just 4.2 per cent. They speak several different dialects, and while they share

Aboriginal peoples
The original inhabitants of North America and their descendants.

First Nations
Refers to all those people called "Indian."

Métis
Refers to people of mixed Aboriginal and European ancestry.

Inuit
Replaces the term *Eskimo* and refers to Aboriginal people who live primarily in Arctic Canada.

Indigenous people
Used interchangeably with the term *Aboriginal people*.

a common culture and traditions there is also linguistic and geographic diversity among the different regions. The Inuit people live primarily in Arctic Canada; almost 75 per cent live in Inuit Nunangat, which stretches from Labrador to the Northwest Territories and comprises four regions: Nunatsiavut, Nunavik, Nunavut, and the Inuvialuit region. The majority, 45.5 per cent of the Inuit population live in Nunavut. Other Aboriginal identities or those who reported more than one Aboriginal identity account for 2.7 per cent of the total Aboriginal population. See Figure 7.1 for a breakdown of the Aboriginal population in Canada and Table 7.1 for the breakdown by province and territory.

The diversity of Aboriginal peoples is further evident when we look more closely at First Nations people, who in 2011 made up 60.8 per cent of Aboriginal Canadians. Within the First Nations group there are 633 First Nations bands, which represent 52 nations or cultural groups and more than 60 languages. Each nation has its own history, spirituality, and traditional political structure. Many First Nations people still prefer to be referred to by the specific nation to which they belong (for example, Cree, Blackfoot, Dene, Maliseet, Mi'kmaq, etc.) (Assembly of First Nations, 2002). The largest percentage (23.6 per cent) of First Nations populations live in Ontario, followed by British Columbia with 18.2 per cent. However, they represent the largest shares of the total population of the Northwest Territories, followed by Yukon, Manitoba, and Saskatchewan (Statistics Canada, 2013a). As well, there is an important distinction between "status" and "non-status" Indians. Status Indians are those who are recognized as Indians under the **Indian Act** and are entitled to certain rights and benefits under the law. They account for 75 per cent of the First Nations people (Statistics Canada, 2013a). Non-status Indians are those who consider themselves Indians or members of a First Nation but are not entitled to be registered under the Indian Act, perhaps because their ancestors were never registered or because they

Indian Act
Sets out certain federal government obligations and regulates the management of Indian reserve lands, Indian moneys, and other resources. The act defines an Indian as "a person who, pursuant to this Act, is registered as an Indian or is entitled to be registered as an Indian."

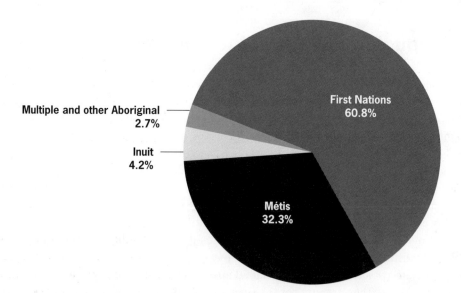

Figure 7.1 Population of Aboriginal People, 2011

Source: Employment and Social Development Canada. (2013). Aboriginal population, Canada, 2011 (per cent). Canadians in Context: Aboriginal Population. In *Indicators of Well-Being in Canada*. Available at www4.hrsdc.gc.ca/.3ndic.1t.4r@-eng.jsp?iid=36.

Table 7.1   Distribution of Population Reporting Aboriginal Identity and Percentage of Aboriginal People in the Population, Canada, Provinces and Territories, 2011

Provinces and Territories	Aboriginal Identity Population	Per Cent Distribution	Aboriginal Identity Population as a Percentage of the Total Population
Canada	1,400,685	100.0	4.3
Newfoundland and Labrador	35,800	2.6	7.1
Prince Edward Island	2,230	0.2	1.6
Nova Scotia	33,845	2.4	3.7
New Brunswick	22,615	1.6	3.1
Quebec	141,915	10.1	1.8
Ontario	301,425	21.5	2.4
Manitoba	195,900	14.0	16.7
Saskatchewan	157,740	11.3	15.6
Alberta	220,695	15.8	6.2
British Columbia	232,290	16.6	5.4
Yukon	7,705	0.6	23.1
Northwest Territories	21,160	1.5	51.9
Nunavut	27,360	2.0	86.3

Source: Ministry of Industry. (2013). In Statistics Canada, *Aboriginal Peoples in Canada: First Nations People, Métis and Inuit, National Household Survey, 2011*, p. 9. Available at: www12.statcan.gc.ca/nhs-enm/2011/as-sa/99-011-x/99-011-x2011001-eng.pdf.

lost their status under former provisions of the Indian Act. Non-status Indians are not entitled to the same rights and benefits that are available to status Indians (Assembly of First Nations, 2002). A further distinction is that some First Nations people live on-reserve while others live off-reserve. In 2011, nearly half (49.3 per cent) of First Nations people lived on-reserve. However, the percentage of First Nations people with registered Indian status who live on-reserve or off-reserve varies from province to province. Similarly, the distribution of non-status Indians varies considerably.

Evidence of Health Inequality

Study after study has shown that on virtually all measures the quality of life and health outcomes for Aboriginal peoples in Canada remain significantly worse than those of non-Aboriginal Canadians (Adelson, 2005; Health Council of Canada, 2005; First Nations Regional Health Survey (RHS) (2012); Loppie Reading & Wien, 2009; Royal Commission on Aboriginal Peoples, 1996a, b; Allan & Smylie, 2015). Despite their diversity, Aboriginal Canadians tend to have higher rates of chronic illnesses, such as diabetes and cardiovascular diseases, lower life expectancy, higher rates of suicide and higher levels of psychosocial stress. In this chapter, we attempt to reveal the "public issues" behind some of these intensely "personal troubles" (Mills, 1959, p. 14). According to C. Wright Mills, if something affects only a few individuals, the problem is best addressed in an individualistic manner by helping the individual concerned. However, if a large number of people experience the same problems, we need to look for the societal roots or social causes; social or structural changes will be necessary to remedy the problem. To understand the root of health disparities for Aboriginal peoples, then, we need to look at the social determinants of health, and their shared history of colonization and oppression, for it is the colonial policies of the Canadian government that historically shaped and continue to shape health determinants *and* Aboriginal peoples' access to care (Allan & Smylie, 2015). The impact on health is evident in testimonies by residential school survivors (who testified before the **Truth and Reconciliation Commission** [TRC]):

Truth and Reconciliation Commission (TRC)
Established in 2005 to reveal the truth and document the individual and collective harms perpetrated against Aboriginal peoples by church-run residential schools, and to guide a process leading toward reconciliation with Aboriginal families and between Aboriginal peoples and non-Aboriginal communities (TRC, p. 27).

> Those schools were a war on Aboriginal children, and they took away our identity. First of all, they gave us numbers, we had no names, we were numbers, and they cut our hair. They took away our clothes. . . . They took away our moccasins. . . . (Doris Young, p. 192)[1]

> Children . . . were not allowed to speak their mother tongue. I remember several times when children were slapped or had their mouths washed out for speaking their mother tongue. . . . Residents were admonished for just being Native. (Michael Sillett, p. 200)

> What is even worse is that they started to sexually take advantage of me and abuse me, not one, not two, but many, many people for a very long time, until I was sixteen . . . I became very sick and anorexic, and really started to go downhill . . . I had no desire to live. (Sonia Wuttunee-Byrd, p. 206)

> I've got chronic bronchitis today. . . . [T]hey used to put us in these little skinny red coats that weren't even warm enough for winter. . . . Both of my lungs are 50% scarred from having pneumonia seven times in residential school. (Ruby Firth, p. 206)

Getting an accurate and complete assessment of the health status of Aboriginal peoples is difficult since the same information is not systematically collected for all three Aboriginal groups. This is due in part to "the multi-jurisdictional complexity of health services to First Nations and Inuit" (Health Council of Canada, 2005, p. 16). Neither Health Canada nor the Ministry of Indian and Northern Affairs, for example, collect specific health information on the Métis population. In addition, the indicators for Aboriginal people may be either incomplete or lacking in comparison to those available for the population as a whole (Health Council of Canada, 2005).[2] However, the data collected show that on virtually every known indicator of health status, the health of Aboriginal peoples is

---

1. These excerpts were all taken from the Summary Report of the Truth and Reconciliation Commission, TRC, 2015.

2. The health statistics collected and the reporting of these varies for the different groups. This is the case even for First Nations peoples; there is separate reporting for those living on-reserve and those living off-reserve. In some instances, the reported data are not for the same years, thus making it difficult to compare.

poorer in comparison to the rest of the Canadian population (Health Council of Canada, 2005; Loppie Reading & Wien, 2009).

Life expectancy is one valuable indicator of a population's health status. Overall, the life expectancy of Aboriginal peoples is estimated to be anywhere between five to fourteen years less than that of non-Aboriginal Canadians. However, life expectancy differs not only by sex—in all cases women's life expectancy was higher than men's—but also by Aboriginal group.[3] For example, life expectancy for Métis people was highest among the three Aboriginal peoples although still significantly below that for non-Aboriginal peoples. Until recently, there were no national life-expectancy data for Inuit because information was not collected for Inuit deaths that took place in the provinces (Wilkins, Uppal, Fines, Senecal, Guimond, & Dion, 2008).

Although declining steadily, the **infant mortality** rates among Aboriginal peoples are estimated to be higher than the rate for the general population. Infant mortality rates are an important measure of the well-being of infants, children, and pregnant women because they are associated with a variety of factors, such as maternal health, quality of, and access to medical care, and socio-economic conditions. For on-reserve First Nations people, the rate of infant mortality is estimated at 7 deaths per 1000 live births, compared to 5 deaths per 1000 for the general population. However, because of limitations in how data are gathered, it is generally agreed that this figure is an underestimation of the actual rate of infant deaths. In Nunavut, where approximately 85 per cent of the population is Inuit, the estimated infant mortality rate is 16 deaths per 1000 (Butler-Jones, 2008). In their review of studies on infant mortality in Aboriginal communities, Smylie et al. (2010, p. 147) found that the infant mortality rate for status Indians living off-reserve and Inuit ranged from 1.7 to over 4 times the rate for non-Aboriginal Canadians. Rates of infant mortality for Métis are unknown (Health Council of Canada, 2005; Smylie et al., 2010). As Smylie et al. point out, this lack of reliable data impedes the ability of public health workers to address the conditions that lead to infant illness and death.

Adult Aboriginal peoples are more likely than other Canadian populations to die from cardiovascular diseases; from external causes, such as accidents, poisoning, and violence; from respiratory disorders; and from various forms of cancer. For example, acute myocardial infarction (heart attack) rates among First Nations are around 20 per cent higher and stroke rates are almost 50 per cent higher than among non-Aboriginal Canadians (Health Canada, 2005b). The prevalence of diabetes among Aboriginal Canadians is three to five times higher than that of the general population (Canadian Diabetes Association, 2012). Tuberculosis also continues to be a major health problem for all Aboriginal peoples; in fact, tuberculosis infection rates are 8 to 10 times higher than the national average (Pan American Health Organization, 2007, p. 174). Aboriginal women experience a disproportionate burden of ill-health and disease, including higher rates of heart disease, cervical and gall bladder cancer, HIV/AIDS, and mental illness (Allan & Smylie, 2015, p. 15).

For a comparison of the prevalence of selected health conditions among Aboriginal Canadians with the general Canadian population, see Figure 7.2. As well, Aboriginal peoples are significantly less likely than non-Aboriginal peoples to rate their health as excellent or very good (Gamer et al., 2010, p. 3).

infant mortality
Refers to the number of infants who die in the first year after birth per 1000 births.

---

3. Different dates are compared based on the availability of data.

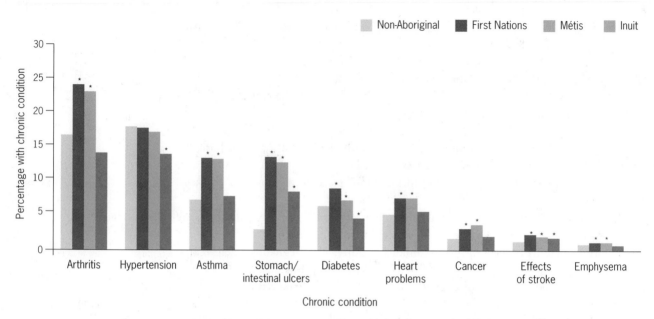

Figure 7.2 Age-Standardized Prevalence of Selected Health Conditions, Aboriginal Identity Group with General Canadian Population

*significantly different from estimate for non-Aboriginal population (p<0.05)

Source: Garner et al., (2012). Figure 2: Prevalence of diagnosed chronic conditions, by Aboriginal identity group, off-reserve population aged 20 or older, Canada, 2006/2007. In Statistics Canada, *The Health of First Nations Living Off-Reserve, Inuit, and Métis Adults in Canada: The Impact of Socio-economic Status on Inequalities in Health*, p. 3. Available at: www.statcan.gc.ca/pub/82-622-x/82-622-x2010004-eng.pdf.

Aboriginal peoples are overrepresented in the HIV epidemic and infected at a younger age (Larkin et al., 2007; Public Health Agency of Canada, 2011c). In 2011, an estimated 8.9 per cent of Aboriginal Canadians were living with HIV/AIDS even though they only make up 4.3 per cent of Canada's population. However, there were slightly fewer new infections than in 2008 (Public Health Agency of Canada, 2011c).

Depression, suicide, injury, and poisoning are a major concern for Aboriginal peoples. Injuries, for example, are considered a leading cause of death among the First Nations people (Bougie et al., 2014). The death rate for injuries and poisoning is four times higher for First Nations and Inuit than for the general population. And suicide among Aboriginal peoples between the ages of 10 and 19 years is 4.3 times higher than among the rest of the country; among all ages of Inuit, suicide is 11 times higher (Pan American Health Organization, 2007, p. 169). It has been estimated that suicide rates among First Nations people are two to three times higher (First Nations Regional Health Survey, 2012, p. 217). Among some sectors of First Nations youth, the rate is five to six times higher than for non-Aboriginal peoples (Smylie, 2009, p. 293). In Attawapiskat, a remote community of about 2,000, 11 youth attempted suicide in a single day (April 2016). Suicide rates for Métis are unknown (Health Council of Canada, 2005, p. 31), although suicide has been identified as a major concern among Métis communities (Our Voices, 2009). Aboriginal women experience higher rates of both spousal and non-spousal violence and more severe forms of violence, and are more likely to be victims of homicide than non-Aboriginal women (Allan & Smylie, 2015, p. 16).

Certain behaviours are associated with people's poorer health status. Smoking, for example, is a **risk factor** for certain types of cancers, heart disease, and stroke (Tjepkema, 2002). The 2008/10 First Nations Regional Health Survey (RHS) (2012, p. 99) reports that approximately 57 per cent of First Nations adults living on-reserve smoked daily or occasionally. Data from the Canadian Community Health Survey collected from 2007–10 show that the smoking rate for First Nations people living off-reserve was 32 per cent; for Métis it was 30 per cent, and Inuit 39 per cent, compared with 15 per cent for non-Aboriginal people (Gionet & Roshanafshar, 2013, p. 6). Heavy alcohol consumption can be another predictor of poor health; however, the statistics suggest a more complex reality. While Aboriginal Canadians are more likely to drink heavily than non-Aboriginal people, Inuit and First Nations people were also more likely to have abstained from alcohol in the past year than non-Aboriginal people; 34 per cent of Inuit and 29 per cent of off-reserve First Nations people had not consumed alcohol compared with 24 per cent of non-Aboriginal people (Gionet & Roshanafshar, 2013).

Prior to 1940, diabetes was rare among Aboriginal peoples but is now considered to have reached epidemic levels in some communities (Gionet & Roshanafshar, 2013, p. 7). Diabetes is significantly more prevalent among First Nations living off-reserve and Métis (Gamer et al., 2010, p. 3). Dr Jay Wortman, who is researching the health effects of diet in First Nations communities, hypothesizes that the high prevalence of diabetes is the result of a shift from traditional Aboriginal diets based on wild regional foods, such as fish, seafood, moose, elk, deer, and seasonal plants and berries, to the carbohydrate-laden diets of today. He argues that the traditional diet provided plenty of protein and fat with little in the way of carbohydrates; previously, diabetes and metabolic syndrome (a cluster of risk factors for both heart disease and diabetes) were unheard of (Schanfarber, 2007).

risk factors
Conditions that are thought to increase an individual's susceptibility to illness or disease, such as abuse of alcohol, poor diet, or smoking.

Social Production of Aboriginal Ill Health

Various historical documents have confirmed that Aboriginal peoples in Canada were in good health upon the arrival of the Europeans (Boyer, 2014, pp. 11–12; Health Council of Canada, 2005, p. 3). Rather, the European explorers were the ones more likely to be sick. Aboriginal healers provided those who were interested with herbal remedies and suggested unfamiliar cures. However, hundreds of thousands of Aboriginal peoples got seriously sick or died after their encounters with Europeans: "Famine and warfare contributed, but infectious diseases were the great killer. Influenza, measles, polio, diphtheria, smallpox and other diseases were transported from the slums of Europe to the unprotected villages of the Americas" (Royal Commission on Aboriginal Peoples, 1996b, Volume 3, Chapter 3, 1.1, p. 2). Diseases imported from overseas produced epidemics that forever altered the "social and biological structure of Aboriginal communities" (Waldram et al., 1995, p. 23, cited in Boyer, 2014, p. 12). These diseases significantly reduced the Aboriginal population and the subsequent decline has been referred to as "genocide or a holocaust" (Royal Commission on Aboriginal Peoples, op.cit.).

Sociological approaches to understanding health disparities look for social patterns and social determinants of health; these suggest that people are not randomly afflicted by disease and illness. As we shall see in the following discussion, the inequities in Aboriginal peoples' health today are a consequence of fundamental structural inequalities related to the dispossession of Aboriginal peoples and their continued economic and political marginalization. Socio-economic disadvantage can be seen in poor housing, low educational achievement, high unemployment, poverty, food insecurity, etc., experienced by a large majority of Aboriginal Canadians. The health disparities within Aboriginal groups and compared to non-Aboriginal people need to be understood within the context of this broad range of **social determinants of health** (Loppie Reading & Wien, 2009). Such an approach is a shift from reliance on lifestyle choices (smoking, drinking, exercise) as the most important predictors of health to acknowledging social and economic characteristics of individuals and populations as essential to explaining and predicting health outcomes (Galabuzi, 2012, p. 98).

social determinants of health
Refers to the social, economic, and political environments in which people live and that determine their health. Examples of social determinants include housing, job security, working conditions, education, environment, social exclusion, and gender.

Using the Social Determinants of Health

As one of the richest countries in the world, Canada is well placed to right past wrongs and ensure that all Canadians, including Canada's First Peoples, are able to enjoy living conditions that promote health and well-being. The biggest barrier at this time appears to be the political will of those who are experiencing privileged access to societal resources. . . .

—Smylie (2009, p. 298)

Social and economic conditions are important predictors of health outcomes for both individuals and populations. Good employment and job security, for example, provide people with the economic means needed for decent housing and food security. Poverty increases one's risk of developing chronic diseases, and growing up in poverty has a long-term impact on childhood development. As well, poor people are often marginalized from participation in their community and may lack a sense of social connectedness, so critical for mental health. And while Canada has a publicly funded universal health-care system, those who experience racism and discrimination find their health care is compromised. On every social determinant, Aboriginal peoples are at a disadvantage. In the words of the **Royal Commission on Aboriginal Peoples** (RCAP), "Aboriginal people endure ill health, run-down and overcrowded housing, polluted water, inadequate schools, poverty and family breakdown at rates found more often in developing countries than in Canada" (Royal Commission on Aboriginal Peoples, 1996a, p. 31). By comparing the situation of Aboriginal Canadians with non-Aboriginal peoples in terms of social determinants of health, we can see the many levels of disadvantage.

Royal Commission on Aboriginal Peoples (RCAP)
Created by the Canadian government in 1991 to address economic, social, and political issues related to First Nations, Métis, and Inuit peoples in Canada. The commissioners held 178 days of public hearings and visited 96 communities.

unemployment rate
Estimates the proportion of people who are not employed but who are actively looking for work.

Research indicates that income is an important predictor of health status and that those in the lowest quintile consistently have a lower life expectancy, higher levels of infant mortality, and a higher rate of morbidity (Auger & Alix, 2009). Income is dependent on employment. When we look at labour force data, we see that Aboriginal Canadians experience significantly higher levels of unemployment than non-Aboriginal peoples (Smylie, 2009, p. 291; Loppie Reading & Wien, 2009, p. 10). For example, in 2006, the **unemployment rate** for First Nations people was two to three times higher than for non-Aboriginal peoples (Gionet, 2009a, p. 56; Smylie, 2009, p. 281). Similar differences exist for Inuit and Métis. Aboriginal peoples today disproportionately rank among the poorest of Canadians and experience far greater income inequality than the rest of Canadians (Wilson & Macdonald, 2010, p. 6). In 2006, the median annual employment income for Aboriginal peoples was $18,962 or 30 per cent lower than that of the rest of Canadians whose median income was $27,097 (p. 9). As indicated in Figure 7.3 below, Métis were comparatively better off than other Aboriginal groups but still significantly below that of the non-Aboriginal population. In all cases, including the non-Aboriginal population, men had a higher income than women. Those with higher income have access to higher quality resources, including better housing, adequate nutrition, and access to clean water, all of which can impact health (Gamer et al., 2010, p. 16). Living in poverty means not having access to material resources or general control over one's life. Poverty breeds anxiety, insecurity, low self-esteem, and feelings of hopelessness. These forms of psychosocial stress have been linked to violence and addictions, poor mental health, diabetes, high blood pressure, and depression (Loppie Reading & Wien, 2009, pp. 9–10).

Research shows that children living in poverty have a greater chance of experiencing a variety of physical, social, and economic disadvantages later in life (Raphael, 2014). The child poverty rates for Aboriginal peoples are much higher than the average in Canada. While the child poverty rate for non-Aboriginal children in 2006 was 15 per cent, 40 per cent of Aboriginal children live below the poverty line (Macdonald & Wilson, 2013, p. 13). Status First Nations children were most likely to live in poverty: 50 per cent live below the poverty line (p. 12). Aboriginal children in poverty are more likely to live in overcrowded and poor quality housing, both of which can lead to chronic health problems.

With respect to education, another social determinant, Aboriginal peoples are also severely disadvantaged. It is significant that levels of post-secondary education for Aboriginal peoples have improved over the past 30 years (Smylie, 2009, p. 291); however, they are still below the Canadian average. In 2006, only 42 per cent of First Nations people (25–64 years of age) had completed some post-secondary education compared to

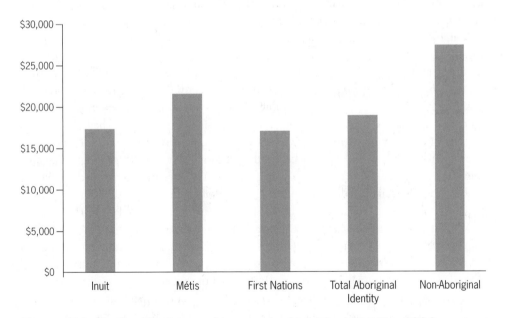

Figure 7.3 Median Employment Income by Aboriginal Identity, 2006

Source: Wilson, D., & Macdonald, D., (2010). Table 4: Median employment income by Aboriginal identity (2006). In Canadian Centre for Policy Alternatives, *The Income Gap Between Aboriginal Peoples and the Rest of Canada*, p. 10. Statistics Canada, (2006). *2006 Census of Population.* Statistics Canada, Catalogue no. 97-563-XCB2006009. Available at: www.policyalternatives .ca/sites/default/files/uploads/publications/reports/docs/Aboriginal%20Income%20Gap.pdf.

61 per cent of the non-Aboriginal population. Furthermore, only 7 per cent had a university degree compared with 23 per cent of non-Aboriginal people. Inadequate education often means poor literacy and limited employment skills which in turn can lead to poverty and social exclusion (Loppie Reading & Wien, 2009, p. 12).

Environmental contaminants are threatening the health of Aboriginal peoples (Boyer, 2014, p. 21; Loppie Reading & Wien, 2009, p. 17). Moreover, contamination of wildlife, fish, vegetation, and water has destroyed traditional lifestyles. Water quality has especially been a serious problem for First Nations reserves. In October 2005, the plight of people living on the Kashechewan reserve in Northern Ontario hit the media. Dr Trussler, chief of staff at Weeneebayko General Hospital, which serves as a base hospital for the people on the James Bay Coast, described the conditions on the reserve as "atrocious" (Rusk, 2005, p. A5). Raw sewage was being pushed into the water-treatment plant by the tides in James Bay, and since the plant was not working properly *E. coli* bacteria flourished. The local school had to be closed as a result. The high levels of chlorine put into the water to try to kill the bacteria further aggravated skin diseases, which were endemic in Kashechewan. Dr Trussler felt that the only solution to this problem was to relocate the people, which the government eventually did. While this may be an extreme example, Kashechewan's problem with its drinking water was not an isolated incident. According to Dr Trussler, "[t]here's 100 native communities in Canada currently under a boil-water advisory" (p. A5). Such water problems lead to a probability of cases of hepatitis A (Rusk, 2005, p. A5). Nearly 25 per cent of First Nations on-reserve households have water that is deficient in quantity or quality; of those, 2 per cent have no water service (Health Canada, 2009a, pp. 34–5). Water quality continues to be a problem. Although there are legally enforceable drinking water standards in the provinces and territories, these protections do not exist for drinking water for reserve lands (Boyer, 2014, p. 20). In her report, the Auditor-General was critical of the government's failure to improve the living conditions for First Nations people living on reserves (Office of the Auditor General of Canada, 2011).

Housing and living conditions are known to directly or indirectly impact people's health (Butler-Jones, 2008, p. 45). Overcrowding and inadequate housing with poor indoor air quality can lead to respiratory diseases, tuberculosis, allergies, mental health problems, and the spread of potentially deadly viruses. Although housing conditions for Aboriginal peoples have improved in the past decade, according to the 2006 census Aboriginal peoples are four times more likely than non-Aboriginal people to live in overcrowded conditions and three times as likely to live in a dwelling in need of major repairs, although conditions varied greatly among Aboriginal groups, as well as by where they lived (Statistics Canada, 2008a). First Nations people are five times more likely to live in crowded homes; the situation is especially dire for those living on-reserve. On First Nations reserves, 44 per cent of houses are in need of major repairs compared to 7 per cent of those in the general population (Gionet, 2009a, pp. 57–8). As a group, Inuit suffer the worst overcrowding (Boyer, 2014, p. 18): they are 10 times more likely to live in crowded conditions and 4 times more likely to live in homes in need of major repairs (Gionet, 2008, p. 60). Dramatic levels of overcrowding may account for the fact that Inuit children have among the highest rates of severe lower respiratory tract infection in the world (Smylie, 2009, p. 292).

Food insecurity can lead to various health complications, from malnutrition to obesity (Gionet & Roshanafshar, 2013). Healthy eating requires that individuals have economic and physical access to sufficient and nutritious food. Inadequate income, employment status, and geographic isolation are significant barriers to food security for Aboriginal peoples. Data (see Figure 7.4) show that all three Aboriginal groups are more likely to experience household food insecurity than non-Aboriginal peoples (Gionet & Roshanafshar, 2013). High rates of poverty, environmental pollution—which has affected traditional food systems—and climate change as well as high rates of diet-related disease are further indications that "[f]ood insecurity is an urgent public health issue for Aboriginal people in Canada" (Power, 2008, p. 95). In remote or isolated areas, foods such as fresh fruit and vegetables are both scarce and costly. In this context, it should be remembered that First Nations people were forced to relocate from agriculturally valuable or resource-rich land onto remote and economically marginal reserves (TRC, p. 1). When Aboriginal peoples lost their connection to their land, they were forced to give up their traditional diet for one similar to the dominant culture. Not only is this new diet now costly for them to maintain, according to Dr Wortman it also leads to serious health issues such as diabetes (Schanfarber, 2007). In the words of one First Nations woman, "Almost everyone eats canned food here. . . . Buying fresh food is so expensive. Ten pounds of potatoes will cost you $20.00" (Linda Wynne, quoted in Strauss, J., *The Globe and Mail*, October 31, 2005, n.p.). Similarly, a study conducted in 2001 found that a healthy food basket for a family of

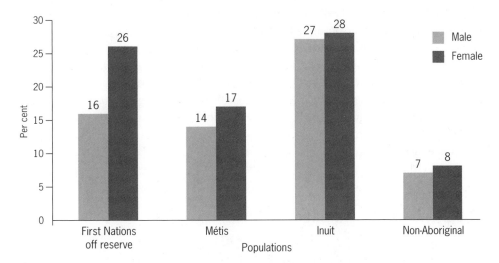

Figure 7.4 Household Food Insecurity by Aboriginal and Non-Aboriginal
Population by Sex, Aged 12 and Over, Canada

Notes:
1. The data were age standardized to the Aboriginal identity population, 2007–2010.
2. The difference between the estimate for each Aboriginal population and the estimate for the non-Aboriginal population is statistically significant.
3. Inuit data do not include Nunavik and some remote communities.
4. Food insecurity: indication of compromise in quality and/or quantity of food consumed or reduced food intake and disrupted eating patterns.

Source: Gionet, L., & Roshanafshar, S. (2013). Chart 4: Moderate or severe household food insecurity by Aboriginal and non-Aboriginal populations and by sex, aged 12 and over, Canada. In Statistics Canada, *Select health indicators of First Nations people living off reserve, Métis and Inuit*, p. 9. Available at: www.statcan.gc.ca/pub/82-624-x/2013001/article/11763-eng.pdf.

four in a northern Inuit community cost $327.00 compared to $135.00–$155.00 in southern cities (Smylie, 2009, p. 292).

Many have argued that socio-economic factors alone cannot explain the poor health of Aboriginal peoples (Allan & Smylie, 2015; Loppie Reading & Wien, 2009; Galabuzi, 2012). Rather, **racism** and **social exclusion** play a significant role in generating and maintaining health inequities. "Racial and social exclusion have been a reality for Aboriginal peoples since first contact with British colonizers" (Loppie Reading & Wien, 2009, p. 22). Social exclusion, Galabuzi (2012, p. 97) explains, is manifest through "forms of oppression that order institutional arrangements and power relations" that marginalize particular groups and limit their ability to participate fully in society, including key societal institutions such as the economy, the political system, and the educational system. Economic exclusion means unequal access "to normal forms of livelihood and differential economic or labour market participation" (p. 99). The inability to secure a decent job and a decent wage leads to income disparities and poverty. As we have seen, Aboriginal peoples have a disproportionate exposure to poverty, as a result of high unemployment, substandard housing, low income, and lower levels of education, all of which are associated with lower health status. Poverty and social inequality "breed alienation and marginalization" and ultimately social unrest and often violence (Galabuzi, p. 105).

Racism is one of the many types of oppression that Aboriginal peoples have had to endure (Battiste & Henderson, 2012, p. 93) and it continues to create barriers to Aboriginal peoples' participation in societal institutions. Although the levels of racism affecting particular groups is difficult to measure, results from one survey indicate that nearly 40 per cent of First Nations adults living on-reserve said they had experienced racism in the 12 months prior (Loppie Reading & Wien, 2009, p. 23). Research suggests that groups subject to racism have more negative health outcomes due to the stress associated with living in a racially charged environment. It is a primary source of traumas and other distresses that exacerbate such conditions as mood disorders, hypertension, and drug and substance use (Galabuzi, 2012, pp. 108–9).

racism
A set of false beliefs that one racial group is naturally superior to another group based on biological differences. It perpetuates notions of cultural superiority and inferiority and is one basis for social exclusion and discriminatory practices.

social exclusion
A process whereby some groups in society are denied access to material and social resources, thereby excluding their full participation in society. It produces inequality in outcomes.

The Legacy of Colonialism

> The policy of colonization suppressed Aboriginal culture and languages, disrupted Aboriginal government, destroyed Aboriginal economies, and confined Aboriginal people to marginal and often unproductive land. When that policy resulted in hunger, disease, and poverty, the federal government failed to meet its obligations to Aboriginal people. That policy was dedicated to eliminating Aboriginal peoples as distinct political and cultural entities . . . [it was] a policy of cultural genocide.
>
> —*Honouring the Truth, Reconciling for the Future: Summary of the Final Report of the Truth and Reconciliation Commission* (2015, p. 134)

The health problems that Aboriginal people face today can be traced directly to colonialism (Boyer, 2014). "Following European contact, the health of Aboriginal peoples declined dramatically" (p. 56). In 2007, at the International Symposium on the Social Determinants of Indigenous Health, it was agreed that the ongoing effects of **colonialism/colonization** is a critical social determinant of health (Smylie, 2009, pp. 281–2). Many, if not all, of the factors that underlie the health inequities endured by Aboriginal peoples in Canada—the

colonialism/colonization
A process by which one nation imposes itself economically, politically, and socially upon another.

forced relocation of communities, the loss of lands and resources, the creation of the reserve system, the forced removal of children and subsequent placement into residential schools, policies of cultural suppression and forced assimilation, and ongoing racist attitudes—are all a terrible part of the legacy of colonialism in this country (Adelson, 2005; Boyer, 2014; Royal Commission on Aboriginal Peoples, 1996a; Smylie, 2009). However, the initial contact between the first European newcomers and the first peoples (Aboriginal peoples) of this land, which is now Canada, was that of "cautious co-operation" (Royal Commission on Aboriginal Peoples, 1996a, p. 7) and acceptance of each other's right to co-exist as distinct and independent. Despite prejudices and stereotypes between the two culturally divergent societies, individuals and groups worked, traded, and sometimes lived together for long periods of time, and even intermarried. The offspring of these unions were later recognized as having a distinct identity—the Métis people (Royal Commission on Aboriginal Peoples, 1996b, Volume 1, Part One, Stage 2, p. 6).

This early co-operation between Aboriginal and non-Aboriginal peoples was formalized in treaties and in the Royal Proclamation of 1763: it offered protection and recognized Aboriginal nations as autonomous political entities with a right to have their own land and govern their own affairs. With the influx of more immigrants came a shift in power in favour of non-Aboriginal peoples, both in terms of population and economic and military strength. Aboriginal peoples were no longer viewed as valued partners but were seen as "impediments to progress" (Royal Commission on Aboriginal Peoples, 1996a, p. 9). In the 1800s, protection soon came to mean cultural assimilation and domination: "[It] took the form of compulsory education, economic adjustment programs, social and political control by federal agents. These policies, combined with missionary efforts to civilize and convert Indigenous people, tore wide holes in Aboriginal cultures, autonomy and feelings of self-worth" (Royal Commission on Aboriginal Peoples, 1996a, pp. 8–9). This was, in essence, what Justice Murray Sinclair, chair of the TRC and Canadian Chief Justice Beverley McLachlin termed "cultural genocide."

To accommodate colonial expansion, Aboriginal peoples were forced off their land onto reserves to make room for a new economy based on timber, minerals, and agriculture. This forced relocation of Aboriginal peoples from their traditional lands onto reserves destroyed their culture and their economic livelihood, which was tied to these lands (Royal Commission on Aboriginal Peoples 1996b, Volume 3, Chapter 3). Food and clothing materials, which were acquired by hunting, trapping, and fishing, quickly diminished. These changes further disrupted the traditional style of life as well as their diet, which further affected the health of Aboriginal peoples (Health Council of Canada, 2005). Research of the Royal Commission and the testimonies made at the TRC shows that the effects of relocation continue to be felt today and continue to manifest in ways such as the negative health status of Aboriginal peoples (Royal Commission on Aboriginal Peoples, 1996b, Volume 1, Part 2, Chapter 8, p. 5; TRC, 2015). In the words of survivor and Anishinaabe Elder Fred Kelly:

> To take the territorial lands away from a people whose very spirit is so intrinsically connected to Mother Earth was to actually dispossess them of their very soul and being; it was to destroy whole Indigenous nations. Weakened by disease and separated from their traditional foods and medicines, First Nations peoples had no defence against further government encroachments on their lives. (TRC, p. 277)

assimilate/assimilation
Refers to the expectation that Aboriginal peoples and immigrants will give up their culture and become indistinguishable from the dominant Canadian majority.

Canadian Confederation was negotiated without reference to Aboriginal nations. The country's first prime minister, Sir John A. Macdonald, made clear that it was his government's policy to "**assimilate** the Indian people in all respects with the inhabitants of the Dominion" (Royal Commission on Aboriginal Peoples, 1996a, p. 11). Aboriginal peoples were completely excluded as active participants. The British North America Act made "Indians, and the Lands reserved for the Indians" subject to government regulation (Royal Commission on Aboriginal Peoples, 1996a, p. 11). The act legalized the removal of Aboriginal communities from their homelands to government-controlled reserve lands. Parliament passed laws, codified in the Indian Acts of 1876, 1880, 1884, and later, which eliminated traditional Aboriginal governments, confiscated valuable resources located on reserves, outlawed important cultural ceremonies, such as the potlatch and the sun dance, and imposed European standards of marriage and parenting. Traditional healing methods were decried as witchcraft and idolatry (Boyer, 2014).

The residential school systems, which came into being in 1849, are considered by many one of the worst legacies of colonialism (TRC, 2015). These government-funded, church-run institutions were part of the government's assimilation plan, first codified in the 1857 Civilization of Indian Tribes Act. The intent of residential schools was to educate, to "civilize," that is, to assimilate and integrate Aboriginal peoples into the dominant European society. When the Indian Act was amended in 1884, attendance at residential schools became mandatory for status Indians under age 16. Children were taken from their families at a young age to a place where their language, customs, and culture were suppressed (TRC, 2015). In place of their traditional belief systems, they were required to adopt Christianity. They were forcefully taught either English or French and were severely beaten if they were caught speaking an Aboriginal language. As a result, the bonds between Aboriginal children and their families and nations were broken. As indicated in Table 7.2, the human costs of this psychological violence are still seen today in the survivors of the residential school system and their families.

The Indian Act of 1876 spelled out who was considered an Indian and who was not. According to the act, the term *Indian* applies to "Any male person of Indian blood reputed to belong to a particular band, any child of such person, and any woman who is or was lawfully married to such person" (Indian Act, 1876, excerpted in Smylie, 2009, p. 287). Under this act, any woman who married an Indian gained Indian status and any of the benefits that accrued, while an Aboriginal woman who married a non-Indian lost her Indian status and rights. (This was changed with the 1985 amendment to the Indian Act, which reinstated Indian status to such women.) The Indian Act also excluded Métis who had received scrip—transferable land or cash allowances. Following the act, Aboriginal peoples who lived on reserves were required to carry an identity card every time they stepped off reserve land. The Indian Act legitimated the authority of the federal government to intervene in the affairs of Aboriginal peoples. It was a powerful vehicle for breaking up Aboriginal societies in its attempt to assimilate Aboriginal peoples into the mainstream culture (Royal Commission on Aboriginal Peoples, 1996b, Volume 1, Chapter 4, Stage 3, p. 4).

Historical research indicates a clear link between the social inequalities created by colonialism and the diseases, disabilities, violence, and early death experienced by Aboriginal peoples (Loppie Reading & Wien, 2009, p. 20). Colonialism created conditions of physical, psychological, economic, and political disadvantage that led to the loss

Table 7.2   The Impact of Residential Schools on First Nation Adults Living on Reserve, 2002–2003

Residential School Characteristics	Per Cent
Proportion of adults attending	20.3
Proportion of those attending reporting a negative impact on their overall health and well-being	47.3
Belief that parent's attendance at residential schools negatively affected the parenting they received as children	43.0
Most frequently mentioned elements of the residential school experience that contributed to the negative impact on health and well-being of survivors:	
Isolation from family	81.3
Verbal or emotional abuse	79.3
Harsh discipline	78.0
Loss of cultural identity	76.8
Separation from First Nation or Inuit community	74.3
Witnessing abuse	71.5
Loss of language	71.1
Physical abuse	69.2

Source: Loppie Reading, C., & Wien, F. (2009). Table 20: The impact of residential schools on First Nation adults living on reserve, 2002–03. In *Health Inequalities and Social Determinants of Aboriginal Peoples' Health*. Prince George, BC: National Collaborating Centre for Aboriginal Health, p. 22. Available at: www.nccah-ccnsa.ca/docs/social%20determinates/NCCAH-Loppie-Wien_Report.pdf.

of dignity and self-esteem of Aboriginal peoples. Today, "[m]any Aboriginal people are suffering not simply from specific diseases and social problems, but also from a depression of spirit resulting from 200 or more years of damage to their cultures, languages, identities and self-respect" (Royal Commission on Aboriginal Peoples, 1996b, Volume 3, Chapter 3, p. 3). This loss of spirit is manifest in negative behaviours, such as alcohol and substance abuse, suicide, injuries, and violence. As Katherine Copenace, a residential school survivor testified, "When I got older, I had thoughts of suicide, inflicting pain on myself which I did. I used to slash my arms, pierce my arms, my body and I destroyed myself with alcohol which the government introduced of course" (TRC, 2015, p. 206). The executive director of a treatment centre in the Northwest Territories explains how colonialism destroys the heart of a peoples.

> The oppressed begin to develop what they call "cultural self-shame" and "cultural self-hate" which results in a lot of frustration and anger. At the same time . . . we begin to adopt our oppressors' values, and in a way, we become oppressors ourselves. . . . (cited in Royal Commission on Aboriginal Peoples, 1996a, p. 35)

Agnes Mills, another residential school survivor poignantly stated, "[O]ne of the things that residential school did for me, I really regret, is that it made me ashamed of who I was.... And I wanted to be white so bad, and the worst thing I ever did was I was ashamed of my mother . . . because she couldn't speak English" (Agnes Mills, p. 201).

The marginalization of Aboriginal people today through social exclusion and racism is evidence of the continuation of colonization today (Boyer, 2014; Battiste & Henderson, 2012). The recent death of Tina Fontaine, a young First Nations woman found murdered in Winnipeg's Red River, points once again to the grim statistics: in the past three decades, nearly 1200 Aboriginal women have gone missing or been murdered. Although they make up only four per cent of the population, Aboriginal women constitute 16 per cent of the country's female homicides (Reid, 2014). Professor Sinclair, a University of Winnipeg Aboriginal studies professor quoted in *The Globe and Mail*, calls this "the most important epidemic facing this country" in which "racism, sexism and colonialism play a part" (Carlson & Mahoney, 2014, p. A1). The newly elected president of the Canadian Association of Chiefs of Police recognizes the systemic nature of this problem when he states that society needs to tackle issues of poverty, poor housing, racism, and the disadvantage of Aboriginal peoples, "because if you can't fix those issues, we can't fix the crime issues because it's an endless circle" (Quan, 2014). Furthermore, as journalist Andrew Coyne (2014) correctly points out, it is Aboriginal people—both men and women—who suffer vastly disproportionate rates of murder and other violent crimes compared to non-Aboriginal Canadians. The root causes of deprivation, poor health outcomes, and violence are to be found in the devastating legacy of colonialism.

Improving Health for Aboriginal People

A beginning point for addressing health disparities faced by Aboriginal people is to understand and respect Aboriginal peoples' perspectives on health and wellness. It is equally important to acknowledge Aboriginal peoples' authority in health care.

Although there may be specific differences among and within Aboriginal groups, there are many commonly held shared beliefs (Boyer, 2014; Healthy U, n.d.). Unlike the biomedical approach, which separates the body from other aspects of the person, Aboriginal concepts of health and healing are holistic. Aboriginal peoples take the view that all living things are interdependent and well-being flows from the balance of the physical, spiritual, mental, and emotional elements of personal and collective life. These components are intertwined. The medicine wheel (circle) represents the inseparability of the individual, the family community, and the world: "The circle embodies the notion of health as harmony or balance in all aspects of one's life. . . . Human beings must be in balance with their physical and social environments . . . in order to live and grow" (Royal Commission on Aboriginal Peoples, 1996b, Volume 3, Chapter 3, Conclusion, p. 4). Aboriginal peoples view disease as indicating an imbalance between an individual and the world around him or her (Boyer, 2014, p. 29). Health, therefore, requires more than just attending to an individual's physical body; it is a matter of achieving balance and harmony within one's self and with the community. The Aboriginal view of health and illness is similar to the WHO's definition of *health* as a "state of complete physical, mental and social well-being and not merely the absence of disease or infirmity" (see https://apps.who.int/aboutwho/en/definition.html).

Historically, Aboriginal peoples engaged in a variety of healing practices, many of which remain important today (Boyer, 2014). Traditional ceremonies are a means for communities to connect to nature—Mother Earth—and are considered an important aspect of maintaining health. As indicated by the many speakers who testified before the Royal Commission on Aboriginal Peoples and the Truth and Reconciliation Commission, respecting the cultures, traditions, and beliefs of Aboriginal peoples is essential for healing to occur. Their vision of health care includes having services and programs founded on an integrated, or holistic, view of human health; integration of traditional medicine, values, and healing practices into all health and social services; redesigning programs to more fully reflect Aboriginal values and diverse cultures; and greater autonomy for Aboriginal peoples to develop and deliver their health-care services (Royal Commission on Aboriginal Peoples, 1996b, Volume 3, Chapter 3, section 2.4).

The Report of the Royal Commission on Aboriginal Peoples (RCAP) affirmed what Aboriginal peoples had been saying for some time: that "self-determination for Aboriginal peoples is an immediate necessity" (1996b, Volume 3, Chapter 3, section 2.4, p. 4), of which reclaiming control over health and social services is one aspect. Despite improvements, "the persistence of ill health and social dysfunction in Aboriginal communities demonstrates that existing services fail to connect with real causes" (Volume 3, Chapter 3, section 2.4, pp. 4–5). The report included the following recommendation and called for a new strategy:

> [That] Aboriginal, federal, provincial and territorial governments, in developing policy to support health, acknowledge the common understanding of the determinants of health found in Aboriginal traditions and health sciences and endorse the fundamental importance of:
>
> - holism, that is, attention to whole persons in their total environment;
> - equity, that is, equitable access to the means of achieving health and equality of outcomes in health status;
> - control by Aboriginal peoples of the lifestyle choices, institutional services, and environmental conditions that support health; and
> - diversity, that is, accommodation of the cultures and histories of First Nations, Inuit, and Métis people that make them distinctive within Canadian society and that distinguish them from one another. (1996b, Volume 3, Chapter 3, section, 2.4, pp. 6–7)

A holistic approach would address the interconnectedness of the physical, spiritual, emotional, and social dimensions of well-being and the social determinants of health that contribute to ill heath. Aboriginal authority over health care would ensure that programs and services reflect the priorities of the community as well as increase their effectiveness. As there is a relationship between ill health and feelings of powerlessness, giving people control over their life circumstances would also improve their health outcomes. Furthermore, there is a need to respect differences within Aboriginal cultures and communities, and provide culturally appropriate programs to reflect this diversity.

Nesdole et al. (2014) argue that the key social determinants commonly used in public health research are inadequate for addressing health disparities in First Nations populations, since these do not incorporate the world view of Aboriginal peoples. They suggest a need to broaden the determinants to include a more holistic and historical perspective. A conceptual framework proposed by Loppie Reading and Wien (2009)—the Integrated Life Course and Social Determinants Model of Aboriginal Health (ILCSDAH)—appears to do this. As they explain it, the ILCSDAH-model "depicts life stages, socio-political contexts and social determinants as nested spheres of origin, influence and impact; each affecting the other in temporally and contextually dynamic and integrated ways . . . [it] incorporates four dimensions of health across the life course, including, physical, spiritual, emotional, and mental" (p. 25). Determinants are divided into "proximal" factors that have a direct impact on physical, emotional, mental, or spiritual health, such as health behaviours, physical environments, employment, income, and food security; "intermediate" determinants, including health-care systems, community infrastructure, resources, and cultural continuity, are considered the origins of the proximal determinants. "Distal" determinants have the most profound influence on the health of populations; these are the political, economic, and social contexts that construct proximal and intermediate determinants. Loppie Reading and Wien note that although intra- and inter-group differences exist among Aboriginal peoples and need to be taken into account, "colonialism, racism and social exclusion, as well as repression of self-determination" are the distal determinants within which all other determinants are constructed (p. 20). This intersectional approach is complementary to Aboriginal perspectives on health and integrates cultural and scientific knowledge to address the multi-faceted dimension of Aboriginal health (Reading, 2009).

The impact of racism and discrimination must also be acknowledged. As Tang and Browne (2008) argue, negative stereotypes and racial profiling of Aboriginal peoples impact the care they receive in clinical settings, such as being denied treatment because it was assumed that they were drunk or "trouble makers" (p. 120). These experiences of discrimination resulted in a reluctance to access health services, even in cases of urgent need. Allan and Smylie (2015, pp. 27–8) cite the case of Brian Sinclair, an Aboriginal man who died of a bladder infection after waiting 34 hours without receiving treatment in the emergency department of a Winnipeg hospital. Several of the staff "testified they had assumed Mr. Sinclair was in the ER to warm up, watch TV or sleep off intoxication . . . others reported they never saw [him] despite the fact that his wheelchair partially blocked the same part of an aisle of the ER for more than 24 hours."

Changes in the Provision of Health Services for Aboriginal People

Early government policies around health care were provided on an *ad hoc* basis (Boyer, 2014, p. 72). Initially health care to Aboriginal peoples was provided by an assortment of RCMP agents, officers, and missionaries, and then later by a growing number of nurses and doctors employed by the federal government. In 1945, Indian health services were transferred from Indian Affairs to Health Canada, and by 1962 Health Canada was providing direct health services to status First Nations people and to Inuit in the North (Health Canada, 2011b). However, these health services operated on a biomedical model; providers were usually non-Aboriginal and had little or no understanding of the cultural practices, traditions, and values of Aboriginal Peoples (Royal Commission on Aboriginal Peoples, 1996b, Volume 3, Chapter 3, section 1.1, p. 4).

Partly in response to Aboriginal peoples' protests over proposed cuts to non-insured health benefits, the federal government in 1979 introduced a new Indian Health Policy that recognized its legal and traditional responsibilities to Aboriginal peoples, including its special responsibility for the health and well-being of First Nations peoples and Inuit (Health Canada, 2007b). The policy states, in part, that improving the health status of Aboriginal communities must be built on three pillars:

1. Community development, including socio-economic, cultural, and spiritual development;
2. Improving communications and encouraging a greater involvement of Aboriginal peoples in the planning, budgeting, and delivery of health programs; and
3. Providing resources to assist Aboriginal communities to take a more active role in public health activities and decisions affecting their health.

Its goal was to integrate Aboriginal health services with traditional health systems in ways that were more collaborative with Aboriginal peoples (Boyer, 2014, p. 74). The need for a consultative process with Aboriginal peoples and community control was further echoed in Justice Thomas Berger's 1980 Report of the Advisory Commission on Indian and Inuit Health Consultation.

In 1988, the federal government's Indian Health Transfer Policy made it possible for Aboriginal peoples to design health programs and services and allocate funds according to community priorities. Then, in 1995 the federal government's Inherent Right to Self-Government Policy further recognized that First Nations and Inuit have the constitutional right to shape their own forms of government in accordance with their needs, and provided greater flexibility to bands to establish program priorities (Health Canada, 2005c). There were important benefits of transfer, including flexibility in the use of funds and ability to adapt services to local needs; however, the program has been criticized for failing to recognize health as an Aboriginal treaty right, for reproducing pre-existing dependent relationships, for not formally recognizing the role of traditional healers, for the cap on funds regardless of need, and for not funding the training of First Nations health-care professionals (Adelson, 2005, p. s58).

The federal government's 1998 document Gathering Strength—Canada's Aboriginal Action Plan provided a framework for establishing new partnerships with First Nations, Inuit, Métis, and non-status Indians as a response to the Royal Commission on Aboriginal Peoples' recommendation. It included a Statement of Reconciliation that offered the following apology: "To those of you who suffered this tragedy at residential schools, we are deeply sorry," and a commitment to affirm the contributions of the Métis people (Gathering Strength, 1998). Another important aspect of the plan was the establishment of the Aboriginal Healing Foundation (AHF), a not-for-profit corporation governed by a board of directors made up of representatives (male and female) from all three Aboriginal groups. The mission statement of the AHF reads in part:

> Our mission is to provide resources which will promote reconciliation and encourage and support Aboriginal people and their communities in building and reinforcing sustainable healing processes that address the legacy of physical, sexual, mental, cultural, and spiritual abuses in the residential school system, including

intergenerational impacts. . . . Our goal is to help create, reinforce and sustain conditions conducive to healing, reconciliation, and self-determination. (Aboriginal Healing Foundation, n.d.)

A notable aspect of the AHF is its involvement in the health of all three Aboriginal groups: First Nations (status and non-status), Métis, and Inuit.

The Medical Services Branch of Health Canada was, in 2000, renamed the First Nations and Inuit Health Branch (FNIHB) "in recognition of the unique status and needs of First Nations and Inuit in Canada" (Health Canada, 2008c). In part its mandate was to establish a renewed working relationship with First Nations and Inuit, including the transfer of direct health services. Today, the FNIHB works with First Nations governments to provide or support community-based health programs, including primary care services in remote and isolated areas, to First Nations people who live on-reserve and in Inuit communities, as well as drug, dental, and ancillary health services to all First Nations and Inuit people regardless of residence. Métis and non-status First Nations are not eligible for FNIHB programs and services; instead, they obtain health-care services from provincial or territorial sources (Health Council of Canada, 2005, p. 16). A recent research initiative, Pathways to Health Equity for Aboriginal Peoples, with funding from the federal government, will consider ways to improve and implement programs that address health inequities for all Aboriginal groups (CIHR, 2012a).

According to the Health Council of Canada (2013b), there are many examples of respectful collaborations and partnerships between government and First Nations, Inuit, and Métis communities. These include various health services and programs directed and administered by Aboriginal communities. As well some mainstream institutions have included Aboriginal-specific programs and services or employed Aboriginal staff in specialized roles (Allan & Smylie, 2015). However, the commitments made in the 2003 health accord with regard to addressing the health disparities of Aboriginal peoples were "largely unrealized following the change in federal government in 2006 [which saw the election of a Conservative government]" (p. 36). The newly elected Liberal government (2015) has promised to foster new relations with First Nations built on respect and partnership. The government has also promised targeted funding for First Nations education and infrastructure, and to implement the recommendations of the Truth and Reconciliation Commission. If implemented such measures could help address the cycle of poverty and the health disparities of Indigenous peoples.

Conclusion

Despite some improvements over the past couple of decades, Aboriginal Canadians fare more poorly on virtually every measure of physical and mental health than non-Aboriginal Canadians. On every social determinant of health, Aboriginal peoples also fare much worse. In terms of poverty, educational levels, unemployment, income, food security, and living conditions, etc., the gap between Aboriginal and non-Aboriginal Canadians is significant (Boyer, 2014; Gionet, 2008, 2009a, b; Health Canada, 2009a; Loppie Reading & Wien, 2009). Health determinants such as economic factors, social environments, personal health practices and behaviours, and physical environments, however, do not exist in isolation from each other; rather they all interconnect to determine one's health status (Raphael, 2009c).

These health inequities are the result of fundamental structural inequalities related to colonialism and the economic and political marginalization of Aboriginal peoples to which it gave rise. Loppie Reading and Wien (2009) remind us that in addition to general social determinants of health, there are what they call the "distal" determinants specific to Aboriginal peoples, namely colonialism, racism, and social exclusion, as well as repression of self-determination. However, the discourse of neo-liberalism obscures these structural inequalities by proclaiming that individuals are responsible for the state of their health. It also mitigates against solutions in proclaiming that "everyone should be treated the same," while glossing over the unequal power relations—yet nothing perpetuates inequality more than the equal treatment of unequal individuals. As Tang and Browne (2008, p. 109) have argued "'race' *matters* in health care as it intersects with other social categories including class, substance use, and history to organize inequitable access to health and health care for marginalized populations."

While there are promising indications that Aboriginal peoples will be given greater control and design in the delivery of health services, the question remains whether governments will provide the necessary resources. An even greater question is whether there is a will to address the structural inequalities that perpetuate the health inequities of Aboriginal Canadians.

Summary

- On virtually all measures of quality of life and health, Aboriginal Canadians fare significantly worse than non-Aboriginal Canadians.
- To understand the root cause of health disparities, we need to look at structural inequalities and explore a broad range of social determinants of health.
- There are some differences among the groups, but in general, Aboriginal peoples are disadvantaged on all health determinants, including income, employment, housing, food security, and education.
- The impacts of colonization have been identified internationally as fundamental determinants to which all other social inequalities are linked.
- Colonialism, forced assimilation, residential schools, racism, and social exclusion have had a profound influence on the health of Aboriginal Canadians.
- Aboriginal peoples have a holistic concept of health that views all living things as interdependent; well-being flows from the balance of the physical, spiritual, mental, and emotional elements of personal and collective life.
- To improve the health status of Aboriginal peoples requires addressing structural inequalities and the legacy of colonialism as well as respecting Aboriginal peoples' approach to their health and health care.

Key Terms

Aboriginal peoples
assimilate/assimilation
colonialism/colonization
First Nations
Indian Act
Indigenous peoples
infant mortality

Inuit
Métis
racism
risk factors
Royal Commission on
  Aboriginal Peoples
  (RCAP)

social determinants of
  health approach
social exclusion
Truth and Reconciliation
  Commission (TRC)
unemployment rate

Sociological Reflection: Racism in Medicine

Apply the four parts of the sociological imagination template (discussed in Chapter 1) to identify the influence of racism in medicine in terms of the following:

- Historical factors: What are some early examples of racism in medicine?
- Cultural factors: In what ways has racism influenced popular understanding of illness suffered by Aboriginal Canadians?
- Structural factors: How has racism affected modes of health-service delivery for Aboriginal Canadians in terms of quality, accessibility, and appropriateness?
- Critical factors: In what ways have racial stereotypes been addressed in the health-care system? How effective do you think they have been?

Discussion Questions

1. Using specific examples, explain how social determinants of health intersect with health behaviours in the case of Aboriginal peoples.
2. What are the pathways by which racism and social exclusion negatively impact the health of Aboriginal peoples?
3. How do Aboriginal peoples' perspectives on health and well-being differ from that of non-Aboriginal people? Why is it important to understand this difference?
4. What do you consider are the most important structural factors in explaining health disparities between Aboriginal Canadians and non-Aboriginal Canadians? Why?
5. What will it take to achieve health equality between Aboriginal and non-Aboriginal Canadians?
6. What are some major differences between mainstream health services and those designed and controlled by First Nations people?

Further Investigation

1. Critically analyze the assertion that racism and the legacy of colonialism continue to perpetuate structures of inequality that lead to poor health outcomes for Aboriginal peoples.
2. How might one reconcile holistic approaches to health and health care that are integral to Aboriginal peoples' understanding of health with the dominant

biomedical approach to illness practised by most health-care providers in Canadian society? Given the differences, what strategies would be most effective in providing appropriate health care to Aboriginal peoples?

Further Reading

Adelson, N. (2005, March/April). The embodiment of inequity: Health disparities in Aboriginal Canada. *Canadian Journal of Public Health, 96*, s45–s60.

Allan, B., & Smylie, J. (2015). *First peoples, second class treatment: The role of racism in the health and well-being of Indigenous peoples in Canada.* Toronto, ON: Wellesley Institute. Available at: www.wellesleyinstitute.com/wp-content/uploads/2015/02/Report-First-Peoples-Second-Class-Treatment-Final.pdf.

Boyer, Y. (2014). *Moving Aboriginal health forward.* Saskatoon, SK: Purich Publishing Ltd.

Loppie Reading, C., & Wien, F. (2009). *Health inequalities and social determinants of Aboriginal Peoples' health.* Prince George, B.C.: National Collaborating Centre for Aboriginal Health. Available at: www.nccah-ccnsa.ca/docs/social%20determinates/NCCAH-Loppie-Wien_Report.pdf.

Royal Commission on Aboriginal peoples. (1996b). *Report of the royal commission on Aboriginal Peoples.* Ottawa, ON: Indian and Northern Affairs.

Smylie, J. (2009). The health of Aboriginal peoples. In D. Raphael (Ed.), *Social determinants of health* (2nd ed.) (pp. 281–99). Toronto, ON: Canadian Scholars' Press, Inc.

Truth and Reconciliation Commission (TRC). (2015). *Honouring the truth, reconciling for the future: Summary of the final report of the Truth and Reconciliation Commission of Canada.* Available at www.trc.ca/websites/trcinstitution/File/2015/Findings/Exec_Summary_2015_05_31_web_o.pdf.

Web Resources

Aboriginal Healing Foundation
www.ahf.ca

Assembly of First Nations
www.afn.ca

Centre for Aboriginal Health Research
www.uvic.ca/research/centres/cahr/

Congress of Aboriginal Peoples
www.abo-peoples.org

Inuit Tapiriit Kanatami
www.itk.ca

Canadian Institutes of Health Research: Institute of Aboriginal Peoples' Health
www.cihr-irsc.ca.ca/e/8668.html

Métis National Council
www.metisnation.ca

National Aboriginal Health Organization (NAHO)
www.naho.ca

Native Women's Association of Canada
www.nwac.ca

Our Voices, First Nations, Métis and Inuit
www.aboriginalgba.ca

CHAPTER 8
Environmental Links to Health: Making Connections

Zelda Abramson

Despite the dangers of mining, Canada did not close its last asbestos mine until 2012 (after ending production in 2011), and it took until 2015 for Health Canada to admit officially that any exposure to inhaled asbestos is dangerous.

DANGER

ASBESTOS
CANCER AND LUNG DISEASE HAZARD

KEEP OUT

AUTHORIZED PERSONNEL ONLY

RESPIRATORS AND PROTECTIVE CLOTHING ARE REQUIRED IN THIS AREA.

Overview

- What role do the petrochemical and nuclear industries play in determining health and illness?
- What are the barriers to linking ill health to environmental factors?
- Why do many governments prefer a policy of risk assessment over the precautionary principle?
- Why are poorer communities at greater risk for environmental health effects?

On any day we do not give much thought to the air we breathe and the water we drink or use for cleaning and bathing. Our relationship to the food we eat is more complex, a factor of what we can afford to buy. Nevertheless, we are told that we need to eat a well-balanced diet, a mix of fruits, vegetables, grains, and dairy products. We assume that everything we buy is safe because it is neatly packaged on the shelves of our grocery store. In this chapter, we take a closer look at whether our air, water, and land are safe for consumption and to what effect our environment has on our health. We also provide various frameworks in which to understand (1) why it is so difficult to link health effects to the environment and (2) the complex relationships between industry, the state, and environmental health policies.

Introduction: Making Connections

I am fortunate to live in the Annapolis Valley, in a small community that overlooks the Minas Basin of the Bay of Fundy. I refer to this area as an oasis, not only for the milder climate compared to other places in the Maritimes, but also for its exquisite beauty. The Annapolis Valley is the breadbasket of Nova Scotia: the land is rich and fertile and the crops are plentiful. The valley, as it is commonly referred to by locals, is bedded between North and South Mountains. North Mountain is the barrier between the farmland and the Bay of Fundy, home of the world's highest tides.

Early every morning I walk my dog at a local reservoir, popular for swimming and walking. The reservoir is located at the base of South Mountain and overlooks Cape Blomidon, the red sandstone bluffs that guard the entrance to the Minas Basin. According to Mi'kmaq mythologies, Blomidon was the home of the first man, Glooscap, who was bestowed with wondrous power.

One warm summer morning, I am startled to hear the sound of a tractor. There is a fog-like cloud surrounding the noise. Just below the reservoir is an apple orchard that gets sprayed at least three times during the growing season, a fellow dog-walker soon thereafter informs me. On these days, we should not be walking the dogs and I am told to leave immediately. As I leave the reservoir, I look for signs announcing that pesticides are in use or signs telling dog owners to keep their dogs on lead for the next few days in order to keep them away from the orchard. There are no such signs. Months later, in the fall, the dogs are drawn to the apples that have fallen on the ground. They eat as many as they can before their owners pull them away. I begin to worry as I recall that day of spraying. How safe is this beautiful place? How safe are the children who swim in the reservoir? How safe is my dog and all his dog friends? I ask a fellow dog walker if there have been any studies in this area that looked at cancer rates and animals in agricultural areas. "I do not know of any," he answers but then adds, "my last two dogs died of cancer."

In this chapter, we examine the complex relationship between our environment and our health. There are three ways the physical environment can affect our health and that is through air, land, and water: we breathe the air, eat from the land, and drink the water. Should the air, water, and land become contaminated with pollutants, intuitively we would think that our health might be compromised. However, proving that this is the case has been enormously challenging.

Rachel Carson in her groundbreaking book *Silent Spring* alerted the world to this possibility 50 years ago. Carson made the public aware that certain chemicals known as organic compounds (used for pesticides and herbicides) are highly persistent in the environment. Such chemicals are stored in animal tissues—in mother's milk, for example—and they cause water contamination and, in turn, kill fish, and have led to the decline of some bird populations. Carson's book was a bestseller both in North America and Europe and at the same time was highly criticized by the agricultural chemical industry, who launched an attack on Carson's professional integrity and credibility. Carson was accused of being sinister, hysterical, and bland. Despite the industry's efforts, a presidential advisory committee was formed and it supported Carson's findings. In 1972, one of the chemicals, DDT (discussed below), was banned. Rachel Carson, however, died in 1964 of breast cancer.

She is seen today as the leader of the contemporary environmental movement, and her research and viewpoints have inspired this chapter.

Rachel Carson in *Silent Spring* repeatedly refers to World War II as a pivotal time of change that led to the development of (1) the petrochemical industry, which includes the manufacturing of a wide range of synthetic products, from pesticides to plastics; and (2) the nuclear industry, which not only includes atomic bombs but also refers to the subsequent development of nuclear energy and nuclear medicine.

The Petrochemical Industry: Links to Health

The petrochemical industry manufactures synthetic products largely using raw materials, such as crude oil (petroleum) and gas. The resulting products include plastics, paints, detergents, and synthetic fabrics, such as polyester, rubber, and fertilizers. Carson argued that carcinogens are produced from these industries in such great amounts that their effects are felt throughout our environment.

The Industry's Effect on the Air We Breathe

On very hot and humid summer days when temperatures break 30 degrees Celsius, should you live in Toronto, it is increasingly common to hear that all elderly people, people with asthma, and young children should avoid going outdoors. Should you fly over Toronto during such blistering hot and humid days, you will notice a purple haze that clouds the city. This purple haze is more commonly referred to as smog. The source of smog is from ground-level ozone, which is formed through a chemical reaction of pollutants from industrial plants and vehicle emissions combined with sunlight and stagnant air. That is why smog is mostly a summer problem.

There are four known health effects from smog: respiratory diseases, such as asthma; cardiovascular disease; allergies; and neurological effects, such as lower IQ. Illnesses related to air pollution can result in more medication use, medical consultations, hospital admissions, and in the worst case, premature death (Environment Canada, 2015, n.p.); approximately 5900 deaths a year, according to Health Canada, are related to air pollution. Emissions from industrial plants "include about seventy different known or suspected human carcinogens" (Steingraber, 2010, p. 179).

Not all ozone is bad, however. High in the atmosphere, there is an ozone layer that protects the earth from harmful ultraviolet radiation from the sun. However, the earth's ozone layer is also a victim of industrial pollution. In the late 1970s, the depletion of the earth's ozone layer was linked to a chemical called chlorofluorocarbon (CFC). Developed in the 1930s, CFCs were believed to be safe and were widely used, such as in aerosol spray propellant, refrigeration, and air conditioning.

A depleted ozone layer has the potential of causing serious health problems around the world, including increased risk of serious sunburn, which in turn leads to an increased risk of skin cancer and cataracts (eye damage), and immunosuppressive diseases and pre-mature aging of the skin (Depletion of the Ozone Layer, 2013). Certain forms of skin cancers are known to be caused by ultraviolet radiation, and scientists claim that "a sustained 10% depletion of the ozone layer would lead to a 26% increase in non-melanoma skin cancer. This could mean an additional 300,000 cases per year world wide" (Depletion of the Ozone Layer, 2013, n.p.).

The Montreal Protocol is an international treaty to address and eliminate the causes of ozone depletion. It was first introduced in 1987 and at that time it was signed by 24 countries and the European Economic Community. Since then, there have been numerous adjustments to the original document, and in 2009, this treaty was signed by 196 governments who committed to phasing out just under 100 chemicals that are linked to depleting the earth's ozone layer. The worst recorded year to date in ozone depletion was in 2006 (NASA Earth Observatory, 2012). However, the United Nations Environmental Program (2014) recently reported that the earth's protective ozone layer is recovering, but there are still many difficult challenges to ensure continuous monitoring of human activity.

The Industry's Effect on the Land that Feeds Us

The effect of the petrochemical industry is specifically noteworthy with regard to the manufacturing of pesticides for use in modern agriculture. The history of pesticides dates back to the 1880s when sulphur was applied to grape plants to combat a fungal disease known as powdery mildew. Shortly thereafter, Paris green (an arsenic-containing compound) was sprayed on potato plants to ward off the Colorado potato beetle, an insect that causes serious damage to potato plants, often eradicating whole crops. By the late 1890s, there were 42 insecticides that were available on the market. The petrochemical industry revolutionized agriculture and today there are approximately 40,000 pesticide products available for use. In 1939, a Swiss chemist by the name of Paul Müller developed a compound called dichlorodiphenyltrichloroethane, more commonly known as DDT. DDT was used in World War II to control insect- and parasite-causing diseases in humans, such as typhus, malaria, and yellow fever (Wargo, 1996). During the 1940s, pesticides "conveyed an image of responsible and scientific land stewardship" (p. ix).

Many advantages to pesticide use were offered, including the following: pesticides greatly increase crop productions without rotating crops; they are highly cost effective and one farmer is able to work a large piece of land efficiently; there is decreased soil loss; and produce is picture-perfect, which consumers have grown to demand. Although not scientifically based, the common belief at that time was that these pesticides were safe as they disintegrated into the environment (Wargo, 1996). However, the wonders of DDT were not as innocuous or as easily controlled as originally believed; insects very quickly become resistant to pesticides, and pesticides persist in the environment and collect in plant and animal tissues and "penetrate the germ cells to shatter or alter the very material of heredity upon which the shape of the future depends" (Carson, 1962, p. 8).

DDT belongs to a group of chemicals commonly referred to in the environmental movement as persistent organic pollutants, better known as POPs. Initially there were a dozen of these chemicals, known as "the dirty dozen"; in 2009, nine more chemicals were added to this list. According to Schapiro (2007), "if The Hague had a list of chemical war criminals . . . POPs chemicals would be on it" (pp. 67–8). They "act like light switches of toxicity upon the human body" (p. 68). When released into the environment, POPs are long-lasting and are spread through soil, water, and air. When they enter the body (of humans, fish, birds, and animals), they accumulate in fatty tissues, and concentration levels increase at high levels of the food chain. POPs have been linked to cancer, nervous system and reproductive disorders, and birth defects. As well, they are known to be **endocrine disruptors**.

endocrine disruptors
They mimic natural hormones circulating in the body, either enhancing or blocking the production of these hormones.

When wildlife moves from place to place, so too do the POPs. And POPs have been found throughout the world, often thousands of miles from the source of use. Thus, dioxin emitted from a smokestack in Indiana, according to Johansen (2002), can be found in the breast milk of women living in Nunavut. The Arctic, which in our minds is pristinely clean, is in fact "one of the most contaminated places on Earth—a place where Inuit mothers think twice before breast-feeding their babies because high levels of dioxins and other industrial chemicals are being detected in their breast milk and where a traditional diet of 'country food' has become dangerous to the Inuit's health" (p. 479). Johansen explains that the Arctic acts as a "cold trap," storing industrial pollutants (p. 480). Consequently, POP levels found in the blood and fatty tissues of the Inuit living in the Arctic are "five to ten times greater than the national average in Canada or the United States" (p. 480).

DDT was banned in the United States in 1972 and in Canada in 1974, more than 10 years after Rachel Carson's damning evidence (Steingraber, 2010). Although DDT has been banned, Steingraber (2010, p. 10) informs us that the chemical continues to be present around us. First, since DDT is long-lasting, it continues to be present in the soil. What this means is that DDT residues can still be found in food crops. Second, DDT residues are found on certain birds and freshwater fish. Third, it is commonly found in hazardous waste sites. Fourth, traces of DDT are detected in carpet dust. Fifth, DDT is not banned in all countries and can be carried through global air currents. Finally, DDT has been found to surface in the deep waters of the Great Lakes.

The Industry's Effect on Farming

Pesticide use since World War II has changed the face of farming. Farming has become more intensive with each acre of land producing higher yields. The smaller farms with a range of crops are less common; typically, larger farms produce fewer crops planted over greater acreage. Even though the number of farms has steadily declined since 1961, crop production has increased where "the real value of production tripled" (Agriculture and Agri-food Canada, 2006, 3). According to Sparling and Laughland (2008), "large farms carry the economic clout in both revenue and profits" (p. 4).

The ability to rid any plant of disease or fungus enhances crop productivity and increases profits for farmers but at what cost to the environment and human health? What effect has pesticide use had on the environment? Box 8.1 illustrates how pesticides affect our soil.

PEI Potato Farming: A Case Study

Prince Edward Island (PEI), aside from *Anne of Green Gables*, is well known for its ruby-red soil and potatoes; as a result, the province is particularly vulnerable to late blight fungus, one of the most serious potato diseases worldwide. Although PEI's soil conditions are ideal for growing potatoes, the high humidity also provides an ideal growing environment for the dreaded fungus. Because PEI is so small, fields are very close to one another. Should one field become infected, there is a strong likelihood that all fields will follow. In order to prevent crop infections, all potato growers take preventative measures (Blight Alert, 2008). Thus, PEI potatoes receive up to 20 dousings of chemical sprays in each growing season, which can cost the farmer up to $100,000 a year (The Perfect Potato, 2002). In 1999, torrential rainfalls hit PEI and tonnes of the red topsoil were swept away. For days after, the colour of the rivers was red. Then, dead fish appeared on the banks of the rivers and stream (Spills Lead to Fisheries Act Convictions, 2000, n.p.).

The PEI government introduced new laws in 2002 to limit the amount of runoff from the potato fields (Agricultural Crop Rotation Act, 2002). However, according to CTV's *W5* "The Perfect Potato" (2002), "In one month alone, enforcement officers spotted nearly 100 violations. But only a couple of farmers have been charged, with minimal fines of about $200.00" (p. 4). Farmers say they spray because they need to, not because they want

Box 8.1 Soil Erosion

Soil erosion occurs when the topsoil is rapidly removed by wind or water. Each year in Canada, tonnes of soil are lost in this way. Soil erosion is problematic for many reasons. The topsoil is the most fertile part of the soil, and, should it be removed, the soil's stability is weakened. During a surface runoff, the soil is deposited into rivers, lakes, and reservoirs, clogging these water systems. Clogged water systems increase the likelihood of flooding, thereby destroying the habitats of fish as well as other aquatic life (Trautmann et al., n.d.). The topsoil also carries manure, fertilizers, and pesticides, and these chemicals are potentially threatening water safety for fish, animals, and humans.

to (2002). Consumers demand perfect fruits and vegetables; and to please their consumers, farmers need to use lots of chemicals to avoid insect infestation. Farmers would prefer not to spray. Aside from the cost, farmers are also concerned that spraying may have adverse effects on their health. This concern has been denied by physicians and the PEI Department of Public Health:

> I asked the doctor one time, was it connected? And he told me, flatly, no. That there was no possible connection that he could make. And that's what I wanted to know. That was five years ago. So if I had even an inkling that I was doing something that caused my wife to be sick or somebody else's wife to be sick, I wouldn't do what I do. (The Perfect Potato, 2002, p. 2)

Linda Van Til, an epidemiologist for the PEI Department of Health, believes that cancer trends in PEI are no different than those in the rest of Canada (Delaney, 2006). However, Dr Matsusaki, who was relatively new to PEI in 2006 and worked in numerous emergency rooms across Canada and the United States, disagrees that cancer is not a problem in PEI: "Nowhere, nowhere did I see cancer that in any way resembles the cancers that I saw when I came to PEI" (Mittlestaedt, 2006, n.p.). Matsusaki believes the source of cancer is the pesticides used on potatoes.

The estimated cancer rates for men in PEI reveal that, compared with men in the rest of Canada, men in PEI have higher incidence rates of, to name a few, prostate, melanoma, and multiple myeloma. The incidence rate of prostate cancer in PEI is the highest in Canada (131/100,000 compared to 104/100,000 in Canada) (Canadian Cancer Statistics 2013).

In addition to the cancers mentioned above, brain cancer and non-Hodgkin's lymphoma also occur at higher rates but "these excesses are more modest" (Steingraber, 2010, p. 66). Multiple myeloma and leukemia are higher in rural areas than in industrial ones.

It is curious, then, that the PEI Department of Health claims that cancer rates in PEI are similar to other places in Canada. What would it mean for the government to admit there is a health problem and that pesticides are to blame? What policies are in place to protect citizens from pesticide residues? According to Albritton (2009, p. 112), the answer to the latter question is not straightforward as we do not know who determines what is an acceptable limit of pesticide residue. How do we establish safe limits given the diversity of people's body size, age, and health status, and is there a synergistic effect with pesticides and other chemicals? Although pesticide use has dramatically increased over the past couple of decades, the lack or absence of research on pesticide residues and policies identifying safety standards is disconcerting (Albritton, 2009).

Carson, in the early 1960s, identified three forms of silence that ultimately serve industry, not people. Two forms of silence continue to be relevant today: (1) environmental debates occur and stay behind closed doors of government offices; and (2) "the hushed complicity of many individual scientists who were aware of—if not directly involved in documenting—the hazards created by chemical assaults on the natural world" (Steingraber 2010, p. 18). With silence comes protection. Who is the government protecting, if not its citizens? In October 2015, Canadians elected a Liberal government who on the surface is committed to environmental protection and transparency. Time will tell if this proves to be the case.

How Agribusiness Controls Food, the Environment, and Our Health

Farming today is part of an integrated larger system that not only includes produce growers but also suppliers, distributors, and food manufacturers. This network is referred to as **agribusiness** and it is intricately linked to local and global markets. This section uses McDonald's food and the coffee industry as two examples that illustrate how corporations control the manufacturing of food, the environment, and our health.

John McKinlay (2005), an epidemiologist, coined the term **manufacturers of illness**. McKinlay argues that "in addition to producing material goods and services, [corporations] also produce, as an inevitable byproduct, widespread morbidity and mortality" (pp. 551–2). McKinlay illustrates that the food industry is a good example of how corporate profits contribute to ill health; yet ultimately, individuals are held accountable for their health. Since the 1960s, there has been a widespread decline in dietary standards in the United States and this is illustrated by increasing rates of overweight and "obesity."[1] In fact, McKinlay believes that being overweight "has reached epidemic proportions" (p. 555). More than half of all Americans are overweight and this is also true for Canadians. Table 8.1 charts percentages of overweight and "obese" Canadians from 2008 to 2012. Overall, there has been a small but consistent increase during this time period. There are differences by gender where proportionally more men than women are overweight and "obese" as well as differences by provinces and territories. Of note, rates of "obesity" and overweight are very high in eastern Canada and in the territories. Is it a coincidence that higher rates of poverty are observed in these regions?

McKinlay (2005) provides evidence of how the food industry developed a campaign to shift our "image of food" away from healthy basic staples, such as dairy products, fruits, and vegetables, to food that is synthetic and highly processed. Highly processed foods are cheaper to produce and this way "makes good economic sense" (p. 555). But the consumer cost for corporate profit is poor nutritional value. Processed foods contribute to what is referred to as diseases of civilization or lifestyle diseases that afflict people living in Western countries. The diseases often include cardiovascular diseases and certain cancers, which are caused by alcohol and fat consumption, possibly in combination with environmental pollution.

Some students may say we have choice in what we eat and how we eat. In this way, should a health problem arise, the individual is held responsible. However, the reality is that this is not the case; indeed, choice is socially and culturally constructed. Two examples are (1) poverty and (2) mass media and advertising.

Individuals who live in poverty have limited choices in what foods they can eat (Green et al., 2008). Their choice depends on the money they have, which often does not allow them to purchase fresh fruits and vegetables, or the foods they get from food banks. In both instances, the food is likely processed. Eating highly processed food is linked to an array of chronic diseases, cardiovascular disease (heart disease, stroke, and atherosclerosis) being the most prevalent (Green et al., 2008).

George Ritzer in 1993, drawing on Weber's theory of rationalization, coined the term **McDonaldization** to capture "the process by which the principles of the fast-food

agribusiness
Farming today is part of an integrated larger system that not only includes produce growers but also suppliers, distributors, and food manufacturers.

manufacturers of illness
Corporations who not only manufacture material goods and services—their products can also produce illness and death.

McDonaldization
A term coined by George Ritzer to expand Weber's notion of rationalization; defined as the standardization of social life by rules and regulations, such as increased monitoring and evaluation of individual performance, akin to the uniformity and control measures used by fast-food chains. These principles are now applied to other sectors, both locally and globally.

---

1. "Obese" and "obesity" are contested concepts by some critical scholars; they suggest that *fat* is a more appropriate term.

Table 8.1 Body Mass Index,[2] Overweight or "Obese," Self-reported, Adult, by Sex, Provinces and Territories, 2008–2012 (%)

	2008	2009	2010	2011	2012
Canada	**51.1**	**51.6**	**52.3**	**52.1**	**52.5**
Males	58.6	59.2	60.9	60.1	59.9
Females	43.5	43.9	43.7	44.2	45.0
Newfoundland and Labrador	**63.5**	**64.6**	**63.2**	**69.3**	**63.2**
Males	69.3	75.7	69.1	77.0	72.4
Females	58.0	53.9	57.6	61.9	54.2
Prince Edward Island	**59.5**	**59.0**	**56.6**	**57.6**	**61.3**
Males	67.2	68.3	67.1	67.2	70.7
Females	52.1	50.5	46.1	48.0	52.6
Nova Scotia	**63.2**	**60.3**	**61.1**	**61.0**	**60.5**
Males	66.2	66.9	68.1	67.9	69.5
Females	60.3	54.1	54.6	54.5	52.1
New Brunswick	**61.0**	**62.9**	**62.8**	**59.4**	**60.8**
Males	69.1	67.3	66.0	63.1	69.7
Females	53.1	58.9	59.7	55.8	52.4
Quebec	**48.0**	**49.2**	**51.8**	**50.1**	**50.8**
Males	56.0	56.3	60.7	58.0	58.0
Females	40.1	42.1	42.8	42.3	43.6
Ontario	**51.6**	**51.4**	**52.6**	**52.3**	**52.9**
Males	59.3	58.7	60.9	59.9	60.7
Females	43.9	44.1	44.3	44.8	45.2
Manitoba	**54.5**	**58.0**	**60.7**	**58.4**	**56.3**
Males	61.2	65.0	68.5	64.4	65.5
Females	47.7	50.9	52.9	52.2	46.6
Saskatchewan	**59.7**	**58.6**	**58.9**	**59.4**	**59.5**
Males	67.1	65.3	67.6	67.0	68.8
Females	51.9	51.5	49.9	51.6	49.8
Alberta	**52.4**	**55.1**	**51.6**	**52.2**	**53.1**
Males	60.4	63.8	59.9	62.0	58.4
Females	43.7	45.3	42.3	41.6	47.4
British Columbia	**45.1**	**45.1**	**44.4**	**46.6**	**46.5**
Males	52.1	54.2	54.9	55.7	54.0
Females	38.2	36.0	33.7	37.5	39.2

2. Note that the Body Mass Index has been criticized as a tool, both because it does not differentiate between fat and muscle (it measures mass indiscriminately), and because the cut-off points for who counts as "obese" and "overweight" have changed over time and by culture, and are not the best fit for all body types. However, for now it is the easiest way to measure "obesity" fairly accurately amongst greater sample sets (McGinty, 2014).

Table 8.1 continued

	2008	2009	2010	2011	2012
Yukon	**51.3**	**54.3**	**51.8**	**55.0**	**51.5**
Males	56.9	58.3	55.6	59.8	60.3
Females	45.4	50.1	47.8	49.9	42.2
Northwest Territories	**62.5**	**62.8**	**54.2**	**60.7**	**61.9**
Males	61.2	66.3	62.3	65.0	61.3
Females	64.1	59.1	45.6	55.5	62.6
Nunavut	**61.9**	**51.0**	**60.1**	**58.2**	**54.4**
Males	69.0	49.9	56.8	62.0	51.6
Females	52.6	52.1	64.1	53.6	58.1

Note: This indicator is measured out of 18 years and over only.

Source: Statistics Canada, CANSIM, table 105-0501 and Catalogue no. 82-221-X.

restaurant are coming to dominate more and more sectors of American society as well as the rest of the world" (Ritzer, 2008, p. 1). The emphasis of McDonaldization is on profits at the expense of food quality. Thus, the food is highly processed and is high in fat, salt, and sugar. The food industry is well aware that there is an addictive quality to fat, sugar, and salt, especially in children. Foods that are high in nutrients, in contrast, taste bland. The preference for fast food, which develops in childhood according to Birch (1999), continues into adulthood and "can promote patterns of food preference and intake that foster the development of overweight and obese individuals" (p. 57). In this way, an aggressive advertising campaign that is geared to children not only lays the groundwork for lifelong customers but also for chronic health conditions.

The growth of the international food industry has not only contributed to widespread **morbidity** and **mortality**, but it also has resulted in deforestation to accommodate intensive farming. The coffee industry is one such example. Since the 1970s, a coffee craze emerged in North America and the demand for coffee skyrocketed; this resulted in a change in the way coffee is grown. Coffee has now become second to oil in dollar value and is traded globally.

morbidity
Rates of illness.

mortality
Rates of death.

The old way of growing coffee was underneath a canopy of trees (called an overstorey) because the coffee plant was intolerant of sunlight. The overstorey also protected the coffee plant from any harsh weather and provided natural mulch to preserve the soil quality and reduce the number of weeds (Perfecto et al., 1996). This way of growing coffee could not meet the growing demand and, between the early 1970s and the early 1990s, the United States Agency for International Development (USAID) invested approximately $80,000,000 to "technify" the coffee industry in the Caribbean and Central America by replacing the shade coffee plant with new varieties that tolerate sun (Rice & Ward, 1996). These plants produced more plants per acre (a four- to six-fold increase) and more coffee crop per tree (Perfecto et al., 1996).

However, in order to maintain the high-yield crops, lots of spraying was needed (remember there was no overstorey that provided protection to the plant). Coffee has become the third most heavily sprayed crop after cotton and tobacco (Pendergast, 2010).

Pesticides that have been banned in Canada, the US, and many European countries continue to be used on coffee. This is problematic both for consumers of coffee and for coffee plantation workers. Coffee that is sprayed with chemicals that are illegal in Canada continues to be imported, and consumers are unknowingly being exposed to pesticide residues. Thus, according to Steingraber, "our diets have one foot each in lifestyle and environment" (1998, p. 61).

Linda Diebel, an investigative journalist for the *Toronto Star*, describes the harsh conditions of coffee workers in plantations in Guatemala as "a brutal place of working children, starvation wages, bonded labor, threats and intimidation, plastic sheeting for shelter, lack of sanitation and flooding, high infant mortality, bone-breaking work and far too many deaths from easily preventable, and treatable, diseases" (1997, n.p.). More recent reports reveal that little has changed since 1997 (Zamora, 2013). Research from Tanzania showed that workers did not wear protective gear when spraying and were not informed about proper procedures (no mixing instructions) for applying pesticides (Ngowi et al., 2001). Zamora (2013) found that even with proper training and gear, coffee farmworkers are exposed to hazardous work conditions.

The story of coffee illustrates how agribusiness and governments turn a blind eye and allow crops that have been sprayed with pesticides that are legally banned in their own countries to be sold here. It also shows how the most impoverished people living in cash-strapped economies are exposed to harsh and dangerous working conditions. Their choice is either not to work and be unable to support their family or to work and be exposed to serious health risks.

How Farming Is Linked to Our Drinking Water: Walkerton, a Case Study

This section examines the relationship between farming, government regulation, and our drinking water. Although water and food are regulated in similar fashions, acceptable levels are more rigorous for water than for food. That being said, water can still be contaminated by pesticides yet fall below the regulated criteria. In theory, water is regulated on an ongoing basis. However, this was not the case in Walkerton, Ontario. Walkerton, according to Prudham (2004), "is an example of broad regulatory failure and the systematic production of environmental risks by neoliberal governance reforms" (p. 344).

In May 2000, Walkerton, a small town in southwestern Ontario surrounded by rich agricultural land, appeared on the front pages of all newspapers in Canada when the town's drinking water became contaminated with *Escherichia coli*, better known as *E. coli*. Typically *E. coli*, a bacterium that lives in the intestines of mammals, is transmitted through eating meat that is undercooked or drinking milk that is not pasteurized. Walkerton is the first known case in North America of water-borne *E. coli*. The bacterium can wreak havoc on the intestines causing fever and diarrhea, which may lead to dehydration, to an increase in blood pressure, to lower red blood cell and platelet counts, and, in the worst case, to death. In Walkerton, 2300 of the town's approximate population of 5000 fell ill, and there were seven deaths (Schabas, 2002).

The source of the *E. coli* was in one of the town's wells, Well 5, which was dug in 1978 and was located next to a farm of cattle, on low-lying land (Perkel, 2002). It was not a deep well and from the onset the water showed signs of contamination. The Ministry of the Environment approved Well 5 with the understanding that the water be disinfected and routinely tested. The ministry also recommended that the land surrounding Well 5 be declared a protection zone to reduce the risk of contamination by agriculture and that Well 5 be viewed as an interim source of water supply for Walkerton. These recommendations were never signed upon, nor did the ministry oversee whether its recommendations were implemented.

In May 2000, Walkerton experienced many days of heavy rain, and on Friday May 12, according to Perkel (2002, p. 59), "[the] storm had pushed a lethal bacterial predator down beneath the emerging crops and fertile soil in the aquifer that fed the well that was being pumped to the taps of the town" (p. 60). The water from Well 5 had been contaminated from the adjacent land where 95 cattle roamed (Prudham, 2004). The strain of *E. coli* found in Well 5 lives in the guts of cattle and is spread through the cattle's feces. If water that is contaminated by the feces is ingested by humans, the results are catastrophic. On May 15, the local Public Utilities Commission (PUC), in routine fashion, sampled the local water supply. Of note, a water sample of Well 5 earlier in May had found bacteria (not *E. coli*) in both the raw and treated water; no one in the PUC, however, seemed concerned. The results for the May 15 test were faxed to the PUC on May 17 and the results showed that the water sample was contaminated with *E. coli*.

The first patients with symptoms (bloody diarrhea, vomiting, cramps, and fever) of *E. coli* were treated on May 15, and four days later the Medical Health Office (MHO) was informed that there were several patients experiencing these symptoms. The MHO contacted the PUC, who offered assurances that the water was safe, even though tests showed bacteria and *E. coli* present in the wells. Each day thereafter, more cases of illness were reported and the PUC held firm that the water was safe. The MHO warned the community not to drink the water and began doing independent water tests. On May 23, the MHO's test results revealed the water was contaminated with *E. coli*. The PUC in response admitted knowing this and also informed the MHO that water from another well, for some time, was not being chlorinated due to equipment failure. The suppressing of information of tainted water, or the "silence" as Carson would say, did not only occur locally, but Ontario's Ministry of the Environment was also implicated. The ministry had in fact received information in April, one month before the crisis erupted, that the water supply in Walkerton was bad, but municipal water systems were "as the highest-level ministry managers had decided, a non-priority" (Perkel, 2002, p. 120).

The premier of Ontario at this time was Mike Harris, a Conservative whose policies were shaped by a neo-liberal ideology known as the "Common Sense Revolution." Harris's government was committed to reducing the deficit and lowering taxes through deep cuts to or elimination of certain government programs. Thus, the Common Sense Revolution, which rolled back environmental regulations, created the conditions that allowed the Walkerton tragedy to occur (Prudham, 2004). The government in this instance was the "manufacturer of illness." The Walkerton story "serve[s] as a reminder that social regulation of nature under late capitalism is meant to protect us from the self-regulating market, and not the other way around" (p. 357). The Ontario government's neo-liberal policies of "fiscal austerity, administrative de-regulation and re-regulation; and privatization" (p. 344) contributed to the tragedy by "undermin[ing] agricultural and water quality regulation" (p. 344).

The health effects of the contaminated water in Walkerton are long lasting. An ongoing Walkerton health study as a result of the tainted water shows some children have lasting kidney problems; those residents who experienced severe gastroenteritis are at increased risk for high blood pressure and kidney damage (Canadian Press, 2008).

The Petrochemical Industry and Plastics: Links to Health

Look under your sink; what do you see? Look in the refrigerator; what do you see? Look in your bathroom cabinet; what do you see? Chances are you will see plastic. Dishwashing detergent, stainless steel cleaner, yogurt, milk, Tupperware, and medicine are mostly all stored in plastic containers. So, why are plastics a problem?

In 2008, CBC produced a documentary called *The Disappearing Male*, which asks the question, "Are males an endangered species"? The film is based on a study (Mackenzie et al., 2005) that showed decreasing numbers of male children being born in Aamjiwnaang, a First Nations community. Particularly noteworthy is that Aamjiwnaang is located near Sarnia, Ontario, and borders on what is known as Chemical Valley, named for the large numbers of petrochemical plants. Examining birth records from 1984 to 2003 (see Figure 8.1), Mackenzie et al. (2005) showed there has been a substantial decrease in births of baby boys in the 10-year period between 1993 and 2003. The ratio of boys to girls born in this time period is 46 to 132, compared to 105 to 100 overall in Canada. Although

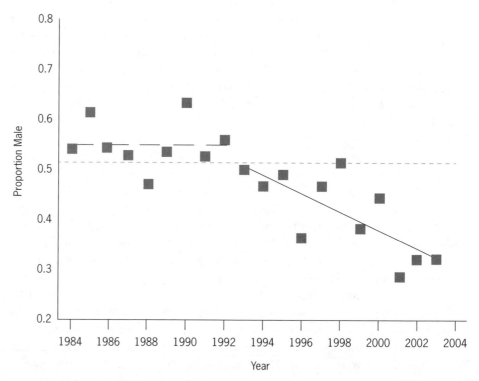

Figure 8.1 Proportion of Live Male Births for Aamjiwnaang First Nation, 1984–2003

Source: Mackenzie, C.A., Lockridge, A., & Keith, M. (2005). Declining sex ratio in a First Nation community. *Environmental Health Perspectives, 113*(10), doi:10.1289/ehp.8479.

definitive conclusions are difficult to make because "several potential factors may be contributing to the observed decrease in sex ratio" (p. 1297), the researchers nevertheless believe "the close proximity of this community to the large aggregation of petrochemical industry and potential exposures to compounds" explains the difference (p. 1297).

A decade earlier, Colborn et al. (1996), in their book *Our Stolen Future*, documented the catastrophic effect certain chemicals have on the reproductive systems of some animal species, such as a dramatic decrease in sperm count over two decades (1970s to 1990s); numerous cases of alligators with shrivelled penises and testicles; feminized male behaviours; and female infertility. Colborn argued that there were 51 man-made chemicals, although thousands were yet to be tested, that disrupt or scramble hormonal communications. The chemicals to which Colborn is referring are PCBs and DDT, as Rachel Carson had pointed out more than a decade earlier.

These chemicals are known as endocrine disruptors, which either mimic natural hormones such as estrogen circulating in the body, thus enhancing estrogens' effect or they "block or interfere" with the production of these hormones. They are also known as "environmental estrogens" (Larkin, 1995, p. 25). In women, estrogen is necessary for normal sexual development and a healthy reproductive system. Should the body produce too little estrogen in women of child-bearing age, infertility may result; too much estrogen increases a woman's risk for cancer of the uterus and breast, and gallbladder disease. Men's bodies produce much lower levels of estrogen than women's. Too much estrogen in a man's body, however, can reduce sperm production and testes growth (Larkin, 1995). Environmental estrogens come from "industrial products and byproducts, such as chemicals used to make plastic packaging or those contained in pesticides . . . and may also be used as ingredients in cosmetics" (p. 25). Environmental estrogens also include synthetic estrogen products, such as the birth control pill, hormone replacement therapy, and diethylstilbestrol, better known as DES (see Box 8.2).

Plastics: An Estrogen Mimicker

In the late 1980s two cell biologists, Ana Soto and Carlos Sonnenschein, were studying the relationship between estrogen and breast cancer and made an "accidental discovery." In one of their plastic test tubes, they found that breast cancer cells with no estrogens began to divide in similar fashion to those containing estrogen. Soto, in an interview, said, "We spent four months trying to figure out where the unknown estrogen came from until we verified that it was something shedding from the test tubes that we used to store the serum components" (Taube, 2009, n.p.). The researchers were able to isolate those test tubes that leaked estrogen. Ana Soto describes their findings:

> It turned out to be nonylphenol, an antioxidant that's also used in the synthesis of detergents. Carlos and I published our findings and then went looking for other places where nonylphenol was used. It turned out that it's also in the spermicides used in condoms and in creams applied with diaphragms . . . right there we knew it could be a big problem. (n.p.)

Soto and Sonnenschein found that nonylphenol is estrogenic, and the nonylphenol test tubes made breast cancer cells grow faster. Since this finding, many more chemicals have been recognized as estrogen mimickers.

Surfactants and plasticizers are two widely used groups of synthetic compounds. Surfactants are added to detergents, herbicides, paint, shampoo, hair conditioners, shaving cream, spermicides, and adhesives, to name a few, to allow for either adherence or lubrication: for example, paint, which is smoothly applied to a wall; and shaving cream, which allows the razor to glide easily on the skin. A team of English researchers found that surfactants could stimulate breast cancer cell growth and possibly feminize male fish (Steingraber, 2010, p. 111). Although there have been numerous reported incidents of fish "with hormonal abnormalities consistent with exposure to estrogenic substances in river-borne sewage" (p. 112), it is not clear whether the feminization of fish in these sewage waters is totally due to sewage polluted with surfactants or to an "exposure to natural and synthetic estrogens found in women's urine" (p. 112). (Think about the birth control pill.)

Phthalates, perhaps the most well-known plasticizers, have been widely used to make plastics soft and flexible; however, phthalates are also estrogen mimickers. When first marketed, phthalates were ubiquitous; they were widely used, for example, in baby products, such as soothers, toys (the rubber ducky), and jars for baby food; as well as in plastic wraps for food and plastic containers that store food; in shower curtains, shampoo bottles, and even perfume. When either ingested or inhaled (remember babies put everything in their

Box 8.2　Synthetic Estrogen

DES was commonly prescribed to pregnant women to prevent miscarriage between the mid-1940s and 1971. DES was discovered in 1938; it was seen as a pharmaceutical breakthrough as it was the first time a drug with estrogenic effects was marketed in pill form. DES was approved in the United States by the Food and Drug Administration in 1941, even though preliminary research on laboratory animals found that DES "caused cancer and problems with sexual development in laboratory animals" (Langston, 2008, n.p.). An estimated 5 million women took DES when pregnant. The first studies that challenged the safety of DES appeared in 1952; they revealed that DES had no beneficial effect in high-risk pregnancies and there was some evidence that DES increased the risk of miscarriage. But these studies were largely ignored until the late 1960s.

The case of DES is particularly instructive as it "provide[s] one of the first confirmed examples of how these chemicals can affect not only those who are directly exposed but also future generations" (Chatterjee, 1996, p. 18). Beginning in 1968, an American gynecologist identified a link between eight young women who were diagnosed with a rare form of vaginal cancer and their respective mothers, who used DES during their pregnancies. Although eight cases is not a large number by any means, it raised suspicion because there were only three other similar cases previously reported in the medical literature. Cancer was not the most common side effect; other more common side effects included miscarriages, ectopic pregnancies, and premature births in daughters of DES users; and epididymal cysts (testicular masses), undescended testes, higher risk for prostate cancer, and low sperm count and motility in their sons. Women who took DES were also at a higher risk for breast cancer.

mouths), phthalates become absorbed by the cells of the pituitary gland, which regulates several different hormonal systems, including sex hormones. Phthalates have been found to reduce testosterone levels, which can then lead to sexual malformations (Schapiro, 2007). Swan and her colleagues (2005) tested the urine of 134 pregnant women from the United States Midwest and California for phthalate levels. They found that the anogenital distance (AGD) (the distance between the anus and the scrotum) in their newborns was "shortened and testicular descent impaired in boys whose mothers had elevated prenatal phthalate exposure" (p. 1061). In an interview with Schapiro (2007), Swan expressed concern that phthalates may account for "the feminization of infant boys" (p. 47).

In 1999, the European Union, drawing on European and American research, placed a temporary ban on six phthalates, and in 2004 the ban became permanent. In the United States, a ban on the manufacturing and selling of children's products using certain types of phthalates with concentrations greater than 0.1 per cent was enacted in August 2008 and the law came into effect in February 2009. And in Canada on June 19, 2009, a decade later than in Europe, the government announced a ban on six phthalates (DEHP, DINP, DBP, BBP, DNOP, and DIDP) used in children's toys and products. Although phthalates have been banned in children's products, they continue to be used in prescription and over-the-counter drugs with timed-release coating (Cone, 2008, n.p.), and according to Maia James (2013), it is impossible to avoid phthalates as they are in everything, examples being shampoo, nail polish, laundry detergent, car interiors, food, and water.

The Nuclear Industry: Links to Health

At the same time the petrochemical industry was hitting its stride around the Second World War, the nuclear industry added to the melee with the introduction of its own toxic materials. The difference between chemicals and radiation, according to Bertell, is "whereas chemicals must touch us or be consumed by us with water or in food in order to poison us, radiation is able to harm us even at a distance" (1999, p. 43). Radiation is typically classified into electromagnetic and particulate radiation. Electromagnetic radiation is either ionizing, which comes from radioactive material, or non-ionizing. Examples of ionizing radiation are X-rays, microwaves, and radio waves. Sunlight hitting the earth's surface is an example of non-ionizing radiation. Particulate radiation is responsible for the atomic bomb, which the Americans dropped on Hiroshima and Nagasaki in August 1944. More than 100,000 people died immediately and many more thousands experienced acute radiation syndrome, which included fever, nausea, vomiting, bloody diarrhea, hair loss, bruising, mouth sores, and ulcers (Radiation Health Effects, 2007). Individuals exposed to radiation were diagnosed with cancers such as multiple myeloma, a cancer with previously low incidence in Japan. Radiation is also used to support nuclear reactors for nuclear energy. The **growth imperative**, since the end of World War II, led to energy demands beyond the scope of hydroelectric plants. As such, nuclear electricity was developed and today comprises over 16 per cent of the world's electricity (World Nuclear Association, 2009). In order to generate nuclear energy, nuclear reactors are needed "to make steam to generate electricity." It goes without saying that nuclear energy has been the source of much worldwide controversy. Hossay, for example, says, "Necessary safety measures meant that it was more expensive than initially promised;

growth imperative
Economic growth that is long term and sustained, supported by government policies that promote free markets.

and the problem of disposing of waste with a dangerous life in thousands of years proved politically difficult" (2006, p. 75).

In order to support both nuclear reactors and nuclear weapons, extensive uranium mining is necessary, which has led to health problems of its own. Uranium is usually found in land that has been of little use. Bertell points out that "it is no coincidence it has been found primarily on the lands of Indigenous Peoples" (1999, p. 47), as is the case in Canada. Canada is the world's largest producer of uranium, producing 20.5 per cent of the world's output. The only active mine today is in northern Saskatchewan, which exports 80 per cent of its production to nuclear electric utility customers worldwide. Although lung cancer has been linked to uranium mining, other health effects are difficult to establish (Elias et al., 1997). In one study of Navaho children living in New Mexico, researchers reported a statistically significant increase in birth defects, stillbirths, and deaths in children born near uranium mine dumps. Yet the researchers were unable to link the health effects to "reported duration of exposure, and other possibilities may explain the increase, including paternal employment in the mines, which was marginally significantly associated with the elevated risk for adverse outcome" (p. 47).

Dr David Maxwell (2008), a Nova Scotia emergency medicine physician and retired professor of family medicine and emergency medicine at Dalhousie University, unequivocally believes that "radioactivity damages cells" (n.p.). In an interview with the Environmental Health Association of Nova Scotia, Dr Maxwell said that radiation causes "chromosome breaks, which cause genetic defects, pregnancy losses, lowered fertility and all the things that happen when you disrupt people's genetic makeup" (n.p.). As well, uranium is an endocrine disruptor that when ingested can "cause neurologic damage or endocrine damage." Ingestion can occur when drinking water or eating food that is contaminated with uranium, or through hand-to-mouth activities when touching contaminated soil. Should a fire occur in a uranium storage facility, uranium deposits are re-suspended into the air and can be carried by wind.

The accident at the Chernobyl nuclear plant in Ukraine on April 26, 1986, is an example of the profound effects of a nuclear accident on a community, if not a continent. Two explosions occurred within the plant that led to numerous fires and a 10-day intense graphite fire responsible for the dispersion of radionuclides and fission fragments high into the atmosphere (Chernobyl, 2002, n.p.). The Chernobyl power plant was located in a populated area. There were over 100,000 people living within a 30-km radius of the plant and all were evacuated. However, most European countries experienced the effects of deposited radionuclides: Austria, Eastern and Southern Switzerland, parts of Southern Germany, and Scandinavia experienced the greatest amounts. The effects on the environment and on health from the nuclear accident were both immediate and long term. Contamination of forests, waters, and agricultural land occurred in Belarus, Ukraine, and Russia. Agricultural land that is highly contaminated will produce food with excessive levels of radionuclides. There continues to be concerns over levels of radioactivity of food products, such as berries, mushrooms, and game meat, from forested areas in Ukraine, and although drinking water for the time being appears to be safe, contamination of fish may be a long-term problem.

There were 31 deaths, and 134 people needed treatment for acute radiation syndrome shortly after the accident. To date, there are higher incidences of thyroid cancers, breast cancers and brain tumours. However, there is some evidence that the exposed population may also be at risk for prostate and stomach cancer, and cancer of the blood (Pflugbeil,

Table 8.2 Thyroid Cancer in the Gomel Area (Belarus) for 13 Years Before and 13 Years After the Chernobyl Catastrophe

Age	1973–85	1986–98	Increase
0–18	7	407	58-fold
19–34	40	211	5.3-fold
35–49	54	326	6-fold
50–64	63	314	5-fold
>64	56	146	2.6-fold

Source: Pflugbeil, S., Claussen, A., & Schmitz-Feuerhake, I. (2011). Table: Thyroid cancer in the Gomel area (Belarus) for 13 years before and 13 years after the Chernobyl catastrophe. In German Affiliate of International Physicians for the Prevention of Nuclear War, *Health Effects of Chernobyl: 25 years after the reactor catastrophe*, p. 29. E. Lengfelder et al.: Aus der Tschernobyl-Katastrope lernen. Jod-Prophylaxe auf alle Altersstufen ausweiten [Learning from the Chernobyl catastrophe. Extend iodine prophylaxis to all age groups]. MMW-Fortschr. Med. 41(2000)355-356. [German.] Available at: www.chernobylcongress.org/fileadmin/user_upload/pdfs/chernob_report_2011_en_web.pdf

Claussen, & Schmitz-Feuerhake, 2011). A child's risk of developing thyroid cancer will be life-long (see Table 8.2) (Pflugbeil, Claussen & Schmitz-Feuerhake, 2011). As well, the research of Danzer and Danzer (2011, p. 51) found those affected by radiation exposure report "lower levels of life satisfaction as well as higher probabilities of suffering from depression or psychological traumas (post-traumatic stress disorders)."

The challenges of storing nuclear wastes in combination with the risks of another nuclear disaster for many environmentalists mean that nuclear energy is not a viable solution to the increasing demand of energy. Instead, the solution lies in "solar, wind, hydro, geo-thermal, and biomass energy—coupled with rapid improvement in the efficiency with which power is used" (Flavin, 2006a, n.p.).

The Nuclear Industry's Links to Environmental Racism

In the 1980s, civil rights activists brought people's attention to the fact that many African Americans in the United States were disproportionately living in communities that neighboured with industries that emitted wastes that were either carcinogenic or that led to other serious health outcomes, such as breathing problems and miscarriages (Westra & Lawson, 2001). **Environmental racism** is now used to describe how disadvantaged communities are disproportionately exposed to environmental health factors and disasters brought about by government or industrial policies. In theses instances people have little choice in terms of where they live and where they work (see Box 8.3). The most compelling example of environmental racism in Canada is that of First Nations people living on reserves.

This environmental racism is evident in the number of communities in Canada whose members live their daily lives with unsafe water even though Health Canada's water program mandates the "protection of public health from microbiological pathogens, chemical and physical, and radiological contaminants found in drinking water and recreational water supplies" (Assembly of First Nations, 2009, n.p.). According to the Assembly of First

environmental racism
A term used to describe how disadvantaged communities are disproportionately exposed to environmental health factors and disasters brought about by government and/or industrial policies.

Nations, "20 per cent of communities live with contaminated water," and "there are currently 93 boil water advisories in First Nations communities across the country, some of which are long-standing" (Halpin, 2009, p. 18). Although in principle First Nations people should have access to the same water quality as all Canadians, at this time there are no legislative and regulatory frameworks to ensure this occurs. Neskantaga chief Roy Moonias responded to this injustice by saying "Nowhere else in Canada would anyone accept this. . . . It's a violation of our fundamental human rights. . . . We're being treated as second-class citizens" (quoted in Petersen, 2008, n.p.).

First Nations people depend on water for "fishing, hunting and spiritual practices" (McCurdy, 2001, p. 20). The struggle for many First Nations groups throughout North America is that both their land and water have been contaminated by mining, petrochemical plants, and hydroelectric dams. As well, according to Laduke (1999), reservations "have been targeted" for nuclear waste dumps (p. 2). The Great Lakes, which drain into the St. Lawrence River, for example, are home to one-quarter of all North American industry, and "puts the Akwesasne [Mohawk] reservation downstream from some of the most lethal and extensive pollution on the continent" (p. 15). All these industries used PCBs (one of the POPs) until they were banned in 1978. In the meantime, PCBs contaminated the air, water, and soil, and then moved through the food chain. PCBs have been linked to "liver, brain, nerve and skin disorders in humans, shrinking testicles in alligators and cancer and reproductive disorders in laboratory animals" (p. 15). Breast cancer is the number one cancer among First Nations women, and in Ontario, these rates are increasing.

First Nations people have higher rates of infectious diseases; higher rates of certain chronic diseases, such as diabetes and heart disease; and higher rates of birth defects,

Box 8.3 Environmental Racism

Africville was a Black settlement in the north end of Halifax, Nova Scotia, where "blacks became a poorly educated, economically marginalized and socially excluded subculture in Nova Scotian society that governments felt no obligation to respect" (McCurdy, 2001, p. 99). Africville, from its beginning (in the mid-1850s), was environmentally attacked. For example, by the late 1800s, the residents of Africville were neighbours to "an oil plant/storage complex, a fertilizer plant, a rolling mill, two slaughter houses, a coal handling facility, a tar factory, a tannery, a shoe factory, several stone-crushing facilities, a foundry, and a fertilizer-producing plant" (McCurdy, 2001, pp. 101–2). Africville was home to waste-disposal pits and in the 1950s, the city council of Halifax "moved the open city dump to Africville because it was too much of a 'health menace' to locate anywhere" (p. 102). Africville is an example of the relationship between race, class, and exposure to environmental hazards. Being poor and Black limits the choices of where to live. At the same time, the government feels entitled to pollute land where poor people live. McCurdy (2001) points out that "Africville was a victim of the NIMBY [not in my backyard] principle which was practiced in many predominant white urban and suburban communities in North America" (p. 107).

such as cleft palate, club foot, and Down syndrome. Moreover, both men's and women's life expectancy is shorter than their non–First Nations counterparts. (See Chapter 7 on the health of Aboriginal peoples.) Some of these differences can be attributed to social determinants of health, such as income and education; however, another important determinant is environment. The contamination of their air, land, and water by industry has direct and indirect effects on health. For example, there are noted birth defects as those listed above; higher incidences of leukemia, lung, and renal cancers (López-Abente et al., 1999, 2001); and chromosome aberrations (Au et al., 1995) for people either working in or living close to uranium mines. Many First Nations reserves are located in close proximity to either active or closed uranium mines. The effect of contamination through industry or mining has changed First Nations' people's traditional way of living (Laduke, 1999). Unable to either fish or farm, in combination with limited income, has meant a diet high in carbohydrates and low in protein. In this instance, poor eating is an outcome of environmental devastation (see Box 8.4 for another example of environmental influence on the health of First Nations people in Canada).

Challenges in Linking Health to the Environment

There are numerous cases of communities or groups of people coming together to try and make sense of what they perceive to be clusters of serious illnesses emerging in their respective communities (see Box 8.5 for one such example). Should a cluster of illness arise, the community typically is confronted with resistance from public health officials because "common people" are unable to "grasp the statistical concept of randomness" (Steingraber, 2010). It is very difficult to meet the criteria of scientific rigour statistically. First, reaching statistical significance with a small sample is challenging. And second, a researcher cannot ask a group of citizens to stay in an area, which is potentially contaminated, so they can have a decent case-control study.

> In cluster studies, **epidemiologists** look for an increase over and above some background level, but if the people in the background are also becoming increasingly contaminated, the researchers are paddling a boat in a moving stream [and] differences are harder to see. (p. 76)

epidemiology
The statistical study of patterns of disease in the population. Originally focused on epidemics, or infectious diseases, it now covers non-infectious conditions, such as stroke and cancer.

Another challenge of linking cancer to the environment has to do with lag time. Cancer generally occurs many years after exposure to a contaminant, complicating exposure assessment. As a result, researchers rely on records and on people's memory (Steingraber, 2010). Old records may be incomplete or nonexistent and people's memories are fragile and thus often unreliable. As well, there are a multiple of factors that may lead to cancer, such as environmental exposure to pesticides, to fires (think about the smoke billowing high above the Hudson River after the September 11 bombing of the World Trade Center in New York City), and to cigarette smoking. Or there may be trace amounts of residues in any one item—let's say food—which is deemed to be safe, but perhaps there is a cumulative effect. As Carson (1962) explains, "any single supposedly 'safe dose' may be enough to tip the

Box 8.4 Oil Sands and First Nations

The Alberta oil sands (found in Athabasca, Cold Lake, and Peace River) spans approximately 20 per cent of Alberta—140,000 square kilometres of Alberta (Pembina Institute, n.d.). To put this into perspective, this area is marginally less than the state of Florida. The Great Canadian Oilsands Company which is now known as Suncor Energy opened the first oil sands mine in 1967. As of January 2014, there are more than 100 active mines in Alberta (www.oilsandstoday.ca/whatareoilsands/Pages/RecoveringtheOil.aspx). Oil sands are comprised of sand, water, clay, and bitumen which is "oil that is too heavy or thick to flow or be pumped without being diluted or heated" (What are Oil Sands?). Ninety-

© iStock.com/Daniel Barnes

This photo captures some of the scale of the environmental impact of the oil sands development in Alberta. Most of the water shown here is in "tailing ponds," no longer safe to drink. You can also see some of the air pollution being released from the processing plants. Do you think that the development of the oil sands is a form of environmental racism?

seven per cent of Canada's oil reserves are found in the oil sands. Only Venezuela and Saudi Arabia have larger oil reserves than those in Canada (see Figure 8.2).

The four key environmental concerns in relation to oil sands development are (1) the amount of water consumption used by the industry; (2) the amount of land disturbed (some land is permanently disturbed) by mining; (3) the management and storage of toxic waste; and 4) the amount of greenhouse gas and air pollution emissions (Grant, Angen, & Dyer, 2013, p. 2). These concerns have been minimized by supporters of oil sands mining, arguing that emissions from oils sands only represent a minutiae of the world's greenhouse gas emissions (p. 1).

However, recent research by Kelly et al. (2009) and Kirk et al. (2014) found that oil sands wastes or tailings are leeching into groundwater and bleeding into the Athabasca River. The tailings "can reach levels in fish and wildlife that may pose health risks to human consumers" (Kirk et al., 2014, p. 7374). This study was downplayed by a spokesman for Environment Canada, who was reported in *The Canadian Press* as saying, "This study does not provide proof that the oilsands process water may be reaching the Athabasca River at the sites examined. Techniques are being further developed and applied to a wider range of shallow groundwater locations in the area to repeat these results and to further assess regional tailings pond/groundwater interactions" (Federal Study Confirms, 2014, n.p.). The reporter also interviewed a spokesman for the Canadian Association of Petroleum Producers who claimed that the water quality of the Athabasca River is safe: "Current tailings pond and groundwater monitoring in the oilsands shows no substances being released or predicted to be released in quantities or concentrations that would degrade or alter water quality" (Federal Study Confirms, 2014, n.p.).

The effect of oil sands mining has had a particularly adverse effect on First Nations people (Milisew Cree and the Athabasca Chipewyan First Nation [ACFN]) living in Northern Alberta. Birds, fish, animals, waterways, and traditional plant life are all at risk. Prior to the federal election of October 2015, the First

Nations people were in a continuous battle with then Prime Minister Stephen Harper, who backed the expansion of oil sands mining by petroleum companies over the needs and treaty rights of the people (Whittington, 2014). According to David Schindler, a freshwater biologist, the treaty

> support[s] native people living a subsistence lifestyle 'til the sun quits shining and the rivers quit flowing, which, I guess, cynically, is what they're trying to do up there with industrial development. It gives you a creepy feeling to be part of a society that has this little regard for native people. It's downright racist. (Bocking, 2012, n.p.)

Consequently, the health, rights, and culture of the ACFN are violated. For many years, the ACFN had voiced concerns about the health status of their people due to environmental contamination.

Even though a cancer incidence report of the ACFN community has been recently completed by the government, according to Chief Allan Adam, the report is fundamentally flawed: the community was not involved in the study, and the conclusions to the report were puzzling. Although the findings revealed that there were three cases of bile duct cancer when zero cases should have been reported, and there were higher than expected levels of both cervical and lung cancers, the report concluded that "cancer in the community was not higher then [sic] expected" (Athabasca Chipewyan First Nation, 2014, n.p.). Chief Adam challenged the methodology of the report arguing that the findings were not peer reviewed, and that there is a disjuncture between the report's findings "that cancer is not higher than expected . . . [and] the fact that people are getting sick and people are getting cancers." He therefore calls for a peer-reviewed study, one that is "done in partnership with our communities" (ACFN, 2014, n.p.).

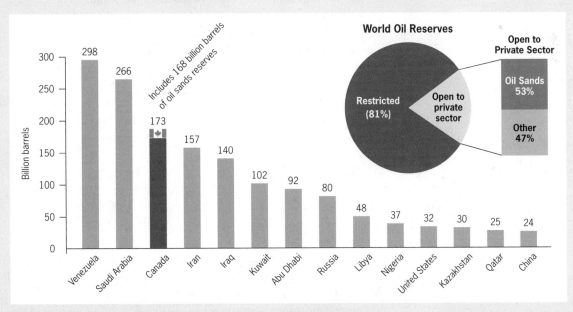

Figure 8.2 International Comparison of Crude Oil Reserves

Source: Canadian Association of Petroleum Producers. (2014). Slide 9. In Canada's oil & natural gas. October 24, 2014. www.capp.ca/~/media/capp/customer-portal/documents/253802.pdf. International Energy Statistics, US Energy Administration.

scales that are already loaded with other 'safe doses'" (p. 237). Isolating a single cause, therefore, is often difficult. Finally, people move not only within their community but also to different geographical regions or even countries. A physician who is untrained in environmental health may not think about asking "Where did you live on September 11, 2001?"

Risk Assessment, Prove Harm, and the Precautionary Principle

This chapter discussed how chemicals such as pesticides were approved for use even though their full effects on human health were unknown, how drugs were marketed even though research on animals showed there were adverse effects, and how governments deny responsibility when a toxic hazard occurs. **Risk assessment** is the process governments use to assess a chemical's potential for injury on humans and the environment. Risk assessment determines government policies on, for example, acceptable levels of drug residues in beef or pesticide residues in food; the amount of bacteria or other pollutants that are allowed in drinking water; acceptable levels of toxic chemicals being emitted from petrochemical plants; radiation limits for technicians working in hospitals; and workplace safety (Montague, 2004).

risk assessment
The process governments use to assess a chemical's potential for injury on humans and on the environment.

There are three components to risk assessment: (1) estimating how hazardous the chemical is; (2) estimating the number of people exposed to the chemical and at what levels exposures occur; and (3) estimating the potential for harm among those exposed to the chemical (Montague, 2004). To assess risk, a mathematical probability is presented that calculates the risk of ingesting or being exposed to a certain chemical. The role of government policy-makers, then, is to decide whether one in a million deaths is an acceptable level or to decrease the risk to what *is* deemed acceptable.

Thus, risk assessment is a highly political process, requiring value judgment (Hossay, 2006); assumptions, not science, shape decision making around risk assessment (McBane, 2005). Montague (2004) argues that the process of risk assessment is fundamentally biased to large corporations who can manipulate the outcomes of research to their benefit. This is done by hiring scientists who "can select and manipulate the data and choose particular assumptions (often silently), thus allowing them to reach almost any conclusion they set out to reach. Then they package it as 'science' even though the conclusions are based on judgment and is not in any way reproducible" (p. 30). Or, more insidiously, corporations are partnered with governments, with each working for their own agenda.

Asbestos, widely used as a fire retardant, is a known carcinogen and is no longer used anywhere in Canada. However, mining of asbestos continues to be active in Quebec, and the asbestos is exported to countries in the global South, in particular to India. Simpson reports that "asbestos represents 11 per cent of Québec's exports to India, a tidy sum of $427-million" (Simpson, 2010, p. A5). The manufacturers of asbestos focus on profit and not on health; the workers need jobs to support their families. But why are the federal and provincial governments complicit in selling carcinogenic material to countries in the global South instead of putting a stop to this practice? According to Simpson, the "fear of offending Québec has put a sock in the mouth of federal governments, and fear of losing a few votes has forced Québec governments into acrobatic flight of hypocrisy to defend the indefensible" (p. A5).

prove harm
Scientific proof that a product is harmful.

Partnered with risk assessment is the notion of **prove harm**: unless there is scientific certainty that harm exists, "anything goes" (Montague, 2004, p. 25). For example, the

Box 8.5 Shannon, Quebec

Communities that have been situated next to old dumpsites may be at higher risk for cancer although this is difficult to prove. Shannon, Quebec, is one such community. Shannon is a community of 2000 residents just outside Quebec City. It also neighbours a military complex, Base Valcartier. In the 1970s the military buried vast quantities of trichloroethylene (TCE) residues.

TCE is an industrial solvent used to degrease metal parts; it is also used in paint removers, spot removers, and rug cleaners. In 2007, the Canadian Environmental Protections Act mandated a 65 per cent reduction in TCE use as it is recognized as a possible human carcinogen. Animal studies have also shown there is a possible link in rats between TCE exposure and kidney and testicular tumours; and in mice, to pulmonary and liver tumours.

In 1997, the military found that its drinking water was contaminated with TCEs and as a result changed its drinking water supply. However, the military did not notify the town of Shannon until 2000, and residents continued to drink water contaminated with TCE 200 times the safe level. The residents of Shannon were convinced that cancer was rampant and rates were much higher compared to those generally in Canada. After much denial from the province, in 2009 a team of Montreal researchers supported what the community knew:

> . . . through DNA testing a common pattern in the cancerous tissue of patients exposed to TCE, a pattern not seen in other cancerous tissues. . . . "Here in Shannon we have a population of maybe 4,000 . . . and actually I have 12 cancers of the brain. It's at least 12 times more than it should be." (Researchers Find Link, 2009, n.p.)

Even though the government now recognizes there is a link between TCE and cancer, it refuses to acknowledge that this is the case in Shannon; the Shannon residents "were not exposed to high enough concentrations over a long enough period to become ill" (DND denies blame, 2010, n.p.). Their struggle continues.

World Trade Organization's rules state that there can be no restrictions placed on products for unknown health effects or if there is no definitive evidence that the product is unsafe, even though safety concerns have been raised (Hossay, 2006). In this way, business is protected at the expense of an individual's health, and the burden of proof is placed on the consumers to prove the product unsafe before protective action will occur. Steingraber (2010) argues that the prove harm approach is "tantamount to running an uncontrolled experiment using human subjects" (p. 282). Instead, she calls for an upstream approach, one that prevents harm before it occurs.

The **precautionary principle** is one such approach. The basic tenet of the precautionary principle is to safeguard human life so that "public and private interests should act to prevent harm before it occurs. It dictates that indication of harm, rather than proof of harm, should be the trigger action—especially if delay may cause irreparable damage"

precautionary principle
The principle of taking into account not just known risks, but also potential risks, even if the evidence for those potential risks is weak. In these circumstances (e.g., a drug), the precautionary principle would say that the product should either not be marketed or should be marketed under significant restrictions.

(Steingraber, 2010, pp. 281–2). In this way, the burden of proof is not on the public to demonstrate that harm has occurred but, rather, the burden is on industry to prove the product is unequivocally safe.

Conclusion

In Canada, we have ignored Rachel Carson's warnings from 50 years ago. There is some evidence that the precautionary principle is taking hold in Europe (Raffensperger & Tickner, 1999; Steingraber, 2010), but in Canada there is less room for optimism. According to a press release put forth by the Canadian Environmental Law Association, the federal government's proposals that manage toxic chemicals "are neither preventive nor protective for Canadians, [and] . . . we are giving industry a free pass to continue with business as usual" (Canadian Environmental Law Association, 2008, n.p.). It appears that Canada's government commitment lies in a risk-assessment approach and that the government has demonstrated no interest in adopting standards based on the precautionary principle.

Summary

- Drawing on Rachel Carson's research, this chapter examines the complexities between our environment and our health and the difficulties and strategies involved in proving these linkages.
- The widespread use of pesticides and herbicides and their effect on health and the environment is studied through the PEI potato industry and pesticide use. Cancer rates, particularly those linked to pesticide use in PEI, for both men and women, have steadily been increasing at a faster rate than in all of Canada.
- The networks of agribusiness are described using examples of McDonaldization and the coffee industry. Both produce widespread environmental devastation as well as health hazards to workers in large part through heavy pesticide use. Pesticides, banned in Canada, continue to be used on coffee, and consumers are unknowingly being exposed to pesticide residues.
- The manufacturing of synthetic compounds such as plastics in everyday consumption are examined. Plastics are known to be estrogen disruptors, which either mimic or block estrogen production. Estrogen disruptors can increase the risk for cancer in women and reduce sperm production and testes growth in men.
- The nuclear industry is examined in relation to the health effects of mining uranium, radiation, and nuclear power plants. Lung cancer is an occupational health hazard among mine workers, and birth defects and stillbirths have been observed in communities situated close to mines. In Chernobyl, thyroid cancer is particularly high among children exposed to radiation due to fire at the nuclear plant.
- Environmental racism and popular epidemiology are described using the examples of Africville, Nova Scotia; First Nations communities; and Shannon, Quebec. Disadvantaged communities, where people have little choice in terms of where

they live and work, are disproportionately exposed to environmental health factors and disasters brought about either actively by government and/or industrial policies or passively through silence—turning a blind eye or denying that a problem exists.

- The frameworks of risk assessment, burden of proof, and the precautionary principle are examined. Canada adopts a prove harm approach where the burden of proof is on the public to demonstrate harm.

Key Terms

agribusiness

endocrine disruptors

environmental racism

epidemiology

growth imperative

manufacturers of illness

McDonaldization

morbidity

mortality

precautionary principle

prove harm

risk assessment

Sociological Reflection: Frederick Street and Burden of Proof

Maude Barlow and Elizabeth May published the book *Life and Death on Canada's Love Canal* based on the lives of residents living on Frederick Street in Whitney Pier, a neighbourhood in Sydney, Nova Scotia. Whitney Pier was not just any neighbourhood; it was home to a steel plant and North America's worst toxic waste site. The emissions from the steel plant were a toxic soup of chemicals. The book reports the conditions that residents of Whitney Pier endured: high cancer rates, heart and lung diseases, headaches, nosebleeds, respiratory infections, dying pets, and even one report of a dog glowing in the dark. After many deaths and illnesses and arsenic appearing in basements, and frustrated by the government's lack of concern and inaction, the residents organized an association and successfully challenged the government to evacuate the residents of Frederick Street and to demolish the homes. The homes on neighbouring streets, however, continue to stand and be inhabited as the government does not see that it is its responsibility to provide further aid.

- Reflect on some of the reasons why you think the government initially resisted helping the residents of Frederick Street.
- How is Frederick Street an example of environmental racism?
- Some health scholars believe that the starting point of health regulation is the precautionary principle. Others counter by arguing that such a policy would work against the economy. What do you think?

Discussion Questions

1. On heavy smog days in large urban areas, do you think that private vehicles should be banned?
2. Farmers say they use lots of pesticides because they have no choice; this is what the market demands. Should the government subsidize organic farming? Is this a problem or a solution?

3. What role, if any, should the government play in preventing another Walkerton from occurring?
4. Why are those members of our society who are most economically disadvantaged at greater risk for health problems related to our environment?
5. Why is the Canadian government so resistant to shifting from a risk-assessment model to one based on the precautionary principle?

Further Investigation

1. The relationships between consumers, farmers, and the manufacturers of food are complex and not straightforward. Describe how each of these groups affects food policies surrounding food costs and availability.
2. What role does the state play and what role should the state play in ensuring that food products are safe for consumer use? Your answer should include a discussion of risk assessment and precaution.

Further Reading

Albritton, Robert. (2009). *Let them eat junk: How capitalism creates hunger and obesity.* Winnipeg, MB: Arbeiter Ring Publishing.

Brown, P., & Mikkelsen, E.J. (1997). *No safe place: Toxic waste, leukemia, and community action.* Berkeley, CA: University of California Press.

Carson, R. (1962). *Silent spring.* Cambridge, MA: The Riverside Press Cambridge.

Colborn, T., Dumanoski, D., & Peterson, M.J. (1996). *Our stolen future: Are we threatening our fertility, intelligence, and survival? A scientific detective story.* New York, NY: Dutton Penguin.

Gibbs, L.M. (1998). *Love Canal: The story continues . . .* Gabriola Island, BC: New Society Publishers.

Laduke, W. (1999). *All our relations: Native struggles for land life.* Cambridge: South End Press.

May, E., & Barlow, M. (2000). *Frederick street: Life and death on Canada's Love Canal.* Toronto, ON: HarperCollins Publishers Ltd.

McGinty, J. (2014, August 15). Much-criticized body mass index endures as a fatness guide. *The Wall Street Journal.* Retrieved from http://www.wsj.com/articles/much-criticized-body-mass-index-endures-as-a-fatness-guide-1408148146

Perkel, C.N. (2002). *Well of lies: The Walkerton water tragedy.* Toronto, ON: McClelland & Stewart Ltd.

Schlosser, E. (2002). *Fast food nation: The dark side of the all-American meal.* New York, NY: Perennial.

Steingraber, S. (2010). *Living downstream: An Ecologist's personal investigation of cancer and the environment* (2nd ed.). Philadelphia, PA: Da Capo Press.

Web Resources

Alternatives Journal: Canada's
  Environmental Voice.
www.alternativesjournal.ca

Canadian Centre for Occupational Health
  and Safety
www.ccohs.ca

Canadian Environmental Law Association
www.cela.ca

DES Action
www.desaction.org

Earth Trends, Environmental Information
http://earthtrends.wri.org

Environmental Defence Fund (EDF)
www.edf.org

Environmental Research Foundation:
  Rachel's Environment & Health News
*www.rachel.org/?q=en/newsletters/
  rachels_news/956*

Environmental and Workplace Health
*www.hc-sc.gc.ca/ewh-semt/contaminants/
  index-eng.php*

Environment Canada
www.ec.gc.ca/default.asp?lang=en

Gimme the Good Stuff
http://gimmethegoodstuff.org

Greenpeace International
www.greenpeace.org

PlanetFriendly
www.planetfriendly.net/health.html

Science Watch: Tracking Trends &
  Performance in Basic Research
*http://sciencewatch.com/ana/st/
  bis/09sepBisSoto*

Scorecard: The Pollution Information Site
www.scorecard.org

Sierra Club
www.sierraclub.org

Statistics Canada: Case Study: Ozone Layer
  Depletion and the Montréal Protocol
*www.statcan.gc.ca/edu/power-pouvoir/
  ch5/casestudy-edudedecas/5214797
  -eng.htm*

World Nuclear Association: Representing
  the People and Organisations of the
  Global Nuclear Profession
www.world-nuclear.org/info/inf32.html

PART 2
The Social Construction of Health and Illness

I enjoy convalescence. It is the part that makes illness worth while.

—George Bernard Shaw, *Back to Methuselah*

The second dimension of the social model of health is the social construction of health and illness. *Social construction* refers to the socially created characteristics of human life—the way people actively make the societies and communities in which they live, work, and play. Differences in values, religions, traditions, and ways of life generally are manifestations of the social construction of reality. In other words, human life and the way we interact with one another is neither "natural" nor inevitable and varies between cultures and over time. Social construction, when applied to how we view health and illness, reveals that assumptions about normal/abnormal, right/wrong, and healthy/unhealthy reflect the culture of a particular society at a given point in time. Our understandings of health and illness are shaped also by intersecting social identities, including gender, class, ethnicity, age, and sexual orientation.

Social construction is rooted in the symbolic-interaction perspective and focuses on individuals and the way they create meaning. However, we need to keep in mind the social and economic contexts in which meanings are constructed. Not all groups of people have equal status in society; some have more power than others to shape the way meanings are constructed. Knowing how people view their health and health-care experiences provides an important lens, but we must not lose sight of the fact that social determinants have an effect on the health status of different groups and their use of health services, which in turn may influence their interpretations of their experience.

Part 2 consists of three chapters that examine how culture, power, social identities, and economics play a part in socially constructing notions of health and illness.

- Chapter 9 looks at medicalization and how aspects of life have increasingly come under medical scrutiny, and the social consequences of such. It also considers who has power to define behaviours as illnesses.
- Chapter 10 examines our understanding of "normalcy" and the social construction of disability. It also looks at the meanings and experiences of chronic illness for individuals.
- Chapter 11 explores changing social attitudes to aging, death, and dying, which, while biological realities, are distinctly social processes.

CHAPTER 9
The Medicalization of Society[1]

Sharyn L. Roach Anleu & Jennie Hornosty

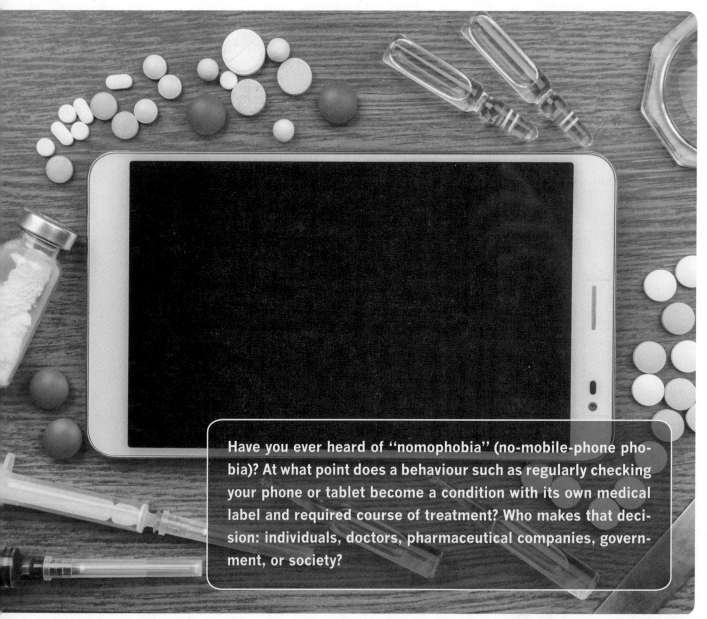

Have you ever heard of "nomophobia" (no-mobile-phone phobia)? At what point does a behaviour such as regularly checking your phone or tablet become a condition with its own medical label and required course of treatment? Who makes that decision: individuals, doctors, pharmaceutical companies, government, or society?

© iStock.com/CJ_Romas

---

1. This is the title of Peter Conrad's 2007 book, which provides a comprehensive overview of medicalization and its effects.

Overview

- How do certain areas of human life come to be defined, or not, as medical issues?
- Who defines social expectations?
- What social forces promote medicalization?
- What are the individual and social consequences of medicalization?

What is defined as sickness and how it gets treated are related to the larger social and political milieu. Is shyness a sickness? When is being short considered abnormal? When is behaviour, such as very active children or gambling, indicative of an illness in need of medical treatment? How did homosexuality, once considered pathology, become acknowledged as normalized behaviour? The concept of sickness, as Freidson (1988) has argued, is not a neutral scientific concept but is fundamentally a moral one that designates certain behaviour as desirable and normal and other behaviour as deviant. Throughout its history, psychiatry has played a critical role in designating various forms of behaviour as evidence of mental illness that requires therapeutic intervention. Psychiatry has developed notions of normal (and deviant) behaviour in such areas as sexual behaviour and identity, mental health, gambling, alcohol and drug use, criminal behaviour, eating, reproduction, and child development. Today, we have what Conrad (2007, p. 133) refers to as "shifting engines of medicalization" and new market-based forms of medicalization.

Introduction: The Social Process of Medicalization

Why does deviation from certain behaviours and expectations become defined and treated as illness or as a medical phenomenon requiring intervention and treatment by medical personnel? The **medicalization** of behaviour considered deviant is a historical and social process, and is the outcome of professional and social-movement activity. The dominance of the medical model in explaining certain types of behaviour or conditions means that the emphasis is on the individual, who must be treated in some way in order to restore conformity or health, rather than on the social environment. When society accepts these definitions, the medical profession becomes an agent of social control that has been given the power to certify individuals as being sick. Medicine continues to play a key role in medicalization; however, other forces, such as the pharmaceutical industry, consumer groups, biotechnological discoveries, and health insurance, are today important "engines of medicalization" (Bell & Figert, 2012; Conrad, 2007; Sulik, 2011). This chapter outlines the concept of medicalization and examines the relationship between medicalization and social control. It looks at the role of psychiatry in identifying and regulating **deviance** and

medicalization
The process by which non-medical problems become defined and treated as medical issues, usually in terms of illnesses, disorders, or syndromes.

deviance
Behaviour or activities that violate social expectations about what is normal.

the role of pharmaceutical companies in manufacturing illness. It also considers some of the social consequences of medicalization.

Several kinds of questions can be asked regarding the concept of deviance: What causes or motivates someone to deviate from social expectations? Who defines those expectations? What kinds of sanctions are invoked and under what conditions? What is the relationship between various forms of **social control** (for example, between legal regulation and medical intervention)? To what extent does the type of deviance or societal reaction depend on gender, age, socio-economic status, ethnicity, sexual identity, or other social attributes and structural inequalities? Medicine is one kind of social audience; it is concerned with identifying various conditions as deviations from a model of health and well-being that makes assumptions and values about normality.

social control
Mechanisms that aim to induce conformity or at least to manage or minimize deviant behaviour.

Medicalization and Social Control

In every society, medicine, like law and religion, defines what is normal, proper, or desirable. Medicine has the authority to label one man's complaint a legitimate ill-ness, to declare a second man sick though he himself does not complain, and to refuse a third social recognition of his pain, his disability, and even his death. It is medicine which stamps some pain as "merely subjective," some impairment as malin-gering, and some deaths—though not others—as suicide.

—Illich (1976, p. 65)

Increasingly, human experiences are coming under medical scrutiny with numerous aspects of daily life being defined as medical issues, resulting in what Ivan Illich (1976), a critic of the medical establishment, has called "the medicalization of life." Is this med-icalization due to an actual increase in medical problems or to better reporting? Or is it that some aspects of life and behaviour that once were considered normal are now sub-ject to medical diagnosis and treatment? *Medicalization* describes the process whereby non-medical problems or phenomena become defined and treated as medical issues, usually in terms of illnesses, disorders, or syndromes (Conrad, 2007; Conrad et al., 2010). Successful medicalization means that the dominant form of social control is therapeutic and that individuals diagnosed as deviating from a model of health confront a new set of normative expectations stemming from the **sick role**.

sick role
A concept used by Talcott Parsons to describe the social expectations of how sick people should act and of how they are meant to be treated.

While the sick role legitimates some kinds of social behaviours and imposes a new set of social norms (and social control), access to this status is not automatic. The manifesta-tion of certain physiological conditions is not the only or indeed a necessary prerequisite for contact with institutionalized medicine. For example, individuals or social groups deemed "at risk" due to prevailing medical and social norms may be subject to medical surveillance in the name of preventing or reducing the so-called **risk** behaviour. Public health programs may target certain groups,[2] such as Aboriginal peoples, female-headed households, gay men, or young people, for early intervention or education in order to pre-vent drug addiction, child abuse, suicide, or crime.

risk/risk discourse
Refers to "danger"; *risk discourse* is often used in health-promotion messages warning people that certain actions involve significant risks to their health.

The medicalization thesis posits that physical conditions do not, by their nature, con-stitute illness; rather, they require identification and classification, which entail subjective

2. These assumptions are generally based on stereotypes.

and value-laden considerations—that is, they are socially constructed. **Social construc-tionism** counters medicine's claims to be scientific, objective, and disinterested. Like Illich (1976), Eliot Freidson (1988) argues that medicine actively and exclusively constructs ill-ness. Rather than disinterestedly detecting symptoms and physiological causes, medical practice involves interpreting and judging what is normal and abnormal—determining which circumstances are suitable for medical intervention and which are not. The symp-toms do not speak for themselves; they are neither self-evident nor naturally occurring. Indeed, their interpretation and categorization are informed by social values and assump-tions about what constitutes health (normal) and illness (deviant). The key to medicaliza-tion is definition; illness is not *ipso facto* a medical problem but, rather, becomes defined as such. The success of the medical profession in monopolizing definitions of health and illness provides it with considerable authority and scope for social control. For example, Foucault (1978, p. 136) argues that medicalization exemplifies a modern mechanism of power by which to discipline the individual body and optimize its capabilities while also regulating the species body (population) (cited in Bell & Figert, 2012, p. 777). Illich (1976) popularized the term **social iatrogenesis** to talk about the extent to which medicine has gained control over every stage of the life cycle, beginning with prenatal check-ups to mon-itor a fetus's development to the decision to not resuscitate at the end of life. In his view, modern medicine creates illness and disease in its attempt to deal with pain and sickness.

Within this context, **empirical** research identifies the social conditions under which certain illnesses emerge, and it analyzes the effect of medical practitioners' claims on the development of conceptions of illness. Conrad (2007) explains that early studies of medicalization focused on the medicalization of deviance; however, today the concept is applied to broad areas of human life that now are subject to medical interpretation and intervention. Some behaviours, such as alcoholism, mental disorders, substance addic-tion, gambling, that were once deemed immoral, sinful, or criminal have been given med-ical meaning, moving them from badness to sickness. The process of medicalization also has created new categories, such as attention deficit hyperactivity disorder (ADHD), erect-ile dysfunction (ED), premenstrual syndrome (PMS), and post-traumatic stress disorder (PTSD). Other aspects of life have also been medicalized, including anxiety and mood, infertility, menopause, sexuality, aging, and death.

Discussions of medicalization often refer to psychiatry as the primary example or prototype of medical social control. Such discussions tend to emphasize the negative and coercive aspects of social control, in contrast to medical **discourses** that focus on med-ical intervention as positive and necessary for health and well-being. There is criticism of theorists such as Illich, Zola (1972), and Navarro (1976) who view medicalization as wholly negative and coercive—as something that should be averted. Critics also suggest that arguments about medical imperialism—and about medicine's displacement of reli-gion and law as a source of social control—are exaggerated, rhetorical, and not borne out in practice (Strong, 1979). It is pointed out that medicalization can also confer certain benefits, including legitimation of the conditions as real rather than imaginary; access to the sick role; and access to insurance. Szasz (2007), while highly critical of medical-ization and the role of psychiatry, does recognize this and argues that there is a distinc-tion between medicalization from above, by coercion, and medicalization from below, by choice. Likewise Conrad (2007) notes that medicalization describes a process and that it is important to distinguish between a condition that most people would agree is truly

social construction/ constructionism
Refers to the socially created characteristics of human life based on the idea that people actively construct reality. Notions of normality/ abnormality, right/wrong, and health/illness are subjective human creations that should not be taken as natural or universal.

social iatrogenesis
Iatrogenesis is a concept popularized by Ivan Illich that refers to adverse effects caused by, or resulting from, medical treatment. *Social iatrogenesis* refers to the process by which biomedicine extends its domain over every stage of life.

empirical
Describes observations or research that is based on evidence drawn from experience. It is distinguished from something based only on theoretical knowledge or other kinds of abstract thinking process.

discourse
A domain of language use that is characterized by common ways of talking and thinking about an issue (for example, the discourses of medicine, madness, or sexuality).

medical, such as epilepsy, and the medicalization of life's normal processes, such as menopause or aging.

The medicalization thesis today focuses on both dimensions; that is, on how medical categories are increasingly applied to all parts of life, and, how, at the same time, people have internalized medical perspectives and actively seek or demand medical remedies (Conrad, 2007). Catherine Kohler Riessman in her seminal article "Women and Medicalization: A New Perspective" (1983) acknowledges the feminist critique of medicalization and the sexual politics embedded in conceptions of sickness; however, she argues that medicalization involves a symbiotic relationship in which "both physicians and women have contributed to the redefining of women's experience into medical categories" (p. 3). Physicians medicalize experience because of their specific beliefs and economic interests, but at the same time "[w]omen collaborate in the medicalization process because of their own needs and motives, which in turn grow out of the class-specific nature of their subordination" (pp. 3–4).

Types of Medicalization

Historical analyses and case studies identify the ways that various phenomena come to be defined in medical terms and to be viewed as warranting medical intervention. Medicalization is not necessarily fuelled solely by the efforts of the medical profession: developments in biotechnology, consumer health movements, and market forces—especially profit-driven pharmaceutical and insurance companies—can successfully advance the emergence of new medical categories (Conrad, 2007; Ebeling, 2011; Sulik, 2011). Medicalization occurs on several levels:

- *Conceptual level*, at which a medical vocabulary is used to describe or define an issue or problem, but medical professionals and treatments may not be involved. For example, alcohol abuse, interpersonal problems, depression, seasonal affective disorder (SAD), and some criminal activities may be defined as pathological or as evidence of sickness or mental impairment, but their management—although it may be viewed as therapeutic—does not necessarily entail intervention by medical personnel.
- *Institutional level*, at which organizations may adopt a medical approach to particular problems and medical personnel may be gatekeepers for the organization, but the everyday routine work is performed by non-medical personnel. Access to some workers' compensation schemes requires a referral from a medical practitioner, even when human services personnel, such as psychologists, counsellors, or social workers, implement the rehabilitation program.
- *Interactional level*, at which medicalization occurs as part of doctor–patient interaction, with the former medically defining and/or treating the latter's problem. The doctor provides a medical diagnosis and prescribes a medical treatment (Conrad, 1992).

The practices and processes that result in greater medicalization at these different levels are diverse. Individual medical practitioners might claim that a problem or set of issues should be in the domain of medicine; however, successful medicalization usually involves collective action and coalitions between different groups (Brown, 1995; Halpern,

1992). Less tolerance of mild symptoms stemming from such things as menstruation, menopause, or erectile dysfunction has spurred a "progressive medicalization of physical distress in which uncomfortable body states and isolated symptoms are reclassified as diseases" (Barsky & Boros, 1995, cited in Conrad, 2007, p. 6). Patients and support groups may lobby with medical practitioners to have a condition recognized as a medical problem and thus gain access to the benefits that medicalization might entail. However, giving a condition—or set of symptoms or behaviour—a medical label does not necessarily reduce other deviance designations or stigmatization.

Conrad and Potter (2000) show how in the 1990s the largest attention deficit [hyperactivity] disorder (AD[H]D) support group in the US combined its efforts with a giant pharmaceutical firm (the manufacturer of Ritalin, a major treatment for hyperactivity), with medical professionals, as well as with the media to successfully extend the diagnosis of AD[H]D to adults. ADHD among adults is generally the result of self-diagnosis; after reading about the disorder and believing it applies to them, they seek professional confirmation of their new identity. As a result, they interpret all their difficulties through the lens of ADHD. Without this self-labelling, adult ADHD would not have become the foremost self-diagnosed condition to explain everyday events such as poor motivation, job failure, and lack of success (Conrad, 2007). Similarly, post-traumatic stress disorder (PTSD), originally applied to Vietnam War veterans to diagnose anxiety, sleep problems, and flashbacks emanating from their combat experience, has been extended to survivors or witnesses of horrendous accidents and crimes, such as earthquakes, sexual abuse, and murder.

Medicalization can involve defining natural biological processes as something that requires pharmaceutical, surgical, or therapeutic intervention. For example, the inevitable process of aging can be perceived as entailing deviation from social norms regarding youth, vitality, performance, and appearance. As we discuss later, this is evidenced in the emerging discourse around male menopause and male sexual performance. Medicalization also includes the broadening of pre-existing medical categories to include more potential sufferers and situations. The process is dynamic—not "simply doctors colonizing new problems or labeling feckless patients" (Conrad and Potter, 2000, p. 560).

Attempts to medicalize a problem or expand a medical category vary in their level of success. The support and agreement of individual medical practitioners or professional medical associations often bolster claims for biomedical explanations and intervention; although there are medical practitioners who resist claims for medicalization. In a recent article published in the *National Post* (Kirkey, 2014), a Montreal psychiatrist, Dr Joel Paris, cautions against the growing use of antidepressants for ordinary sadness and mild depression. He suggests that the diagnostic criteria for "major depressive disorder" are so flexible and elastic that at least half of the population will meet the criteria at some point in their life, like the common cold.

Medicalization today is being reconstituted through the development of technoscientific biomedicine (Clarke et al., 2005). Such processes are situated within political-economic contexts: "In the biomedicalization era, what is perhaps most radical is the **biomedicalization** of health itself. In commodity cultures, health becomes another commodity, and the biomedically (re)engineered body becomes a prized possession" (p. 447). Within a context of cutbacks to health-care funding, individuals are told that their health is an ongoing individual moral responsibility. Risk and surveillance practices are institutionalized and shape both the technologies and discourses of biomedicalization. Rather

biomedicalization
Describes increasingly complex, multi-sited, and multi-directional processes of medicalization.

than illness, the "normal" is problematized (Clarke et al., 2005, p. 447). According to Clarke et al. (2010), the increasing reliance on technoscientific biomedicine extends and reconstitutes medicalization processes, thus marking biomedicalization as one of the primary social forces transforming the twenty-first century (cited in Sulik, 2011, p. 464).

The History and Role of Psychiatry in Medicalization

The emergence and dominance of a medical approach to madness (later to be redefined as mental illness) began in the late-eighteenth century. Despite the lack of cures or explanatory theories of madness, physicians assumed a small but central role as gatekeepers of the asylums: from 1774, a physician's certificate was required for commitment to a British asylum. As Michel Foucault (1988) observes,

> The physician . . . played no part in the life of confinement. Now he becomes the essential figure of the asylum. He is in charge of entry . . . the doctor's intervention is not made by virtue of a medical skill or power that he possesses in himself and that would be justified by a body of objective knowledge. It is not as a scientist that *homo medicus* has authority in the asylum, but as a wise man. (p. 270)

The decline of the Church, the scientific discoveries of the Enlightenment, and the humanitarianism of the Renaissance all aided physicians' professional dominance in this area and fostered a unitary conception of mental illness as a disease: that is, a single illness category to encompass diverse conditions and symptoms. By the end of the eighteenth century, the notion of mental illness as a topic of medical and scientific interventions was becoming the dominant conception of madness (Conrad & Schneider, 1992). Around the same time, reformers sought to eliminate the physically punitive aspects of life in the insane asylum and to reinforce the benefits of moral treatment. Physicians successfully argued that as both moral and medical responses were appropriate to manage madness, they should have a monopoly on dispensing both. This was especially important since they were unable to show the physiological causes of mental illness and had not demonstrated any cures. The asylum emerged during the nineteenth century as the state's solution to the increasing numbers of people identified as insane. The history of psychiatry and its authority is inextricably intertwined with this development. Even so, there was considerable optimism and hope that new scientific advances in medicine would be able to solve problems associated with mental illness (Conrad & Schneider, 1992). The separation of deviants was an essential precondition for the development of a medical specialty (the forerunner of psychiatry) that claimed to possess specific expertise in dealing with madness. This, in turn, further legitimized the concept of mental illness as a distinct phenomenon (reflecting and caused by an underlying pathology), rather than the amorphous cultural view of insanity that had previously prevailed and that had emphasized demonological and non-human influences (Scull, 1975, 1977). During the nineteenth century, psychiatrists identified ill health, religious anxiety, disappointed love, pecuniary embarrassment, acid inhalation, suppressed menstruation, and general poor health as causes of mental illness. Their interventions included physical restraints, cold baths, tooth extractions, and surgery of the brain and reproductive systems. By the close of the nineteenth century, a whole range of new personal problems paralleled enormous social changes, especially in the US. Everyday problems became defined as nervous diseases, providing a focus for new professional groups.

The first Canadian asylum was built in 1714 in Quebec for female patients (Robb et al., 1934, cited in Sinha, 2009). By the mid-nineteenth century, asylums were established in the Atlantic provinces as well as in Ontario and Quebec, and by the end of the century, asylums were erected in western Canada (Moran, 2009). At the end of 1931 in Canada, a

DEPARTMENT OF HEALTH FOR ONTARIO
MENTAL HEALTH DIVISION

ELECTROSHOCK TREATMENT RECORD

Date	Time	No. Shocks	Resistance	Voltage	Glissando Time	Duration of shock (secs.)	Type of Response	Grand Mals to date	Medication and Clinical Notes
Jan 22/62								1	
Jan 24/62								2	
								3	
Feb 2/62								4	
Feb 12/62								5	
								6	
								7	
Mar 30/62								8	
								9	
								10	
								11	
								12	
								13	
								14	
								15	
Jan /67	1	—	120	1.6	.20	CMH	1	
Jan 23/67	1	—	120	1.6	.15	GM+	2	A70
Jan 25/67	1	—	120	1.6	.15	GM+	3	A70
Jan 27/67	1	—	120	1.6	.15	GM	4	A70
Jan 30/67	1	—	120	1.6	.15	GM	5	A70
Feb 1/67	1	—	130	1.6	.15	GM	6	A70
Feb 3/67	1	—	120	1.6	.15	GM	7	A70
Feb 6/67	1	—	120	1.6	.15	GM	8	A60
Feb 8/67	1	—	120	1.6	.15	GM+	9	A60
Feb 10/67	2	—	120/140	1.6	.15/.25	GM++	10	A70

Form 324-25M-60-1261

The Archives of Ontario RG 10-337

This photo is a record of electroshock treatment from a patient case file from 1967. Electroshock treatment was once used ubiquitously to subdue patients who could not (or who refused to) behave "normally," including as an intervention for homosexual people. Seeing how medical interventions have changed over time can help us to untangle individual needs and abilities from societal expectations.

total of 32,059 individuals were registered in these mental institutions. The most common psychosis reported was dementia praecox and manic-depressive (Agnew, 1933). By 1960, there were 75,000 patients; one-half had been there for more than seven years (Richman & Harris, 1983, p. 65). The growth of asylums consolidated the professional development of psychiatrists; however, psychiatry was not approved as a medical specialty until 1934 (Neff et al., 1987). Although psychiatrists successfully monopolized the treatment of insanity by officially defining it as a medical condition with identifiable causes, moral judgments and lay concerns still influenced diagnosis. Insanity was an elastic concept—a category of residual deviance—that could be applied to a variety of individuals whose deviance stemmed from poverty, homelessness, or physical disability. Unlike confinement in other custodial institutions, commitment to an insane asylum entailed neither a trial, a fixed term of internment, nor the legal protection associated with criminal proceedings (Sutton, 1991).

Case studies of psychiatric hospitals illustrate the power of psychiatric diagnosis, the pervasiveness of psychiatric discourse, and the high status of psychiatrists (Goffman, 1961). A stark example is provided in D.L. Rosenhan's article "Being Sane in Insane Places" (1973). He describes an experiment in which eight sane people gained secret admission to psychiatric institutions. The pseudo-patients claimed that they had been hearing voices, but upon admission to the hospital ward ceased simulating any symptoms of abnormality. The only people who detected that they were not suffering from a psychiatric condition were the other patients, not the medical staff. Indeed, the label "schizophrenic"—that is, the diagnosis—determined psychiatrists' and nurses' perceptions and interpretations of the pseudo-patients' behaviour, even when it was completely "normal" (p. 253).

Close links exist between mental hospitalization and social control. Erving Goffman's classic study of a state mental hospital shows that very few of the everyday activities of the institution are devoted to therapy or treatment; most activities are oriented to maintaining the organization, performing routine tasks, and achieving social control among the patients. The psychiatrist's presence is brief and the input non-specific (Goffman, 1961). Mental institutions also play a role in wider social policy and in the regulation of sub-populations that are identified as problematic.

deinstitutionalization
A policy of moving patients in mental institutions out into community-based living arrangements and health centres. In theory, such policies are meant to be supported by extensive community resources to "break down barriers" and better integrate the mentally ill into the community.

The process of psychiatric **deinstitutionalization** began in Canada in the 1950s with a shift in care from mental institutions to community-based living and care-giving arrangements and community health centres (Morrow et al., 2008). It was driven by a number of interdependent factors including the availability of psychotropic (mood-altering) drugs, the rise of psychoanalysis and other therapies, widespread criticism of the coercive nature and the failure of mental institutions to cure or adequately treat mental illness, concerns about legal rights of those with mental illness, and cost containment (Morrow et al., 2008). Although, some have suggested that the driving force was the government's desire to save money by eliminating the fixed cost of mental institutions (Niles, 2013, p. 69). Between 1960 and 1980, all the provinces instituted some elements of deinstitutionalization; however, there was tremendous variation in timing and the rates of bed closures (Sealy & Whitehead, 2004, p. 250). Developing an alternative mental health delivery system, however, did not proceed smoothly or rapidly. According to the Public Health Agency of Canada (2006a), the community services available may at times be inappropriate, provide inadequate coverage, or lack sufficient resources to provide the needed psychiatric services. Without the necessary community resources, individuals may "fall through the cracks"; they may find themselves destitute, on the streets, or in prison (p. 154). According to Morrow et al., "[i]n some instances, deinstitutionalization has meant the shift of beds from large psychiatric institutions to the back wards of hospitals and/or the application of institutional treatment models characterized by paternalism and coercion in community settings . . . [or] the criminalization of people with mental health problems, such that . . . [they] are institutionalized in corrections facilities rather than treated in hospitals or other health care facilities" (2008, p. 2). While some would argue that mental health services and supports are somewhat better now (Ballon, 2011), others caution that reduced social expenditures and cost-cutting by all levels of government will further erode the needed services, such as housing, income support, and employment opportunities, for those with mental illness. The growing visibility of poverty, homelessness, and addictions in major Canadian cities may lead some community leaders, as in the case of Vancouver, to call for re-institutionalization (Morrow et al., 2008).

The Growth of Psychiatry

As an emergent occupation and as a segment of the medical profession, psychiatry has developed notions of normal behaviour, or normativity, in areas such as sexual behaviour and identity, mental health, alcohol and drug use, eating, reproduction, and child development. Medicalization today encompasses more than just psychiatry, but in the words of Thomas Szasz, "[p]sychiatry is medicalization, through and through" (2007, p. xx). Psychiatry seeks to locate a pathological basis within the individual for such "deviance" and views certain types of behaviour as evidence of addiction, syndromes, conditions, personality disorders, or other mental illnesses. It attempts to attribute causes to—or, perhaps more accurately, to identify sites of intervention on the basis of—individual rather than social factors. Psychiatry has been instrumental in giving some behaviours, such as alcoholism, mental disorders, substance addiction, and gambling, that were once deemed immoral, sinful, or criminal, medical meaning, moving them from badness to sickness. At the same time, it also has created new categories, such as attention deficit hyperactivity disorder (ADHD), erectile dysfunction (ED), premenstrual syndrome (PMS), and post-traumatic stress disorder (PTSD).

Other significant developments in the history of psychiatry include the rise of psychoanalysis and the introduction of psychotropic drugs. Psychoanalysis enabled psychiatrists to help people who were anxious and depressed and who experienced problems with everyday life, as well as to treat those labelled insane. Sigmund Freud, a physician and a neurologist, provided a new approach to understanding personal problems. He replaced a biological model with a psychogenic explanation and intervention that was based on free discussion (by the patient) in the context of a relationship with the therapist (Conrad & Schneider, 1992). The rise and influence of a therapeutic culture that ensued has been met by critics lamenting the dominance of psychiatry that has resulted in a privatization of social control and the extension of the cult of the individual (Wright, 2011).

Another important development extending the influence of psychiatry was the availability of new psychotropic (mood-altering) drugs in the 1950s, used both in mental institutions and to enable more people to be discharged and treated outside the hospital, further extended the influence of psychiatry. However, the use of prescription drugs raised questions of compliance and self-medication. While drug treatment reinforced the medical model of mental illness, the curative effect is contested, and critics argue that the drugs merely sedate, and thereby regulate, the behaviour of people identified as mentally ill. In the 1960s, criticisms of psychiatry, the unitary conception of mental illness, the social control functions of mental hospitals, and the so-called therapeutic relationship became more evident. Proponents of the labelling perspective doubted that diverse symptoms, behaviours, and conditions constituted a single classification of mental illness. Thomas Scheff, for example, argues that mental illness became almost a label of convenience for a range of norm-breaking behaviour that could not be accommodated within other types of deviance. He termed this behaviour "residual deviance" to include crime, alcoholism, and illness (Scheff, 1966, pp. 31–54). Commentators identified enforced drug therapy—which violated patients' rights by denying them informed consent and due process—as an unacceptable outcome of the influence of psychiatry in the mental health and criminal justice systems (Kittrie, 1971). Thomas Szasz (1961, 1973), one of the strongest proponents of the anti-psychiatry movement, maintains that medicine's replacement of the Church as the institution of social control merely redefines and re-labels deviance with medical terminology. He argues that the term *mental illness* is widely used to describe something that is very different from a disease of the brain, and suggests that problems in living derive from the stresses and strains inherent in social interactions among complex human personalities in modern societies (1960, p. 113).

A contemporary example of a controversial psychiatric classification, and associated diagnosis and treatment, is that of "personality disorder." The past 20 years has seen a rapid elaboration of this category in the **Diagnostic and Statistical Manual of Mental Disorders** (DSM). In the latest version, DSM-5, personality disorder is defined as "an enduring pattern of inner experience and behaviour that deviates markedly from the expectations of the individual's culture, is pervasive and inflexible, has an onset in adolescence or early adulthood, is stable over time and leads to distress or impairment" (American Psychiatric Association, 2013, p. 645). It identifies 12 kinds of personality disorders. Nonetheless, personality disorders do not include obvious organic or psychological impairment but are identified through their interpersonal effects, including chaotic and distressing relationships, instability of identity, or incurred criminal records (Manning, 2000; Pickersgill, 2012). The DSM distinguishes personality disorders according to such descriptive terms as "odd and eccentric" and "anxious and fearful" (Nuckolls, 1997, p. 52), thus attesting to the classification's broad scope. The DSM-5 has 15 new diagnoses, including hoarding, excoriation (skin picking), caffeine withdrawal, cannabis withdrawal, and binge eating disorder. However, it has met with considerable critique and controversy, including its role in the medicalization of normality, from psychiatric and psychological practitioners (Pickersgill, 2014). According to psychiatrist Allen Frances, the DSM-5 would "expand the territory of mental disorder and thin the ranks of the normal" (cited in Pickersgill, p. 522). In an article in *Psychology Today* (December 2, 2012), Frances suggested that DSM-5 would start "a half a dozen or more new fads which will be detrimental to the misdiagnosed individuals."

Diagnostic and Statistical Manual of Mental Disorders (DSM)
A manual published by the American Psychiatric Association that lists all mental health disorders for both children and adults. It also indicates causes, types of treatment, and prognosis.

Another ambiguous psychiatric or psychological classification is depression, or more specifically, "depressive disorders." Some suggest that the recent and continued popularity of **Prozac**—the antidepressant drug—can be explained to some extent by the increasing tendency of individuals to redefine life's problems, stresses, anxieties, and disappointments as evidence of depression. Prozac is not only prescribed to people suffering serious disturbances; its application is more ordinary: "a formulation that could improve the lives of people with minor disturbances and distresses" (Conrad & Potter, 2000, p. 571). A

Prozac
A new type of medication (selective serotonin reuptake inhibitor [SSRI]) introduced in 1987 to treat depression.

recent report by the OECD (2013) shows that Canadians had the third highest consumption of antidepressants among OECD nations. See Figure 9.1.

It is estimated that 42.6 million prescriptions for antidepressants were filled in 2012, part of the nearly $1.8 billion antidepressant drug market in Canada (Kirkey, 2014). Psychiatrist David Healy, in his controversial book *Let Them Eat Prozac* (2003), shows the role of the drug industry in promoting mood-altering drugs such as Prozac while minimizing the potential serious side-effects, such as increased risk for suicide. More recently shyness has emerged as a new "crippling affliction" that doctors argue can be appropriately treated with various psychotropic medications (Scott, 2006). Similarly, grief has been medicalized, subsuming it under depression. The result is that unprecedented numbers of people, with what was formerly viewed as the ordinary distress of living are taking psychotropic medications (Kleinman, 2012, p. 609).

The history of psychiatry, its interrelationships with allied occupations and other segments of the medical profession and the influence of wider social changes all illustrate unevenness in the process of medicalization along with great shifts in psychiatric

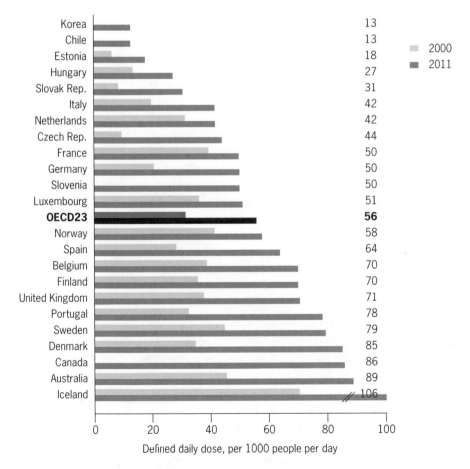

Figure 9.1 Antidepressant Consumption by Country

Source: OECD. (2013). 4.10.4: Antidepressants consumption, 2000 and 2011 (or nearest year). In *Health at a glance 2013: OECD indicators: Pharmaceutical consumption.* OECD Publishing, p. 103. Available at: www.oecd-ilibrary.org/docserver/download/8113161ec041.pdf.

knowledge and treatments. As a profession, psychiatry has never been completely successful. Its claims to provide precise and exact explanations are questioned, and its ability to demonstrate etiology is difficult, making psychiatry particularly vulnerable to the criticism that its knowledge base is socially constructed and historical. Arguably, then, psychiatry's jurisdiction over certain conditions and patients stems from its own self-interested quest to achieve and maintain professional status.

Other Interests in Medicalization

Social movements, consumers, occupational groups, and pharmaceutical corporations have also played a significant role in the medicalization process. For example, Alcoholics Anonymous (AA) is a hybrid organization that combines elements of the disease model of alcoholism with a spiritual program emphasizing individual change and recovery and the achievement of inner peace (Valverde & White-Mair, 1999). Another example, the National Alliance for the Mentally Ill (NAMI), one of the most influential mental health organizations in the US (with affiliates now in Canada), grew from concerns that the families of the mentally ill had insufficient input in the management of their afflicted relatives. This organization believes that mental patients are not capable of holding and exercising rights, and criticizes the legal extension of rights to individuals involuntarily committed to mental institutions. It maintains that psychotherapeutic approaches—which may view family dynamics rather than a chemical imbalance as responsible for disease—stigmatize caregivers, and that the patient's legal right to refuse medication establishes an inappropriate adversarial relationship between patients and their families (Milner, 1989).

Other research shows that teachers and family members have been particularly influential in the construction of hyperactivity in children as evidence of a psychiatric disorder, namely attention deficit [hyperactivity] disorder (AD[H]D) (Lloyd & Norris, 1999, pp. 505–8). In Britain, as elsewhere, active parents' organizations articulated their rights and the right of their children to be classified as having a medically defined disorder requiring prescribed medication, thus rejecting a more social model of the deviantization of certain childhood behaviours. In a Canadian study, Malacrida (2004) found that teachers were primarily responsible for labelling a child as having ADD/ADHD. Mothers she interviewed said that although they saw their child as different in early childhood, "it was really only once the child went to school that these differences came to be identified as problematic enough that the child was identified for formal intervention" (p. 67). Mothers also stated that their decisions to medicate their children were the result of indirect school pressure, such as constant phone calls and questions as to whether the child was still on medication. On the other hand, British educators had a "strong antipathy" toward medicalizing childhood behaviour problems (p. 70). This difference in attitude, according to Malacrida, might be explained by fewer alternatives available in Canadian schools for maintaining classroom discipline. It also may reflect the different degrees of medicalization of ADD/ADHD in each culture.

The pharmaceutical industry has played a major role in the expansion of medicalization through its ability to market "diseases" and then sell drugs to treat them. This idea is captured in the concept of **pharmaceuticalization**, namely the "transformation of human conditions, capabilities and capacities into opportunities for pharmaceutical

pharmaceuticalization
A complex socio-technical process whereby health "problems" are constructed as having pharmaceutical solutions which includes the successful mobilization of consumers wanting access to drugs.

intervention" (Williams et al., 2011, p. 711). It is a process whereby social, behavioural or bodily conditions are deemed to be in need of treatment by medical drugs (Abraham, 2010, p. 604). For example, the popularity of Prozac (fluoxetine), marketed as a drug to help people feel better, created a social context in which it became acceptable to use medications to deal with a variety of life's problems. The influence of Prozac has so shaped our language, culture, and assumptions about health and sickness that we speak of living in the "Age of Prozac" (Currie, 2005. p. 1). Ebeling (2011) describes how symptom checklists—developed collaboratively by drug marketers and medical practitioners and available on the Internet—transform the patient into a consumer to achieve the aims of a drug company. She writes, "[s]ymptom checklists are tools of consumer recruitment for marketing, where consumers perform self-diagnosis that is harmonized with the symptoms that the sponsored drug is approved to treat, and through this self-diagnosis, are empowered to demand a diagnosis that will call for a treatment option that points to a branded drug from their doctors" (p. 831).

Women and Medicalization

Women's life experiences are more likely to be medicalized than men's (Bell, 1987; Berenson, et al., 2009; Davis, 1996; Lorber, 2000; Riessman, 1983). Women may be more vulnerable to medicalization because their bodies and physiological processes deviate from the so-called ideal male norm (Riessman, 1983). Furthermore, women's bodies come under increased medical scrutiny because of the beauty ideal in Western society. While much of this could be considered the result of patriarchy, medicalization is effective only if, at least to some degree, there is acquiescence on the part of those involved. For example, Riessman (1983) explains the complex set of reasons for why women were supportive of the medicalization of pregnancy and childbirth at the beginning of the twentieth century, including their desire to be free from pain and their belief that surgical techniques of doctors were superior should there be complications.

The menstrual cycle is another aspect of the reproductive body that has been increasingly medicalized. Some women have been active participants in the construction of premenstrual syndrome (PMS) as a disorder and successfully sought its inclusion in the DSM. Berenson et al. (2009) note that the discovery of this new period of disease evolved from accounts of individual women, who reported menstrual-related difficulties to their doctors. From this small sample, PMS was expanded to include *all* menstruating women as sufferers. It is significant that the original term was *premenstrual tension*; the use of the term *syndrome* indicates increased medicalization. The DSM-5 is the first edition of the DSM to include premenstrual dysphoric disorder (PDD) in the body of the text (American Psychiatric Association 2013, pp. 171–2). Paula Caplan suggests this inclusion is an indication that emotional displays such as anger and irritability that are considered normal in men are seen as a mental disorder in women (cited in Daw, 2002).

Both medical and popular literatures emphasize the negative, debilitating symptoms of PMS. An analysis of popular magazines and self-help books shows that PMS is portrayed in a generally negative tone, which effectively defines how a normal woman should feel or behave in contrast to an "abnormal" woman, who experiences PMS. Women themselves use the PMS label to dismiss or explain what is described as their "deviant" behaviour: "Don't mind me, I'm PMSing" (Berenson et al., 2009, p. 243). Popular discourse identifies the causes as physiological and focuses on women's hormones as the source of the problems. Intervention and alleviation of the symptoms—ranging from dizziness, backache, and lack of concentration to decreased school or work performance, mood swings, and irritability—include drug therapy and management of individual lifestyles through diet, exercise, and rest, rather than considering the relevance of social, structural, or cultural factors (Markens, 1996; Martin, 1987). In the twenty-first century, the medicalizing process of PMS is taking a new twist. New technological advances in the form of different types of birth control pills allow females to hormonally curtail or eliminate menstruation altogether (Berenson et al., 2009).

The medicalization of PMS presents a dilemma for women: on the one hand, it legitimizes the experiences of premenstrual symptoms as real and worthy of medical and public attention, but on the other, it reasserts the pathology of women's bodies, especially their reproductive systems, and views women's actions and thoughts as being determined by biology (in this case, by their hormones). Opponents worry that medicalization could lead to stigmatization and result in sex discrimination. This is an example of a situation in which some medicalization, but not necessarily psychiatrization, may be helpful in order to have complaints taken seriously by medical practitioners, and for strategies to be adopted for alleviating or managing symptoms. For example, research on chronic fatigue syndrome and fibromyalgia finds that diagnosis—that is, medicalizing a condition during consultation—can enable patients to explain their symptoms and to feel more in control of their situations; they are not dismissed as having imagined their symptoms or as malingerers. On the other hand, medicalization that reflects preconceived notions about gender-specific behaviour—for example, that women are naturally emotional, hysterical, or prone to depression or hypochondria—is unhelpful (Broom & Woodward, 1996).

Some surveys indicate that depression and some anxiety disorders are more frequent among women, while antisocial personalities and alcohol and drug abuse or dependence are more common among men (Aneshensel et al., 1991). Regardless of marital status, women tend to report more depression than men (Simon, 2002). Research also shows that twice as many psychotropic drugs (drugs that affect the mind) and SSRI antidepressants (of which Prozac is one) are prescribed for women as for men (Currie, 2005). The differences between men's and women's responses to life events stem from different gendered expectations about appropriate emotions; sadness is more appropriate for women and anger for men. Sadness is related to affective and anxiety disorders, including depression (Simon, 2005). Also it is more culturally acceptable for women to express their psychological problems and symptoms, whereas dominant forms of masculinity make it more difficult for men to admit and talk about their feelings. Furthermore, women may actually experience more stress and sadness related to their historical roles in the context of their families and workplaces, including demands of caregiving, violence, poverty, and lack of social supports (Currie, op.cit.). However, pharmaceutical companies aggressively promote the bio-chemical theory of depression despite questionable scientific evidence as to the effectiveness of SSRIs (Currie, op.cit.; Healy, 2003), of whom the largest consumers are women.

The medicalization of women's lives today has historical parallels. In the nineteenth century, dominant medical theories linked a woman's uterus and ovaries to irrationality, emotional disorder, and mental disease. Indeed, the term *hysteria* derives from the Greek word for *uterus* and refers to what was regarded as a quintessential female condition, indicated by weeping, fainting, screaming, tantrums, and moodiness (Turner, 1987, p. 89) . . .

The diagnosis of hysteria became a general label for abnormal or non-conforming behaviour on the part of women, and medical intervention became a form of social control. Currently, the diagnosis of hysteria is very rare (it is not included in the DSM). The decline of hysteria as a diagnostic category today indicates changes in gender norms and the activism of women in resisting medicalization, as well as changes in medical knowledge (Seale & Pattison, 1994). Nevertheless, the stereotype of the hysterical woman remains, and behaviour that in the past may have resulted in a diagnosis of hysteria may today be diagnosed as depression, a personality disorder, or PMS.

Men and Medicalization

In much the same way that medicalization of women's bodies is related to conceptions of femininity, the medicalization of men's bodies is connected to notions of masculinity. As Conrad (2007) explains, the medicalization of male aging, baldness, and sexual performance is rooted in a masculine identity that embodies physical strength and energy, hirsutism, and sexual vitality. Although such medicalization is driven by medical and pharmaceutical enterprises, it is also embraced by "men's own concerns with their masculine identities, capacities, embodiments, and presentations" (p. 23). In Western cultures, normative masculinity is strongly connected to sexual performance, in particular, heterosexual erectile achievement (Connell, 1995, cited in Vares & Braun, 2006). The contemporary construction of male menopause as a medical disorder is closely tied to this equation of masculinity and sexual potency (Marshall, 2007; Wienke, 2005).

Growing old was once viewed as normal, inevitable, and unalterable; however, by the late 1990s, male aging and sexuality were medicalized. Male menopause, now referred to as **andropause** or ADAM (androgen deficiency in the aging male) was reconceptualized as an age-related physiological disorder treatable with testosterone therapy with all aging men considered to be at risk (Marshall, 2007, p. 510). Although andropause is not an easily identifiable condition, testosterone was "marketed as a miraculous substance to help healthy men restore or enhance their masculinity" (Conrad, 2007, p. 33). In other words, what were once considered "normal" changes in sexual performance as men aged became pathologized as sexual dysfunctions (Marshall, 2006).

> **andropause**
> Defined as an age-related decline in testosterone levels. It is often considered the male equivalent of menopause.

In 1998, Viagra was introduced as a "cure" for erectile dysfunction, considered a key symptom of andropause, with a promise to restore "natural," "normal" sexuality. Initially intended for older men or for erectile dysfunction associated with medical problems such as prostate cancer, Viagra was soon marketed so as to include virtually all men who might have any insecurity around sexual performance. The interest in Viagra, the fastest selling drug in history, capitalized on previous media attention to what was portrayed as a "crisis in masculinity," in which men were considered powerless and emasculated (Vares & Braun, 2006, p. 316). Viagra advertisements put "the spotlight on the performing penis as integral to masculinity. Viagra thus becomes a pill not only for repair, but also to enhance or improve, both erectile functioning and masculinity" (p. 325).

Two new popular drugs to treat erectile dysfunction, Cialis and Levitra, were approved in 2003. Although these drugs function in much the same way as Viagra, their promotional strategies in effect expand the notion of erectile dysfunction to include any erectile difficulties at any age, whether occasional problems or problems with erection quality. According to Wienke (2005), Cialis and Levitra are marketed as "lifestyle drugs" which enhance "natural" sex and suggest that sexual functioning involves more than the ability to attain and maintain an erection; rather it is the "erectile quality" that is important. For example, sport-theme ads are used to market the drugs to a youthful and healthy male demographic, not only to men with erectile dysfunction, but to large segments of the male populace who "just need a little help" (p. 47). The intended users are all whose erections could be "improved." By promising "to take male sexuality to a new level of performance and sexuality. . . these drugs introduce new standards for functional sexuality and create new medically treatable deviations" (Wienke, 2005, p. 51). Although the medicalization of male sexual performance has constructed the male body in potentially harmful ways, it could be argued that advertisements for Viagra, Cialis, and Levitra have "also helped de-stigmatize erectile dysfunction, making it a topic men and women could more freely discuss without embarrassment or shame" (Conrad, 2007, p. 44).

Masculinity today is also intertwined with appearance; in particular men are concerned about their hair (Ricciardelli, 2011). Research on the psychological effects of hair loss has shown that men who experience hair thinning felt less attractive, had lower self-esteem, and were frustrated and stressed about their hair loss (Cash, 2001, cited in Ricciardell, p. 185). In her study of 14 Canadian men, Ricciardelli (2011) found that appearance norms associated with ideal masculinity always included "well-styled hair or at a minimum a full head of hair" (p. 189). All her respondents were concerned with the potential for hair loss and balding and eagerly shared strategies for dealing with such loss, including best styles to disguise the hair loss. Some of the men discussed surgical interventions if necessary to counteract baldness. Respondents appeared to view hair as "a project that could be worked on and 'improved'," perhaps as one way of meeting idealized standards of masculinity (p. 196). Numerous marketing strategies target the male consumer to "improve" their appearance and invest in themselves. Treatments for hair loss or baldness are not new, but the medicalization of baldness is gaining momentum due to new medical treatments being developed for hair loss (Conrad, 2007). Now that balding is viewed as a "treatable disease," in order to remain attractive, men are encouraged to seek treatments in much the same way that women resort to liposuction or to Botox injections for wrinkles.

Medicalization of the body reinforces stereotypes of masculinity and femininity, and turns the body into a commodity in constant need of technological help.

Towards Demedicalization?

Conrad (2007) has argued that medicalization is uneven and bidirectional. Just as segments of the medical profession gain exclusive or partial jurisdiction over managing certain behaviour or individuals whom they define as pathological and sick, they also lose jurisdiction. The term **demedicalization**, the reverse of medicalization, denotes that an issue is no longer defined in medical terms and that medical intervention is no longer thought to be appropriate. Masturbation, for example, is a behaviour that has now been demedicalized whereas in the nineteenth century it was considered a disease in need of medical treatment. While not completely demedicalized, childbirth has been transformed. For example, midwifery, once illegal in Canada, today is a regulated profession in most provinces and territories. The availability of birth centres such as those in Quebec, staffed by midwives who follow a woman through her pregnancy, provide low-tech and more natural alternatives for childbirth. On the other hand, the growth of medical technology

demedicalization
The reverse of medicalization—that is, when a behaviour once defined in medical terms is no longer defined as such.

has made fetal monitoring and ultrasounds routine even in low-risk cases. The direction over childbirth remains a contested area between medical specialists and advocates of natural childbirth.

Another example is homosexuality, which arguably has been demedicalized. Demedicalization does not necessarily indicate that the behaviour in question ceases to be subject to normative evaluation and social control. In 1973, as a result of social activism, in particular the gay liberation movement, and the work of individual psychiatrists, the American Psychiatric Association agreed that homosexuality was not an illness and voted to exclude it from the DSM (Conrad & Schneider, 1992). This change did not mean that homosexual people were no longer subject to discrimination or were no longer viewed as "deviant." Despite changing official definitions, the growing support and recognition of Gay Pride, and the fact that same-sex marriage is legal in places like Canada and the United States, there remain people who view homosexuality as immoral and something that should be condemned. The readiness with which many people have associated gay men and AIDS in Western societies attests to their lack of integration and acceptance. Because of the increasing prevalence of the human immunodeficiency virus (HIV), gay men (as well as intravenous drug users, sex-trade workers, and others) are subject to increasing medical scrutiny, albeit in a different form. Sadly, some still view the contraction of AIDS as just deserts for engaging in risk behaviour or for deviating from moral precepts.

Conclusion

Medicalization has transformed the normal into the pathological, and medical ideologies, interventions, and therapies shape our notions of acceptable behaviour and states of being (Conrad, 2007). Although medicalization was once associated mainly with psychiatry, today other branches of medicine and social forces, such as the pharmaceutical industry, consumer rights groups, patients, and health insurance companies are equally important in promoting medicalization of all aspects of life. Normal processes such as aging are framed as medical problems or pathologies. Excessive consumerism is labelled "compulsive buying" that "needs" to be treated similar to other disorders, such as obsessive-compulsive behaviour, substance abuse, and depression (Lee & Mysyk, 2004). Shyness is constructed as a social problem that can and should be treated by medications, cognitive-behavioural therapies, and/or self-help materials (Scott, 2006). Emotions such as grief can now be a type of disease (i.e., depression) (Kleinman, 2012). Hoarding (the desire to accumulate and save things) is thought to be a form of obsessive-compulsive disorder.

The medicalization discourse focuses on the individual as the source of the problem; it diverts attention from social, economic, and ideological factors, or social determinants of health that may either contribute to or cause certain behaviours or illness. Depression, for example, is treated predominantly with psychotropic medications while social environments that feed depression are not altered (Conrad, 2007). Notions of what constitutes "normality" or "deviance" are neither objective nor obvious, but rather are social constructions that emerge in particular social and political contexts and reflect the views of powerful groups in society, be they religious or scientific. It is a means by which dominant groups can exercise control over others in society. As Caplan states, "The act of naming is an act of power. To assign a name is to act as though we are referring to something that exists, something real" (cited in Lee & Mysyk, 2004, p. 1716).

The scope and direction of medicalization is intensifying in new ways as a result of the technoscientific revolution. Biomedicine now has the potential to transform biological processes of human life forms, often transforming life itself: "The scope of biomedicalization processes is thus much broader, including conceptual and clinical expansions through the **commodification of health**; elaboration of risk and surveillance; and innovative clinical applications of drugs, procedures, and other treatments" (Clarke et al., 2005, p. 444). New technologies will pervade even more aspects of everyday life. Clarke et al. go on to suggest that in the biomedicalization era, risk and surveillance practices will be the ways by which health is achieved and maintained. Since all individuals are always at risk of becoming ill, the focus in the biomedicalization era "is no longer on illness, disability, and disease as matters of fate, but on health as a matter of ongoing moral self-transformation . . . health itself becomes something to work *toward*," not something that we take as a given (Clarke et al., 2005, p. 447). In the future, it is conceivable that our bodies and lives will be constructed and altered through technoscientific tools to create new social identities.

There are social consequences to medicalization (Conrad, 2007). One benefit is that medicalization extends the "sick role" to a wider range of ailments and behaviours and thus reduces individual blame for the problem. Medications have significantly improved the lives of many individuals suffering from various conditions such as depression, bipolar disorder, ADHD, and fibromyalgia. Medical labels can be instruments of empowerment and social recognition that assist individuals and disease-based social groups to legitimate their grievance and even blur the line between experts and laypersons (Chaufan et al., 2012). On the negative side, medical labels become "instruments of professional expansion, social control and corporate dominance, serving to pathologize normal functioning, unduly reinforce gender norms, or persuade the public that technical, rather than structural solutions is what is needed to address major health concerns whose roots are social and political in origin" (Chaufan et al., 2012, p. 789). Another danger is that transforming all difference into pathology diminishes our tolerance for and appreciation of the diversity of human life" (Conrad, 2007, p. 148). *Normal*, *expected*, and *acceptable* are increasingly being defined by biomedicine and pharmaceutical companies.

commodification of health
Treating health as an object or commodity that can be purchased or marketed.

Summary

- "Normal" and "deviant" are not objective concepts but are socially constructed and reflect the social and the political contexts in which they emerge.
- Medicalization is the process whereby non-medical problems or phenomena become defined and treated as illnesses, disorders, syndromes, or problems of adjustment. Medicalization can occur on at least three levels: the conceptual, the institutional, and the interactional.
- The medicalization thesis looks at how medical categories are applied to all parts of life and how people actively internalize these perspectives and seek medical remedies.
- Psychiatry has always been involved in the identification and regulation of deviance, and is the primary example of medical social control. With

deinstitutionalization and the emergence of other mental health providers, psychiatry has lost some of its power.

- Consumer groups, social movements, parents, occupational groups, the media, and health insurance companies are today important engines of medicalization.
- Both men's and women's lives have been subject to medicalization.
- Behaviours once medicalized can become demedicalized.
- Medicalization focuses on "treating" the individual and diverts attention away from the social environment and structural factors that influence human behaviour.
- Medicalization today is being transformed through developments in technoscientific medicine and pharmaceuticalization.
- There are both positive and negative dimensions to medicalization.

Key Terms

andropause	Diagnostic and Statistical	Prozac
biomedicalization	Manual of Mental	risk/risk discourse
commodification	Disorders (DSM)	sick role
of health	discourse	social constructionism
deinstitutionalization	empirical	social control
demedicalization	medicalization	social iatrogenesis
deviance	pharmaceuticalization	

Sociological Reflection: Role of Media and Peer Groups in Medicalization

Increasing aspects of life are being medicalized. Behaviour such as shyness and grieving and processes such as aging are coming under medical scrutiny. For medicalization to be successful, however, people have to buy into the problem as being real. What role do the media and peer groups play in this process? List some examples from your experience that illustrate this.

Discussion Questions

1. Discuss how notions of "normal" and "illness" have changed over time. What are the reasons for these changes?
2. What are some social consequences of medicalization? Are there times when medicalization is more harmful than helpful? When might that be the case?
3. What are some consequences for the individual and society when behaviours such as shyness, excessive shopping, bereavement, or seasonal affective disorder become medicalized?
4. Has deinstitutionalization brought about the demedicalization of various problems? Explain.
5. How might biomedical and technological discoveries alter how we view the normal body and health?

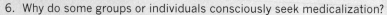

6. Why do some groups or individuals consciously seek medicalization?
7. In what ways could looking at social determinants of health be useful in understanding an illness or behaviour that has been constructed as deviant?

Further Investigation

1. The decline of the welfare state and acceptance of a neo-liberal ideology runs parallel with an increasing emphasis on individuals to take responsibility for their own health and well-being. What role, if any, does the growing medicalization of society have in promoting this point of view? Explain.
2. Critically analyze the proposition that psychiatry remains one of the most powerful institutions of social control in contemporary societies.
3. Critically assess, with examples, how men's and women's bodies have been subject to medicalization. What role do dominant conceptions of femininity and masculinity play in this process?

Further Reading

Conrad, P. (2007). *The medicalization of society*. Baltimore, MD: The Johns Hopkins Press.

Conrad, P., & Schneider, J. (1992). *Deviance and medicalization: From badness to sickness* (2nd ed.). Philadelphia, PA: Temple University Press.

Goffman, E. (1961). *Asylums: Essays on the social situation of mental patients and other inmates*. Garden City, NY: Anchor Press.

Moynihan, R., & Cassels, A. (2005). *Selling sickness: How the world's biggest pharmaceutical companies are turning us all into patients*. Toronto: Greystone Press.

Sulik, G. (2011). "Our diagnoses, our selves": The rise of the technoscientific illness Identity. *Sociology Compass*, 5(6), 463–77.

Szasz, T. (2007). *The medicalization of everyday life*. Syracuse, NY: Syracuse University Press.

Zola, I.K. (1972). Medicine as an institution of social control. *Sociological Review, 20*, 407–584.

Web Resources

Alcoholics Anonymous
www.aacanada.com

Canadian Mental Health Association
www.cmha.ca

Canadian Psychiatric Association
http://publications.cpa-apc.org/browse/sections/1

Centre for ADD/ADHD Advocacy, Canada
www.caddac.ca/

Canadian Institute for Health Research, Institute for Neurosciences, Mental Health & Addictions
www.cihr-irsc.gc.ca/e/8602.html

Health Canada, Healthy Living (Mental Health)
www.hc-sc.gc.ca/hl-vs/mental/index_e .html

Mood Disorders Society of Canada
www.mooddisorderscanada.ca/

Public Health Agency of Canada: Report on Mental Illnesses
www.phac-aspc.gc.ca/publicat/miic-mmac/

Schizophrenia Society of Canada
www.schizophrenia.ca

CHAPTER 10
Constructing Disability and Living with Illness

Jennie Hornosty

Think about the buildings in which you live and go to school, the ways you commute to class, and the places you go after class to hang out: How many of these buildings and services are designed for wheelchair use? How many bank machines or restaurant menus have braille characters? How does the way we design social spaces contribute to what it means to be disabled?

Overview

- What is "normalcy"?
- What are the main approaches to understanding disability?
- How do illness and disease differ?
- What is chronic illness, and what is the experience of those who live with chronic illness?
- What is the prevalence of "disability" in Canada?

This chapter discusses the human body as a socio-cultural phenomenon rather than simply a biological one. It examines dominant approaches for understanding disability and the implications of these for social policy. As well, the chapter looks at how disability and chronic illness are socially constructed and can act as barriers to inclusion. It considers the meanings that disability and chronic illness can have for different individuals.

Introduction: The Body as Social Construct

If asked about the human body most people would describe it in biological terms. This assumption that the body is simply a biological and natural phenomenon is the dominant discourse in medicine and the allied health sciences. Such a perspective does not consider that there is anything social or cultural about the human body, except perhaps such superficial aspects as clothing, hairstyle, and body shape. This biological perspective also fails to recognize that people may experience their bodies differently. Certain aspects of the human body are, of course, given and immutable—for example, all humans are born and must die and all humans experience pain and illness. But as sociologists and anthropologists have pointed out, the ways that people understand and experience their bodies are mediated through social, cultural, and political processes. As we have seen in Chapters 6 and 7, different groups have different beliefs, understandings, and experiences of health and illness. There are also social and cultural differences as to what constitutes a healthy body or an ideal body. A sociological approach to the body is the notion that we both are and have a body. In other words, people's bodies are central to their self-identity; it is the thing or container in which we present ourselves to others, and through which we experience the world.

Constructing Disability

It is often assumed that a disability such as deafness, cerebral palsy, mental retardation or blindness poses an insurmountable barrier to the enjoyment of a normal life, one replete with challenges, joys, success and failure. Life with a disability is perceived as tragic.

—Lepofsky (1985, p. 312, cited in McCoy, 2001, p. 22)

> When we think of bodies, in a society where the concept of the norm is operative, then people with disabilities will be thought of as deviants.
>
> —Davis (2010, p. 7)

What is *disability* and what does it mean to be defined as "disabled"? For Michael Oliver, scholar and disability rights activist, disability is a form of social oppression that arises from definitions and practices that seek to exclude individuals seen to deviate from the socially constructed norms of the "able bodied." From this viewpoint, disability is a product of exclusionary practices. He suggests that such exclusionary practices in a capitalist society designate certain attributes as productive and acceptable, namely those able to meet the needs of economic production and the workplace; those who do not possess these attributes are seen as abnormal or deviant and, hence, of less value. Furthermore, these practices reinforce an ideology of individualism, which tends to portray disability as a feature of the individual. In this context, the state's role is to ensure that social order is maintained by regulating eligibility for state benefits such as a disability pension (Bury, 2004, pp. 271–2).

In media representations and social policy discussions, disability is constructed as "a personal problem of tragic proportions requiring the assistance of the helping professions" to allow individuals to live as "normal" a life as possible (Titchkosky & Michalko, 2009, p. 2). Disabled people frequently are seen as "other," that is, they are grouped together as objects of experience, as symbolic of something that "normal" people are not (Wendell, 2010). Davis (2010) argues that the notion of the "average man" and with it the concept of normalcy and the social process of disabling is a configuration that arose at a particular historical moment, namely during the period of industrialization. Disability is conceived of as something "abnormal" and "unnatural" that happens to some individuals because of an illness, disease, or accident (Titchkosky & Michalko, 2009) and is something "normal" people fear or dread. Today, disability studies scholars are interrogating this view of disability by suggesting that it is the construction of normalcy that creates the problem. Titchkosky and Michalko (2009, p. 7) write that

> [D]isability studies conceives of disability as a socio-political phenomenon, one that marks an occasion to interrogate what we "normally" think of and experience as "normal life." After all, it is this taken-for-granted character of "normal life" that generates disability in the first place. As marginalized as we disabled people are, we live in and with the cultural understanding that we live on the margins of a centre or on the margins of what we have been calling normalcy. We recognize that the centre builds its environment—both physical and attitudinal—from the blueprint or standard of normalcy, and we recognize that, for the most part, this blueprint does not include us.

In other words, normalcy should not be viewed as a taken-for-granted "natural" phenomenon, but rather, it is to be understood as **socially constructed**. If the centre is human-made, as Titchkosky and Michalko (2009) suggest, then it can be constructed to be otherwise. How one defines disability is not simply a matter of language or science; it is also, as Oliver (2004) suggests, a matter of politics and has implications for social policy and how people are treated. In the quotation below, Wendell makes the same point.

social construction
Refers to the socially created characteristics of human life based on the idea that people actively construct reality, meaning it is neither natural nor inevitable. Therefore, notions of health/illness are subjective human creations that should not be taken for granted.

. . . how a society defines disability and whom it recognizes as disabled are of enormous psychological, economic and social importance, both to people who are experiencing themselves as disabled and to those who are not but are nevertheless given the label. . . .

There is no definitive answer to the question: Who is physically disabled? . . . Disability has social, experiential and biological components, present and recognized in different measures for different people. (Wendell, 1989, p. 108)

Today, there are various social theories and new critical approaches applied to the study of "disability" (see for example Goodley et al., 2012 and Titchkosky & Michalko, 2009); however, historically there have been two main competing models of interpreting disability: the individual (biomedical) model and the social model.[1]

Disability as Individual Pathology

A biomedical approach to disability locates the problem within the individual. That is, disability is constructed as an individual condition or pathology that requires ongoing medical intervention to help the individual function as normally as possible. This perspective focuses on an individual's functional limitations and is concerned with medical diagnosis and treatments for the so-called dysfunction (Rioux & Daly, 2010). In focusing on individual medical conditions as the causes of disability, the individual model locates the "problem" as a fixed condition of individuals' bodies that results in a "handicap" (Smith, 2009). This impairment is thought to be permanent and to inevitably lead to a life-long dependency on those who are non-disabled. From this perspective, disability is framed as a "personal tragedy," and the implicit assumption is that people with impairments or disabilities are abnormal. But, as Titchkosky and Michalko (2009) and others have argued, we need to ask, what is a "normal" body and who decides?

In other words, the individual model is based on an essentialist notion of disability that associates being disabled with fixed characteristics as seen from the perspective of non-disabled people and experts (Smith, 2009). Viewing disability as individual pathology legitimizes a medical infrastructure that "rests on notions [of] *normality* and the dichotomy between normal and pathological" (Lewis, 2010, p. 161). Or as Oliver (2009, p. 24) puts it, the "aim is to restore the disabled person to normality, whatever that may mean . . . or to a state that is as near normality as possible." Since disabilities are seen as located in individuals' pathologies, the medical profession and other health-care providers can act as gatekeepers to determine who is entitled to certain accommodations, benefits, specialized training, etc., all of which are tied to medical certification. One example of this is student accessibility centres in universities. Students are eligible for accommodations, such as having access to note takers, writing their exams in separate rooms, having extra time to complete exams, or carrying a reduced full-time course load (and still be considered a full-time student), only if they are deemed worthy of such accommodations.

---

1. Although often the terms *people with disabilities* and *disabled persons* are used interchangeably, Shakespeare (2010, p. 269) writes that *disabled people* signals a social model approach, whereas *people with disabilities* signals a mainstream approach.

In certain situations—such as with "learning disabilities"—to be eligible for these accommodations, students require some form of medical documentation. These accommodations are considered privileges, not rights, and students have to apply for them on a regular basis. What is not acknowledged in such an approach is the possibility that the problem is not a student's inability to learn but, rather, is a function of the way academic material is traditionally conveyed and the way standardized testing procedures are used to evaluate whether the material has been properly mastered. Such policies and practices, Smith (2009, p. 16) argues "render disabled people as passive and powerless targets of intervention through non-disabled expertise." A major critique of the individual model is its failure to look at societal factors, including discriminatory attitudes, social exclusion, and lack of opportunities, as real obstacles to disabled individuals from leading the sorts of lives they would like. "Rather than adjust social environments to meet differing bodily needs, medical interventions seek to cure the individual 'abnormal' body" (Lewis, 2010, p. 161). However, today, even those who adhere to the essentialist individual model generally recognize there is a complex relationship between "bodily structure" and social environments that structure disabled peoples' experiences.

Disability as Social Pathology

[D]isability, according to the social model, is all the things that impose restrictions on disabled people; ranging from individual prejudice to institutional discrimination, from inaccessible public buildings to unusable transport systems, from segregated education to excluding work arrangements . . . the consequences of this failure do not simply and randomly fall on individuals but systematically upon disabled people as a group who experience this failure as discrimination institutionalised throughout society.

—Oliver (2009, p. 21)

The social model of disability can be viewed as the polar opposite of the individual model: it locates disability within society, not the individual, and provides a structural approach to understanding disability. From this perspective, disability is not a bodily or mental attribute of the individual but, rather, results from society's failure to provide appropriate services to ensure the needs of disabled people are fully taken into account (Oliver, 2009). The social model does not deny the existence of impairment or functional limitations, but instead emphasizes that "[d]isability is something imposed on top of our impairments by the way we are unnecessarily isolated and excluded from full participation in society" (Oliver, 1996, quoted in Freund et al., 2003, p. 160). In other words, whether an impairment becomes a disability is contingent on society and peoples' social environments. See Table 10.1 which summarizes some of the key differences between the individual and social models. If Braille were the main method of written communication, blindness would not be a disability. People in wheelchairs are considered disabled because there are physical barriers to their mobility. Freund et al. (2003) explain that until the 1940s many of the inhabitants of Martha's Vineyard (a community in Massachusetts) were deaf but were not marginalized in any way. The entire community, including those who were able to hear, used sign language as a natural and ordinary form of communication. Those with impaired hearing were treated no differently from those who were not: they worked, married, and were not thought of as being significantly different. Similarly, without the availability of eye glasses or large print, many people would be considered "disabled." These examples suggest that whether something is constructed as a disability is dependent on the physical, social, and cultural environment in which people live, and is influenced by normative practices and people's attitudes. In her 1984 Royal Commission on Equality in Employment, Judge Rosalie Abella makes a similar point. Abella identifies four groups of people who have been and are disadvantaged in the workplace as a result of **systemic discrimination**: women, visible minorities, Aboriginal peoples, and people with disabilities. She writes that

> Persons with disabilities experience some limitation of their work functioning because of their physical or mental impairment. But the extent to which their disability affects their lives on a daily basis—that is, handicaps them—is very often determined by how society reacts to their disability. A disabled person need not be handicapped. (1984, p. 39)

According to Rioux and Daly (2010, pp. 349–51), there are two analytically separate approaches within a social pathology framework: the *environmental* approach and the *rights-outcome* approach.

The environmental approach highlights how environments construct disability through the failure to accommodate people's differences and needs. Imagine, for example, how your life might be different if all of a sudden the dominant mode of communication was sign language or if physical spaces were designed only for people in wheelchairs.

systemic discrimination
A form of discrimination that arises from the way that organizational structures, policies, practices, and procedures operate (unrelated to the requirements of the job), which while appearing neutral have a discriminatory effect on certain groups of people.

Table 10.1 Disability Models

The Individual Model	The Social Model
personal tragedy theory	social oppression theory
personal problem	social problem
individual treatment	social action
medicalization	self-help
professional dominance	individual and collective responsibility
expertise	experience
adjustment	affirmation
attitudes	behaviour
care	rights
control	choice
individual adaptation	social change

Source: Modified slightly from Oliver, M. (2009). The social model in context. In Titchkosky, T. & Michalko, R. (Eds.), *Rethinking Normalcy*. Toronto: Canadian Scholars' Press, Inc., p. 22.

Yet, the lack of elevators in many public buildings routinely makes spaces inaccessible for people who have mobility impairment. Or, those who are visually impaired cannot use automated banking machines without assistance, if the keys do not have Braille characters. Standardized methods for assessing learning outcomes put those who learn differently at a disadvantage, and construct those differences as learning disabilities. In other words, some people are excluded from the mainstream of social life, not as a result of their individual limitations but as a result of the failure of social environments to accommodate people's differences. Policies that emanate from this approach would focus on ways to minimize societal barriers, such as changing building codes, employing principles of barrier-free design or adapting curricula (Rioux & Daly, 2010, p. 350). The goal is to modify the environment to accommodate a wide spectrum of bodies (Freund et al., 2003).

A recent CBC TV News report (2014, September 17, www.youtube.com/watch?v=SE_VNRGYtU0) suggests that this may now be happening. The segment entitled "Inspiration for Innovation: How Disabilities are Changing Big Business" focused on how innovations in technology, such as Google's "self-driving car," will make the world more accessible for everyone. The aim, in the words of one spokesperson, is that their focus is "not special products for special people," but rather products that are of benefit to everyone. The reason for this, they admit, is that it makes "good business sense" since "the disabled population is the largest growing population in the world." However, while one can be cynical about motives, there is reason to be optimistic that innovative technology could play a part in creating a more inclusive environment.

The rights-outcome approach, Rioux and Daly (2010, p. 350) write, "moves beyond calls for adaptations to environments, reflecting a shift that has taken place over the past 20 years in the paradigm of disability from a medical welfare model to a human rights model." This approach underscores respect for diversity, the right to autonomy and the inherent self-worth of all individuals; the provision of accommodations and supports is considered a basic right, not a privilege. The focus is on ensuring that principles of human rights are being adhered to and that all systemic barriers to equal opportunities are eliminated. In Rioux's words (2009, p. 216), "[i]t is about equal outcome and entitlement, and about freedom and agency." One such example is Judge Rosalie Abella's recommendations for removing systemic barriers in employment for people with disabilities (as well as the other three disadvantaged groups).

There is an important distinction made from a human rights perspective between *equality* and *equity*. Unlike the principle of equality where the underlying premise is that everyone must be treated the same, *equity is about ensuring fairness through a recognition of difference*. The former is concerned only with equal opportunity while the principle of equity addresses equality of outcome or equality of condition as the basis of equality. For example, it is often argued, and is legally the case, that everyone in Canada has the same or equal opportunity to get a good education. However, this ignores that fact that not all Canadians begin at the same starting point; those from privileged backgrounds have many greater advantages than those who live in poverty. To achieve equity requires that the underlying structural or systemic inequalities be addressed first. Similarly, as discussed in Chapter 4, although all Canadians are entitled to the same level of health care not all have the same (or equitable) access to health-care services. To ensure that all people have the same or equal rights may require implementing different provisions for different groups of people. As a result of hearing a claim by three deaf applicants, the 1997 Canadian Supreme Court decision in *Eldridge v. British Columbia* affirmed this when it ruled that the provincial government was discriminatory in its health-care services because it did not include sign-language interpreters as an insured service nor did it require hospitals to provide such services. The court stated that

> to argue that governments should be entitled to provide benefits to the general population without ensuring that disadvantaged members of society have the same resources to take full advantage of those benefits bespeaks a thin and impoverished vision of S 15(1) [the equality provisions in the Canadian Charter of Rights and Freedoms]. (Cited in Rioux, 2010, p. 103)

The social model underscores the connection between the personal and the political; it changed the discourses around disability and provided the foundation upon which disabled people began to organize collectively. "Social model thinking mandates barrier removal, anti-discrimination legislation, independent living and other responses to social oppression" (Shakespeare, 2010, p. 268). It became a basis for advocacy to give disabled people autonomy and control in their lives (Oliver, 2004). The disability rights movement that emerged in the 1970s further challenged the existing discriminatory attitudes and exclusionary practices toward those with impairments. See Box 10.1 for a brief history of the disability rights movement in Canada.

Criticisms of the Social Model

The core of the social-model message, Oliver (2009) writes, is that it is society that has to change, not individuals: the "change will come about as part of a process of political empowerment of disabled people as a group" (p. 24). Similarly, Shakespeare (2010) argues that the social model has been "effective *instrumentally* in the liberation of disabled people" and "effective *psychologically* in improving the self-esteem of disabled people and building a positive sense of collective identity" (p. 269). However, the social model has also come under scrutiny and critique from both disabled people and those working in the field of chronic illness. A major criticism is that the social model does not adequately address the personal experiences of impairment, an important aspect of many disabled peoples' lives (Shakespeare, 2010; Oliver, 2004, 2009). French (1993) argues that her visual impairment imposes certain restrictions—for example, her inability to recognize people, to see colour, or to read non-verbal cues—that cannot be eliminated by applying principles of the social model (cited in Oliver, 2004, p. 284). The problem with the social model, Shakespeare (2010) suggests, is its failure to recognize that not only does society disable people with impairments, but also do their bodies.

A related criticism is that the social model does not take into account the pain and suffering that accompanies impairment. Jenny Morris (1991) acknowledges the importance of the social model in helping people understand the disabling barriers and attitudes that accompany disablement. However, she feels the model has also pushed aside the experiences of disabled people's bodies:

> . . . there is a tendency within the social model of disability to deny the experience of our own bodies, insisting that our physical differences and restrictions are entirely socially created. While environmental barriers and social attitudes are a crucial

Box 10.1 The Disability Rights Movement in Canada

In Canada and the United States, the disability rights movement began in the 1970s as disabled people came together to challenge a society that did not fully recognize their rights. A basic human right is the right to equality in society. Encouraged by the successes of the 1960s social movements, people with disabilities argued for the right to participate as autonomous individuals on the same basis as others in society and to shape their own lives. They rejected the predominant attitude that people with disabilities should be treated as charity cases, and they demanded recognition of their rightful place in Canadian society as citizens with equal rights. They fought against discriminatory policies and practices that placed people with physical and mental impairments at a disadvantage and lobbied to have their rights included in human rights legislation and the Canadian Charter of Rights and Freedoms. When the Canadian Human Rights Act passed in 1976–7, it became illegal to discriminate against individuals because of their disability, and thus gave disabled persons the same rights as others.

In 1976, the Coalition of Provincial Organizations of the Handicapped (COPOH) was formed by provincial organizations that came together to form a national organization; in 1994, the organization changed its name to the Council of Canadians with Disabilities (CCD) to reflect a new membership structure and provide a national voice for disability organizations. The organization has lobbied for legal changes, developed coalitions, organized national forums, and supported provincial organizations concerned with the rights of persons with disabilities. COPOH was instrumental in developing skills and strategies used by leaders of the Canadian disability rights movement to challenge the federal government's first-draft omission of disability in the Canadian Charter of Rights and Freedoms. One of the most important victories for the disability movement was its success in entrenching the rights of Canadians with disabilities in the Constitution and in the Charter, which became law in 1982. Section 15 (1) of the Canadian Charter of Rights and Freedom reads as follows:

> Every individual is equal before and under the law and has the right to the equal protection and equal benefit of the law without discrimination and, in particular, without discrimination based on race, national or ethnic origin, colour, religion, sex, age or mental or physical disability.

part of our experience of disability—and do indeed disable us—to suggest that this is all there is to it is to deny the personal experience of physical or intellectual restrictions, of illness, of the fear of dying. (Quoted in Oliver, 2009, p. 25)

In response to these criticisms, Oliver, who coined the term "social model of disability" (Shakespeare, 2010, p. 267), states that the model is not an attempt to deal with personal restrictions of impairment; rather "the social model has insisted that there is no causal relationship between impairment and disability" (Oliver, 2009, p. 25).

The social model has also been criticized for not adequately incorporating other oppressions, such as racism, sexism, and homophobia (Oliver, 2009). Susan Wendell (2010) argues that what is needed is a theory of disability that integrates feminist theory since feminist thinkers "have raised the most radical issues about cultural attitudes to the body" (p. 337) and show how similar attitudes have contributed to women's oppression. On a related point, Bell (2010) criticizes what he sees as the assumption in disability studies that "the disabled community is a monolithic one struggling against the same oppressors" (p. 375) and does not address the rich diversity, such as racial and ethnic, within disability communities. The social model, according to Stienstra (2002) needs to be reworked within an intersectional framework (cited in Driedger & Owen, 2008, p. 9).

As mentioned earlier, new critical approaches in disability studies understand disability as something that is "fluid and shifting" and "an integral part of the essential diversity of human life." Disability is understood as a legitimate way of being in the world. As Titchkosky and Michalko (2009) write, "Disability is as legitimate and valuable a part of who we are as is our gender, race, sexuality, ethnicity . . ." (p. 6). From this perspective, disability is not a problem that needs to be solved; rather disability disrupts normalcy as something taken for granted and allows for the possibility to interrogate normalcy as the object of study. In doing so, it becomes possible to show how disability comes to appear as a problem in the first place (Titchkosky & Michalko, 2012).

Some have argued that there is a complex relationship between disability and chronic illness (Driedger & Owen, 2008; Stone, 2008). However, before considering how chronic illness is constructed and how there may be overlaps with disability, we need to first consider meanings of illness.

Understanding Illness: It's Not Just Biological

The ideal of health . . . embodies a particular culture's notions of well-being and desired human qualities.

—Freund et al. (2003, p. 126)

Health and illness are often thought of as medical categories; however, sociologists argue that these are also social phenomena that cannot be understood fully by biomedical criteria. Rather, we need to explore individuals' understanding of their bodies and their health beliefs. Several studies have pointed to the importance of lay health beliefs in people's understandings of the body which do not conform to orthodox medical views (see, for instance, Kleinman & Seeman, 2000; Lock, 2000) and have demonstrated how health beliefs may vary between different social and cultural or ethnic groups. See, for example, our discussion in Chapter 7 of Aboriginal peoples' conception of health.

A sociological approach emphasizes that our understandings and definitions of illness are mediated through factors such as culture, class, ethnicity, and age. In other words, illness is not an objective state but is dependent on how individuals define their situation or experience. Put another way, illness is socially constructed; that is, our meanings of illness are shaped through our interactions with others. These meanings are also influenced by an individual's identity, time, and place. People may have the same disease, but they may experience it and react to it quite differently (Brown, 2000). For example, a diagnosis of rheumatoid arthritis will have different meanings for a competitive skier than for a writer. Similarly, a 65-year-old would likely think differently than a 22-year-old about such a diagnosis. People's behavioural responses can also vary. An elderly person with a heart condition might severely restrict her physical activity whereas a 30-year-old with a heart problem might change his dietary habits and embark on a physical exercise program as a way to manage his condition.

Social class is another factor that can mediate one's understanding of illness. For example, in his study of different social-class groups in a rural northeast community of Nova Scotia, Kenneth Davidson (1969) found significant differences among the three groups in terms of how they conceived of disease and illness. For example, many of those in Class III (those with little training or education, high seasonal unemployment) tended to take a stoical view of illness and suffered considerable pain and discomfort before they sought medical help or defined themselves as being ill. By comparison, respondents in Class I (those who had achieved high professional, occupational, and educational status) and II (the majority of wage earners in the community, including trades and small business owners) were much more likely to seek medical attention early on for a wide range of symptoms. Explanations for illness also differed among the three groups. The majority of people in Class III took a fatalistic approach when explaining their illnesses, attributing it to things such as "bad luck" or "God's will" (p. 239) whereas those in Class I and II were more likely to explain most illnesses as the consequence of viruses and other pathogenic agents. Not surprisingly, Davidson also found different approaches to treatment and curing among the three groups.

Similarly, Zborowski's (1952) oft-cited study of pain experiences among different ethnic groups calls into question our assumption that people experience pain in a universal way that can be objectively measured and compared. A common question patients are asked when they present with pain is this: "On a scale of one to ten, with one being the least and ten being the highest pain, how would you rate the pain you are currently experiencing?" The answer is thought to be helpful to doctors and physiotherapists in determining what they should prescribe or what treatment options they should consider to manage the patient's pain. However, in a qualitative study involving patients from four ethno-cultural groups—Jewish, Italian, Irish, and "Old American stock"—Zborowski (1952) found that there were important cultural differences in whether and how patients acknowledged pain, their attitudes and reactions to pain and their willingness to accept pain-relieving drugs.

To say that illness is socially constructed, however, is not to deny that viruses and diseases objectively exist. In everyday life, the terms **disease** and **illness** are frequently conflated into the term *illness*; however, it is important to distinguish between them. Simply put, disease is located in the body; it is a biophysical condition, something that doctors diagnose as such, and is treated through biomedical interventions. However, its distribution, as we have seen in Chapters 4, 6, and 7, is nevertheless affected by social factors, such as class, race, sex, ethnicity, and education. Illness is a more subjective phenomenon; it is something that people experience when they believe that they are not well and may be considered an **embodied** experience. Illness refers to "how the sick person and the members of the family or wider social network perceive, live with, and respond to symptoms and disability" (Kleinman, 1988, pp. 3–6, as cited in Freund et al., 2003, pp. 147–9).

A further distinction is **sickness**, which refers to the actions a person takes, as discussed by Parsons in his concept of the **sick role**. While in many cases individuals diagnosed with

disease
Refers to a biophysical condition diagnosed by a medical practitioner.

illness
The subjective response to a disease.

embodiment
The lived experience of both being a body and having a body.

sickness
Refers to the actions an individual takes while sick, including taking on the sick role.

sick role
A concept used by Talcott Parsons to describe the social expectations of how sick people should act and of how they are meant to be treated.

a disease may think of themselves as being ill and take on the sick role, this is not always the case as we saw in Davidson's (1969) study of the three groups as discussed above.

When do individuals consider symptoms to be indicative of ill health? Irving Zola (2000) points out that the process by which people construct symptoms as illness is a complex one. Neither the obviousness of a symptom, the medical seriousness, nor objective discomfort can account for the point at which a person "converts" to a patient, according to Zola. Rather, he found, the reason people sought medical treatment was related to their social-psychological circumstances, such as an interpersonal crisis, perceived interference with social or personal relations, or interference with work or physical activity. Zola concluded that while the symptoms were there, the perceptions of those symptoms differed considerably by different ethnic groups. People bring different world views to the ways in which they frame an etiology. "[T]he very labelling and definition of a bodily state as a symptom as well as the decision to do something about it is itself part of a social process" (pp. 212–13).

A further distinction is made between acute disease/illness and chronic disease/illness. An **acute illness** typically develops quickly, generally lasts for a short period of time, and often goes away without the use of medications or surgery. It is by definition transitory. Common examples of acute diseases are colds, the flu (including H1N1), eye infections, headaches, tonsillitis, appendicitis, pneumonia, as well as more serious diseases such as severe acute respiratory syndrome (SARS) and the Ebola virus. Those with an acute illness may take on the sick role. During our lifetime, all of us will experience many acute illnesses; however, our concept of who we are will not be changed as a result of such illnesses. A **chronic illness**, on the other hand, is ongoing, recurrent, non-communicable (except for HIV/AIDS), often degenerative, and has no known cure. Examples of chronic diseases include AIDS, diabetes, arthritis, asthma, cancer, heart disease, Alzheimer's disease, multiple sclerosis, Parkinson's disease, rheumatoid arthritis, emphysema, and fibromyalgia. Individuals with a chronic disease face a number of common problems in terms of everyday life, including the need to constantly manage their illness. Although from the view of the sufferer an acute illness can be problematic, disruptive, and even life threatening— such as in the case of Ebola—it does not permanently alter the ill person's sense of **self**. A chronic illness, on the other hand, is a rupture in our relationship with our body, the self, and the world (Williams, 2004).

According to the World Health Organization (WHO), chronic diseases are the most significant cause of death globally, accounting for an estimated 36 million deaths yearly. In Canada, three out of five people over the age of 20 live with a chronic disease, and four out of five are at risk (Public Health Agency of Canada, 2013). Cancer, cardiovascular disease, diabetes, and chronic respiratory disease are the leading causes of death and morbidity; also the proportion of people dying from chronic conditions is constantly increasing (Elmslie, n.d.). Data from the WHO profile of non-communicable diseases (NCDs) for Canada estimates that in 2014, 67 per cent of deaths will be attributed to one of the four major chronic diseases and another 22 per cent will be the result of other NCDs (WHO, July 2014). Chronic disease affects all groups of people; however, as we have seen, there is an increased prevalence among those in vulnerable communities, such as Aboriginal peoples, those who are socio-economically disadvantaged and among the aging population. Chronic illnesses tend to affect more women than men; depression, chronic fatigue syndrome, fibromyalgia, and lupus, for example, are primarily "women's diseases" (Driedger & Owen, 2008, pp. 2–4).

acute illness
An illness that develops quickly and is short-lived.

chronic illness
An illness that is ongoing, often lasts a lifetime, and has no known cure.

the self
A concept used by George Herbert Mead to refer to a core identity. For Mead the self is a social product that emerges through our interaction with others.

Table 10.2   Selected Chronic Diseases in Canada by Sex, 2010–2011 (%)

	Both	Males	Females
High blood pressure	18.0	17.8	18.2
Arthritis	16.7	12.7	20.6
Mood or anxiety disorder	10.4	7.6	13.1
Asthma	8.6	7.2	9.9
Diabetes	6.5	7.4	5.7
Heart disease	5.2	6.0	4.3
Cancer	2.0	2.0	2.1
COPD	2.9	2.5	3.2
Stroke	1.2	1.2	1.2
Alzheimer's disease or dementia	0.4	0.5	0.4

Source: Public Health Agency of Canada. (2014). Chronic Conditions by Sex. In *Chronic Disease Infobase.* Available at: http://infobase.phac-aspc.gc.ca:9600/PHAC/dimensionMembers.jsp?l= en-us&rep=i3E02D8DB9D30499BA2D25581E2A1B441#

Over three million Canadians cope with serious respiratory diseases, such as asthma, chronic obstructive pulmonary disease, lung cancer, influenza and pneumonia, bronchiolitis, tuberculosis, cystic fibrosis, and respiratory distress syndrome (Public Health Agency of Canada, 2008a). The Canadian Cancer Society estimates that two in five Canadians (41 per cent of women and 45 per cent of men) will develop cancer in their lifetimes (Canadian Cancer Society's Committee on Cancer Statistics, 2014). Of Canadians 35 years or older, 4 per cent reported being diagnosed with chronic obstructive pulmonary disease (COPD) (Public Health Agency of Canada, 2011c). In 2008/09, more than 2.3 million Canadians were living with diabetes, of whom 90 per cent have type 2 diabetes; nearly two-thirds (61 per cent) reported having at least one complication as a result (Public Health Agency of Canada, 2011d). As well, 1.3 million Canadians report having heart disease diagnosed by a health practitioner and about 300,000 are living with the effects of a stroke (Public Health Agency of Canada, 2009b). Data collected from the Canadian Community Health Survey 2010/2011 provides self-reported health information, including chronic disease, for those 12 years and older. See Table 10.2. Collectively, these statistics tell a frightening story of ill health for large numbers of Canadians. But what does it mean to live with a chronic illness and how does it impact on individuals' lives?

Constructing Chronic Illness

Living with a serious illness takes effort and devours time. It also means overcoming stigmatizing judgments, intrusive questions, and feelings of diminished worth.

—Charmaz (1993, p. 2)

Has there ever been a time when you've felt frustrated because you're just not physically well enough or strong enough to do something you wanted to do? Have you wondered how your life would be different if you had multiple chemical sensitivities or constant back pain? Especially when we are young, many of us take our bodies for granted and assume that our bodies will do whatever we want them to do. As the popular expression goes, it is only a matter of "mind over body." Being ill is not only inconvenient; experiences of illness remind us of our limitations and our dependencies, and our ultimate mortality. Our sense of who we are and our social relationships are intimately connected with our bodies and their everyday functioning. Being chronically ill is disruptive and disorderly (Freund et al., 2003). Serious illness changes who one believes oneself to be and alters how one sees one's body as operating in and with the world (Swoboda, 2008). Grills and Grills (2008) write that chronic illness is marked with uncertainty: "an uncertain understanding of self, an uncertain framing of illness, and an uncertain future" (p. 54).

George Herbert Mead states that the self is a social product that arises only in interaction with others. For Mead, the self is "that which can be an object to itself"; it is "reflexive," that is, it can be both subject and object (Mead, 1964/1934, p. 140). Our human uniqueness stems from our ability to reflect on our experiences; the self is not present at birth but evolves through our interaction with others. While in some respects our sense of who we are—that is, our identity—is shaped in the early years through a process of socialization, the self is also fluid. Chronic illness often challenges and disrupts our earlier sense of self. While chronically ill people experience physical pain and psychological distress, another aspect of the suffering is the loss of self. In the words of Kathy Charmaz, "chronically ill persons frequently experience a crumbling away of their former self-images without simultaneous development of equally valued new ones. The experiences and meanings upon which these ill persons had built former positive self-images are no longer available to them" (1983, p. 168).

Freund et al. (2003) write that chronic illness often leads to a radical assessment of one's self in relation to one's past and one's future, in light of changed and changing capacities (p. 149). The extent of disruption to the earlier self with the onset of a chronic illness depends on a number of factors, including the severity of the illness, its visibility to others, and its perception by others. Susan Wendell (2001) reminds us that any practical concept of chronic illness has to be patient-centred or illness-centred, rather than simply being based on diagnosis or disease classification. Not all who have what might be understood as a chronic illness take on an illness identity (Stone, 2008). For example, see Box 10.2 for a story about Katy. An illness identity, Charmaz (1995) tells us, is an incorporation of chronic illness or disability into one's sense of self (cited in Sulik, 2011, p. 464).

stigma
A physical or social trait, such as a disability or a criminal record, that results in negative social reactions, such as discrimination and exclusion.

Certain chronic illnesses, such as HIV/AIDS, for example, carry a great deal of **stigma**. Advanced stages of multiple sclerosis can mean total dependence on others for assistance with mundane everyday activities. An individual with diabetes can often manage to hide the illness from co-workers; someone with severe rheumatoid arthritis often cannot. People with chronic illnesses may face a number of common problems in terms of organizing their social environments, in terms of the attitudes of others, and in terms of their sense of self. For example, relationships with family members and the individual's wider social network may need to be re-examined. Becoming dependent can mean that normal rules of reciprocity and mutual support may need to be altered or abandoned. Bodily states may need to be closely monitored; time must be devoted to the management of symptoms and medical regimes (Bury, 1982). Having a chronic illness makes a person's life less predictable and controllable: *Will I get worse? Will I be able to go on this planned vacation? If I take on this demanding but interesting project, will I have another heart attack?*

Box 10.2 Katy's Story[1]

Katy, an accomplished academic in her 40s, is respected for her ideas, her teaching, and her calm, reasoned approach to issues. As a result, she is often asked to sit on committees at both a national and local level. She is energetic, outgoing, athletic, always cheerful, considerate of others, and eternally optimistic, the kind of person everyone enjoys being around. You would never know from a casual acquaintance with Katy that, on a daily basis, she needs to be vigilant about where she goes, where and how she travels, and what she eats. If she is not careful, she will be physically ill for days. People are often surprised to learn that Katy has multiple chemical sensitivities. Among the many things she reacts to are perfumed scents, smoke, environmental pollution, household and commercial cleaning products, paint, various construction materials, whiteboard markers, and freshly paved asphalt. Her home is the only place that she knows for certain will not make her ill.

Katy lives with unpredictability—she never knows for certain when something will trigger a reaction. She has had to leave concerts before they even began because someone in the audience was wearing a scent. She hesitates to travel to countries where smoking is not banned in public places. In fact, she minimizes her travels as much as possible because the cleaning fluids used in hotel and conference rooms can trigger a severe headache and nausea. On a sunny and warm day she is hesitant to eat on patios in restaurants because someone outside may light up a cigarette. Doctors have told her to eliminate certain foods from her diet to help her immune system so she has to watch carefully what she eats. When travelling, Katy carries a face-mask and often an air purifier with her; even during daily walks with her dog, she sometimes wears a mask because roads that are being paved or emissions from the pulp mill 100 kilometres away affect her breathing.

She has sought help from both conventional doctors and alternative health practitioners. In some cases, the seriousness of her condition has been questioned or attributed to psychological factors, such as the possibility of earlier trauma. It has been suggested that maybe her problems are "all in her head." Some acquaintances and colleagues were initially skeptical about the seriousness of her illness or the severity of her symptoms if she is exposed to chemicals and pollutants. As one person remarked, "I didn't really believe it until I saw it [the physical reaction] with my own eyes."

Does Katy suffer from a chronic illness? The answer is yes and no. Her multiple chemical sensitivities profoundly affect her behaviour on a daily basis. However, despite any medical definition, Katy's self-identity, that is, her sense of who she is, has not changed. Occasionally Katy might say with some frustration "that my body is really starting to wear me down." But on a daily basis she does not define herself as a person who has a chronic illness or a disability.

---

1. Based on a true story, although some descriptors have been changed.

226 | **Part 2** The Social Construction of Health and Illness

For many, having a chronic illness can result in a loss of independence. In a society that prides itself on self-sufficiency and individual responsibility, this loss can threaten a person's sense of self because it impairs the ability to participate as an equal in social relationships. Many chronically ill persons subscribe to this ideology and view dependency as something negative, as a loss of a so-called normal life. In Charmaz's words, "Values of independence and individualism combine to intensify the immobilizing effects of chronic illness" (1983, p. 172). As a result, former friendships may become strained or lost altogether; the chronically ill individual may retreat into his or her own world and shun social relationships. For example, the pain from fibromyalgia is more acute at some times than others so individuals with fibromyalgia may not know ahead of time whether they will feel well enough to attend a social function. If they frequently decline social invitations for fear that they may not be able to go, or accept invitations but later need to send regrets, it may only be a matter of time before such invitations are no longer issued. Also, as Freund et al. (2003) explain, for some people pain, requirements of treatment, and lack of access to everyday activities foster isolation; others may socially withdraw because they are unable to deal with the chronic problems, thus setting in motion a spiral of increasing isolation: "The less one can or wants to do, the less one socializes; but the less one socializes, the more others withdraw, and in turn the more the person with a chronic illness withdraws" (p. 150). In other words, over time the chronically ill individual can become marginalized from social activities, which results in a **diminished self**. However, as we saw in Katy's story not everyone takes on an illness identity. Also, there may be gender differences in response to chronic illness: constructions of masculinity that place greater emphasis on autonomy and independence for men may make it more difficult for them to preserve their sense of self (p. 151).

Chronic illness affects not only an individual but it can also have an impact on family and other close members of the sufferer's social network, who may feel the disruption of the illness (Freund et al., 2003, p. 151). The onset of a chronic illness may lead to financial crises and family strain, and the necessity of giving up paid employment or reducing hours of works can create economic hardships. As a result, the individual or family may be forced to live economically marginal existences or to drastically alter their lifestyles. In her interviews with women with a chronic illness, Hansen (2008) found that fear of job loss lead many women to minimize or conceal the reality of their condition at work, which could be both physically and psychologically demanding. In situations where a chronically ill person was the sole or primary caregiver, other arrangements needed to be made. Depending on the circumstances this can be both costly and lead to family strain. One of Charmaz's (1983) interviewees, the older sister of a woman with anorexia nervosa, explained her frustration with the disruption to her life this way: "it is very hard to keep my life up and positive when I am constantly drained . . . because it does take a lot out of me to deal with my sister . . . same with my mother, it takes a lot of energy and I do get angry" (p. 179).

Sociologists have suggested that people with chronic illnesses need to construct a new sense of self as their former self-images disappear. Our emotions around chronic illness and our definition of self, including whether we feel valued, are produced in ongoing social interactions with family, friends, co-workers, and health-care providers. Charmaz reminds us that supportive friends and intimates play a major role in bolstering the ill person's self, maintaining ongoing relationships, and minimizing the potential

diminished self
The term that Charmaz (1983) uses to refer to the loss of a previously valued identity.

for discrediting experiences. But what happens to people who find themselves in a foreign environment? In her study with Cantonese-speaking immigrant women in Canada, Joan Anderson (1991) shows that multiple factors influence a person's ability to manage chronic illness. She writes that for an immigrant woman, "the difficulties in living with a chronic illness are exacerbated by the experience of uprooting from her homeland and resettling in a new country. She must deal with her marginality, social isolation and alienation in a foreign culture" (p. 710). Furthermore, the lack of English language skills made it difficult to communicate with English-speaking health professionals.

Anselm Strauss and Barney Glaser's (1975) now classic work on chronic illness points to the limitations of a biomedical approach for understanding the complexity of chronic illness. They argued, as have others, that it is important to understand the subjective experience of living with chronic illness. For example, there are certain demands placed on people with chronic illness and their families in terms of managing a medical regime. Medications must be taken at set times; medical appointments need to be organized and scheduled; and arrangements must be made to ensure the individual is able to get to an appointment. People with a chronic illness must deal with uncertainty about their future, they may need to find ways to cope with social isolation, and they must manage relationships with friends and co-workers.

Different illnesses, of course, affect people's lives in different ways; it is important, therefore, to look at chronic illness in the context of people's lives. Not all chronic illnesses are accorded the legitimacy of being considered a real illness. Some chronic illnesses, such as fibromyalgia or chronic fatigue syndrome, are sometimes *contested*, that is, dismissed as illegitimate or psychosomatic (Moss & Teghtsoonian, 2008, p. 7; Swoboda, 2008). While individuals with contested illnesses "experience profound life disruption similar to that of others with chronic illnesses, questions and judgments regarding illness origins, personal accountability, and the validity of complaints are in the forefront of their illness narratives" (Swoboda, 2008, p. 88). A case in point is that of chronic fatigue syndrome. In her interviews with 50 individuals in the Boston area who had sought help for a debilitating fatigue that significantly interfered with their work and home activities, Norma Ware (1992) found that her interviewees regularly reported two types of delegitimizing encounters as a result of their experience with chronic fatigue syndrome. One type stems from the apparent insignificance of the symptoms in the eyes of many people. Since everyone from time to time has aches and pains, feels fatigued, or has feelings of depression, people would dismiss or trivialize the symptoms with comments such as "You're tired? We're all tired! So what!" The other delegitimizing experience was the result of encounters with doctors. There are no definitive diagnostic tests for the illness, and chronic fatigue syndrome is only just gaining acceptance as a real medical condition. Participants reported that many physicians viewed the illness as psychosomatic—that is, it was considered to be "all in your head." Interviewees also complained of being disbelieved or not taken seriously because they didn't look sick (p. 350). This experience of being repeatedly disconfirmed in their definition of reality lead to self-doubt, suffering in silence, and alienation as a result of deciding to keep the illness secret: "The self-doubt and the threat of stigma, the secrecy and the social isolation that results, the psychological paralysis induced by the ambiguities of the illness, and the shame of being wrong about "really" being sick all contribute to the psychic suffering of the chronic fatigue victim" (p. 355). Delegitimization of one's illness also means that one is not viewed as worthy of sympathy, support, or time off work. As mentioned above, for those with contested illnesses, issues of illness legitimacy are "paramount in their illness experience" (Swoboda, 2008).

Chronic Illness and Disability

Since the 1960s, various attempts have been made to explain the complex relationship between chronic illness, impairment, and disability (Bury, 2004; Oliver, 2004). Although health and social policy, grounded in individual/biomedical assumptions, conflate the two, the reality is that "people with disabilities experience periods of ill health and health in the same way as do all people" (Rioux & Daly, 2010, p. 352). There is a tendency to conflate disability with illness in part, Stone (2008) explains, since many aspects of contemporary society continue to focus on disability as a health issue in need of medical intervention. For example, health measures, like the widely used Disability Adjusted Year Life (DALY) purports to objectively measure how many years of "healthy life" are lost due to ill-health and disability (Rioux & Daly, 2010). This medicalization of disability has been challenged, as we saw, by disability studies scholars and the social model framework. Although some people may have impairments—that is a loss or restriction of some physiological or psychological function—disability can be the result of a genetic disorder, accidents, or trauma rather than the result of a chronic illness (Weiss & Lonnquist, 2006). It is equally true that not all who have a chronic illness are disabled. Yet the World Bank's use of DALY to measure "the global burden of disease" reconstructs illness as disability by turning all illnesses into measures of disability (Rioux & Daly, 2010; Stone, 2008).

Driedger and Owen (2008, pp. 1–4), women who both self-identify as having chronic illnesses and are involved in the disability movement, have been critical of the movement's reluctance to talk openly about the changing nature of bodies, and how chronic illness can disrupt day-to-day tasks, a reality faced by those with chronic illness. In rightly rejecting the biomedical approach, the disability movement, they argue, has not taken into account the physical and mental experiences of the body of the individual. "While some of us may benefit (some of the time) from accessible entrances, all the social transformation in the world will not rid us of pain and fatigue" (p. 8). According to Wendell (2001, p. 17), "chronic illness is a major cause of disability, especially in women . . .; any adequate feminist understanding of disability must encompass chronic illnesses," even though the relationship between the two is a problematic one. She goes on to distinguish "important differences between healthy disabled and unhealthy disabled people that are likely to affect such issues as treatment of impairment in disability politics, accommodation of disability in activism and employment, [and] identification of persons as disabled. . . ." Wendell suggests that there are both similarities and differences between the experiences of chronic illness and experiences of disability, including that of impairment and accommodation. For example, people with some brain injuries have difficulty getting their impairments understood and accommodated, "because they are more like impairments of chronic illnesses—transitory and unpredictable," unlike more stable disabilities. This could include fatigue and intermittent cognitive impairments, such as difficulty concentrating and recalling words, that are exacerbated by fatigue (p. 24). Fatigue, she notes, is "the most common and misunderstood impairment of chronic illness." Coming up with accommodations that take fatigue and pain into account are not as straightforward as providing ramps for those who have mobility impairments, or braille or seeing eye-dogs for those who have visual impairments.

Both chronic illness and disability are embodied experiences. The borders between them are murky. From a disability studies perspective, disability is not a property of an individual body, but is socially created through practices that fail to ensure that the needs of all people are taken into account. In contrast, "illness is something that an individual subjectively feels . . . and it implies suffering on some level" (Stone, 2008, p. 202). Since chronic illness is, by definition, not something that will "go away," "the experience of chronic illness can often resemble the experience of disability" (p. 203).

Canadians with Disabilities

According to the 2012 Canadian Survey on Disability (CSD), about 3.8 million (13.7 per cent of) Canadians aged 15 and older reported being limited in their daily lives because of a disability (Statistics Canada, 2013b). For the purposes of the CSD persons with disability were defined as "anyone who reported being 'sometimes,' 'often,' or 'always' limited in their daily activities due to a long-term condition or health problems, as well as anyone who reported being 'rarely' limited if they were also unable to do certain tasks or could only do them with a lot of difficulty" (Statistics Canada, 2013b p. 3).[2] Problems related to pain, and mobility and flexibility limitations were those most frequently reported. Twenty-six per cent of people who reported disabilities were classified as having a "very severe" disability. The severity score was determined by taking into account the number of disability types, the intensity of difficulties and the frequency of activity limitations.

See Figure 10.1 for a distribution of types.

Not surprisingly, the survey shows that the disability rate in Canada varies by age and sex. The proportion of women reporting a disability (14.9 per cent) is higher than men (12.5 per cent) in all age groups, except for those aged between 15 and 24 where the rate for men is slightly higher (0.2 per cent difference). The prevalence of disability increased with age: 33.2 per cent of seniors (those aged 65 or older) reported a disability compared to 4.4 per cent for those between ages 15 and 24. The type of reported disability also varied by age. Young people (15–24) mostly reported mental/psychological, learning, and pain disabilities. Among those aged 45–64 as well as seniors, the most common disabilities were pain, flexibility, and mobility (Statistics Canada, 2013b, p. 4). Rates of reported disability also varied across the country: the percentage of Canadians with reported disabilities was lowest in Nunavut (6.9 per cent) and highest in Nova Scotia (18.8 per cent). The rate for Quebec was 9.6 per cent whereas that for Ontario was 15.4. Some but not all of this difference can be explained by the different demographic makeup of each province.

Barriers to Inclusion in Canada

Historically, disabled people have had difficulties attaining employment and, if they were employed, tended to be marginalized in low-paying jobs with minimal responsibility and little chance of advancement. Channelled out of the mainstream, they were segregated into special schools, workplaces, or residential facilities; they were treated as charity cases

---

2. Because of changes that the CSD made, its results cannot be compared to that of the previously used Participation and Activity Limitation Surveys (PALS). However, like the PALS, it does use self-reported measures to determine the prevalence of disability in a population.

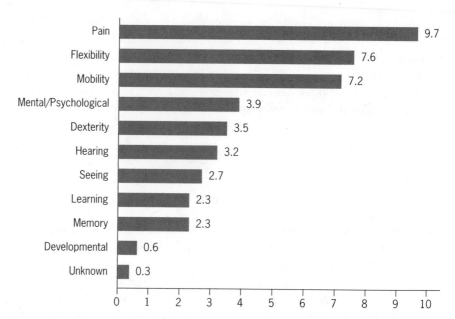

Figure 10.1 Prevalence of Disabilities among Adults 15 Years of Age or Older, 2012 (Per Cent)

Source: Employment and Social Development Canada (2015). *Indicators of Well-being in Canada.*

(McCoy, 2001). In response to the Abella Report, the Canadian government introduced employment equity legislation that mandated federally regulated employers to identify and remove any systemic barriers to employment for persons with disabilities (as well as for the other three disadvantaged groups). The Canadian Human Rights Act prohibits discrimination against people with disabilities; as well, persons with disabilities are protected under the equality section of the Canadian Charter of Rights and Freedoms. In many jurisdictions, efforts have been made to improve accessibility in education and employment. Can we assume, then, that persons with disabilities today participate as equals in society?

According to the Canadian Council on Learning (CCL) a significant number of Canadians with disabilities of working age still experience major barriers to labour-force participation and economic security, from physical barriers that limit mobility to discriminatory hiring practices (Canadian Council on Learning, 2009). Findings from the 2012 CSD indicate that 54 per cent of the working-age disabled population is unemployed compared to the country's general unemployment rate of 6.9 per cent (Sadakova, 2013). Employment profiles for these two groups are also different: disabled persons are more likely to be employed part-time and are also much more likely to experience at least one period of unemployment. The failure to provide workplace accommodation is one obstacle. This could easily be addressed through modifying the workplace, such as adding handrails and ramps, making washrooms more accessible, modifying workstations, improving accessible parking, and having flexible work schedules. Further modifications could include increasing supports, such as sign-language interpreters or assistants, having opportunities for multiple rest breaks, or providing technical aids, such as a computer with Braille, speech recognition software, and recording devices. Although it has been estimated that the costs of providing more workplace accommodations is relatively low, that is, under $1500, "employers are still ignorant about what it takes to hire and accommodate a person with a disability" (Canadian Council on Social Development, 2010, p. 219). Sadakova (2013, p. 1) further suggests that some companies "engage in practices that shut out individuals with disabilities, often right from the application process." Examples he mentions include accepting only online applications (a barrier to the blind if they do not have the right software) and phone screening (an issue for those with cerebral palsy).

It is often argued that disabled people have difficulty finding paid work because of inadequate skills and education. The CCL, for example, states that Canadians with disabilities have markedly poorer literacy skills than non-disabled individuals. However, they point out, part of the reason is that individuals with disabilities often encounter barriers to education, which in turn impedes the development of their literacy skills. Examples of barriers include inaccessible classrooms and transportation; financial issues, including difficulty in applying for financial aid and negative attitudes; and the inability to access needed accommodations for note-taking and exams. However, McCoy (2001) points out that low educational achievement can only partially explain the underrepresentation of disabled people in the labour force. He shows that if we compare university graduates with disabilities to those without disabilities, disabled individuals are still significantly disadvantaged. One study, for example, found that university-educated persons with disabilities had unemployment rates that were almost 10 times higher than for those without disabilities (McCoy, 2001). Furthermore, even with university degrees, disabled people have often been steered toward entry-level jobs that are low paying and offer little employment security or opportunities for promotion (p. 30).

Barriers to employment and education can lead to poverty and poor health. Studies show that disabled Canadians are more than twice as likely to live in poverty as other Canadians (Council of Canadians with Disabilities [CCD], 2010, pp. 228–33). Rates of violence and abuse against people with disabilities are among the highest of any group in Canada. The CCD argues that access to needed supports—whether these are at work, school, or home—"is the central foundation for inclusion and equal participation of Canadians with disabilities" (p. 229). However, according to McCoy, education and training are insufficient mechanisms to ensure employment equity. He agrees with Rioux (1985, p. 611) "that changing attitudes is the only real, long term solution to employment of persons with disabilities" (McCoy, 2001, p. 42).

Conclusion

From a sociological perspective, disability and illness can best be understood as social constructions. While in both situations there may be physiological or psychological dimensions, the impact of chronic illness and disability on the individual depends significantly on the society in which she or he lives. Biomedical approaches individualize experiences and are inadequate for explaining the complex relationship between embodiment and socio-cultural processes. To understand what chronic illness or being disabled means to the individual, one needs to understand how people experience their body and how social interaction and societal arrangements impact on peoples' experiences.

Summary

- "Normalcy" is a socially constructed concept.
- Disability is a form of social oppression that arises from exclusionary definitions and practices.
- Disability studies scholars interrogate "normalcy" and how the idea of "normal" implies that those who are different from a norm are "deviant" or somehow "wanting."
- How one defines disability has social and political ramifications.
- There are two competing models of disability: the individual model which views disability as an individual pathology; and the social model that locates disability within society and focuses on how societal arrangements and attitudes construct disability.
- Both disability and chronic illness are embodied experiences.
- Illness is a subjective experience, and our understanding of our illnesses is mediated through culture, class, ethnicity, age, etc.
- Having a chronic illness can affect one's sense of self and have major impacts on how one manages one's daily activities.
- Although disability and chronic illness are often conflated, there are important differences between them as well as similarities.
- In 2012, 13.8 per cent of Canadians aged 15 and older reported being limited in their daily lives because of a disability.
- Disabled people are often excluded from participation as equal members of society.

Key Terms

acute illness	embodiment	sick role
chronic illness	illness	social construction
disease	the self	stigma
diminished self	sickness	systemic discrimination

Sociological Reflection: What Is the "Normal" Body?

Most societies have idealized notions of the body for women and men. The bodies of disabled people or those with chronic illnesses are often regarded as abnormal or diseased. Reflect on the following:

- What is implied when we say that some bodies are "abnormal" or "disabled"?
- What role does the media play in reflecting and reinforcing dominant notions of normalcy? Think of examples.
- What role does stigma play in upholding idealized notions of the body?

Discussion Questions

1. How do people's socio-cultural beliefs about illness affect their illness behaviour?
2. In what ways might having a chronic illness lead to a "loss of self"?
3. What does it mean to say that both chronic illness and disability are embodied experiences?

4. What sorts of societal barriers exist for people with disabilities? How can these be changed?
5. Why might some people with a medically defined chronic illness not accept an illness identity? See Katy's story (see Box 10.2).
6. What are the major limitations of an individual/biomedical approach to understanding disability?
7. What is "normalcy" in relation to bodies?

Further Investigation

1. Using library resources, do some research on the disability rights movement in Canada. How many chapters are in existence? What is their membership composition? What are their goals and major accomplishments? Have there been any setbacks?
2. Research and compare two chronic illnesses. What sorts of different challenges would individuals with these illnesses face? What similar experiences might they share?

Further Reading

Charmaz, K. (1993). *Good days, bad days: The self in chronic illness*. New Brunswick, NJ: Rutgers University Press.

Davis, L. (Ed.). (2010). *The disability studies reader.* (3rd ed.) New York: Routledge.

Driedger, D., & Owen, M. (Eds). (2008). *Dissonant disabilities: Women with chronic illnesses explore their lives.* Toronto: Canadian Scholars' Press/Women's Press.

Dossa, P. (2009). *Racialized bodies, disabling worlds: Storied lives of immigrant Muslim women.* Toronto, ON: University of Toronto Press.

Strauss, A., & Glaser, B. (1975). *Chronic illness and the quality of life.* St. Louis, MO: Mosby.

Titchkosky, T., & Michalko, R. (Eds.). (2009). *Rethinking normalcy.* Toronto: Canadian Scholars' Press, Inc.

Wendell, S. (1996). *The rejected body: Feminist philosophical reflections on disability.* New York, NY: Routledge.

Web Resources

Canadian Arthritis Network
www.arthritisnetwork.ca

Canadian Cancer Society
www.cancer.ca

Canadian Diabetes Association
www.diabetes.ca/

Council of Canadians with Disabilities (CCD)
www.ccdonline.ca

Chronic Illness Community, Support and Resources
www.healingwell.com

Disabled Peoples' International (DPI)
www.dpi.org/

Disability and Society
http://www.tandfonline.com/toc/cdso20/current#.VFLV5kvd7nd

Disability Rights Promotion International (DRPI)
www.yorku.ca/drpi/

Disability Studies Quarterly (DSQ)
www.dsq-sds.org/

Heart and Stroke Foundation
www.heartandstroke.ca

CHAPTER 11
Aging, Dying, and Death in the Twenty-First Century

Jennie Hornosty & Maureen Strazzari

ing Grannies say

MAKE LOVE NOT WAR...

...how else can you become a Granny?

Members of the Raging Grannies march for action on climate change. How does this image of aging differ from the image that might usually appear in advertisements, movies, or television? What social expectations do we have of our elderly citizens?

Overview

- What are the prevailing social attitudes toward aging, death, and dying?
- What are the experiences of the elderly in Canada?
- What is ageism?
- How do individuals experience death and dying?

This chapter is concerned with the social construction of aging, death, and dying today with a focus on Canada. Some experts involved in institutional policy decisions argue that the aged are a "social burden," placing a strain on health and other resources as they become frail and immobile. Others point out that "70 is the new 50"; many seniors, they stress, live healthy and active lives into old age. While death, statistically, is postponed until old age for most non-Aboriginal Canadians, there is an increased awareness of the risks associated with contemporary living and of ever-emerging new risks, which generate fears of death and suffering, even among the young. Medical life-and-death decisions have become complex as the boundaries between life and death have become blurred. Significantly, these decisions are being made within an environment of economic rationalism, with pressure on medical and health professions to cut health-care costs. Medical, legal, and other discourses associated with the process of dying have provided a contemporary language for discussing death, but these discourses do not address "ontological insecurity" (Giddens, 1991)—that is, existential concerns that are likely to emerge in the experience of dying.

Introduction: The Changing Nature of Aging

Biological life and death are not of themselves the reality that people experience and to which they respond. What is perceived as real and normal about events and processes such as aging, dying, and death is **socially constructed**, and depends on the historical, social, and cultural contexts in which they occur and are given meaning. At the beginning of the twenty-first century in Canada, for example, the death of a young person is considered tragic because it is premature. Not too far back in history, however, it was normal for the young to die; to reach old age was extraordinary.

Age structures are shifting radically as populations age, and it is predicted that this phenomenon will continue to have profound implications within the areas of health and medicine, as well as in the broader social, political, and economic spheres. See Figure 11.1 for an illustration of Canada's age and sex structure in 2014. These social processes are deeply connected with people's lives. Anthony Giddens (1991) argues that a characteristic of "late modernity" (i.e., present-day society) is the interconnection of individual experiences with **globalization**. People may have little, if any, personal contact with death, but television brings graphic and selected images of death and dying from around the globe into their homes. The current media hype around the Ebola virus outbreak in parts of West Africa

**social construction/
constructionism**
Refers to the socially created characteristics of human life based on the idea that people actively construct reality, meaning it is neither natural nor inevitable.

globalization
Political, social, economic, and cultural developments—such as the spread of multinational companies, information technology, and the role of international agencies—that result in people's lives being increasingly influenced by global, rather than national or local, factors.

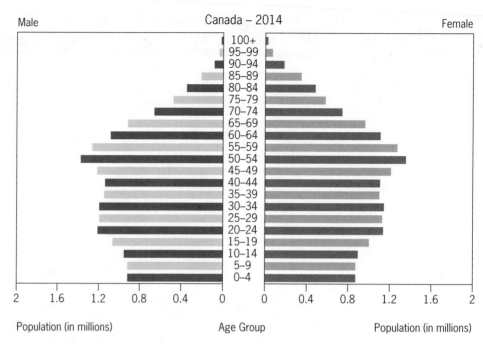

Figure 11.1 Population Pyramid of Canada

Here's a numerical breakdown of the Canadian population distribution according to age: 0–14 years: 15.5%, 15–24 years: 12.7%, 25–54 years: 41%, 55–64 years: 13.5%, and 65 years and over: 17.3%.

Source: IndexMundi. (2014). Canada Age Structure. Available at: www.indexmundi.com/canada/age_structure.html. CIA World Factbook, 2015.

is a case in point. At the institutional level, international agencies influence national policies, which affect individuals. Recommendations of the WHO, for example, become translated into Canadian health policies, reflected in health promotion and education activities, which assist people to maintain their health into old age. These are contemporary resources and strategies, and they are replacing traditional relationships (Giddens, 1991).

As Giddens (1991) argues, life in late modernity is profoundly different from life in earlier times. In his analysis, the contemporary social world is forever changing, with an array of novel resources, previously unimaginable, becoming available to individuals to create their own lifestyle, while traditional linkages, such as close family ties, lose significance. Giddens (1991) acknowledges that disadvantaged groups are marginalized or excluded from the new opportunities. Moreover, death, he argues, has been sequestered from social life. Not only has it physically been removed to the hospital, but questions and anxieties arising from the universality of human finitude have, at least until very recently, been repressed. And today, in times of personal crisis—for example, severe illness or bereavement—people are more likely to seek guidance from modern experts, such as doctors or counsellors, than from religious leaders.

The terms *lifespan* and *life cycle* are representative of changes in life as people age. In past eras, the life cycle linked the generations and resonated with the seasonal cycles of nature. The cyclical notion of renewal following death provided death with meaning. No effort was required to believe in life after death, as it appeared to be perfectly natural that this was so. The lifespan, by contrast, is linear. It has a definite beginning and end. In response, people today emphasize what can and ought to be done to improve the quality of the lifespan and to extend it. As a result, differences, even conflict, between generations are highlighted—for example, between the baby boomers and Generation X. The baby boomers, stereotypically, are accused of spending their children's inheritance or, conversely, of becoming the "sandwich" generation, "caught between parents who are living longer and children who won't leave home" (Sampson, 2000, p. 7).

The health and medical care that elderly people can expect to receive is the result of institutional planning and strategies. Other social responses to the aging population come from those experts who contribute to bodies of knowledge that affect experiences of aging and old age. Expert knowledge informs health and medical practices and influences or directly advises government policy-makers. In Canada, people continue to die in hospitals, but hospices and palliative care have come to be associated with dying. In February 2015, the Supreme Court of Canada struck down a ban on doctor-assisted suicide although opinions about the new ruling among health and medical professionals are deeply divided. The wider social context within which health and medicine are practised—especially economic and political concerns about escalating **public health** and medical costs—cannot be excluded from consideration. What are the consequences of all these conditions for the ways that aging, death, and dying are experienced?

public health
Public policies and infrastructure to prevent the onset and transmission of disease among the population, with a particular focus on sanitation and hygiene, such as clean air, water and food, and immunization.

Aging: A Socially Constructed Process

There are considerable differences in social and cultural responses to old age and hence in meanings and experiences associated with old age. Subjectively, people have very different views of when old age begins. To children, 30 years of age can seem old but in today's society, where everyone is encouraged to lead a healthy, active lifestyle, many in their 60s, 70s, and 80s do not think of themselves as old. It has been suggested that since people in affluent countries live "longer, healthier and more productive lives than ever before" (Giddens, 2006, p. 179), it is no longer useful to categorize people aged between 60 and 80 years as "old" and those between 80 and 100 as "very old." Even the number of centenarians will increase (Poole, 2014, p. 301). Canada, for example, saw an increase of 25.7 per cent in the number of centenarians between 2006 and 2011, making them the second most rapidly growing age group (Statistics Canada, 2012b).

Aging today is constructed differently than in the past. The portrait of aging over the past three decades has shifted from "the acceptance of aging as a gradual process of decline and dependency" to a view of aging "as individual achievement and social contribution" (Raymond & Grenier, 2013, p. 118). The "Third Age" (generally thought of as the period immediately post-retirement) is increasingly portrayed as a period of opportunities for self-fulfillment. The Internet is replete with sites for advice on "active" and "healthy aging," covering everything from nutrition, finances, and exercise to dating tips. *Healthy Aging* (http://healthyaging.net) and *Zoomer* (www.everythingzoomer.com) provide practical ideas for those 45 plus to improve their physical, mental, financial, and social well-being. In today's consumerist society, ageless faces and "taut and terrific" bodies are displayed in the media as the norm to be desired and achieved. Anti-aging theorists, such as Deepak Chopra, argue that while chronological age (age from birth) cannot be altered, biological age (functioning of body) and subjective, psychological age (how young a person feels) can be changed. Older people can be rejuvenated by means of, for example, meditation, injections, cosmetics, exercise, vitamins, nutrition, detoxing, fasting, and surgery. Nature no longer determines aging processes involved in the diminishing sexual prowess of men, who can now become sexually youthful with the help of pharmaceutical aids. To be "old" today does not mean the same that it did 50 years ago.

Population Aging in Canada

In 2011, the first members of Canada's baby boom generation turned age 65 (CIHI, 2011). Our population profile is rapidly changing: seniors (those ages 65 and over) constitute the fastest growing population group in Canada, accounting for 14.8 per cent of the population in 2011 (Statistics Canada, 2012b). It is predicted that by 2015, seniors will outnumber youth (those 14 and under). Low fertility, longer life expectancy, and the effects of the baby boomers (those born between 1946 and 1965—the largest birth cohort in Canada's recent history) are the major factors contributing to the aging of Canada's population. By 2036, it is estimated that seniors will comprise between 23 per cent and 25 per cent of the population (Statistics Canada, 2010b, p. 50). However, Aboriginal Canadian seniors (in 2011) comprised only 5.9 per cent of the reported Aboriginal population (Employment and Social Development Canada, n.d.). Figure 11.2 shows the past and projected growth of the subgroups of seniors in the country. However, keep in mind that seniors are a diverse group in terms of health status, living arrangements, and financial situation, as well as gender, ethnicity, sexual orientation, and Aboriginal status.

Life expectancy for non-Aboriginal Canadians, for both men and women is considered high. In 2012, the life expectancy at birth for females was 84 years and for males, 80 years

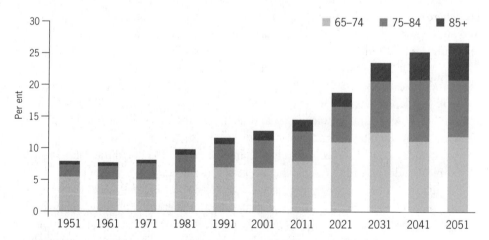

Figure 11.2 Seniors by Age Subgroups, as Percentage of the Total Population, Canada, 1951–2051

Source: Trainor, C. & Geran, L. (2011). Slide 4, Seniors by age as a percentage of the total population, Canada, 1951–2051. In Canadian community health survey (CCHS)—Healthy Aging. Statistics Canada, Demography Division. CANSIM: tables 052-0005 and 052-0006. Presented at RDC Network Conference 2011. Available at www.rdc-cdr.ca/sites/default/files/leslie_geran_rdc_2011_10_03_e_healthy_aging.pdf.

(WHO, 2014) as compared to 1921 when the life expectancy was 61 years for females and 59 years for males (Statistics Canada, 2010a). It is projected that by 2036 the life expectancy for women will be 87.3 years and for men, 84 years (CIHI, 2011, p. 15). Women form the majority (55.6 per cent in 2010) of the population of Canadian seniors, although their proportion vis-à-vis men is projected to decline (in 2036, for example, they would comprise 53.4 per cent of seniors) as the gap between women's and men's life expectancy continues to narrow (Milan & Vézina, 2011). And since women tend to live longer than men, many women will be alone as they age. Of the Aboriginal seniors in 2001, 54 per cent were women and 46 per cent were men (Turcotte & Schellenberg, 2007).

There are some notable geographical differences across Canada in terms of the seniors' population. According to the 2011 Census of Population, the proportion of seniors is lowest in Nunavut (3.3 per cent) and generally low in both other territories compared to the rest of the country, followed by Alberta at 11.1 per cent. The highest proportion of seniors live in the Atlantic provinces; in all four provinces, seniors account for 16 per cent or more, with the highest being in Nova Scotia at 16.6 per cent. This can be explained in part by the net outflows of young adults seeking work and lower immigration levels. In Ontario, seniors make up 14.6 per cent and in Quebec, 15.9 per cent of the population. The percentage of seniors in British Columbia is 15.7 per cent (Statistics Canada, 2012b). Approximately 75 per cent of all seniors live in a metropolitan or urban area (Health Canada, 2002a).

Population aging is occurring around the world although there are significant discrepancies both between and within countries. For example, in some poor countries in Africa, life expectancy is around 41 or 42 years (WHO, 2014). Although the proportion of seniors in Canada is predicted to rapidly increase, Canada's population is one of the youngest

© iStock.com/Tomwang112

Is population aging a sign of economic and social progress (i.e., a benefit), or is it a precursor of a looming crisis that threatens the sustainability of our health-care system, pension plans, and social programs (i.e., a burden)?

among the G8 countries; only the United States and Russia had a lower proportion of seniors than Canada in 2011(Statistics Canada, 2012b).

Aging and Retirement

"Retirement, as a social institution, emerged in modern industrialized societies at the beginning of the twentieth century" (McDonald & Donahue, 2011, p. 401). It is a mechanism by which workers are moved out of the labour force in an organized way. Historically, the social definition of "old age" for men[1] was tied to paid employment and determined by the age of retirement. Workers remained in the paid labour force as long as they could or until they were laid off because they were no longer considered productive, that is, they were considered "too old" to work. When the means-tested Old Age Pension Act was first introduced in Canada in 1927, it applied to persons 70 years or older. It was only in 1965 with a new federal act that the age of eligibility for pension benefits dropped from 70 to 65. Age 65 became the generally accepted age for retirement and the time at which one became "a senior."

The workplace has changed dramatically from the time when men were the breadwinners and women the homemakers: Women have entered the workforce in large numbers; capitalism has globalized; casual work has increased at the expense of full-time work; and workers face constant job insecurity. The majority of "baby boom" women who first entered the labour market in the late 1960s will constitute the first female cohort to have spent most of their adult life in the labour force, and thus qualify for their own retirement pensions (McDonald & Donahue, 2011, p. 402). Many workers are retiring early and in some cases this is not simply a matter of choice. Workers, now referred to as "human resources," become redundant as their skills become outdated or as companies downsize or shift their production or services offshore. The growth in non-standard work—that is, part time or casual—means fewer workers have benefits such as access to employer pension plans. The global financial crisis of 2007–8 meant massive job losses (especially in the manufacturing and service sectors), reduced household finances, major declines in the stock market, and the shrinking of pension funds. Between the mid 1970s and mid 1990s, the median age of retirement in Canada for men declined by three years (from 64.5 to 61) and by five years for women (from 65 to 60) (Public Health Agency of Canada, 2009d). However, recent job losses, failure of some employer pension plans, and loss of investment income may mean that millions of Canadians are forced to work well into what many had planned would be their retirement years. The elimination of mandatory retirement in most jurisdictions in Canada extends the protection against age discrimination to those over 65 and gives baby boomers an option of when to retire. In an effort to reduce growing government pension costs, however, some Western European countries are now extending the pension age to 67 or 68 years.

Pension plans are intended to provide some economic security for seniors in their retirement years. Canada, like many European countries, has a compulsory earnings-related retirement pension system, the Canada Pension Plan (CPP).[2] Every employed person over 18 must pay into the CPP, with half of the total contributions being paid by

---

1. Women did not enter the paid labour force in significant numbers until the late 1950s in Canada.
2. Quebec has its own retirement pension plan called the Quebec Pension Plan.

the employer. Retirement benefits normally begin at age 65, although one can apply for reduced pension benefits as early as age 60 or defer for up to five years for an increased pension. It is estimated that about three-quarters of seniors' income comes from the public retirement income system (the Old Age Security (OAS) and the Canada/Quebec Pension Plans) and from private retirement pensions (Public Health Agency of Canada, 2009d). The government also provides a Guaranteed Income Supplement for those with very low incomes, of whom approximately 65 per cent are women (Service Canada, n.d.). However, for over two-thirds of seniors the main source of income comes from the CCP/QPP and the OAS, rather than from private plans. Indeed, fully 60 per cent of the Canadian workforce does not have access to a workplace pension plan (CARP, 2010). Privately managed pension plans are both costly and especially vulnerable to market downturns. Unless there is pension reform, the prospects of economic security for seniors in the future does not seem promising.

Relative to other similar countries, Canada does well in ensuring an adequate standard of living for its seniors due to its public retirement income system (Conference Board of Canada, 2013a). However, since the mid-1990s, the poverty rate for seniors has been rising, reaching 12.3 per cent in 2010. Of those, almost 60 per cent were women (Conference Board of Canada, 2013a). Older women tend to have lower incomes because their wages were less then men's and because they live longer. An increasing number of seniors are using food banks. In its 2010 report, Food Banks Canada reported that 7.2 per cent of its users were persons over 65, a 9 per cent increase from 2009; in Ontario, senior usage of food banks increased to 12 per cent and, in Manitoba, to 15 per cent in 2010 (Food Banks of Canada, 2010).

In many countries across the globe, including Canada, a current concern associated with increasing aging populations is the looming prospect of fiscal strain on governments, particularly in financing pensions and health care, in what has been characterized as an aging "tsunami" (Znaimer, 2010). This is occurring at a time when **individualism** and **economic rationalism** have become dominant ideologies; individuals are expected to be personally responsible for their own retirement income (Macintyre, 1999). Despite the global financial downturn, the "blame the victim" message chastises Canadians for not saving enough for retirement (McDonald & Donahue, 2011, p. 414). Young people are reminded constantly by financial institutions and governments that they must plan ahead and start saving now for their retirement years. Aging baby boomers, now heading into retirement and who had reasonably expected to receive an old-age pension, are being labelled a burden and selfish for not sufficiently planning for their own retirement. Public pressure is mounting on the government to reform the public pension plan to improve pension accessibility and provide an adequate retirement income for all seniors. At the same time, concerns are expressed that the younger generation will need to pay higher taxes in order to finance the government pension plan.

In contrast to what occurred during much of the twentieth century, it is likely that experiences of aging in the twenty-first century will be individualized. Not all people have the ability to save for retirement. Many older Canadians have expressed concerns about the adequacy of their income in retirement (McDonald & Donahue, 2011, p. 410). Growing income inequality in Canada means that some individuals have more disposable income during their working years than others to invest or pay higher levels of superannuation in order to maximize their retirement income. Seasonal workers, minimum-wage workers,

individualism/ individualization
A belief or process supporting the primacy of individual choice, freedom, and self-responsibility.

economic rationalism/ economic liberalism
Terms used to describe a political philosophy based on small-government and market-oriented policies, such as deregulation, privatization, reduced government spending, and lower taxation.

casual workers, and homemakers are not in a position to invest for their retirement but will remain solely dependent on the government pension plan. For many, retirement will be difficult or need to be postponed. The structure of inequality is further reproduced in the senior years.

Ageism in Today's Society

ageism
A term, as with *sexism* and *racism*, that denotes discrimination but based on age.

Ageism, according to Hepworth (1995), is "prejudice against older people collectively stereotyped as a section of the population disqualified by reason of their chronological age from making a full contribution to society" (p. 177). A popular belief is that the elderly are not valued in our technological society because the knowledge they have acquired over their lifetime is irrelevant, whereas in bygone days the aged were respected for their wisdom. Historical studies indicate, however, that attitudes toward the elderly have fluctuated over time and between cultures (Bytheway, 1995). The significant question is how ageism is constructed in today's society. Although there is a growing recognition of the contributions made by seniors and near seniors, the workplace is in many respects ageist. Older workers encounter negative attitudes and stereotypes about their abilities, and they experience more difficulty finding employment (National Seniors Council, 2011). Many workers in their 40s and 50s, especially males, are considered too old for retraining after being made redundant.

Stereotypical views of old age also contribute to ageism. Old age is associated with memory loss, incontinence, lack of cleanliness, making mistakes, slowness, becoming argumentative or withdrawn, or acting childishly. Old age is considered something to be feared, as it is increasingly associated with becoming demented. This embedded view is in sharp contrast with the contemporary value placed on youth, health, and fitness. There is little wonder that for many, old age has become something to postpone as long as possible. Moreover, aged people may themselves internalize ageist views, their feelings of self-worth diminished by their loss of youth, fitness, and choice. Ageism can also result in the progressive exclusion of elderly people from the social world, a situation for which Mulkay (1993) has coined the term **social death** and which can occur well before biological death.

social death
The marginalization and exclusion of elderly people from everyday life, resulting in social isolation.

The current use of the term *agelessness* may be perceived as introducing a positive attitude to old age, but this is questionable. Molly Andrews (1999) cautions that it is a seductive term, allowing us to believe "we can transcend age" (p. 301). Such an anti-aging stance denies the importance of individuals' biographies in terms of the role played by unique life experiences in the aging process. The mass media, in their variety of forms—television, films, magazines, billboards, and the Internet, particularly through advertising—provide contradictory stereotypical images of age. Elderly people may be presented as incompetent or chronically ill. Chivers (2011) argues that despite the salience of "boomer" culture, "Hollywood remains committed to ageist universalizing stories that dramatize loss" (Katz, 2012, p. 254). Advertisements promoting retirement financing or housing, on the other hand, are accompanied by images of a smiling and contented older couple. The media also promote the idea that people can remain ageless; for example, a recent television ad for an anti-inflammatory prescription medication had this as its slogan: "Defy aging: Speak to your doctor" (the caption listed the name of the medication). The ad itself featured youthful seniors engaged in various sorts of physical activities. Remaining youthful is valorized. Various products such as skin creams, vitamin supplements, hormone therapy, and

Botox injections promise to make older people look younger and remain healthier. These stereotypical images oversimplify and discount the diversity of seniors' lives, as these are shaped by different gender, ethnic and cultural backgrounds, or their **class** positions and health status.

Stereotypical and ambivalent images of aging and old age are also constructed by experts. Specialized forms of knowledge inform the practices of medical and health professionals as well as the practices of bureaucrats and others involved with making policies that affect the aged or aged care. The construction of age by experts establishes images of what is considered normal for particular age groups, with contradictory results. On the one hand, old age is presented as a burgeoning social problem; as more people live longer they become an economic and social burden. On the other hand, the aged are portrayed as being "cool" and responsible for their own quality of life, with the potential to remain healthy and active participants in society. For example, see the 2012 DVD produced by the Public Health Agency of Canada (PHAC), "Seniors Are Cool" (PHAC, 2014, found at www.youtube.com/watch?v=xszPdSfk-AQ). The PHAC also publishes numerous pamphlets, tips, and fact sheets informing seniors on how they can take responsibility for remaining healthy and active (Public Health Agency of Canada, 2009a). Both approaches are ageist constructions, contributing to stereotypical views.

class (or social class)
A position in a system of structured inequality based on the unequal distribution of power, wealth, income, and status. People who share a class position typically share similar life chances.

How Old Age Is Perceived as a Social Burden

Rather than celebrating the longevity of populations as an achievement, this trend is being viewed increasingly with dismay, both nationally and internationally. Indeed, current concern about the perceived burden of the aged is said to be reaching the level of hysteria, with a "sense of impending crisis" (Walker, 1990, p. 378). There is a prevalent belief that Canada's aging population will wreak havoc on the health-care system. In February 2010, Parliamentary budget officer Kevin Page released a report warning that elderly benefits and health-care costs associated with aging will require Ottawa to hike taxes or cut spending by at least $20 billion over the coming decade (Hui, 2010). Population aging, the federal Department of Finance warns, leads to slower economic growth and reduced revenues while at the same time it "puts pressure on pubic expenditures, notably for age-related programs such as elderly benefits and health care" (Simpson, 2014, A 15). A recent poll (2013) of Canadians found that 6 out of 10 surveyed lacked confidence in the health system's ability to care for the rapidly aging population (Kirkey, 2013).

Sociologists Susan McDaniel and Monica Boyd both dispute these dire predictions that aging seniors will be an economic burden. Boyd notes that many elderly people are choosing not to retire immediately; rather than becoming a drain on the system, she suggests the future elderly will be contributing, productive members of the economy. McDaniel argues that the dire predictions are based on incorrect assumptions. The mistake is that people involved in policy-making think that the health-care needs of the elderly in the future will be the same as those who are 85 today. According to McDaniel, "people who are 85 now were born in a time when smoking was chic, they sometimes went through the Depression– they're an entirely different person" (quoted in Hui, 2010). The lifestyles of baby boomers and those who will enter retirement in the future is qualitatively different. Today's seniors are more physically active and socially engaged than those in previous generations (Hui, 2010). While it is true that the elderly have more health problems than younger Canadians, which is reflected in higher health-care expenditures, the data need to be interpreted carefully. Znaimer (2010) argues that although statistics show that 90 per cent of seniors visited a doctor in the past 12 months, it is interesting to note the relatively high percentages of Canadians in other age brackets who also consulted a physician within the same period: 82.8 per cent of those aged 45 to 64, 80 per cent in the 35- to 44-year-old bracket, and 85 per cent of children under the age of 12. Since advancing age is associated with declining health, physician visits tend to increase at older ages: "But when the level of need and the other characteristics were controlled, the relationship between age and physician consultations was less clear" (Health Reports, 2007, p. 27).

According to health economists Morgan and Cunningham (2011, p.68), "there is a gap between rhetoric and reality concerning healthcare expenditures and population aging . . . although decades-old research suggests otherwise." Based on their research, they concluded that the future effects of population aging on health-care spending will continue to be small. Similarly, in a 2011 report released by the Canadian Institute for Health Information (CIHI) (2011), the authors state that while health spending per capita on seniors is more than four times that of non-seniors, the rate of spending growth for seniors was actually lower over the past 10 years than the rates for non-senior adults. Population aging added less than 1 per cent to public-sector health spending each year. With the exception of spending on long-term institutional care, aging has only had a modest effect on public-sector health expenditures. Rather, new technologies and increasing pharmaceutical costs are major drivers of growing government health-care expenditures. Also overlooked is the fact that the majority of seniors continue to contribute significantly to the economy and health costs through their taxes.

Depictions of seniors as major economic burdens foster ageism and ignore certain facts. Overall the financial situation of seniors in Canada has actually improved over the past 25 years (Turcotte & Schellenberg, 2007; CIHI 2011). Although there has been a recent troubling rise in poverty rates among seniors, these figures remain relatively low. A significant number of seniors still participate in the labour force, increasing from 6 per cent in 2000 to 13 per cent in 2013 (Government of Canada, 2014, p. 9). Home ownership is also relatively high among seniors: in 2001, 75 per cent of seniors between ages 65 and 74 owned their own homes (Turcotte & Schellenberg, 2007, p. 69). More importantly, depictions of seniors as burdens ignore the many contributions they have made during their lifetime and continue to make to society. For example, past contributions to the economy during their working lives, taxes paid during that time, the unofficial caring and financial assistance provided to adult children and grandchildren, and the various volunteer activities they engaged in are all discounted in such a depiction, and the benefit of these services to the well-being of the country is ignored. For example, more than one-third (36 per cent) of Canadian seniors volunteer with formal voluntary organizations and devote on average 223 hours per year. The economic value of these contributions in market terms amounts to more than $5 billion annually (Mei et al., 2013). Nearly one quarter of seniors are engaged in providing unpaid care for friends and family members as well as taking care of their healthy grandchildren (Faid, 2013). Further, stereotyping the aged as a collective social burden also has sexist implications because the majority of older people are women. Finally, anxiety about the baby boomers becoming a bourgeoning social burden neglects the growing influence of aged people with disposable income as a market sector for a range of services.

© iStock.com/fotokostic

Twenty two per cent of adults aged 65–74 and nine per cent of those aged 75 and over help with child care. Collectively, older adults spend more than 4 million hours on unpaid child care each week, and their time is valued at an estimated $4.4 billion per year.

People's experience of aging is complex as power, wealth, and health are unequally distributed among the aged and those who will age in the future. Social class, **gender**, and **racism** may be contributing factors in determining whether people retire with chronic health problems, resulting from long years of repetitive or heavy manual work, or whether they retain positions of power for many more years as members of boards of directors or as consultants. It needs to be acknowledged, for example, that socio-economically disadvantaged seniors have poorer health status than their wealthier counterparts. And low-income seniors are "more likely to live in neighbourhoods with fewer health-promoting features" (CIHI, 2011, p. 16). The growing gap between the rich and the poor, which is likely to continue into people's retirement years, and neo-liberal policies will exacerbate these inequalities. With the increase in casual and part-time work at the expense of full-time employment, it will be difficult for many younger people to save for their future retirement. The causes, however, do not lie with these "victims" of global capitalism and economic rationalism but with government policies that fail to address structural inequalities. It is well to remember that terms are never neutral. While experts warn that the aging masses are likely to be a *social burden*, this term is not directed at, say, ex-politicians, most of whom retain substantial benefits at public expense throughout their retirement.

gender/sex
Refers to the socially constructed categories of feminine and masculine (the cultural values that dictate how men and women should behave), as opposed to the categories of biological sex (female or male).

racism
Refers to a set of false beliefs that one racial group is naturally superior to another group based on biological differences. It perpetuates notions of cultural superiority and inferiority and is one basis for social exclusion and discriminatory practices.

Health, Well-being, and the Needs of Seniors

Seniors today, according to the CIHI (2011), are healthier than previous generations, and are generally healthy well into their later years. In fact, "the health status of younger seniors appears more similar to that of adults younger than age 65" (p. 17). Ninety-seven per cent of seniors in general are satisfied with their lives (Butler-Jones, 2010). In terms of physical health, 44 per cent of seniors perceived their health to be excellent or very good and 70 per cent self-rated their mental health as excellent or very good (Butler-Jones, 2010, pp. 20–1). Seniors' functional capacity, that is the ability to carry out everyday tasks, varies with age: a large majority of those 85 years and under reported no limitations in functional capacity whereas one-quarter of all seniors 85 years and older reported a moderate or more severe limitation (CIHI, 2011, pp. 17–18). Seniors are more likely than non-seniors to have chronic health conditions; in 2009, 83 per cent of women and 79 per cent of men living in a non-institutional setting reported having at least one chronic condition, of which the most common was high blood pressure: 52 per cent for women and 45 per cent for men, followed by arthritis, diabetes, and heart disease (Milan & Vézina, 2011, p. 27). Although a large number of seniors at one time smoked, less than 10 per cent smoke now. And "obesity"[3] rates among seniors age 65–74 have declined although the rates for older seniors have risen (CIHI, 2011, p. 19). However, over half (57 per cent) of seniors were considered physically inactive, which can in turn lead to increased "obesity" and more chronic diseases in later life (Butler-Jones, 2010, p. 28). The reasons that seniors are less physically active are often related to external barriers such as cost, adverse weather, and lack of accessible and affordable recreational activities.

One area of growing concern is the abuse and neglect of seniors, often a hidden and unreported crime. While the exact numbers are not known, it is estimated that between 4 per cent and 10 per cent of seniors experience some form of abuse from a family member, friend, or caregiver (Butler-Jones, 2010, pp. 40–1). Abuse can be physical, psychological, emotional, or financial. Children and spouses were the most common perpetrators of violent crimes against seniors reported to the police. In a 1999 survey, 7 per cent of seniors reported that they experienced some form of emotional or psychological abuse and 1 per cent reported financial abuse. More research is needed in the area, but we do know that such abuse and neglect will have significant negative impacts on the physical and social well-being of seniors, resulting in physical frailty and increased depression.

Geographic mobility of seniors is low: most prefer to "age in place" in their own homes (Northcott & Petruik, 2011). According to the 2011 population census, 92.1 per cent lived in private households, either alone, as part of couples, or with others; the remaining 7.9 per cent lived in collective dwellings such as residences for senior citizens, nursing homes, or hospitals (Statistics Canada, 2012b). Not surprisingly, the prevalence of seniors living in institutional facilities such as nursing homes and long-term care hospitals is age-related; 29.6 per cent of seniors aged 85 and over lived in special care facilities. However, since the early 1980s, the percentage of seniors living in residential care settings has declined. Two-thirds of long-term care residents are women, which is explained in part by women's higher longevity, higher levels of chronic illness, gender-based poverty, and less access to informal community-based supports (Penning & Votova, 2009). Some seniors living in their home need occasional assistance from home-care services to help them manage their daily lives. Seniors who live in **assisted living** arrangements also require some assistance, but not the type of full-time care provided in long-term facilities (Health Council of

assisted living
Where individuals live somewhat independently in apartment units but receive assistance with meals, housekeeping, and personal health care.

---

3. This is the term used by public health and medical professionals, although critical scholars who argue such terms pathologized natural body-weight diversity contest it. See for example Rothblum & Solovay (Eds.), 2009.

Canada, 2012). Although the importance of home care is acknowledged by governments, "there is no shared understanding of what home care should look like for seniors—no shared vision, common principles, or collective standards" (p.8). Such care is not available on a universal basis; mostly it falls outside the realm of **Medicare**. As well, provinces vary in the services they offer, eligibility criteria differ, and there is variability in user fees (Canadian Association on Gerontology, 2011). In 2009, 4 per cent of seniors reported that they had at least one unmet need for professional home care, and nearly two-thirds attributed this to their inability to pay for the service (Hoover & Rotermann, 2012).

Medicare
Canada's universal health-care program, which is funded and administered by federal, provincial, and territorial governments.

Community-based home-care services were formally introduced in the 1970s as a way of potentially limiting the number of seniors requiring residential institutional care. They encompass a variety of supportive, therapeutic, and personal health services which make it possible for those with minor physical limitations or social needs to live at home (Penning & Votova, 2009). As with residential care, home-care services are delivered by both public and private sources, on both a for-profit and not-for-profit basis. Different provincial and territorial health-care programs cover costs associated with home care and most provinces offer a mix of publicly and privately funded services. For most seniors, however, sources of support and assistance are informal, provided by family members, friends, or others in the community. Nearly 70 per cent of care was provided by close family members; approximately one in five Canadians 45 years and older provided care to a senior in 2007 (Cranswick & Dosman, 2008). One-third of seniors who resided in care facilities also received personal care as well as assistance with transportation from family and friends. In many cases family members, most often the female members, have multiple caring responsibilities, such as looking after dependent children as well as aged parents, or providing assistance to their adult children and grandchildren, as well as an aged spouse or parent.[4] Many also juggle paid employment with caregiving responsibilities.

Without appropriate government resources, the burden of home or community care, to a very large extent, falls back on families and in particular on those in the family who are willing and able to take up and maintain the responsibility of caring for their elderly relatives. There is significant variation across Canada in terms of eligibility for professional home-care services and whether clients need to pay (Health Council of Canada, 2012). Doctors are under pressure to free up hospital beds when people no longer need acute care; however, seniors who are discharged before being able to resume their own care may require intensive home-support services. Services for those with chronic problems may not be a priority, and thus seniors must fend for themselves, pay for services if they can afford it, or rely on voluntary assistance or family support.

Increasingly, health and health care today are being commodified within a profit-driven health-care marketplace (Coburn, 2004): "Older adults and other health service users are being encouraged to consume in the name of health, lifestyle, and independence, as well as to 'shop for services' and pay privately for care that enables independent living for as long as possible" (Penning & Votova, 2009, p. 359). This is evident in the promotion of self-care, including the emphasis on "being informed" and taking personal responsibility for one's health.

---

4. Adults who are raising their own children and at the same time taking care of their parents are referred to as the "sandwich generation."

"Healthy Aging"

Recognition of the discriminatory effects of ageism, especially in a world that is rapidly aging, has prompted resistance to the notion of the aged as a social burden. This cause has been assisted through Laslett's identification of a stage in life that has become known as the "third age." Laslett states that nearly all elderly are, or have the potential to be, healthy and active, and many are highly productive. Conceivably, the length of this period could be extensive as the biological limits of the human lifespan are uncertain, with predictions ranging as high as 120 years or even well beyond (Laslett, 1989, p. 13).

At the forefront of Canada's social policy agenda on health is the concept of "healthy aging." According to the Public Health Agency of Canada, a "new vision" for healthy aging would be a society that values and supports the contributions of older people; that celebrates diversity, refutes ageism, and reduces inequities; and creates opportunities to enhance independence and quality of life (2011b, p. 4). This vision includes the promotion of "age-friendly communities" as a way to create healthy aging environments that incorporate factors such as universal design, accessible transportation and housing, community support, and access to appropriate health services (Butler-Jones, 2010, p. 4). For example, in an age-friendly community sidewalks are well lit and kept in good shape; buildings have automatic door openers and elevators; and seniors take part in all sorts of community activities, such as visiting museums or libraries, taking courses, or volunteering for charities or civic duties (Public Health Agency of Canada, 2012). In this vision, age is not perceived as a barrier to maintaining a healthy lifestyle. Rather healthy aging has become a moral imperative: to age successfully, a moral duty. The discourse on successful aging, according to Asquith (2009), is dominated by hyper-individualism (cited in Mendes, 2013, p. 179). We know that socio-economic factors, racism, ethnicity, and **social capital**, for example, have significant influences on peoples' experience of aging: however, it is not clear how structural inequalities arsing from these will be addressed through the "healthy aging" agenda.

social capital
A term used to refer to social relations, networks, norms, trust, and reciprocity between individuals that facilitate co-operation for mutual benefit.

Illness, deterioration, and death do not fit into the construction of this idyllic view of healthy aging. Rather, individuals are encouraged to be positive and to concentrate on daily healthy living (choosing and eating healthy foods, making time for daily exercise, coping with stressful situations as they arise) with the "promise" that death can be resisted or postponed. They are reassured by the continuing advancement of medical technologies to combat disease and replace body parts. The result of the construction of healthy aging is the idea of an indefinitely extended and healthy middle age, with death coming quickly at the end of a satisfactory life. Aged people are likely to be more realistic, however, having experienced and continuing to experience losses through their own illnesses or disabilities and through the deaths of those close to them.

According to Laslett (1989), the final stage of life is one of "decrepitude and dependency"; it is when old age is constructed as a "social burden." He suggests that the repercussions are profound for personal relations (in terms of time and effort), especially for families, and for national budgets (in terms of supplying hospital and medical care) (p. 13). That the last years of a person's life are represented by the term *social burden* says much about how we think about peoples' lives. To discuss chronic illness and dependence on the services of others in terms of cost ignores personal suffering as well as the right of everyone, regardless of age, to be treated with dignity.

Dying and Death: How Perceptions Have Changed

Until relatively recently, it was uncommon for people to live into old age. Little could be done to control epidemics, diseases, infections, and childbirth complications. Historian Philippe Ariès (1981) suggests that, because of this, death had to be accepted as fate throughout most of the long history of Western civilization. Fate offered the solace of a better existence in the next world for those who righteously accepted life in this world as a "vale of tears." Slowly, people became aware that life conditions were not completely out of their control and that action could be taken to improve some situations. The Enlightenment—an eighteenth-century intellectual movement—marked the beginning of a growing optimism that there were secular answers to life's problems. Causes and, therefore, prevention, and cures of illness and disease could be discovered. Medical interventions, such as vaccinations and antibiotics, as well as public health measures, introduced through quarantine and sanitary reform, contributed to the decline in disease. Better standards of living—including working conditions, accommodation, availability and affordability of nutritious food, and education—have also contributed significantly to people living longer.

The medical profession came to occupy a position of dominance in the health area, symbolized and institutionalized by the establishment of the prestigious modern hospital. Fighting to save lives became a central task of hospitals, which also became the sites at which deaths occurred when the battles were lost. Dying and death were thus removed from the homes and neighbourhoods where they had always resided, thereby becoming separated from everyday life. The idea that death can be avoided or postponed indefinitely is fostered as people live increasingly longer lives, and younger deaths are seen as premature and abnormal. Optimism is invoked by claims that quality of life can be enhanced or maintained by healthy living. A steady stream of media reports informs people of the promising results of new curative or preventive research findings. Medical technology has become very sophisticated and expensive; people can be kept alive through surgical procedures, such as heart bypasses and organ transplantations, as well as through continually updated pharmaceutical drugs and technological therapies. The mapping of the human genome has produced radical promises for eliminating hereditary diseases.

Somewhat paradoxically, in light of these actual and potential achievements aimed at conquering death together with the institutional sequestering of death, dying and death are now returning to everyday life. The limitations of medical technology's endeavour to eliminate diseases are apparent in the chronic, sometimes debilitating, ailments associated with aging. Also, technology blurs the distinction between life and death: is chemotherapy, for instance, prolonging life or prolonging the dying process? With increasing awareness of risk, and of ever-emerging new risks, life seems dramatically less secure. Death may be lurking in unprotected sex, in contaminated food, in the very air we breathe.

Generally, the death of old people is accepted—they are said to have had their "good innings"—while young deaths are perceived as premature and, therefore, problematic. In Canada, most people die sometime after the age of 65, although mortality rates vary by factors such as socio-economic and Aboriginal status. For example, for Aboriginal Canadians, the average age of death is significantly lower than that for the rest of the population. The lowest mortality rates are among the university-educated, the employed, those in professional and managerial occupations, and those in the top income brackets. Some deaths are not caused by disease—for example, accidents, motor vehicle traffic accidents, suicide, and homicide—but cancer, heart disease, and stroke are the main causes of death in Canada. In 2011, these accounted for 55.1 per cent of all deaths (Statistics Canada, 2014e).

How Death Is Now an Ambiguous Process

Death has become an ambiguous process rather than just a natural event. Brain death has become the accepted criterion for death so that an apparently live patient whose heart is still beating but whose brain no longer functions is declared dead, thus becoming a source of fresh body parts for patients who would otherwise die. Medical intervention can retard the advancement of many diseases that once would have killed more quickly so that it is now possible for individuals to continue their normal social activities for months, or even years, after having been diagnosed with a terminal illness, albeit in a state of uncertainty about their future. Patients are now likely to be informed of their dying status and urged to make preparations for the time when they may no longer be competent to make decisions. They are urged to discuss their preferences for their final stages of life and for their death—for example, for their medical treatment and for their funeral. People can draw up living wills or advance directives, and/or they may give an enduring power of attorney to a trusted person to ensure, as much as possible, that even when dying they maintain control over their lives. The underlying assumption is that all people want to be informed that they are dying, that they all have the knowledge, and the will, to plan ahead—i.e., to consider their potential future circumstances and to choose possible alternative ways of dying—and that their wishes will be adhered to.

New ethical issues have arisen in relation to death and dying, for which there is often no easy solution. People are encouraged to donate organs in order to save lives, but in some countries, there is a black market in organs. There is also the question of how patients are selected as organ recipients. How many Aboriginal people or poor people, for example, have received organ transplantations? Many ethical questions were raised, for example, after the owner of the Senators hockey team, Eugene Melnyk, was given a liver transplant in five days after his public appeal. Challenging ethical questions also arise in relation to dying: for example, in relation to the withdrawal of treatment, at what stage should patients be taken off ventilators? Who decides, and when, whether the lives of patients who have suffered severe brain trauma will continue to be worthwhile? Is it ever ethical to withdraw nutrition and fluid from a patient? Should priority be given, in terms of health-care costs, research, and expertise, to more sophisticated technology and treatment, or to palliative treatment for the chronically ill and dying?

The Search for a Good Death

medicalization
The process by which non-medical problems become defined and treated as medical issues, usually in terms of illnesses, disorders, or syndromes.

The ideal so-called good death, prior to its **medicalization** and prior to the secularization of society, was to die at home, surrounded by friends and neighbours, accepting this last earthly suffering as a preparation for eternal life after death. Death often came early and relatively quickly as there was little that medical therapies or the medical profession could do. In the face of the inevitable, the doctor retreated, leaving the priest to perform the last rites. When the hospital became the place where people were sent to be cured, or to die, no longer was the dying person or the person's family in charge of the dying process. The patient became the property of the hospital, with visiting hours restricted and subject to hospital rules for the convenience of hospital organization and staff. The image of dying in hospital became that of patients attached to an arsenal of equipment in a futile attempt to defeat death, and resulting only in the unnecessary prolongation of their suffering. This is likely to have contributed to prevalent fears of experiencing suffering, degradation, and loss of control during a drawn-out dying period. People are made more fearful by descriptive media accounts of dying with cancer, HIV/AIDS, and dementia.

Palliative care and, more recently, **euthanasia** may be thought of as providing contemporary ideals of a good death. A good death may be envisaged as having a period of time during which the dying individual and relatives prepare for their forthcoming separation, for affairs to be put in order, and for the spiritual side of death to be approached. The aim of palliative care is to alleviate suffering in order to allow for these opportunities. Others may wish to die suddenly and painlessly after living a healthy, active life in old age, and when nature does not oblige, euthanasia or physician-assisted suicide may appear to offer a good death.

euthanasia
Meaning "gentle death," the term is used to describe voluntary death, often medically assisted, as a result of incurable and painful disease.

Palliative Care

Palliative care is an approach to care for those who are living with a life-threatening illness; the focus is on achieving comfort, ensuring respect, and maximizing quality of life for persons nearing death. In Canada, palliative care is provided in a variety of settings, including hospitals, long-term care facilities, hospices, and in individuals' homes on both a profit and not-for-profit basis. The types of services and funding available vary depending on the community in which an individual lives (Health Canada, 2009b). Canadians living in remote and rural areas or those living with disabilities have very limited access to palliative care services (Living Lessons, 2007). Hospices can provide both in-patient care in special facilities and care to patients in their own homes; doctors and nurses working in hospices specialize in palliative care. The aim is to offer comprehensive support by controlling pain and other symptoms as well as addressing the psychological, social, and spiritual needs of the dying person. The first hospice in Canada opened in November 1974 at St. Boniface General Hospital in Winnipeg, Manitoba (Tomczak, n.d.).

In recent years, the limitations of palliative care have been pointed out. Individuals have their own particular needs, and it is argued that, especially as hospices have become more medicalized and institutionalized, tension has developed between maintaining the ideal of a good death and maintaining the hospice organization (McNamara et al., 1994). Palliative caregivers generally have tended to oppose views supportive of euthanasia.

Euthanasia

On February 6, 2015, the Supreme Court of Canada in a unanimous decision ruled that Canadians have the right to physician-assisted suicide where there is "a competent adult person who (1) clearly consents to the termination of life and (2) has a grievous and irremediable medical condition (including an illness, disease or disability) that causes enduring suffering that is intolerable to the individual in the circumstances of his or her condition" (Supreme Court of Canada, 2015, [147]).[5] It should be noted that there was

5. Quebec passed legislation that legalized medical aid in dying in June 2014.

nothing in the court decision that would compel doctors to participate. However, the decision was met with mixed response from doctors and medical groups. Some advocates of disabled people condemned the ruling because it extended to persons with disability and not just the terminally ill, arguing that this devalues disabled peoples' lives. However, those who had worked for years to decriminalize physician-assisted death felt "relief and gratitude" (Martin, 2015, p. A8). A survey in 2014 found that 84 per cent of Canadians supported "assisted dying," a view shared across every demographic including those who identified themselves as Christians and the disabled (Kirkey, 2014). The court gave the federal government 12 months to draft new legislation that would be consistent with its ruling. The recently elected Liberal government, while sympathetic to the decision, has indicated a commitment to hold broad consultations on the issue prior to formalizing new legislation. Justice Minister Jody Wilson-Raybould requested a six-month extension, until August 2016, to draft the new law. The court only granted a four-month extension.

The challenge to Canada's Criminal Code that had prohibited assisted suicide was first made public with the famous case of Sue Rodriguez. The 42-year-old Rodriguez, who had Lou Gehrig's disease, asked the Supreme Court in the early 1990s for the right to kill herself with a doctor's help. She argued that the ban on assisted suicide violated the Constitution by curbing her right to personal liberty and autonomy guaranteed under the Charter of Rights and Freedoms. In a narrow 5–4 ruling in 1993 the court rejected her argument. (See M. Smith, 1993, for a review of the case.) Sue Rodriguez committed suicide in 1994 with the help of an anonymous doctor. Her struggle helped to galvanize right-to-die groups, such as Dying with Dignity, whose mandate is to improve quality of dying and expand Canadians' end-of-life options (www.dyingwithdignity.ca/about/index.php). In September 2013, Dr Donald Low's case furthered support for the right-to-die movement. Low made a passionate plea for medically assisted dying in a video eight days before his death from a brain-stem tumour: "I'm going to die, but what worries me is how I'm going to die . . . I wish they [clinicians who oppose assisted suicide] would live in my body for 24 hours. I'm frustrated with not being able to have control over my own life, not being able to make the decision myself when enough is enough" (www.youtube.com/watch?v=q3jgSkxV1rw).

Euthanasia and physician-assisted suicide provide the medical means of ending life that is perceived as being unbearable, usually, although not necessarily, in relation to terminal illness. With a few exceptions (the Netherlands, Belgium, Switzerland, and the US states of Oregon, Washington, Montana, and Vermont), these actions are illegal in most countries. The word *euthanasia* literally means a "good death" or "dying well," but there are conflicting opinions about what constitutes the practice of euthanasia. The injection of a lethal drug dose by a doctor with the explicit intention of terminating life at the request of a patient who is competent to make decisions is voluntary euthanasia, sometimes referred to as active euthanasia. When a doctor does not directly cause death but prescribes or provides the substance that causes death, it is regarded as physician-assisted suicide. Withdrawing medical treatment from the terminally ill when such treatment is considered to be useless and providing drugs to the terminally ill to relieve pain knowing that this may result in death, have traditionally been accepted as good medical practices. These measures are sometimes referred to as passive euthanasia. The medical profession has generally accepted that while death may be the side effect of pain relief, the intention is to relieve pain, not to end life.

Supporters of euthanasia usually focus on arguments for voluntary euthanasia by appealing to the right of individuals to control their own death. According to this view, legalizing voluntary euthanasia provides justice for all. A law that denies choice is unjust and oppressive to those who decide that life has become unbearable for them or that life has lost any qualities that would make it worthwhile. Opponents of legalized voluntary euthanasia often invoke what is called the "slippery slope" (or "thin edge of the wedge") argument to support their case. They assert that it is not simply a matter of individual rights, but that changing attitudes could eventually lead to the acceptance of some forms of involuntary euthanasia whereby the quality of life of those considered too socially burdensome may be perceived as being not worthwhile. Supporters point out that strong safeguards can be put into place that would protect all persons and that there is no evidence from jurisdictions that allow doctor-assisted deaths that abuse has occurred.

Today, there is no consensus about euthanasia among Canadian doctors. Prior to the Supreme Court ruling, 44.8 per cent thought that physician-assisted death should be legalized while 41.7 per cent thought it should remain illegal (Picard, 2014). However, at the 2014 Canadian Medical Association (CMA) annual general meeting, 91 per cent of delegates voted that should future legislation permit physician-assisted death, doctors should be free to choose according to their conscience as to whether they would participate if requested by a patient (Kirkey, 2014). After the court decision, the CMA stated that it supports patients who seek "medical aid in dying" as well as physicians' choice to participate (CBC News, Feb. 06, 2015).

According to most religions, euthanasia and physician-assisted suicide are morally wrong. Many people, however, no longer accept moral answers based on traditional authority. As Giddens (1991) suggests, although traditional authority, including religion, continues to exist, there are many other competing authorities in the modern world of expertise. When making life-and-death decisions during times of illness, medicine, rather than religion, is likely to be regarded as more significant because of the high value that people place on medical knowledge and technology that can save or maintain life. Medicine remains the area of expertise that controls the knowledge, drugs, and technology associated with health and illness and with the dying process.

Conclusion

Aging is constructed differently in different social and historical contexts. The consequences of population aging have profound social and economic implications for governments, health-care providers, family members, and communities. Although the majority of seniors are active, healthy, and contributing members of society, ageism persists in our society and leads to a view that older people are a social burden. On the other hand, public health policy counters the negative stereotypes with a vision for "healthy aging" and "age-friendly communities."

Death is a social process as well as a biological event. Individuals are encouraged to discuss their end-of-life preferences with loved ones, and make plans for a future without them. The Canadian Medical Association has called for a national end-of-life care strategy that minimizes suffering and places priority on quality of life to the end. Ultimately, dying and death is a solitary experience; its meaning depends on one's faith and existential beliefs. At a societal level, health professionals are under increasing pressure to find methods to achieve cost efficiencies and set priorities for the allocation of health services. The priorities chosen will have a major impact on the quality of life and death experienced by our seniors.

Summary

- Aging is a socially constructed process. Social, cultural, and historical factors shape our understanding of old age.
- People today are living longer, although there are notable differences within and between countries. Aboriginal Canadians, for example, have a lower life expectancy than non-Aboriginal Canadians.
- Canada's population is rapidly aging; projections are that seniors will comprise one-quarter of the population by 2036.
- Population aging has economic, social, and political implications.
- Ageism, that is discrimination based on age, contributes to a view that seniors are a "social burden."
- The reality is that most seniors are healthy and remain active and contribute significantly to the social fabric, for example, as volunteers and caregivers.
- Government policies that promote "healthy aging" ignore structural inequalities that affect people's health.
- Medical intervention and technology are postponing and changing the process of dying.
- Despite a recent Supreme Court decision that ruled Canadians have the right to physician-assisted suicide, there is no consensus in the medical community about euthanasia.
- Proponents of legal voluntary euthanasia argue that individuals should have autonomy in their end-of-life decisions; opponents argue that legalization is a slippery slope that could lead to a disregard for some human life.

Key Terms

assisted living	gender/sex	public health
ageism	globalization	racism
class	individualism/	social capital
economic rationalism/	individualization	social construction
economic liberalism	medicalization	social death
euthanasia	Medicare	

Sociological Reflection: Living in an Ageless World

Imagine a time when medical science has discovered a cure for aging: a one-shot vaccine has been discovered that makes people virtually immortal. Would you take the vaccine? What would be the ramifications of a world in which no one ever grew old, and aging, dying, and death were things of the past?

Discussion Questions

1. In what ways do the media contribute to ageism? Give examples.
2. What does being old mean to you?
3. As you see it, what are the implications of population aging for society? Be specific.

4. How have death and dying changed over the past 50 years?
5. Which groups of people do you think are more likely to agree with legalized voluntary euthanasia? Which groups are more likely to disagree? Why?
6. Why is it important to understand the economic and political factors that affect funding and social services for seniors?

Further Investigation

1. Expanding on the information in this chapter, critically analyze policies that affect the aged in Canada.
2. Critically discuss whether a "good death" is possible. What is the meaning of death in the sense of a good death?

Further Reading

Auger, J., & Tedford-Litle, D. (2002). *From the inside looking out: Competing ideas about growing old*. Halifax, NS: Fernwood.

CIHI. (2011). *Health care in Canada, 2011: A focus on seniors and aging*. Ottawa: CIHI. Available at www.cihi.ca

Denton, M., & Kusch, K. (2006). *Well-being through the senior years*. Ottawa, ON: Social Development Canada.

Northcott, H., & Wilson, D. (2001). *Dying and death in Canada*. Aurora, ON: Garamond.

Snyder, L., & Caplan, A. (Eds.). (2001). *Assisted suicide: Finding common ground*. Indianapolis, IN: Indiana University Press

Turcotte, M., & Schellenberg, G. (2007). *A portrait of seniors in Canada 2006*. Ottawa: Statistics Canada. Available at: http://www.statcan.gc.ca/pub/89-519-x/89-519-x2006001-eng.pdf

Web Resources

Canadian Hospice Palliative Care Association
http://chpca.net

Dying with Dignity Canada
www.dyingwithdignity.ca

Health Council of Canada—Seniors in Need
www.healthcouncilcanada.ca/rpt_det_gen.php?id=348

Public Health Agency of Canada (PHAC) Aging & Seniors
www.phac-aspc.gc.ca/seniors-aines

SocioSite—Death and Dying
www.sociosite.net/topics/health.php#DEATH

Statistics Canada—Seniors
www5.statcan.gc.ca/subject-sujet/theme-theme?pid=70000&lang=eng&more=0

PART 3
The Social Organization of Health Care: Politics, Values, and Professions

Canadians consider equal and timely access to medically necessary health-care services on the basis of need as a right of citizenship, not a privilege of status or wealth.

—Roy Romanow (2002)

One way that Canadians distinguish themselves from Americans is through differences in the two health systems. But this was not always the case, so how did these differences emerge? An understanding of the social organization of health care in Canada today requires us to examine issues of power, ideology, and values in shaping health care and health-care institutions. To understand health care in Canada also requires an examination of the relationship between the state and medical interests, the role of the growing pharmaceutical industry, and how economic and political forces have influenced the delivery of health care. A common theme among four of the chapters is the influence of the medical profession on health policy, on other health professionals, and on the delivery of health care. The influence of the pharmaceutical industry on health policy is the focus of Chapter 14.

The five chapters in Part 3 examine key features of the health system—its history, its structure, and the changes underway—to understand why the health system is organized the way that it is and how it could be otherwise organized.

- Chapter 12 traces the development of Western medicine's dominance of health care and how this dominance is continually the source of challenge and resistance.
- Chapter 13 discusses the history of health care in Canada, the competing interests and politics that shaped, and continue to shape, its publicly funded universal system, and the on-going debate about its future.
- Chapter 14 examines how the profit motive affects the operation of the pharmaceutical industry, and the relationship between the industry and Health Canada.
- Chapter 15 looks at the changing history of nursing in Canada and some of the major challenges and problems faced by nurses today.
- Chapter 16 discusses complementary and alternative medicine and some of the reasons for its growing popularity in the Western world.

CHAPTER 12
Medicine, Medical Dominance, and Public Health

Jennie Hornosty & John Germov

Did you ever dream about being a doctor as a child? Why do you think being a doctor seems so appealing to so many of us when we are young? What do you think prevents most people, particularly people of certain groups, from pursuing that career?

Overview

- What are the origins of scientific medicine?
- What is medical dominance, and how has it been challenged?
- How did Western medicine emerge as the dominant health-care profession?
- What is the role of public health and health promotion?

Medicine today is the dominant health profession. However, medicine as we know it is a fairly recent phenomenon, dating back only to the late nineteenth century. This chapter provides a brief overview of the history of scientific medicine and the underlying assumptions of medicine today. It discusses how medical dominance was established in Canada and looks at some of the challenges to medical dominance. While medical dominance has often been resisted in formal and informal ways, recent challenges, including complementary and alternative medicine, the growth of allied health professionals, the women's health movement, and the involvement of government in the provision of health care, have proved effective in challenging medical power. The concern with public health has its roots in the nineteenth century. Although Canada played a leading role in emphasizing the societal roots of health inequities, health policy today is geared primarily toward changing individual lifestyles.

Introduction: Our Faith in Scientific Medicine

It is hard for us to imagine a time when medicine as it is practised today did not exist. Whether for a regular check-up, or because we are ill or need a doctor's note to explain our absence from work or for a missed exam, most of us have visited the doctor's office for more than one reason. Many of you will have received vaccinations as children, or more recently against viruses such as H1N1. Some of you will have been to a hospital for X-rays, blood tests, or surgery. Although some people seek out what is referred to as alternative medicine or therapies from time to time, most people still have a great deal of faith in doctors. We look to medicine to come up with cures for such things as heart disease, diabetes, blindness, and cancer. When people are asked why they have such respect for medicine, a common response is that medicine is scientific. A scientific approach to illness is, however, a fairly recent development.

The Origins of Scientific Medicine

> To seek to ease pain is natural.
>
> —Silverburg (1966, p. 16, cited in "Hippocrates Biography")

People have always sought ways to relieve pain. All known societies have had theories or explanations about disease and illness. Early societies, for example, attributed sickness

HIPPOCRATES MEDECIN
Grec. Chap. 28.

Stock Montage/Getty Images

Hippocrates is perhaps most famous today for the Hippocratic Oath, a pledge that all new physicians took for centuries. While Canadian doctors today do not take this oath, as it conflicts with the way medicine is practised (e.g., the oath bans abortion), some of the fundamental ideals of the original oath are preserved in modern codes of ethics, which doctors are required to adhere to.

to spiritual or supernatural causes, such as evil spirits, direct intervention by gods, or the work of a sorcerer. When someone got sick, they turned to shamans, who were seen as intermediaries between the natural and spiritual worlds. Shamans used prayer, incantations, spells, and sacrifices to drive away or appease the gods or spirits thought to be responsible for people's illnesses. They also developed certain skills such as using herbal remedies and setting broken bones (History of Medicine, Shamanism, n.d.).

Supernatural explanations for disease were first challenged in classical Greece. Hippocrates (460–377 BCE), generally considered the "Father of Medicine," is credited with laying the foundations of medicine as a science; he rejected superstition and magic and argued that every disease had only natural causes. Hippocrates subscribed to the humoral theory of disease, that is, the belief that each of the four natural elements—air, earth, fire, and water—was associated with a particular humour. He believed that illness resulted when these four humours (blood, phlegm, yellow bile, and black bile) were not in balance and that this could be detected through physical symptoms (Weiss & Lonnquist, 2009).

Early Christianity, however, attributed disease and illness as a punishment for sin or as a test of one's faith and commitment to God. For example, people with disabilities were viewed as sinners or as the offspring of parents who had sinned. This view prevailed until the seventeenth century (Covey, 2005). In the Medieval era, religious dogma dominated explanations of illness and healing practices. Medical practice was initially based in the monastery and controlled by the Church. Although people complemented religious healing with secular healing, physicians represented a form of blasphemy because they did not use religious intervention, such as prayer and penitence, to cure disease. By the second half of the Medieval era, medicine became the responsibility of secular clergy (Weiss & Lonnquist, 2009).

The Renaissance period marks the beginning of a more scientific approach to medical knowledge and practice. This was a period of significant intellectual growth and discovery; the teachings of the Church were being challenged and Christianity began to lose authority and control to the state. The previously accepted humoral theory of disease was rejected, as experimentation, observation, and dissection on the human body led to new discoveries and theories of human anatomy. Medical specialization became more pronounced. Physicians, that is, graduates from a school of medicine, provided diagnosis and treatment to the wealthy. Surgery, however, was practised mostly by barbers and had lower status. These *barber surgeons* learned their skills in apprenticeship, in many cases on the battlefield, performed surgeries, managed open wounds, and repaired broken bones. Apothecaries, the early pharmacists, dispensed herbs and spices, and in the countryside sometimes acted as physicians. The discoveries and advances of this period primarily benefited the wealthy; most people in villages and towns continued to rely on less expensive traditional methods, such as herbal and spiritual healing (Weiss & Lonnquist, 2009; History of Medicine, Renaissance Medicine, n.d.).

The Scientific Revolution in the seventeenth century signalled a revolution in thought and practice that brought about modern science. During this period and the following Age of Enlightenment (in the eighteenth century), science and medical knowledge developed in leaps and bounds; new ideas in physics, astronomy, biology, human anatomy, chemistry, and other sciences replaced the earlier doctrines from Ancient Greece and the Middle Ages. Systematic doubt and empirical verification by experiment became the new paradigm—what we know today as the scientific method. One of the most important medical advancements in the seventeenth century was in physiology and William Harvey's experimental proof that blood is conserved and then circulated through the body by the heart. In the eighteenth century, an Italian physician and professor of anatomy, Giovanni Morgagni, demonstrated that specific diseases could be traced to specific pathology in individual organs—and hence developed the anatomical concept of disease. An Austrian internist, Josef Leopold Auenbrugger, discovered that he could detect fluid in the lungs by tapping on the chest. An English country doctor, Edward Jenner, paved the way for modern immunology with his discovery that persons inoculated with cowpox developed immunity to smallpox, which at the time was a leading cause of death among children. And in the early nineteenth century a French physician named René Laennec invented the stethoscope (Weiss & Lonnquist, 2009; History of Medicine, History of Scientific Medicine, n.d.).

In the nineteenth century, new discoveries, such as improvements in the microscope, X-rays, the discovery of the cell, and the germ theory of disease, revolutionized medicine. The *cell theory*, associated with German pathologist Rudolf Virchow, postulated that diseases begin when there are changes in a healthy cell; treatment, therefore, requires restoring the cell to its normal state. The *germ theory* was advanced by French chemist Louis Pasteur. Pasteur, who invented the process known as pasteurization, demonstrated that micro-organisms (germs) were responsible for infectious diseases in humans and animals and for their transmission among them. Building on the work of Pasteur, Robert Koch, a German doctor, identified specific bacteria that caused specific diseases and formulated a set of rules known as Koch's postulates for determining conclusively whether a particular bacterium was the cause of a particular disease. His work laid the foundations for the science of bacteriology (Weiss & Lonnquist, 2009; History of Medicine, The Rise of Scientific Medicine, n.d.). Along with ongoing medical discoveries, there was also a growing interest in social medicine or what is now often referred to as public health. Links were made between the overcrowding in cities, unsanitary living conditions, and poor working conditions and the spread of infectious diseases such as cholera, typhoid fever, diphtheria, and tuberculosis. Those who fell ill were increasingly being treated in hospitals, which also grew in number. By the end of the century, the science of pharmacology was established. Surgery, which had previously been painful and frequently resulted in an infection, became safer with the development of both anesthesia and antiseptics. Nitrous oxide was first used for anesthesia by American dentists in the 1840s. In the mid-1860s,

Sir Joseph Lister, a British surgeon, discovered that infection was caused by airborne bacteria and that by applying carbolic acid to the wound, dressings, and surgical instruments, which sterilized them, infection could be prevented (Weiss & Lonnquist, 2009; History of Medicine, The Rise of Scientific Medicine, n.d.).

By the twentieth century, scientific medicine and the biomedical approach to illness had gained a great deal of legitimacy. Advancements in technology and the discovery of antibiotics and antiviral vaccines were instrumental in encouraging faith in medicine. Most of the medical technology and medications we take for granted today were developed less than 100 years ago. Ultrasound imaging, CT scans, MRIs, endoscopes, heart-lung machines, kidney-dialysis machines, antibiotics, cortisone, and drugs to treat mental illness, for example, are all products of twentieth-century medicine.

Biomedicine/Scientific Medicine

**biomedicine/
biomedical model**
The conventional approach to medicine in Western societies, based on the diagnosis and explanation of illness as a malfunction of the body's biological mechanisms. This approach underpins most health professions and health services, which focus on treating individuals, and generally ignores the social origins of illness and its prevention.

allopathic medicine
A name given to conventional biomedicine. Treatment of diseases is by drugs, which have effects opposite to the symptoms.

Biomedicine, often referred to as **allopathic** medicine or conventional medicine, is considered to be *the scientific approach* for treating disease and illness. Underlying this approach are certain basic assumptions that have implications for the structure and practice of medicine today. In their book *Wasting Away* (2003), Pat and Hugh Armstrong critically examine the following five such assumptions that form the basis of allopathic medicine (pp. 18–42).

1. The Determinants of Illness Are Primarily Biological

An underlying premise is that mind and body are separate, and that each disease has a specific etiology, that is, each disease has a specific cause (germs, cancer cells) that can be diagnosed by specific medical tests. In narrowing a focus on disease to a biological level, it is easy to minimize other aspects of illness.

This assumption has an impact on the doctor–patient relationship and the way that medicine is practised. Doctors need not ask about social factors or what else is happening in a patient's life. If a patient's complaint has no identifiable biological cause, it may be dismissed as not real or as being "all in one's mind." Hence, doctors generally spend a limited amount of time with their patients. (In many practices the usual allotted time is 15 minutes per patient.) Prescriptions and diagnostic tests are typically the modes of treatment. Walk-in clinics operate on the assumption that only diagnoses of physiological symptoms are necessary for effective treatment.

2. Biomedicine Uses the Engineering Model of the Body

Biomedicine operates within a unified paradigm or model that views the body as a machine. That is, the body is approached as if it was composed of a number of different parts that can be separated and analyzed from each other. Since each disease is thought to be caused by a specific germ, diagnosis and treatment is limited to specific causes and specific parts. Accordingly, doctors are frequently encouraged to specialize in one branch of medicine. Nearly half (49.3 per cent) of practising physicians in Canada today are medical specialists (CIHI, 2014g). While specialization is associated with increased expertise in an area, for the patient with a complicated medical problem such as concomitant heart disease and kidney problems, this can mean having to see many different specialists, each one not having a complete understanding of how the treatment for one may affect the other.

The Armstrongs (2003) explain that this approach to the human body, combined with the doctrine of specific etiology, makes possible a fee-for-service payment, whereby each service or task is calculated to be worth a specific amount, and doctors are reimbursed accordingly. Furthermore, an assumption that treatment can be broken down into specific parts makes possible the rationalization of work in hospitals, whereby the amount of time required for each procedure is calculated to improve efficiency. In the process, the social and psychological needs of individuals are ignored.

3. Health Care Is Primarily about Curing Illness or Disability

The primary role of modern medicine is to cure the patient in order to make them "normal" again. This justifies the provision of the majority of health-care resources to acute-care hospitals with a focus on treating a specific medical condition as quickly as possible. According to Pat and Hugh Armstrong (2003), "management techniques developed in industry are transferred to health care on the assumption that fixing a care part is not much different from fixing a car part" (p. 21). Patients are treated as cases rather than as unique individuals who may have a range of specific physical and emotional needs; increasingly more surgeries are done on an outpatient basis. Focusing on acute care makes it is possible to ignore the effects of social determinants of health, such as unemployment, poverty, and racism, on health.

4. Medicine Is Scientific

The alleged superiority of biomedicine over alternate forms of treatment (e.g., naturopathy) stems from its claim to being a science. An assumption is that all surgical procedures, medications, and tests that doctors use have been proven scientifically. That is, they have been evaluated through experiments using double-blind randomized clinical trials, that there is agreement on what constitutes scientific evidence, and that doctors are value neutral in their practice of medicine. There is a further assumption that all patients with the same illness will have the same symptoms or will have the same pattern of disease development.

These assumptions are all problematic. In New Brunswick, for example, some doctors for moral reasons refuse to prescribe birth control pills or make referrals for abortion. Recently, an Ottawa woman brought the question of whether doctors should be allowed to refuse treatments for religious or moral reasons to the fore after she was refused a renewal for her birth control prescription at a walk-in clinic. The letter she was handed read, "Please be advised that because of reasons of my own medical judgment, as well as professional ethical concerns and religious values, I can only provide one form of birth control—natural family planning" (Yakabuski, 2014). It has also been established that women and men can have very different symptoms of impending heart attacks, and treatments appropriate for one may not be appropriate for the other. And in Chapter 14, Joel Lexchin demonstrates how the profit motive rather than science sometimes drives the pharmaceutical industry.

5. The Doctor Is the Authority and Expert

Allopathic doctors today are considered the "master labellers" of illness. That is, they are the ones who have the power to decide what is considered an illness, what the appropriate treatment is, as well as who provides the treatment. Our abiding faith in everything that is deemed scientific as well as doctors' lengthy educational and clinical training and their ability to convince us that the "doctor is always right" means that most people still look to the doctor as the expert. As a result, patients' views or opinions about their health and health care may be dismissed in the belief that they lack sufficient knowledge. However, as we shall see later in the chapter there is now more public skepticism about medicine's claims.

The Ascendancy of Medical Dominance

> There would never be any public agreement among doctors if they did not agree to agree on the main point of the doctor being always in the right.
>
> —George Bernard Shaw, *The Doctor's Dilemma*

medical dominance
A general term used to describe the power of the medical profession in terms of its control over its own work, over the work of other health workers, and over health resource allocation, health policy, and the way that hospitals are run.

The term **medical dominance** refers to the fact that medicine was, and to some extent still is, the most powerful profession in the health system. It points to the power the medical profession has, despite its limited numbers, to control its own work and that of other health-care workers, and to have influence over health policy and the organization of hospitals. For example, medical doctors in Canada are by no means the largest group of health-care workers. Even though the percentage of doctors is increasing, in 2011, doctors comprised just over 10 per cent of the total health-care professional workforce, compared with nurses, who made up 42.7 per cent, and allied health-care workers (including audiologists, chiropractors, dentists, dieticians, medical laboratory technicians, midwives, occupational therapists, optometrists, pharmacists, physiotherapists, psychologists, radiation technologists, respiratory therapists, speech pathologists, and social workers), who collectively constituted 47 per cent (CIHI, 2013a, p. 11). See Figure 12.1. A number of significant works have examined the issue of professions, particularly the rise of the medical profession (see Freidson, 1970, 1994, 2001; Gillespie, 1991; Larkin, 1983; Navarro, 1976, 1986; Starr, 1982; Willis, 1983, 1989b).

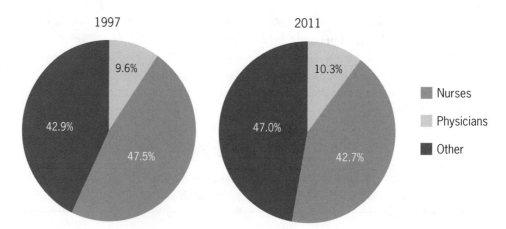

Figure 12.1 Distribution of Health-Care Workers in Canada, 1997 and 2011

Source: Figure 2, "Distribution of Health Personnel in Canada, 1997 and 2011," in *Canada's Health Care Providers, 1997 to 2011—A Reference Guide: Overview and Methodological Notes,* Canadian Institute for Health Information (2013), p. 11. https://secure.cihi.ca/estore/productFamily.htm?locale=en&pf=PFC2161

One factor in the growing dominance of medicine during the twentieth century was the continual advancement of science. No one can deny that scientific medicine has found effective cures for many diseases, and now with the completion of the Human Genome Project medicine potentially will be able to prevent or ameliorate the suffering from genetically caused illnesses. However, we need also to look at the societal factors that help explain medicine's ability to attain power and political influence. Eliot Freidson (1970), a key author in the field of medical dominance, suggests that the professional dominance of medicine is due to doctors' clinical role of diagnosis and treatment; to the ability of doctors to exert control over the knowledge base and occupational territory of other health professions; to the requirement that doctors request and supervise the work of other health practitioners; and to the unequal public status of medicine compared to other health professions. Similarly, Paul Wolpe (1985) argues that "a profession's power rests on its consensually granted authority over a specific, cultural tradition," which is its social capital. This is then institutionalized by the institution's retaining of control over licensing procedures, its education, and self-regulation (cited in Weiss & Lonnquist, 2006, p. 29). The successful medicalization of broad areas of human life such as sexuality, masculinity, aging, anxiety, and mood has also helped consolidate medical dominance. See Chapter 9 for a further discussion. However, as Freidson (1970) points out, the key feature of medical dominance is autonomy, which he defines as the "authority to direct and evaluate the work of others without in turn being subject to formal direction and evaluation by them" (p. 135).

Some specific ways where medical power is evident include the following:

- Only doctors can formally diagnose disease and sign birth and death certificates, and they have significant control over access to non-medical benefits, such as sick leave, workers' compensation, and early retirement due to health reasons.
- Doctors' control of diagnosis and treatment means that they effectively have administrative authority over other health professions. For example, doctors' decisions affect the work of nursing and allied health professionals who are often directly or indirectly responsible to doctor authority, particularly within the hospital system.
- Doctors can control access to a range of therapies through the requirement of a doctor's referral before other health professions can treat a patient.
- Doctors retain the right to set professional standards about treatment, which can affect hospital expenditures and the work of other health-care workers (enacted through licensing laws, which protect medicine from occupational encroachment).
- Doctors control the educational curriculum, as well as the examination and licensing of future doctors.

Another explanation for the ascendancy of medical dominance is found in the writings of Marxists like Vicente Navarro. Navarro's (1988) class analysis leads to his argument that medical dominance occurred in the United States because it served the interest of the dominant class:

Professional power was and is submerged in other forms of power such as class, race, gender, and other forces that shape the production of the knowledge, practice, and institutions of medicine. The power of the professions is subservient to the powerful forces such as the dominant classes that have an overwhelming influence in medicine. (p. 64)

Although Navarro's analysis is based on the ascendancy of medicine in the United States, his basic points are applicable to the Canadian context.

The Emergence of Medical Dominance in Canada

At the time Canada became a nation in 1867, there were few trained doctors, no medical schools, and no medical associations. During most of the nineteenth century and into the early twentieth century, most people did not consult a doctor when they were sick but, rather, visited the more affordable, accessible, and respectable homoeopaths, chemists, Chinese herbalists, spiritual healers, and midwives. Aboriginal peoples for example, used a variety of natural remedies and spiritual practices to treat diseases and illness. Later, settlers brought with them their informal healing practices that predominated until the latter half of the nineteenth century. During that time, medicine had little connection with science (Torrance, 1998). Physicians were scarce and most of the population relied heavily on lay healers. Home remedies made from roots, bark, leaves, and seeds, in addition to whisky, brandy, and opium were the standard fare for treating such things as respiratory and digestive problems.

In the early nineteenth century, doctors had few cures and little scientific understanding of disease; they mostly serviced the wealthy, who resided in major cities and could afford their fees. The general population was highly skeptical of medicine, particularly surgeons, because of the high death rate from post-operative infection (antiseptic only came into use in the 1880s). Although the first hospital in North America was established in Quebec City in the early part of the seventeenth century (Judi Coburn, cited in Armstrong & Armstrong, 2003), it was not until the twentieth century that hospitals became a place for most medical and surgical procedures. Prior to that, hospitals were seen as places for the chronically ill, the poor, and the dying. People viewed hospitals as dangerous places with poor hygienic practices and unqualified practitioners (Armstrong & Armstrong, 2003). Those who were middle class or wealthy were treated at home or in doctors' offices (Torrance, 1998).

There was no cohesive medical profession in the early nineteenth century; rather, there was a continual struggle between the medical practitioners and traditional folk healers, who enjoyed popular support (Blishen, 1991). However, as early as 1795 in Upper and Lower Canada, there were attempts made by physicians, who because of their social origins had connections to political elites, to restrict who could practise medicine. Licensing legislation was in place by 1870 but physicians were unable to achieve hegemonic control of the medical profession until well into the twentieth century (Torrance, 1998).

Formal educational qualifications are a key aspect of professionalization in order to ensure uniform training, socialize newcomers into accepted professional ideologies, and limit the number of those who can practise the profession. In Canada, the first medical school was established in Montreal in 1824, which five years later became affiliated with McGill University. By the end of the nineteenth century, six other medical schools were established: the University of Toronto, Laval, Queen's University, Dalhousie University, the University of Western Ontario, and the University of Manitoba (The Canadian Encyclopedia, Medical Education, n.d.). Today there are 17 university medical facilities in the country. The affiliation with universities both added respectability and served as a means of controlling curriculum and entrance to the profession. In practice, it meant restricting entry to those of higher social class origins and ultimately standardizing curriculum and training (Torrance, 1998, p. 8). The Canadian Medical Association was formed in 1867; this body was given the power to examine would-be practitioners and set curriculum (Blishen, 1991).

"The emergence of medical dominance in Canada took place between the nineteenth century, when medicine lacked power and status, and the early twentieth century, by which time it largely controlled the emerging health means of production" (Coburn, 1988a, p. 94). At a general level, the evolution of medical dominance in Canada followed a pattern similar to that of other capitalist nations at similar levels of economic development. Similar types of institutions were established to provide health care, which included "a hierarchy of healing occupations and professions under a dominant medical profession; hospitals as key institutions; . . . [and] specialized organizations for the training and socialization of health workers . . ." (Torrance, 1998, p. 3). Medicine consolidated its power between the First World War and 1962, the time of the Saskatchewan doctors' strike (Coburn et al., 1983, p. 407).

To gain dominance, physicians needed to restrict the activities of other health occupations, such as pharmacists, and of healers, such as homeopaths and eclectics, who had popular support among citizens. Pharmacists were regularly sought after for medical advice, were able to counter-prescribe drugs for customers, and were powerful enough initially to resist medical attempts to control their profession (Muzzin et al., 1998, p. 381). However, pharmacists eventually agreed to stop prescribing on the condition that doctors stopped dispensing medications: "By the early twentieth century, pharmacy's subordination to medicine was complete" (Torrance, 1998, p. 8). The medical profession also succeeded in bringing nursing under medical control and making it a subordinate profession. Similarly, doctors gained exclusive control over pregnancy and childbirth, and midwifery was relegated to isolated and northern regions of the country. It should be noted, however, that midwifery is becoming increasingly recognized as a preferred choice for women giving birth. In 2012, there were 1080 midwives in Canada (CIHI, 2014a).

This ability of the medical profession to unify and attain professional dominance over competing health-care occupations was strengthened by its connections to elite groups and the **state**. Because of their social origins, their affiliation with elite educational institutions, and their connections with socially and politically dominant groups, physicians were able, with the help of the state, to achieve and maintain their **hegemonic** position. They succeeded either through absorbing competing professions, marginalizing them, or granting them some legitimacy in exchange for subordinate status (Torrance, 1998, p. 4).

Ongoing tensions between physicians and other health-care providers continued well into the twentieth century; however, the key institutions that helped consolidate the power of biomedicine were in place by the beginning of the First World War. The Flexner Report ("Medical Education in the United States and Canada"), which gave rise to modern medical education, was released in 1910. The report, conducted for the Carnegie Foundation, emphasized the need for rigorous academic standards, a curriculum based around biomedicine and scientific evidence, and an apprenticeship system with hands-on clinical training. It "ensured the 'triumph of the specific aetiology paradigm,' the one called scientific medicine," which continues to dominate today (Armstrong & Armstrong, 2003, p. 24). Largely as the result of efforts by Dr Thomas Roddick, a celebrated physician and Member of Parliament, the government passed the Canada Medical

state
A term used to refer to a collection of institutions, including the Parliament (e.g., government and opposition political parties) the civil service, the judiciary, the police, and the military.

hegemony/hegemonic
Dominance or power of one social group, idea, or discourse over another.

Act in 1912, which led to the formation of the Medical Council of Canada. This had the effect of creating a national medical licensing standard and examination procedures across the country.

Medical dominance in Canada, as has been the case elsewhere, was secured and has been maintained by political means. In the Depression years, although doctors suffered a loss of income, the medical profession remained powerful and continued to have a strong influence on developments in health care. During the Second World War, "government practically integrated its policy and planning with that of the profession" (Coburn, 1988a, p. 100). The close relationship at the time between medicine and the state is expressed in a comment made by a medical officer in the Department of Health: "we do our utmost to maintain at every turn the interests of the practitioners of Canada as well as organized medicine" (cited in Coburn, 1988a, p. 101). By post–World War II, the medical profession was almost a private government and took an even more active role in formulating public policy. In the words of Taylor,

> . . . the private government of the medical profession and the public government of the country have become interlocked and, to some degree, interdependent. . . . Organized medicine influences legislative policy with respect to the timing and design of public programmes, guides the choice and structure of administrative agencies, prescribes certain of the administrative procedures, participates in the continuing decisions of administrators, and . . . serves as the governmental agency in the administration of major programmes. (Cited in Coburn, et al., 1983, p. 417)

Challenges to Medical Dominance

Medical dominance has never been absolute; there has always been some resistance, whether from other health professions or the working classes in society who were critical of medicine's elitist class position. However, more recently, several major countervailing powers in society have significantly challenged and constrained medical influence. The first major challenge was the introduction of government-financed and -controlled health-insurance plans implemented in Canada in the 1960s.

The Emergence of the Welfare State

welfare state
A system whereby the government assumes primary responsibility for the welfare of its citizens through programs designed to protect and promote the economic and social well-being of its citizens.

The 1930s and 1940s saw the emergence of the **welfare state** in Canada. Saskatchewan elected the first social-democratic government (the Co-operative Commonwealth Federation) in the country in 1944 on its promise to implement a government hospital-insurance plan, which it successfully did in 1947. But it was Saskatchewan's implementation of a government-controlled provincial medical-care plan in 1962 that led to the 23-day doctors' strike. This strike and the subsequent defeat of the doctors was, Coburn et al. (1983) argue, a "landmark of [a] new era in relationships between the profession and the state" (pp. 418–19); it marked the beginning of a decline in medical dominance. In opposing government health insurance in Saskatchewan and later the recommendations of the Hall Commission to establish a national plan, "the medical profession lost substantial ideological and political influence regarding nonclinical matters" (p. 419).

When the federal government passed the Medical Care Act in 1966, which laid the foundation for **Medicare** in Canada, this diminished some of the power of the medical profession to set wages and the conditions of work. In her discussion of professional power, Elston (1991) argues that economic autonomy, that is, the right of doctors to determine their pay rates, had been an important component of medicine's autonomy. This autonomy was lost with the introduction of government health insurance as doctors now had to negotiate their schedule of fees with their respective provincial or territorial governments. Initially, doctors tried to circumvent some of this control through extra-billing but, ultimately, were unsuccessful; the federal government brought in legislation that made extra-billing illegal.

Furthermore, state-administered health plans provided an opportunity for government surveillance of physicians' local work and income patterns (Coburn, 1988a, p. 103). As well, there were other changes that redefined and delimited the traditional mandate of the medical profession in substantial ways: hospital budgets were closely scrutinized and medical technology was "rationalized" to avoid duplication, which affected the type of care doctors were able to provide (Coburn, 1988a). Administration and management of hospitals increasingly came under university-trained administrators rather than physicians. Coburn et al. (1983) note that a new class of corporate rationalizers (including health administrators, planners and bureaucrats, medical researchers, and doctors in public health) brought in new managerial strategies that constrained doctors' clinical autonomy. This bureaucratic rationalization of hospitals decreased medicine's direct control over its major workplace; doctors became just another, although still powerful, interest group in a large organization. In some instances, governments required hospitals to put emergency room doctors on salary rather than fee-for-service compensation. In many provinces, health services were regionalized and operated under the direction of district health councils, which included lay and other health-care personnel besides doctors (Coburn et al., 1983; Coburn, 1988a).

Government, through funding, was able to control the number of intern and residency training spots available in any year. For example, in the late 1970s governments were successful in getting medical schools to reduce the number of students they accepted and ensure that general practitioners accounted for about 50 per cent of graduates (Coburn et al., 1983; Coburn, 1988a). Also in the 1970s and 1980s, there was a shift in government priorities in health to focus more on disease prevention, health promotion, and **social determinants of health** (see Epp, 1986; Lalonde, 1974; Coburn, 2006). Changes today are part of a changing political economy. Coburn (2006, p. 441) writes that the state has increased its regulatory constraints on all the health professions, including putting public representation on previously autonomous and self-regulatory bodies. Within the Ministry of Health, planners and state bureaucrats have replaced physicians. Professional self-regulation, while still operative in many respects, is significantly different from the previous eras.

The Professionalization of Other Occupations

In addition to managerial reforms that are exerting control over health care, the medical profession is facing challenges from other health occupations which want greater autonomy from medicine. Nurses, optometrists, pharmacists, chiropractors, psychologists, dentists, and other health professionals are asking for a share of government monies and

Medicare
Canada's universal health-care program; funded and administered by federal, provincial, and territorial governments.

social determinants of health
Refers to the social and economic environments in which people live and which determine their health, such as working conditions, income, and education. The quality of these determinants is a reflection of how society is organized and how it distributes its economic and social resources.

are striving to enhance their power and influence in the medical domain. Many of these occupations are professionalized and now have self-governing and licensing bodies. For example, nursing has recently become more critical of the medical profession and has asserted its right to practise independently in the community. Furthermore, an increasing number of Canadians are choosing alternative therapies instead of, or as an addition to, allopathic medicine. This choice is facilitated by supplementary private health-insurance plans, which cover some of the costs of naturopaths, osteopaths, chiropractors, acupuncturists, and massage therapists.

Women's and consumer groups continue to question traditional technological approaches to childbirth and lobby hospitals to provide alternatives, such as family-oriented birthing rooms. The **women's health movement**, long critical of the medicalization of women's bodies, has played an important role in legitimating midwifery as a desirable alternative to physician-managed pregnancy and childbirth. Today, midwives are legal and regulated to practise in most provinces and territories. Advocacy groups such as the Canadian Health Coalition (health-care workers, including nurses and some doctors, seniors, labour groups, churches, and academics) lobby for greater participation by patients and members of the public in health-care reform and an expanded role of non-physician health-care providers. The Canadian Health Coalition criticizes the fee-for-service model, opposes the growing privatization of health-care services, and advocates a community-based, multidisciplinary approach to health-care delivery (Canadian Health Coalition, 2014).

Conflicts within Medicine

Heterogeneity within medicine today is another factor that weakens medical hegemony (Coburn et al., 1983; Coburn, 2006). There are more academic and research physicians whose attitudes, interests, and goals differ from general practitioners and specialists. As well, the orientations of general practitioners often differ from that of specialists, such as those in surgery or cardiology. The latter group tends to focus on acute care and individual treatment, arguing for more money for advanced diagnostic medical technology; doctors in general practice may favour greater decentralization and community-based health care. And there are conflicts within the profession itself. Groups such as the Medical Reform Group of Ontario, formed in the late 1970s as an organization for progressive, socially conscious physicians, advocates for a different model of primary care. For example, the group actively opposed extra-billing and the subsequent doctors' strike in Ontario. It "destroyed the myth of the unanimity of the medical profession in a very visible and repeated fashion" (A Brief History of the Medical Reform Group of Ontario, 1979–1994).

The Demystification of Medicine

An indirect challenge to medical dominance is the growing public skepticism of medical authority as scientific and infallible. People today have higher levels of education and are better informed about health issues. And, although the information is not always reliable, the Internet provides easy access to a vast health literature and a range of health resources, including information on diseases, medications, and suggested therapies. As a result, medicine and medical practice no longer hold the same mystique. The media has also

women's health movement In Canada, included both formal and informal organizations of women that addressed issues ranging from birth control to poverty. The movement did not have a single voice or leader but, rather, encompassed a variety of groups and activities, collectively known as the women's health movement.

played an important role in demystifying medicine and raising ethical questions about certain medical practices.

Medicine has been criticized for being self-serving—placing self-interest over patient or public interest—in the delivery of health services and the treatment of disease. From the public's perception, this was especially evident during both the Saskatchewan and Ontario doctors' strike, discussed in Chapter 13. Professional self-regulation has been criticized as being unable to effectively address issues of fraud, negligence, misconduct, or incompetence among its members. Media exposés of medical fraud and negligence have made the public increasingly aware of the potentially damaging effects of medical treatment, what Illich (1977) referred to as **iatrogenesis**. Various forms of scientific dishonesty have been exposed over the years—particularly scientific fraud in the form of biased medical research (La Follette, 1992); pharmaceutical fraud, such as the promotion of thalidomide and more recently Vioxx and SSRI medications (Braithwaite, 1984; Healy, 2003); and medical technology fraud, such as the marketing of the Dalkon Shield (Cashman, 1989). In addition, serious questions have been raised about the close relationship between medicine and Big Pharma (see Healy, 1997, 2003). In March 2009, students at Harvard Medical School exposed the links that a number of professors had with drug companies after a student became concerned when one of his professors promoted the benefits of cholesterol drugs and belittled the student for asking about side effects. Through his investigations, the student found that this full-time member of the medical faculty was a paid consultant to 10 pharmaceutical companies, including 5 who developed cholesterol medications (*New York Times*, March 3, 2009). In her recent investigation of the pharmaceutical industry's influence in medical education, Kelly Holloway (2014) found that the industry's presence is normalized as a part of medical training, even though some students resisted its presence.

Media attention to cases of medical error and negligence has added to public skepticism about the scientific validity of diagnostic testing and the trustworthiness of doctors' professional opinions. Such cases raise doubts in people's minds about the quality of care they receive from their doctors. After a patient went public in February 2010, a surgeon at a Windsor, Ontario, hospital was required to stop performing surgeries after it was revealed that she performed mastectomies as a result of a misdiagnosis on two women who did not have cancer. It appears the doctor misread the initial pathology report (CBC, 2010). In 2008, a New Brunswick pathologist was stripped of his medical licence after an investigation found that 18 per cent of the cases he diagnosed were incomplete and 3 per cent of the diagnoses were wrong (CBC, 2008). In Newfoundland, a provincial inquiry found that laboratory errors led to the misdiagnosis and incorrect treatment of 383 patients between 1997 and 2005, resulting in 108 deaths (Furlow, 2008). Another recent high-profile case in Canada relating to medical error was that of Dr Charles Smith, once considered a leading expert in the field of pediatric forensic pathology. When an Ontario coroner reviewed 45 child autopsies in which Dr Smith had attributed the cause of death to either homicide or as being criminally suspicious, it was found that Smith made questionable conclusions of foul play in 20 of the cases, 13 of which resulted in criminal convictions. A subsequent inquiry into Smith's professional conduct found that Smith "actively misled" his superiors, and "made false and misleading statements" in court (CBC, 2009).

While it would be unreasonable to assume that the incidents mentioned were the result of deliberate negligence, they do highlight the fact that mistakes by health-care providers

iatrogenesis
A concept popularized by Ivan Illich that refers to any adverse outcome or harm as a result of medical treatment.

are not that uncommon. A past-president of the Canadian Medical Association, Dr Anne Doig, admitted that there are "outright [medical] errors," and urged patients to "ask for a second opinion" prior to making momentous life decisions about their health (Nguyen, 2010). According to Dianne Carmichael (president of Best Doctors Canada, a company that retests medical results), initial diagnoses worldwide are incorrect 22 per cent of the time (Nguyen, 2010). In its analysis of patient safety in Canada, the Canadian Institute for Health Information (CIHI) states that 10 per cent of patients with health problems surveyed reported that they had been given a wrong medication or a wrong dose in the past two years; 15 per cent reported a medical mistake in the care they received, of which nearly half stated that this mistake caused a serious health problem (CIHI, 2007b). Increased public access to health research and information, greater knowledge about health issues, and more scrutiny of medical errors undermine the basis of doctors' once exclusive claim to medical knowledge and authority.

The Face of Medicine Today

According to a report by the CIHI, in 2013 there were 77,674 active physicians in Canada (excluding those who are military, semi-retired, and residents), the highest ever recorded, and a 14.1 per cent increase over the 2009 figure. For the same period (2009–13), the Canadian population grew by 4.2 per cent (CIHI, 2014c). In the past three decades, with the exception of a few years, the number of doctors (including both Canadian and foreign trained) entering the workforce exceeded the number of those leaving. And student enrolment in Canadian medical schools continues to increase (after a steady decline beginning in 1993 to 1999): in 2012, there were 11,375 students enrolled (Association of Faculties of Medicine of Canada, 2013a).

Physicians are quite evenly divided between family medicine and specialty medicine: just over half (50.7 per cent) of all physicians are in family medicine. However, the ratio varies by province; for example, in Saskatchewan 56 per cent of doctors are in family medicine whereas in Ontario and Quebec 49 per cent are in family medicine. The three territories are particularly disadvantaged in terms of the availability of specialists, with the lowest being in Nunavut at 9 per cent (CIHI, 2014g). **Primary health care** is provided predominantly by family physicians and general practitioners working in solo and small-group practices, many of which operate only to share office costs and are reimbursed on a fee-for-service basis. Such a system "discourages physicians from spending time with their patients to explore multiple causes of ill health or to identify disease prevention and health promotion strategies . . . it discourages primary care providers from holding team meetings to discuss patient issues" (Armstrong & Armstrong, 2008, p. 72). There is little opportunity to share medical knowledge or feedback; there is also little scope to monitor physicians' work.

The medical profession is no longer as homogeneous by class and sex as it was before. Pressures for greater diversity in Canadian universities in the 1970s have had some impact on recruitment to medical schools. However, students in Canadian medical school today still come disproportionately from privileged socio-economic backgrounds. In their survey of first-year medical students in Canada, Dhalla et al. found that 17 per cent of the students had parents with household incomes greater than $160,000 as compared with 2.7 per

primary health care
Both the point of first contact with the health-care system and a philosophy for delivery of that care.

cent of Canadian households that had an income greater than $150,000. Nearly half of the students came from neighbourhoods with median family incomes in the top quintile (Dhalla et al., 2002). Dhalla et al. also found that while certain minority groups (Chinese and South Asian) were overrepresented, others, like Black and Aboriginal peoples, were underrepresented. The recently released report *The Future of Medical Education in Canada* (FMEC) emphasizes that more diversity is needed in medical schools. It notes that there has been little progress in attracting applicants from First nations, Inuit, and Métis communities; as well it calls for greater diversity from underrepresented sociocultural and economic groups (Association of Faculties of Medicine of Canada, 2012, p. 18).

Women have benefited from the challenge to medicine's **patriarchal** and elitist tradition, as is indicated in the increased number of women in the physician workforce. Barbara Ehrenreich and Deidre English (1973) were among the first writers to highlight the patriarchal and oppressive role of medicine in the persecution of women healers, who were often accused of being witches. Many scholars have also criticized the patriarchal tradition of medicine for various forms of sexism in the research, diagnosis, and treatment of illness, and in terms of discrimination against female medical students and doctors (see Annandale, 2004; Annandale & Hunt, 2000; Kirk, 1994; Walters, 1994). Although women worked as midwives and nurses in the eighteenth and nineteenth centuries, women in Canada were not allowed to study medicine at university until the late nineteenth century. Dr Emily Stowe, the first Canadian woman to practise medicine in Canada, received her medical training in the United States because no Canadian medical school would accept her. When she returned to Canada in 1867, she practised unlicensed; as an American-trained doctor she was required to take courses at an Ontario medical school and then write the qualifying exams for an Ontario licence. However, no Ontario medical school would admit her. Eventually, in 1870, she was admitted to the University of Toronto and in 1880 obtained her medical licence from the College of Physicians and Surgeons of Ontario. In 1883, Stowe's daughter, Ann Augusta Stowe-Gullen, following in her mother's footsteps, became the first female doctor to graduate from a Canadian medical school—the Faculty of Medicine at Victoria University (Famous Canadian Physicians, n.d.). Yet it took nearly 100 years before the Canadian Medical Association elected its first woman president, Dr Bette Stephenson, in 1974. Not until 170 years after the first medical school in Canada was opened was a woman finally appointed dean of a medical faculty: in 1999, Dr Noni MacDonald was appointed dean of Dalhousie Medical School (Robb, 1999).

The gradual entry of women into the profession began during the second half of the twentieth century. Women today (2012–13) comprise 56.1 per cent of medical school enrolment, a significant difference from 1968–9 when only 14.3 per cent of those enrolled in Canadian medical schools were female. In 1940, only 4.1 per cent of the MDs awarded in Canada went to women. It wasn't until 1966 that the proportion of women receiving medical degrees began to increase steadily, reaching 20 per cent in 1974, 36.8 per cent in 1984, and 44.3 per cent in 1994. In 2013, 57.1 per cent of medical degrees awarded by Canadian universities went to women (Association of Faculties of Medicine of Canada, 2013b).

The composition of the physician workforce in the country is also changing as women become an increasingly larger proportion of practising doctors. See Figure 12.2. Between 2009 and 2013, the number of male doctors increased by 9.2 per cent, while the number of female doctors grew by 22.5 per cent. By 2013, women accounted for over one third

patriarchal
A system of power through which males dominate households. The term is used more broadly by feminists to refer to society's domination by patriarchal power, which functions to subordinate women and children.

feminization
A shift in the gender base
of a group from being
predominantly male to being
increasingly female.

(38.2 per cent) of Canada's doctors; the proportion was higher among family medicine (43.1 per cent) than specialists (33.2 per cent) (CIHI, 2014c). This **feminization** of the physician workforce, which is also occurring internationally, is expected to continue, with a projection that by 2027, half of all the physicians in practice in Canada will be women (CMA, 2007).

Feminization of the profession is likely to have implications for the delivery of medical services; it appears female physicians on average prefer working in urban areas, have a preference for family medicine, and work fewer hours per week (CIHI, 2008a). While women are overrepresented in some specialities such as family medicine, gynecology, and pediatrics, they are underrepresented in others, such as cardiology and surgical specialities (Canadian Health Human Resources Research Network, 2013; Biringer & Carroll, 2012: Phillips & Austin, 2009). Some research suggests that female and male physicians bring different professional and personal values and attitudes, which may be reflected in the way they choose to organize and manage their professional practices (Hedden et al., 2014). It has also been suggested that female physicians are more attuned to psychosocial aspects of patient care and are less likely to accept the status quo in medicine and the technologic focus of the biomedical disease model (Maheux et al., 1990; Williams et al., 1990). Maheux et al. note that their results confirm other findings that suggest female physicians have more social concerns than male doctors and show more interest in educating and counselling patients about health matters. Recent systematic reviews of research on the increasing number of women in medicine found there were some differences in the way male and female physicians practise medicine (Hedden et al., 2014; Canadian Health Human Resources Research Network, 2013). Women physicians tend to work fewer hours and see fewer patients but spend more time with each patient than their male colleagues; they are also more likely to work in partnership or group-based practice

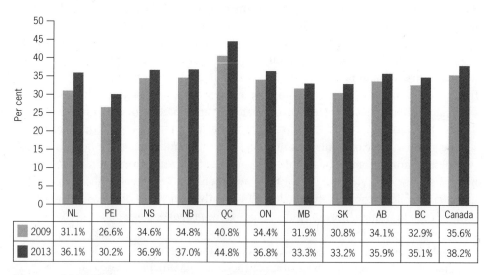

	NL	PEI	NS	NB	QC	ON	MB	SK	AB	BC	Canada
2009	31.1%	26.6%	34.6%	34.8%	40.8%	34.4%	31.9%	30.8%	34.1%	32.9%	35.6%
2013	36.1%	30.2%	36.9%	37.0%	44.8%	36.8%	33.3%	33.2%	35.9%	35.1%	38.2%

Figure 12.2 Proportion of Female Doctors in Canada

Source: CIHI. (2014). Slide 8, More than one-third of physicians were women. In *Physicians in Canada Chartbook 2013*. Canadian Institute for Health Information, 2014. Available at: https://secure.cihi.ca/estore/productFamily.htm?locale=en&pf=PFC2676

rather than solo; and are more likely to see patients with complex psychosocial problems. Some of the difference in hours worked may be explained by the fact that women have responsibilities as child bearers and primary caregivers and organize their practices with these imperatives of family life in mind (Hedden et al., 2014; Burton & Wong, 2004). In their qualitative study of female physicians, Mobilos et al. (2008) found a strong link between the choice of specialty and lifestyle issues; female physicians indicated a strong commitment to maintaining a balanced lifestyle, which required certain career decisions. A more recent study though found that physicians today of both sexes want more time for work-life balance (Biringer & Carroll, 2012). It is not clear what impact the increased representation of women will have on medical hegemony; however, it is possible that gender differences in professional attitudes and practice patterns could fragment the profession further (Coburn et al., 1983).

The Role of Public Health and Health Promotion

The goal of **health promotion** is to improve the health of populations. As explained in the **Ottawa Charter for Health Promotion** it refers to "the process of enabling people to increase control over, and to improve, their health" with the aim of creating more equitable health outcomes for all people (Ottawa Charter for Health Promotion, 1986). The Ottawa Charter indicated a move towards a new **public health** agenda that would encourage greater community engagement and social change.

As discussed in Chapter 1, concerns about public health and disease prevention date back to the 1800s. However, such concerns dissipated as medical treatments improved, and it was not until the 1970s that any significant interest in public health was renewed. When the so-called lifestyle diseases or diseases of affluence (i.e., heart disease, cancer, and stroke) became the leading causes of death in developed countries, governments and health professionals turned their attention to disease prevention. *Health promotion* as a term was popularized through the 1974 Lalonde Report, *A New Perspective on the Health of Canadians*. The report has been criticized for its focus on individual lifestyle and behavioural change as the primary avenue for improving health (Kirk et al., 2014). Nevertheless, it is generally regarded as providing the impetus for global initiatives in health promotion, the major driving force of which has been the World Health Organization (WHO), a United Nations body. The WHO has hosted a series of important international health conferences, out of which emerged a number of highly influential health-policy documents. These include the Alma-Ata Declaration of 1978 (WHO, 1978), which was released at its International Conference on Primary Health Care held at Alma-Ata, and the Ottawa Charter for Health Promotion of 1986 (Ottawa Charter for Health Promotion, 1986).

The Ottawa Charter, which emerged from the First International Conference on Health Promotion in Ottawa, has been a dominant influence over health-promotion approaches in Canada and elsewhere. The model is an attempt to integrate health education and individual behaviour-change strategies, with broader structural strategies that aim to fundamentally reorient health-care services and public policies to address the social determinants of health. It identified for the first time the prerequisites and resources for health (Kirk et al., 2014) including peace, shelter, education, food, income, a stable eco-system, sustainable resources, social justice, and equity (Ottawa Charter for Health

health promotion
Any combination of education and related organizational, economic, and political interventions designed to promote individual behavioural and environmental changes conducive to good health, including legislation, community development, and advocacy. Draws attention to a variety of social determinants.

Ottawa Charter for Health Promotion
A 1986 document produced by the WHO. It was launched at the first international conference for health promotion, held in Ottawa, Canada.

public health
Policies, programs, and services designed to keep citizens healthy and to improve the quality of life. The focus is on enhancing the health status and well-being of the general population rather than just looking at the health of individual persons.

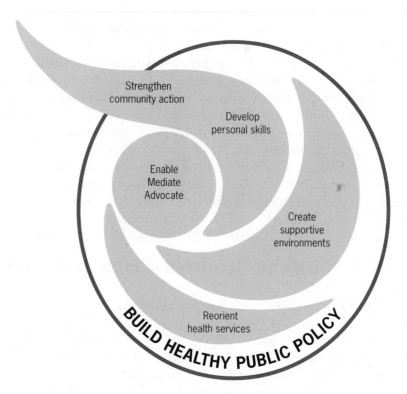

Figure 12.3 Ottawa Charter for Health Promotion

This logo for the Ottawa Charter for Health Promotion has been used by the WHO since 1986. It represents a circle with three wings, held together by the larger circle of public health policy, and incorporates five key areas in health promotion (build healthy public policy, create supportive environments for health, strengthen community action for health, develop personal skills, and reorient health services), with three strategies for achieving these goals (enable, mediate, and advocate).

Source: Reprinted with permission of the World Health Organization (WHO).

Promotion, 1986). Similarly, the Epp Report (1986) took a broad structural approach; it emphasized the need for government policy to focus on reducing inequities between economic groups and identified implementation strategies to foster public participation to strengthen community health services (Raphael, 2008, p. 486). The consistent message of these documents reflects a movement away from focusing on individuals and toward looking at societal factors that influence health, or what we have referred to elsewhere as the social determinants of health. These documents make clear that health professionals and policy-makers not only should educate people about health matters, but they also need to change the social conditions in which people live and involve the community in implementing projects to improve health.

An Individualist Approach

However, despite the developments at the national and international level in support of creating healthy communities, much of health promotion funding in Canada has been narrowly focused around educating people to change their behaviour and lifestyles. On a daily basis, Canadians are bombarded by lifestyle messages from government agencies, public health agencies, and the media that promote healthy diets, physical activity, and the reduction of tobacco use (Raphael, 2008). See for example the Public Health Agency (2013) website on "Health Promotion" (www.phac-aspc.gc.ca/hp-ps/fs-fr/index-eng.php). The underlying assumption becomes all that is needed is to educate people that they are putting their health at risk by smoking cigarettes, eating unhealthy food, drinking too much, and not exercising enough. In this **discourse**, the problem of illness is concep- tualized in terms of "choices" individuals make and their non-compliance with health advice. Some people are said to have "failed" to give up full-cream milk or butter, for instance. Smokers are said to have "failed to understand" that lung cancer and coronary heart disease are major risks of smoking (Borland et al., 1994, p. 369). "Obesity" is blamed on the consumption of too many calories, unhealthy foods, and lack of physical activity (Prince, 2009).

discourse
A domain of language use that is characterized by common ways of talking and thinking about an issue (for example, the discourses of medicine, madness, or sexuality).

ParticipACTION is a non-profit organization that promotes health through individual changes in lifestyle and behaviour. Are there equal opportunities for each of the depicted activities available to every child in Canada?

Government-produced brochures explain the importance of eating lots of fresh fruits and vegetables and wholesome grains. For example, Canada's Food Guide (Health Canada, 2011a), now available in 10 languages in addition to English and French, tells individuals how to make "wise choices" by recommending the amount of daily servings they should eat of fruits, vegetables, and dairy products and emphasizes the importance of choosing lean meats (Health Canada, 2011a). The "Healthy Eating Toolbox" campaign by Health Canada (2013c) helps organizations in "raising awareness and improving understanding of the importance of healthy eating in the day-to-day lives of Canadians." Canada's Physical Activity Guide, produced by the Public Health Agency of Canada, explains the health benefits of being active and warns of the danger of inactivity.

Crawshaw (2013) correctly points out that public health policy has increasingly posited responsibility for well-being with the individual without reference to the wider structural inequalities that have been shown to be the main influences on morbidity and mortality. "Individualized approaches obviate the relational nature of how health behaviours and practices are acted out as part of everyday lives in complex cultural and social contexts" (p. 619). Socio-economically disadvantaged groups experience significant constraints in the sorts of choices they can make. One example comes from a study of food buying in Canada, which looked at five low-income women and how they budgeted for food for their families (K. Travers, 1996). The study found that women's low income reduced their capacity to select appropriate foods or to shop at more distant locations where food was cheaper. Compare, for example, the price of regular ground beef with the healthier choice of extra-lean ground beef. Another significant factor was the pressure to buy certain foods that the women faced from their children, who saw food advertised on television. As Travers explained, teaching someone to budget does not address the structural inequity created by inadequate welfare allowances. In relation to diet, "[h]ealthy choices are not usually easy choices for the socially disadvantaged" (McMichael, 1991, p. 10). In more remote parts of Canada, the cost of fruits and vegetables is prohibitive and frequently not available. These facts seem to have been lost on the last federal government: at the launch of the Harper Government's national Eat Well campaign, the Minister of Health, Leona Aglukkaq, stated "our government wants to provide information to Canadians to help them make healthier food choices" as the best way to invest in the health of children and youth (Health Canada, 2013b).

A Materialist/Structuralist Approach

In contrast to the focus on individual responsibility to change behaviour, an increasing number of sociological contributions to health promotion have focused on the social determinants of health (Raphael, 2009a, b, c). Critics writing from the structuralist perspective argue that the ineffectiveness of the lifestyle approach to health promotion wastes community resources. More importantly, however, they argue that these programs are fundamentally misconceived. The failure of individuals to comply with health warnings is not the problem; the problem is with governments and powerful corporate interests, such as the tobacco lobby, who do not accept responsibility for major diseases in the community. Putting pressure on people to change their lifestyles is, in effect, **victim blaming**, and does nothing to correct the structural causes of ill health (Waitzkin, 1983, p. 215). Structuralists from a neo-Marxist or critical political economy perspective argue that "[t]o focus on

victim blaming
The process whereby social inequality is explained in terms of individuals being solely responsible for what happens to them in relation to the choices they make and their assumed psychological, cultural, and/or biological inferiority.

individual life-styles is to assume an independence and freedom of the individual that is an illusion" (Navarro, 1986, p. 35). They emphasize that there is a need to examine how social determinants of health influence health both directly and indirectly and how political and economic forces shape the distribution of resources, which in turn influences the quality of resources available to different groups of people (Raphael, 2009c). To address inequities in health, health promotion and public health policy must do something about the social and material conditions that frame the decisions that individuals make about their health.

Public Health in Canada

At the beginning of the twentieth century, contagious diseases, such as scarlet fever, diphtheria, measles, whooping cough, and tuberculosis, were the leading causes of death in Canada. Public health activities were largely limited to responding to infectious disease outbreaks, although broader public health initiatives soon emerged. Immunization against smallpox and diphtheria began in Ontario schools; Montreal and Toronto began to pasteurize milk; and some towns began chlorinating drinking water. However, it only was after the First World War that childhood immunization against infectious diseases became commonplace and new scientific discoveries, such as insulin and penicillin, led to treatments for diabetes and infection (Butler-Jones, 2008, pp. 10–12).

The Public Health Agency of Canada (PHAC) was created in 2004, in part as a response to the severe acute respiratory syndrome (SARS) outbreak, to coordinate and establish at a federal level programs to sustain a public health system that would focus on the following (Public Health Agency of Canada, 2005):

- promoting programs to encourage healthy living;
- preventing and controlling infectious and chronic illnesses;
- monitoring health and water safety;
- ensuring emergency preparedness.

The agency is one of five departments and agencies that make up the Government of Canada's Health Portfolio. Part of its mandate is to strengthen public health "consistent with a shared understanding of the determinants of health and of the common factors that maintain health or lead to disease and injury" (Public Health Agency of Canada, 2011a).

The first annual report of the first chief public health officer (Dr David Butler-Jones, 2008) defined public health as "the organized efforts of society to improve health and well-being and to reduce inequalities in health" (p. i). The report focused on inequalities in health status, and on how social and economic determinants contribute to these health inequalities. Dr Butler-Jones's view is that "health inequalities are fundamentally societal inequalities that we can overcome through public policy and individual and collective action" (p. iii). He is clear that social inequalities mediate health, and that physical and social environments have an impact on the choices individuals can make about their health. Addressing child poverty, he suggests, should be a primary focus of governments. This would include income distribution policies and programs so that all families have the necessary resources for healthy child development, adequate housing and infrastructure, post-secondary education, employment, and employment supports (p. 69). However, child poverty in Canada is on the rise.

Why then, one might ask, does the government continue to promote programs and policies targeted at changing individual behaviour, even though there is little evidence to suggest such strategies are effective? Why, given the extent of social inequalities in Canada, are current population-level prevention strategies focused mainly on individual health promotion and education activities (Prince, 2009)? One suggestion is that individualist approaches continue because they are supported by a range of powerful interest groups, not least a range of medical and allied health professionals. As Alan Petersen (1996) argues, "[health] promotion is not a value-free enterprise. It is enmeshed in power relations" (p. 56). An individualist model has widespread support because it makes governments look authoritative and active while at the same time it avoids confrontations that might prove politically costly (Lupton, 1995). For bureaucrats, the model is appealing because the types of targets set—such as getting 20 per cent more Canadians engaged in physical activity—are quantifiable and seem manageable. The individualist model has the support of the medical profession because it expands medical turf and provides work for **epidemiologists**, health professionals, psychologists, and educationalists, many of whom work within the still-dominant positivist tradition (Beattie, 1991). Pharmaceutical companies also stand to benefit when the focus of ill health is on biology and genetic predisposition. As an example, see Wendy Mesley's CBC documentary, *Chasing the Cancer Answer*, which raises questions about why there is so little research on preventing cancer (such as eliminating carcinogens) compared to the dollars spent on finding a medical cure.

epidemiology
The statistical study of patterns of disease in the population. Originally focused on epidemics, or infectious diseases, it now covers non-infectious conditions, such as stroke and cancer.

Although Canada was a leader in the development of health-promotion approaches that recognize the importance of social and economic factors on health status, the government has done little to implement policies that would address social inequalities. Raphael (2009d) suggests that there are political and economic barriers that explain the failure of the Canadian government to implement structural change, namely the ascendancy of neo-liberalism and the dismantling of the welfare state. Neo-liberal ideology promotes a so-called free market, individualism, and a reduction of spending on social programs: "[N]eo-liberalism and neo-conservative ideologies . . . position societal issues, including health and health promotion, as individual issues beyond the concern of governments and their institutions" (Raphael, 2003, p. 401). Crawshaw (2013) adds that social marketing strategies today that promote individual responsibility for health outcomes reflect the market-oriented neo-liberal mode of social organization. As a consequence, there is no support for a social agenda that would improve living conditions and other structural inequalities through state intervention. Some researchers and health-policy advocates remain committed to the visions articulated in the Ottawa Charter. However, the dominant public health approach in Canada today is more in keeping with biomedical traditions and individualized solutions.

Conclusion

The development of medicine and medical dominance occurred during specific conjunctures in history. Challenges to medical dominance, such as the development of Medicare, the rationalization and corporatization of health care, the growth of allied health professionals, the women's health movement, and divisions within the medical profession reflect the dynamic nature of the health system. Medical hegemony has also been challenged by media attention to cases of medical error and negligence and a growing public skepticism of medical claims. The medical profession today is more fragmented in terms of its views and values, and is less homogeneous in its socio-demographic characteristics; most striking is the feminization of medicine. Nevertheless, scientific medicine remains the most powerful health occupation. Although there are groups of doctors who espouse progressive policies, ideologically and politically the medical elite remain aligned with conservative values. Medicine continues to struggle against any encroachment on its privileges; however, its fate "is [ultimately] dependent on the outcome of broader class struggles in Canadian society" (Coburn, 1988a, p. 111).

The Ottawa Charter (1986) signalled a new direction in public health, with an emphasis on social, cultural, economic, and political factors as determinants of health. However, there is a major "disconnect" between the vision espoused in the Ottawa Charter and government practice. Despite vast amounts of research in Canada and elsewhere that demonstrates the link between health outcomes and social inequalities, health promotion and public health policy in Canada has focused predominantly on social marketing strategies to change individuals' habits and lifestyles. Consistent with the philosophy of neo-liberalism, governments have done little to address the underlying structural inequities.

Summary

- Biomedicine operates within a set of assumptions about disease and illness that have an impact on both the practice and structure of medicine.
- Medicine has control over health-care delivery, the nature of medical practice, and the education and certification of its members, as well as influence over health policy.
- Medical dominance in Canada was achieved by political means, including connections to elite groups.
- Main challenges to medical dominance are government-controlled health insurance, allied health groups, demystification of medicine, and divisions within the profession.
- Despite challenges, the medical profession is dynamic and resilient; medical dominance continues to stand the test of time.
- Health promotion can be categorized into two types: individualist social-marketing approaches which aim to change behaviour and lifestyles; and structural materialist approaches that address societal inequities as determinants of health.
- Critics of lifestyle health promotion point to their ineffectiveness in changing behaviour long term and their tendency toward victim blaming.
- Public health policy and health promotion in Canada favour lifestyle messages with little reference to the wider social determinants of health.

Key Terms

allopathic medicine

biomedicine/biomedical model

discourse

epidemiology

feminization

health promotion

hegemony/hegemonic

iatrogenesis

medical dominance

Medicare

Ottawa Charter

patriarchy/patriarchal

primary health care

public health

social determinants of health

state

victim blaming

welfare state

women's health movement

Sociological Reflection: Feminization of Medicine

An important aspect of medicine today is the number of women enrolled in medical schools and the growing number of women who are practising physicians. What might be some of the reasons for this feminization of medicine? How might it influence medical curriculum and the practice of medicine? Do you think that medicine will fundamentally be changed as a result of this? Why or why not?

Discussion Questions

1. What are the major assumptions of a biomedical/allopathic approach to health?
2. How would you define medical dominance, and how was it achieved in Canada?
3. What are the major challenges to medical dominance?
4. In what ways has the profession of medicine changed over the past 100 years?
5. What are the key features of public health in Canada today?
6. What are social determinants of health and why are they considered important?
7. What are the underlying assumptions of individualist health promotion? What are the criticisms made of this approach?
8. What are the major barriers faced by critical scholars who advocate a need to address structural inequalities as the basis for health promotion?

Further Investigation

1. What are the differences in how health promotion is understood through the biomedical model compared with the social model of health? Why do these differences exist? Are there limitations to each of these two models? Can the two be reconciled?
2. There is ongoing debate about the degree to which the medical profession has lost its hegemony. To what extent has government emphasis on accountability and the rationalization of health-care delivery challenged the power of medicine? Can the medical profession regain its former power over health care?

Further Reading

Blishen, B. (1991). *Doctors in Canada: The changing world of medical practice*. Toronto, ON: University of Toronto Press.

Bryant, T. (2009). *An introduction to health policy*. Toronto, ON: Canadian Scholars' Press.

Butler-Jones, D. (2008). *The chief public health officer's report on the state of public health in Canada*. Ottawa, ON: Minister of Health.

Coburn, D. (1998). State authority, medical dominance, and trends in the regulation of health professions: The Ontario case. In D. Coburn, C. D'Arcy, & G. Torrance (Eds.), *Health and Canadian society: Sociological perspectives* (3rd ed.) (pp. 332–46). Toronto, ON: University of Toronto Press.

Coburn, D., Torrance, G., & Kaufert, J. (1983). Medical dominance in Canadian historical perspective: The rise and fall of medicine? *International Journal of Health Services, 13*, 407–32.

Freidson, E. (2001). *Professionalism: The third logic*. Cambridge, UK: Polity Press.

Navarro, V. (1988). Professional dominance or proletarianization?: Neither. *The Milbank Quarterly, 66*(2), 57–75.

Web Resources

Canadian Doctors for Medicare
www.canadiandoctorsformedicare.ca

Canadian Health Coalition
healthcoalition.ca

Canadian Institute for Health Information (CIHI)
www.cihi.ca

Canadian Medical Association
http://cma.ca

Canadian Policy Research Networks (CPRN)
www.cprn.com

Canadian Public Health Association (CPHA)
www.cpha.ca

Medical Reform Group
http://medicalreformgroup.ca

Public Health Agency of Canada
www.phac-aspc.gc.ca

CHAPTER 13
Power, Politics, and Values: The Canadian Health-Care System

Jennie Hornosty

Protestors, including physicians, gather in front of Citizenship and Immigration headquarters to protest proposed cuts to health-care programs for refugees. Should health care be treated as a benefit earned through citizenship? Should it be a commodity that can be purchased? Or should it be treated as a human right?

Overview

- What is the nature of Canada's health-care system?
- Who are the major interest groups and what influence do they have?
- What role do power, politics, and values play in shaping health care?

Most Canadians view government-funded universal health care as a fundamental right of citizenship. However, the Medical Health Act, which became the foundation for Canada's system of Medicare, was only passed in 1966. Its history was fraught with tensions, including two major doctors' strikes. This chapter examines the structure of health care in Canada and the competing interests that shaped its development. It also discusses the growing divide between those who argue for increased privatization of health care and those who defend the basic principles on which Medicare was founded.

Introduction: Is Health Care a Fundamental Right or a Commodity for Purchase?

In his "Message to Canadians," the Honourable Roy Romanow, who was appointed in 2001 as sole commissioner to look at the future of health care in Canada, summarized the core values underlying Canada's health-care system as those of equity, fairness, and solidarity. He went on to note, as have others, that Canadians everywhere are deeply attached to these core values underlying **Medicare**. These values reflect the Canadian view that health care is a fundamental right of citizenship and not a privilege of status or wealth (Romanow, 2002; Armstrong & Armstrong, 2003). Medicare as we know it today only became a reality for all Canadians in 1971. Now, however, there is talk of Medicare being in crisis due to escalating costs, an aging population, and long waiting lists. Certain groups in society are asking the question whether Canadians can afford Medicare and are advocating for more privatization of health-care services. Others argue that there is no crisis in public health-care costs; rather, the escalating costs are related to services purchased from the private sector, such as drug expenditures.

There are competing interests at stake in the current debate about the future of Canada's public health-care system, just as there was earlier when a public health-insurance plan was first introduced in Canada. Two of the most powerful groups were and are doctors and politicians. Underlying the debate about costs is a clash in fundamental **values** and **ideology** about whether health care is an **unalienable human right** to which every citizen is entitled or whether it is a commodity in the marketplace where citizens can purchase what they want or need. Whose interests are being served if Canada abandons its universal health-care system in favour of more privatization? What political forces are driving the push toward greater privatization of health-care services? This chapter provides an overview of Canada's public health-care system, examines the major

Medicare
Canada's universal health-care program, funded and administered by federal, provincial, and territorial governments.

values
Important beliefs and ideals shared by members of a culture or society.

ideology
In a political context, refers to those beliefs and values that relate to the way in which society should be organized, including the appropriate role of the state.

unalienable human right
A right considered to inhere in a person as a human being and that cannot be relinquished by government; sometimes referred to as a "natural right."

historical factors in its development, considers the role of physicians and politicians in shaping health-care policy, and looks at the ideology of neo-liberalism and its impact on health care today.

The Development of Medicare in Canada

As a society, we [Canadians] decided that health is a public good and that the costs of treating illness should be broadly shared. To achieve this goal, we built a system we call "medicare."

—National Forum on Health (1997, p. 4)

The first initiative to establish some form of government health insurance came in 1919 as part of the platform of the federal Liberal Party under Prime Minister Robert Borden. However, it was after the Great Depression that there was renewed interest in a national health-insurance plan. During the Depression, doctors' incomes declined dramatically since patients were unable to pay their bills; the government had to institute a medical relief plan to help pay for doctors' salaries and other medical expenses. Health problems among the population worsened as communicable diseases such as tuberculosis, pneumonia, and influenza spread among the population due to inadequate nutrition and poor housing. During the same period, political radicalism, particularly in the Prairie Provinces and British Columbia, grew (Torrance, 1998, p. 14).

allopathic medicine
A name given to conventional biomedicine. Treatment of diseases is by drugs that have effects opposite to the symptoms.

By the 1930s and 40s, Canadians generally had put their faith in **allopathic medicine**; however, paying for physician and hospital services was difficult for most, including large segments of the working and middle classes. At the time, Canada's health-care system was dominated by private medicine, similar to that in existence in the United States today. Unless people had private insurance or were wealthy, they were forced to rely on charity, sacrifice their life savings, or do without medical treatment: "Canada trailed most Western European countries, Britain, and New Zealand in making health care economically accessible to most of the population" (Torrance, 1998, p. 11). Although most European nations, including England, had established some form of government-administered health insurance by the end of the First World War, doctors in Canada lobbied against the idea, warning that government-funded insurance plans would undermine the spirit of charity and turn physicians into civil servants (Feldberg & Vipond, 2006).

welfare state/social welfare state
A system whereby the government assumes primary responsibility for the welfare of its citizens through programs designed to protect and promote the economic and social well-being of its citizens.

As was the case in Western European countries, a government-funded health-insurance plan was largely brought about as the result of increasing popular pressure for change: "Channelled through interest groups and political parties of the left, public pressure forced reluctant governments and a mostly resisting medical profession to implement limited reforms" (Torrance, 1998, p. 13). It is not surprising that significant government initiatives for a national health plan emerged in Canada in the 1930s. An important player was the Co-operative Commonwealth Federation (CCF) party, which was formed in Calgary 1932. A broad coalition of progressive intellectuals, farmers, and labour groups, the CCF was dedicated to economic reform and to the establishment of a **welfare state**. In 1933, when the party met in Regina, it drafted the Regina Manifesto, which had as one of its key policies state-funded health insurance. The first actual legislation in favour of state medicine was passed in Alberta in 1934 by the United Farmers of Alberta government, but was never implemented by the Social Credit Party, which gained power the following year. In British Columbia, the Liberal government was pressured by the CCF to pass a health-insurance act. Despite popular support in a plebiscite on the issue, the legislation was never implemented, in part due to opposition from the medical profession and partly because the federal government failed to provide any financial support (Torrance, 1998). However, some years later, in 1947, the CCF government in Saskatchewan, with Tommy Douglas as premier, implemented the first public hospital-insurance plan in the country. The plan covered everyone in the province regardless of their ability to pay; money to finance the plan largely came from taxes although those who had the economic means paid premiums (Armstrong & Armstrong, 2008, p. 16).

Ideas for a national health insurance surfaced in both Canada and the United States after the Second World War (Feldberg & Vipond, 2006). World War II reinforced the importance of Keynesian economic theory, which argued for an expanded government role in stimulating the economy and increased government expenditures for social programs to help those in need. This laid the foundation for the **social welfare state**. Canada came out of World War II with a commitment to human rights: "Increasingly, shared responsibility for what were understood as shared risks was a notion that underlined Canadian government activities, rather than the idea that most people got what they deserved in a market economy and must be held responsible for themselves" (Armstrong & Armstrong, 2008, p. 14). The post-war period was one of economic prosperity; it was also a time when more Canadians demanded that government play a central role in providing basic social services, such as health care, unemployment insurance, and pensions.

In 1945, Prime Minister William Lyon Mackenzie King presented a proposal for national health insurance to the Dominion-Provincial Conference on Reconstruction but failed to get agreement from the provinces. Under the terms of the British North America Act, health care was considered largely a provincial matter; several provinces rejected King's plan because they saw it as encroaching on provincial jurisdiction in health. The tension over provincial–federal jurisdiction continues in discussions over Medicare today, a point that will be discussed later in this chapter. However, the federal government reached an agreement in 1948 with the provinces for a national health grants program, which would cover 50 per cent of the costs for approved hospital construction. This initiative helped establish hospitals as the primary place for medical treatment; at the same time, the costs of hospital care increased significantly. Although hospitals were non-profit, they still charged for their services and only 40 per cent of the population had some form of hospital insurance. Many could not afford the costs and defaulted on their hospital bills (Armstrong & Armstrong, 2003, p. 49). In response to mounting debts and increased public pressure for a national hospital-insurance plan, the federal government implemented the Hospital and Diagnostic Services Act in 1957, which covered half of the costs of specified hospital services, on condition that services were provided to everyone on an equal basis. Coverage included meals and accommodation on a standard ward, medications, laboratory and diagnostic testing, and some outpatient services. Tuberculosis hospitals and sanitoria, institutions for the mentally ill, and care institutions such as homes for the elderly, however, were not covered (Armstrong & Armstrong, 2003, p. 50).

Tommy Douglas: Planting the Seeds of Medicare

All my adult life I dreamed of the day when . . . we would have in Canada a program of complete medical care without a price tag.

—Tommy Douglas (quoted by Finn, 2007, p. 1)

Medicare, as we know it today, had its birth in Saskatchewan under the leadership of Tommy Douglas. (See Box 13.1 for a brief overview of Tommy Douglas's life.) During his 1944 provincial campaign as leader of the CCF, Tommy Douglas promised that his party would establish medical, dental, and hospital services "available to all without counting the ability of the individual to pay" (quoted in Badgley & Wolfe, 1967, p. 17).

In 1947, the first step in Douglas's vision of universal health care was put into place; his government introduced a province-wide public hospital-insurance plan, 10 years before the federal government brought in a similar plan. During his first term in government, more than 100 bills were passed, 72 of which were "aimed at social or economic reform"

Box 13.1   Tommy Douglas: A Visionary

Thomas Clement Douglas, better known as Tommy Douglas, "the father of Medicare," was born in 1904 in Falkirk, Scotland, but moved with his family to Winnipeg in 1910. His childhood experience of nearly losing a leg helped shape his passionate commitment to social justice and universal health care. His family was not economically well off, and when he developed a bone disease (osteomyelitis) as a result of an infection, his parents could not afford to pay a bone specialist. Instead, he was put, as a charity patient, in a Winnipeg hospital, where doctors were going to amputate his leg. Had it not been for an orthopaedic surgeon who offered to provide the necessary medical treatment (making amputation unnecessary) for free if his students could observe, Tommy's life might have been much different. Later Douglas recalled, "Had I been a rich man's son instead of the son of an iron molder,

Boris Spremo/The Globe and Mail/The Canadian Press

"We can't stand still. We can either go back or we can go forward. The choice we make today will decide the future of Medicare in Canada." (From a 1984 speech by Tommy Douglas.)

I would have had the services of the finest surgeon, and would not have had to depend on charity for a cure" (Finn, 2007, p.1). As noted in *Tommy's Life Story*, "The treatment [both] saved Tommy's leg—and planted the seed for his vision: universally accessible health care" (Tommy Douglas Research Institute, n.d., n.p.).

and included reducing "the provincial debt by $20 million." He created new government departments, e.g., the Department of Co-operatives, Department of Labour, and Department of Social Welfare (Tommy Douglas Research Institute, n.d., n.p.).

Influenced by his personal experience with illness and his passionate commitment to values of social justice and human rights, Douglas continued his fight for a universal health-care program that would further extend health coverage. By 1959, he was confident that financially the government could extend health-care coverage. In a speech that year on "Prepaid Medical Care," Douglas outlined five basic principles for a proposed comprehensive plan that would cover everyone: (1) prepayment; (2) universal coverage; (3) high-quality service in both urban and rural areas; (4) coverage that was government-sponsored and publicly administered; and (5) coverage that was acceptable both to those providing the service and those receiving it (quoted in Badgley & Wolfe, 1967, p. 22). And in 1960, Douglas fought and won the provincial election on a promise to implement a universal medical-insurance plan, despite massive opposition from Saskatchewan doctors.

Douglas graduated from Brandon College and was ordained as a Baptist minister in 1930. His ministry was shaped by the progressive teachings of the social gospel, which integrated Christianity with struggles for social justice and equality. As a young minister in Weyburn, Saskatchewan, he faced many challenges guiding his congregation through the Great Depression. Through his community work organizing relief programs for local farmers and their families, he saw first-hand the hardships and poverty that many families faced as they struggled to cope with drought and economic depression. Douglas's shift from the pulpit to the political arena arose out of a growing awareness that his relief efforts were incapable of having long-term effects. This was painfully evident when he had to bury two "young men in their 30s with small families who died because there was no doctor readily available, and they hadn't the money to get proper care" (Palpz, 2004, n.p.).

In 1932, Douglas joined the Saskatchewan Farmer Labour Party (later the Co-operative Commonwealth Federation [CCF]) and in 1935 was elected as one of the first CCF members of Parliament. Seven years later, he resigned his seat to become leader of the Saskatchewan CCF, and in 1944 swept the party to victory under the slogan Humanity First and a promise to implement a universal health-care plan, becoming the first social democratic government in North America.

After 17 years as premier of Saskatchewan, Douglas re-entered federal politics as leader of the New Democratic Party (NDP) in 1961, a party formed by a coalition of the old CCF and the Canadian labour movement. There, until he resigned his seat to retire in 1979, he continued to promote a national system of health care and his socialist ideals that the common good should supersede private interests (CBC, 2004). Tommy Douglas died in 1986 of cancer at the age of 82. In 2008, he was voted the Greatest Canadian to have ever lived; his achievements were many and continue to have far-reaching effects.

During the 1960 campaign, the Saskatchewan Medical Association (SMA) launched a political campaign to defeat the CCF government and its socialized medicine. The SMA's tactics remind one of the recent opposition in the United States to health-care reform proposed by President Obama. Publicity kits distributed to doctors equated the proposed plan as similar to that "first enunciated by Karl Marx in his Communistic Theories of the last century . . ." (quoted in Badgley & Wolfe, 1967, p. 31). One document warned that a government plan would endanger the doctor–patient relationship and that any emotional problems "under state medicine [would need to be] referred to a psychiatric clinic or a mental hospital" (p. 33). Four days prior to the election, the SMA placed a full-page advertisement in the daily press that stated, in part,

> Compulsory state medicine has led to mediocrity and a poorer quality of care everywhere it has been put into practice. We believe that compulsory state medicine would be a tragic mistake for this province and it would undermine the high quality of medical care which you now enjoy . . . we refuse to support and service a plan which will lead to a poorer type of medical care. (Quoted in Badgley & Wolfe, 1967, pp. 34–5)

Doctors supportive of the proposed plan were afraid to speak out for fear of retaliation by the powerful medical lobby (p. 34). Despite the massive efforts of the SMA, however, the CCF government was re-elected. In 1961, the CCF government passed the Saskatchewan Medical Care Insurance Act, based on the five basic principles that subsequently became the model for Canada's Medical Care Act in 1966. The medical profession continued its lobby against the proposed universal health plan even though the electorate endorsed it. Despite the government's willingness to meet with doctors prior to passing the Saskatchewan Medical Care Insurance Act in November 1961, the SMA refused to co-operate or negotiate with the government. It was only in April 1962 that a meeting with the president of the SMA took place; however, the SMA proposals were rejected and negotiations broke down. The physicians described their issues as those of professional autonomy and patient care. Premier Lloyd, who replaced Tommy Douglas, characterized the fundamental disagreement as being "whether the people of Saskatchewan shall be governed by a democratically elected legislature responsible to the people, or by a small, highly organized group." He went on to say that the SMA had given notice that unless the act was repealed or doctors were permitted to ignore the act, "the people of the province will be punished by curtailment of medical services" (cited in Badgley & Wolfe, 1967, p. 56).

The government refused to back down, and on July 1, 1962, when the act came into effect, the majority of the 725 practising doctors in the province closed their offices and began what was to become a bitter 23-day strike. Although some 250 doctors provided emergency services in centres designated by the medical profession, only 30 or so actively practised under the act. These doctors worked with citizens to establish the Community Health Services Association and opened a co-operative health clinic in Saskatoon: the Saskatoon Community Clinic opened with two doctors just three days after the strike began. The clinic's co-operative health model subsequently became an alternative to private-practice medicine.

In anticipation of the doctors' strike, the government had secured doctors from Britain and the United States. The strikers underestimated the extent of pro-Medicare sentiment in the province, and initial public sympathy for the doctors began to dwindle quickly. By July

10, it appeared the profession was having difficulty maintaining the strike. With the help of Lord Taylor, a Labour peer and architect of Britain's national health plan who had been invited to the province by the Saskatchewan government, a settlement with the SMA was signed on July 23. Both the government and the doctors made concessions: "Doctors ... had to give way on at least one key principle to reach agreement ending the medical care dispute. This was acceptance of a universal, compulsory medical care plan, long opposed by organized medicine as a threat to doctors' freedom" (cited in Badgley & Wolfe, 1967, p. 72). The government made some amendments to the act, including allowing physicians to opt out and bill patients directly (Frankel et al., 1996, p. 131). In the end, it was clear that the CCF government had triumphed: a universal health plan came to Saskatchewan and the SMA lost some of its power.

Despite the tremendous gains in Saskatchewan for universal health care, Douglas's vision for Medicare has yet to be fully realized. In his view, removing financial barriers was necessary but was only the first phase. His vision involved something more comprehensive: a fundamental restructuring of health-care delivery, with a much greater focus on illness prevention, health promotion, and measures to address the social determinants of health, especially poverty and inequality (Campbell & Marchildon, 2007). This second phase has yet to be implemented.

Federal Developments

The Saskatchewan plan served as the archetype for the Medical Care Act introduced by the federal government in 1966. In 1961, then Prime Minister John Diefenbaker, with pressure from doctors, appointed a Royal Commission chaired by Supreme Court Justice Emmett Hall to consider options for health care. Although not initially a supporter, Hall recommended a national universal plan covering a full range of health services, including doctor care, for all Canadians in his 1964 report of the Royal Commission on Health Services. The subsequently elected Liberal government of Lester B. Pearson acted quickly on Hall's recommendations and introduced the Medical Care Act in 1966 (Armstrong & Armstrong, 2008, pp. 19–29). Despite strong opposition from the Canadian Medical Association, using similar arguments to those used by Saskatchewan doctors, the bill passed in Parliament by a vote of 177 to 2 (Frankel et al., 1996, p. 133).

The Medical Care Act set out four criteria:

- Universality: health services were to be available to all Canadians on an equal basis.
- Comprehensiveness: all necessary medical services were to be covered.
- Public administration: the plan was to be administered on a non-profit basis.
- Portability: the benefits were to be portable across provinces, and were to be guided by accessibility.

According to the act, the federal government would reimburse, or cost share, one-half of provincial and territorial costs for medical services provided by a doctor outside hospitals (Health Canada, 2012a). By 1972, all provinces and territories had established health plans, financed through the cost-sharing formula (Rich, 2008).

The implementation of a universal health care did not impact that negatively on doctors. The plan legitimated allopathic medicine: it maintained the existing model of fee-for-service, private practice, and professional autonomy, and it did not challenge the structure of medical practice or physicians' sole authority to determine care:

> Individual doctors determined what was defined as necessary care and, within the confines of a negotiated agreement with doctors about what should be covered, the governments paid. This power was based on the notion of the doctor as expert, the objective, knowledgeable person who applies proven diagnosis and techniques. (Armstrong & Armstrong, 2003, p. 55)

Medicare had a significant impact on the everyday lives of most Canadians. It eliminated financial barriers, especially for lower income groups, making access to health-care services more equitable. It went a long way toward fulfilling Tommy Douglas's dream of a health-care system where no one was denied treatment because of inability to pay. However, not all costs are covered; for example, prescription drugs, dental and eye examinations, physiotherapy, and counselling are generally not insured under the plan unless the services are provided in hospitals. Those who can afford it, or who have jobs with health-insurance benefits, are able to purchase these and other services through private insurance companies, such as Blue Cross or Manulife. Today, the cost of prescription drugs, in particular, remains a significant obstacle for those living in poverty or in the lower income groups.

Under the Federal-Provincial Fiscal Arrangements and Established Programs Financing Act, 1977 (EPF), the federal government revised its 50–50 cost-sharing agreement with the provinces and replaced it with block funding. This new funding formula involved a combination of cash payments and tax points and meant that provincial and territorial governments would now make the decision of how the health-care dollars would be spent. This new arrangement also meant, however, a cap on cash transfers and required the provinces and territories to shoulder a larger proportion of health-care costs (Armstrong & Armstrong, 2003, p. 56).

According to then federal health minister Marc Lalonde, the intent of this change was to provide flexibility so as to allocate additional resources to preventative medicine (Sawyer, 2006). Regardless, the new funding formula left provincial and territorial governments strapped for cash. A growth in population and an expanded medical-hospital complex in many provinces meant that health-care costs increased dramatically. In response, some provinces implemented **extra-billing** and hospital-user fees (Segall & Chappell, 2000). Citizen groups, such as the Canadian Health Coalition (a not-for-profit, non-partisan organization formed to protect and expand Canada's public health system), soon raised concerns that such practices were jeopardizing equal access to health care as a fundamental right and that these threatened the very foundation of Medicare (Canadian Health Coalition, 2004).

To address growing concerns, another federal commission on health care was convened in 1979, chaired by Justice Emmett Hall. The mandate of the commission was to evaluate whether principles of portability, reasonable access, universal coverage, comprehensive coverage, public administration, and uniform terms and conditions were being achieved, one aspect of which were the effects of extra-billing and user fees. In his report, Canada's National-Provincial Health Program for the 1980s: A Commitment for Renewal, Justice Hall (1980) recommended eliminating user fees and extra-billing; changing mechanisms

extra-billing
An arrangement that allowed doctors to charge patients over and above the set payment schedule, for which the patient was not reimbursed

for physicians' fees; and setting national standards for portability, comprehensiveness, accessibility, public administration, and universal coverage (Health Canada, 2004a). Hall went on to note that certain practices were threatening to create a two-tier health-care system and would violate a basic principle of equal access.

The federal government acted on Hall's concerns and introduced the **Canada Health Act**. The act passed with unanimous approval in 1984 in both the House of Commons and the Senate, despite strong opposition from the medical lobby. The act sets out the primary objective of Canadian health-care policy, which is "to protect, promote and restore the physical and mental well-being of residents of Canada and to facilitate reasonable access to health services without financial or other barriers" (Canada Health Act, 1984, 3, c. 6 s. 3). Under the conditions set out in the act, provincial governments would face dollar-for-dollar penalties if they allowed doctors to extra-bill and hospitals to charge user fees (Rich, 2008). The Canada Health Act, it is argued, strengthened Canada's commitment to equity and universal health care as a fundamental right by prohibiting premiums and extra-billing (Feldberg & Vipond, 2006). It "represented a clear defeat of strong physician opposition" (Armstrong & Armstrong, 2008, p. 28).

Canada Health Act
An act passed by Parliament in 1984, which outlined the five principles of Canada's universal, government-funded health-care system.

Principles of Equity and Justice

The Canada Health Act institutionalized the belief that health care is a right, not a privilege, and that the costs of treating illness should be shared broadly by society. The act also entrenched the five fundamental principles that were to guide health-care delivery in Canada. The provinces and territories were left with the responsibility to manage, organize, and deliver health services; however, they had to adhere to the five principles in order to qualify for federal funds. These principles signalled Canada's commitment to equity as the basis for health policy:

> In order that a province may qualify for a full cash contribution . . . for a fiscal year, the health care insurance plan of the province must, throughout the fiscal year, satisfy the criteria described in sections 8 to 12 respecting the following matters:

- public administration;
- comprehensiveness;
- universality;
- portability; and
- accessibility. (Canada Health Act, 1984, c. 6, s. 7)

Non-compliance with the act would result in the loss of transfer payments for health-care services. See Box 13.2 for excerpts from the Canada Health Act.

The new act was applauded by citizens' groups like the Canadian Health Coalition but strongly opposed by the Canadian Medical Association (CMA); of particular concern was the government's decision to ban extra-billing. Medical associations predicted the act would "destroy the fundamental freedoms of all Canadians" (Rich, 2008, p. 43). In the words of Dr Everett Coffin, then president of the Canadian Medical Association, "Surely, the Canada Health Act is a rape of the spirit, if not the legal stipulations, of the Canadian constitution" (cited in Rich, 2008, p. 43). Aware of the potential loss of transfer payments if they did not act, most provinces quickly introduced legislation banning extra-billing. However, the Ontario Medical Association (OMA), one of the most powerful medical lobby groups in the country, put pressure on the Ontario government to resist such legislation. On June 12, 1986, the OMA escalated its pressure and sanctioned what was to become the longest physicians' strike in Canadian history (Meslin, 1987): approximately 50–60 per cent of doctors closed their offices, withdrew hospital services, cancelled non-emergency surgery, and shut down several emergency departments in the province. The OMA argued the proposed Ontario legislation, Bill 94, was discriminatory, that it would undermine the physician–patient relationship, and turn physicians into civil servants. According to Meslin (1987), the real concern was doctors' determination to protect their economic interests. He writes, "By sanctioning a withdrawal of medical services the Ontario Medical Association sought to make a moral issue out of physicians' right to extra-bill, and to elevate that issue to the same moral plane as the Ontario public's right to universal health care" (p. 13). The Ontario government enacted Bill 94, which eliminated extra-billing, on June 20, 1986; the strike officially ended on July 7, although rotating

Box 13.2 Canada Health Act—Excerpts

(1) In order to satisfy the criterion respecting public administration, the health-care insurance plan of a province must be administered and operated on a non-profit basis by a public authority appointed or designated by the government of the province;

(2) In order to satisfy the criterion respecting comprehensiveness, the health-care insurance plan of a province must insure all insured health services provided by hospitals, medical practitioners or dentists, and where the law of the province so permits, similar or additional services rendered by other health-care practitioners;

(3) In order to satisfy the criterion respecting universality, the health-care insurance plan of a province must entitle one hundred per cent of the insured persons of the province to the insured health services provided for by the plan on uniform terms and conditions;

(4) In order to satisfy the criterion respecting portability, the health-care insurance plan of a province must not impose any minimum period of residence in the province, or waiting period, in excess of three months before residents of the province are eligible for or entitled to insured health services;

(5) In order to satisfy the criterion respecting accessibility, the health-care insurance plan of a province (a) must provide for insured health services on uniform terms and conditions and on a basis that does not impede or preclude, either directly or indirectly whether by charges made to insured persons or otherwise, reasonable access to those services by insured persons; . . . (c) must provide for reasonable compensation for all insured health services rendered by medical practitioners or dentists; and (d) must provide for the payment of amounts to hospitals, including hospitals owned or operated by Canada, in respect of the cost of insured health services.

strikes continued at some hospitals. The Ontario doctors' strike was the second major one in the country in a span of 25 years. The failure of Ontario doctors to force the government's withdrawal of legislation on extra-billing indicated once again that one special interest group would not dictate health-care policy in Canada. The doctors' defeat was another blow to medical dominance.

Universal Health Care under Threat

The early 1990s saw growing concern that Medicare was being eroded. The prime minister of the day, Jean Chrétien, proceeded in 1994 to establish an advisory body, the National Forum on Health (Forum), to consult widely with Canadians and advise government on ways to improve Canada's health-care system. The nature of the politics involved is best summed up in the following words from the National Forum on Health's final report:

> Medicare was not born overnight. Nor was it the outcome of calm, reasoned discussions. Its history is fraught with false starts, difficult and sometimes acrimonious federal/provincial relations, and numerous confrontations between governments and health-care providers and suppliers. (National Forum on Health, 1997, n.p.)

Like previous bodies, the Forum, in its 1997 final report, strongly affirmed the necessity of preserving Medicare as outlined in the five principles of the Canada Health Act: they endorsed public funding for medically necessary services, a single-payer model, and a strong federal/provincial/territorial partnership. Moreover, the Forum recommended that home care be considered an integral part of publicly funded health services; that government provide full public funding for medically necessary drugs as a means of both controlling pharmaceutical costs and ensuring universal access; and that primary care be restructured to include a greater emphasis on prevention and a gradual elimination of the current fee-for-service structure (National Forum on Health, 1997). None of the recommendations have yet been implemented.

In the mid-1990s, troubled by their large budget deficits, the federal government made huge cuts in transfer payments to the provinces, and provincial governments ended the practice of substantial yearly increases in health-care funding (Canadian Doctors for Medicare). Although subsequent budgets restored much of this money, considerable damage to the health-care system had already occurred. A new funding arrangement in 1995 made it difficult for the federal government to enforce the principles in the Canada Health Act, as did a new framework agreement, the Social Union Framework Agreement (SUFA), drawn up in 1999. When the Alberta government passed legislation that allowed private, for-profit hospitals, the federal government did not take effective measures to reverse this development (Armstrong & Armstrong, 2003).

The Report of the National Forum on Health pointed to the growing chasm between the principles and the reality of Medicare. It noted the growing conflicts between health-care providers and governments; that hospitals were closing; that patients were experiencing longer waiting times for surgery; that health-care expenditures had been reduced; that the private sector was encroaching on health care; and that critics of publicly funded universal health care were arguing that Medicare was no longer sustainable (National Forum on Health, 1997).

Amidst ongoing political controversy, the government established yet another commission in 2001 to review the policies and programs that define Medicare. The Commission on the Future of Health Care in Canada (Romanow Commission), with Roy Romanow as its sole commissioner, tabled the final report, *Building on Values*, in 2002. Romanow stated unequivocally that a single, publicly funded health care was critical to ensuring quality services for all Canadians:

> Canadians have been clear that they still strongly support the core values on which our health-care system is premised—equity, fairness and solidarity. These values are tied to their understanding of citizenship. Canadians consider equal and timely access to medically necessary health-care services on the basis of need as a right of citizenship, not a privilege of status or wealth. (Romanow, 2002, pp. xvi)

Medicare, Romanow argued, is as "sustainable as Canadians want it to be" (p. xvi), but the funding imbalance between the federal and provincial governments needed to change.

While he argued that Medicare had served Canadians well, Romanow also pointed to the serious disparities in both access and health outcomes in some parts of the country that needed to be addressed, especially for Aboriginal peoples and for those in the North. Especially important were his major recommendations for change: the establishment of a new Canadian Health Covenant as a guide for the health-care system; the creation of a Health Council to measure and track the system's performance; the expansion of insured services under the Canada Health Act to include diagnostic services and home care; a dedicated cash-only Canada Health Transfer that would provide stable, predictable, and long-term funding to the provinces/territories; and immediate targeted funds to improve access in rural and remote areas, to improve wait times for diagnostic services, to remove obstacles to primary care, to begin a national home-care plan, and to improve drug coverage for expensive therapies (Romanow, 2002, pp. xxiv–xxv).

Despite these recommendations, little has changed. In 2003, a new Accord on Health Care Renewal was signed with the first ministers to direct new money into primary health-care renewal, and a Health Council to monitor progress was established. The federal government committed to a 10-year plan for stable and increased funding to the provinces but failed to provide sufficient accountability measures or enforce the provisions of the Canada Health Act (Health Council of Canada, 2006). On March 31, 2014, the federal government unilaterally terminated the Health Accord.

Fred Chartrand/The Canadian Press

In this photo, Roy Romanow holds up his 2002 report. Romanow concluded that Canadians value health care based on equity, fairness, and solidarity. Do you think this is still true? Are these values still reflected in federal health-care policy?

Health-Care System and Delivery

The organization of Canada's health-care system is largely determined by the Canadian Constitution, in which roles and responsibilities are divided between the federal and provincial/territorial governments. Prior to the creation of Medicare, health care in Canada was for the most part privately funded and delivered. Today, however, 70.1 per cent of expenditures on health care come from public funds, below the average for OECD countries at 73.3 per cent (CIHI, 2014b, p. 85). In addition to administering the Canada Health Act and assisting in the financing of provincial/territorial health-care services through fiscal transfers, the federal government is responsible for delivering health-care services to specific groups (e.g., First Nations people living on reserves, members of the Canadian Forces and the Royal Canadian Mounted Police, eligible veterans, refugee protection claimants, and inmates in federal penitentiaries). Approximately one million people receive **primary** and supplementary **health-care services** directly from the federal government. The federal government also has constitutional authority in some specialized aspects of health care, such as the approval and regulation of prescription drugs and the protection and promotion of health (Health Canada, 2012a).

primary health care
Both the point of first contact with the health-care system and a philosophy for delivery of that care.

In accordance with the principles of the Canada Health Act, each provincial/territorial health-care insurance plan provides complete coverage for all necessary hospital and physician services funded through a single-payer insurance system. It has been suggested that the single-payer system not only ensures greater equity but also is more efficient and cost-effective (Stolberg, 2004). The plans are financed through federal, provincial, and territorial taxation, such as personal and corporate taxes, sales taxes, payroll levies, and other revenues; services are provided free of charge to individuals without deductible amounts, co-payments, or dollar limits. Most provinces/territories also provide some health services that are not generally covered under Medicare to certain groups, such as seniors, children, and social assistance recipients. The scope and nature of these supplementary health benefits, such as prescription drugs, vision care, dental care, and medical equipment and appliances, vary considerably by province and territory (Health Canada, 2012a).

In 2014, physician services accounted for the third-largest health-care expenditure (15.5 per cent), below that of hospitals (at 29.6 per cent) and drugs (at 15.8 per cent) (CIHI, 2014b, p. 42). Over 98 per cent of the expenditures on physician services come from the public sector. Doctors working in private practice provide most primary health-care services, although an increasing number work as part of health-care professional teams in clinics, community health centres, and group practices. Those in private practice are paid a fee-for-service according to the reimbursement schedule negotiated between each provincial and territorial government and the medical associations in their respective jurisdictions. Doctors who work in clinics, community health centres, and group practices are generally paid salaries. The first publicly funded community clinics were established in Saskatchewan at the time of the doctors' strike in 1962. Today there are over 700 community health centres (CHCs) across all regions of Canada. Although called differently in different provinces/territories, all share several characteristics: they provide "not-for-profit," publicly funded services; they are comprised of multidisciplinary health teams including family physicians, nurse practitioners, dieticians, and community health workers who provide primary-care, as well as mental health, public health, and some home-care services; they partner with various local agencies to address the broader "social determinants of health"; and they serve an identifiable community (neighbourhoods or communities of individuals with common characteristics such as youth, seniors, ethno-cultural groups) designed to focus on the most appropriate services and programs for that community (Canadian Association of Community Health Centres, 2015). Health-care delivery by multidisciplinary health teams has been suggested as a way to improve access, increase resources for preventative care, and contain costs (Cohen, 2014; Romanow, 2002; Yalnizyan, 2005).

Private-sector expenditures account for nearly 30 per cent of health-care spending in the country and have risen faster than public-sector expenditure over the past three decades (CIHI 2006a, p. 6). Forecast annual growth for private-sector expenditures for 2013 and 2014 are also higher than those forecast for the public sector (CIHI, 2014b, p. 30). Included are expenses paid through private health-insurance plans, either purchased individually or as part of an employee benefit plan, or out-of-pocket expenses for medications, treatments, medical equipment, etc., that either are not covered by private plans or where an individual does not have a supplementary health plan. For example, most dental services, drugs, counselling, and alternative therapies are paid by private supplementary plans or are paid for directly by the individual. Under most provincial and territorial laws, private insurers are restricted from offering coverage that duplicates that of the publicly funded plans, although there are no restrictions on supplementary health services. See Figure 13.1 For a breakdown of health-care expenditures.

Over the years, Canada's universal health-care system has received positive reviews: "Every successive generation of Canadians [has] enjoyed improved health and physical quality of life" (Yalnizyan, 2005, p. 1). Yet, there are serious disparities in health outcomes within the country, mostly notably for Canada's Aboriginal peoples. There are other disparities as well. People who live in remote and rural areas have less access to health-care providers, medical resources, and advanced hospital care. Those in the Atlantic region have fewer services available than people living in other parts of Canada. Disparities also exist

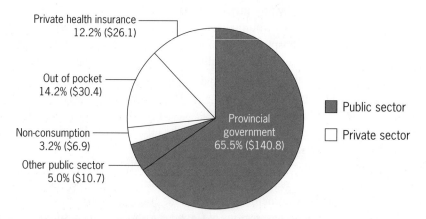

Figure 13.1 Total Health Expenditure by Source of Finance, 2014 (Percentage Share and Billions of Dollars)

Source: CIHI. (2014). Figure 9: Total health expenditure by source of finance, 2014 (Percentage share and billions of dollars. In *National Health Expenditure Trends, 1975 to 2014*, p. 31. Available at: www.cihi.ca/web/resource/en/nhex_2014_report_en.pdf

in terms of waiting times to see a specialist or for surgery, and primary health-care services are more comprehensive and readily available in the richer and more populated provinces. As well, there are disparities between the supplementary health-care services covered by the various provincial and territorial plans. Economic inequality, linked to other determinants of health, is another form of disparity. The income gap between the rich and poor in Canada is growing (Yalnizyan, 2010; OECD, 2011a), and health disparities among income groups is becoming more pronounced (Kondro, 2012). Many Canadians cannot afford to pay for all their health-care needs, such as medications not covered by government plans. Today, Canadians spend more of their own money on prescription drugs than any other category of health expenditure, and those who can not afford prescriptions will do without (Health Canada, 2008a, p. 4; Kondro, 2012). For example, almost one in four Canadians failed to take prescribed medicines because of cost in the last five years (Dutt, 2014).

Income disparity is directly linked to health status and has yet to be addressed by Canada's government.

International Comparisons

Health-Care Expenditures

One of the most contentious issues today concerns the extent that the private sector should be involved in providing health-care services. A common assertion made by the media and by some health-policy experts is that spending on health care is spiralling out of control. Canadians are being told that Medicare has become too costly and is no longer economically sustainable (Romanow, 2002; Skinner & Rovere, 2011). Over the past 40 years, health-care spending has indeed increased in Canada as it has all over the world, both on a per capita basis and as a percentage of the **gross domestic product (GDP)**. Although relatively high in comparison with some other Organisation for Economic Co-operation and Development (OECD) countries, the overall expenditure on health care in Canada, however, is at the level that one would expect given Canada's standard of living and is significantly lower than health expenditures in the United States (CIHI, 2014b; OECD, 2014).

gross domestic product (GDP)
The market value of all goods and services that have been sold during a year.

In 2015, Canada is projected to spend an estimated $219.1 billion dollars on health care, or $6,105 per Canadian (CIHI, 2015). However, among the 20 or so richest countries, Canada's spending levels and growth patterns are not unusual. Canada in 2012 ranked eighth among OECD countries in terms of both per capita health spending and the proportion of GDP spent on health care. Canada's total health-care spending as a percentage of GDP in 2012 represented about one-tenth (10.9 per cent) of its GDP. That same year, the United States, by comparison, spent 16.9 per cent of its GDP on health care (CIHI, 2014b, p. 86). The projections for 2015 suggest that overall health expenditure will represent 10.9 per cent of Canada's gross GDP, a share that has fallen gradually over the past few years (CIHI, 2015). For a comparison of selected OECD countries, see Figure 13.2.

On a per capita basis, Canada's spending was among the top quartile of 29 OECD countries. Canada spent $4569 (US dollars) per individual in 2013; on the other hand, the United States, which had the highest expenditure per individual, spent $9086. The OECD average of total health expenditure per capita for the same year was $3566 (US dollars) (CIHI 2015).

In Canada, as in other OECD countries, both the public and private sectors finance health-care services, although the ratio varies among countries. Public-sector funding

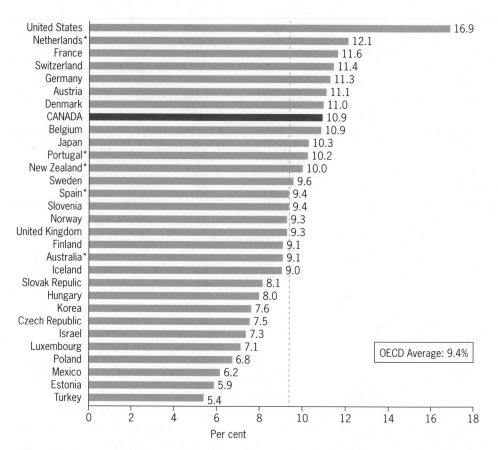

Figure 13.2 Total Health Expenditure as Percentage of GDP, 30 Selected OECD Countries, 2012

Note: *data for 2011.

Source: CIHI. (2014). Figure 42: Total health expenditure as a percentage of GDP, 30 selected OECD countries, 2012. In *National Health Expenditure Trends, 1975 to 2014,* p. 86. Available at: www.cihi.ca/web/resource/en/nhex_2014_report_en.pdf

includes payments by municipal, provincial/territorial, and federal governments and by workers' compensation boards and other social security programs; private-sector funding consists primarily of health expenditures by individuals and private insurance companies. Since 1997, the share of public sector spending as a proportion of the total health expenditure in Canada has remained relatively stable at about 70 per cent. In 2012, it accounted for 70.1 per cent of total expenditure, somewhat less than the OECD average of 73.3 per cent. This is also less than many OECD countries with a comparable standard of living. For example, the Netherlands, Denmark, Sweden, Japan, France, Germany, Norway, Austria, Finland, the United Kingdom, and New Zealand all have higher public health-care expenditures. The Netherlands and Denmark had the highest public-sector share of total health expenditures at 85.8 per cent. By comparison, in the United States the public-sector health expenditure was 47.6 per cent (CIHI, 2014b, p. 89).

Types of service provided for by the public-sector share of health-care finances differs among OECD countries. For example, in Canada the public sector pays for most physician services, whereas in France public funds pay around 75 per cent of physician services; however, public funds in France pay 67 per cent of pharmaceuticals and other medical non-durable goods (CIHI, 2006a, p. 7) whereas in Canada the public sector finances only slightly over 40 per cent of prescription drug costs (CIHI, 2014b, p. 7). Canadians rely more heavily than people in most OECD countries on private insurance and direct-individual payments for health-care services not covered by its Medicare system (Romanow, 2002, p. 26). According to Colleen Flood (2014), "what distinguishes Canada's health system from others is not how little private finance we have but how much private finance we already endure."

Canada is the only country in the world with a universal health-care plan that doesn't provide universal coverage for prescription drugs. Yet, Canadians pay some of the highest drug prices in the world, with average drug prices 30 per cent above the OECD average, trailing only Switzerland and the United States in prescription costs (Dutt, 2014, p. 2). Research shows that patients reduce the use of prescribed medications because of cost: one in 10 Canadians per year who are prescribed medications do not take them because of associated costs, which in turn can lead to further health problems. It is estimated 6.5 per cent of all hospital admissions are the result of non-adherence to medications, at an estimated cost of $7 billion to $9 billion per year (Dutt, p. 3). A growing body of research shows that implementing a national pharmacare program would significantly lower costs, reduce the amount of public spending on drugs, improve access to medications for all, and improve health outcomes for individuals (Morgan et al., 2015; Morgan et al., 2013; Romanow, 2002). A universally funded pharmacare system is "required to ensure equitable access to care" which in turn "will improve health outcomes and generate returns in the form of savings elsewhere in the healthcare system" (Morgan et al., 2013, pp. 2–3). Countries that have integrated prescription drugs as part of their universal health care at little or no cost to patients achieve better access to medicines at significantly lower costs than in Canada. In August 2014, the current president of the Canadian Medical Association publicly supported the call for a publicly funded national pharmacare program (www.canadiandoctorsformedicare.ca/CDM-in-the-News/dr-chris-simpson-cma-president-offers-support-for-pharmacare-plan.html).

Health Status

According to a recent survey conducted by EKOS for the Conference Board of Canada, health care remains a top priority for Canadians, with 90 per cent indicating that health care should be the main priority for national decision-makers, ahead of issues such as the economy and the environment (Muzyka et al., 2012). In general, the health status of Canadians compares favourably to most countries in the world. For example, Canada ranks within the top 10 as measured by the UN's **Human Development Index (HDI)** (Human Development Report, 2014). Over 85 per cent of Canadians rate their health as being very good or good (Conference Board of Canada, 2013b). Although there are major disparities within the country in terms of life expectancy, infant mortality, and premature mortality from various diseases such as diabetes and mental disorders, the health of Canadians overall in comparison to those in similar countries remains very good. A number of factors affect an individual's health: socio-economic, biological, and environmental factors, as well as accessibility of health care. A 2010 survey conducted by the Commonwealth Fund compared experiences of access in 11 countries, focusing on access to care and costs (Schoen et al., 2010). The findings suggest that Canada's system

Human Development Index (HDI)
Provides a composite measure of three dimensions of human development: living a long and healthy life (measured by life expectancy), being educated (measured by adult literacy and gross enrolment in education), and having a decent standard of living (measured by purchasing power parity and income).

Table 13.1 Comparison of Responses to Cost Being a Deterrent in Access to Health Care, in per cent, 2010

	Canada	Australia	US
Did not fill prescriptions or skipped doses	10%	12%	21%
Had a medical problem but did not visit a medical doctor	8%	18%	28%
Had out-of-pocket medical spending of $1000 or more	12%	21%	35%
Had serious problems paying or unable to pay medical costs	6%	8%	20%

Source: Adapted from Schoen et al. (2010). How health insurance design affects access to care and costs, by income, in eleven countries. *Health Affairs, 29*(12), 2326.

is more equitable in facilitating access to needed health care. Especially stark is the comparison with the United States, which still lacks a comparable publicly funded universal health-care system. See Table 13.1.

Transforming Health Care: The Current Debate

In the past decade, calls for increased privatization of health care have gained momentum. Since the beginning of the global economic recession in 2008, the ratio of health expenditures to GDP has stabilized or fallen in most OECD countries. In Canada, for example, health spending has decreased by an average 0.4 per cent in the last four years (after adjusting for inflation and population growth) (CIHI, 2014b, p. 14). Nevertheless, the debate around the sustainability of Medicare and health-care costs continues. The Fraser Institute, for example, continues to argue that "the redistributive, tax-based funding structure of Canada's health system produces rates of growth in health spending that are not sustainable without at least a partial reliance on user-based, private financing" (Skinner & Rovere, 2011, p. 3). In 2005, opponents of Medicare received a boost from the Chaoulli decision in Quebec when the Supreme Court, by a 4–3 vote, declared that Quebec's prohibition of private insurance for publicly insured services violated the provincial Charter of Rights (www.canadiandoctorsformedicare.ca/the-chaoulli-decision.html). As a result of this decision, Quebec agreed to allow private insurers to provide insurance for those doctors who worked exclusively within the private sector. Supporters of Medicare, however, argue that privatizing health-care services not only undermines the basic values of justice on which Canada's Medicare system was founded but also that it is not the way to reduce overall health-care costs (Canadian Doctors for Medicare [CDM], 2011; n.d.; Romanow, 2002; Armstrong & Armstrong, 2008; Canadian Health Coalition, 2008; Yalnizyan, 2005). In the words of Dr Monika Dutt, Chair of Canadian Doctors for Medicare,

> Proponents of two-tier medicine continually tell Canadians that introducing for-profit care will lower costs, but international research consistently shows that these claims are false. When health care becomes a for-profit industry, profit has

to be generated somewhere, which consistently results in higher treatment costs. Additional spending results from the administrative demands generated within for-profit health-care systems as it moves Canada away from the straightforward, single-payer system that we have. The US spends one-quarter of their hospital budgets just on administering the plethora of insurance companies, private payers, and HMOs, and dumping billions into marketing and promotion. We believe that our health-care budget is better spent on providing treatment to Canadians rather than covering marketing and administrative costs. (Dr Monika Dutt—quote provided in private correspondence with Ms Katie Raso, Communications and Outreach Officer, Canadian Doctors for Medicare, January 2015)

Although there are competing views about how to fix Canada's health-care system, there is agreement that things need to be improved. Wait times for primary-care appointments, to see a specialist, or for elective surgery is of major concern. According to the Canadian Institute for Health Information (CIHI), significant efforts have been made in improving access and shortening wait times within the last decade; however, a 2010 comparison of 11 Commonwealth countries showed that Canada's wait-time performance is poor. Canadians waited the longest for a specialist appointment: 41 per cent reported waits of two or more months. Less than 50 per cent of Canadians reported being able to see a doctor or nurse the same day or the next day when sick (CIHI, 2012a, pp. 13–15). To address the ongoing concerns, CIHI recommended that demonstrably successful wait-time strategies, including financial incentives, clear benchmarks, and effective use of technology be implemented more broadly (p. xiv). In one of its last reports,[1] the Health Council of Canada (2013a) echoes these recommendations. It went on to state that "the results of the last ten years make it clear that we need to do things differently" to achieve better outcomes in the future, "with an overarching aim of achieving equity" for all Canadians (p. 34).

A Clash of Values: A Public . . . or Private . . . Future?

The debate over private, for-profit health care continues to generate considerable interest and opposition. According to Dr Brian Day, former president of the Canadian Medical Association (2007–8) and owner of Vancouver's for-profit Cambie Surgery Centre, Canadians should have the freedom and choice to spend their own money on their health care however they wish, including to obtain faster treatment (Day, 2012). He has launched a Charter challenge, to be heard at the BC Supreme Court originally in March 2015,[2] alleging that BC's Medicare laws that limit for-profit delivery of medically necessary services and restrict extra billing violate Section 7 and 15 of the Charter of Rights and Freedoms. In his view, health care should be treated like any other commodity on the market, with an individual buyer choosing where and how to spend her or his health-care dollars. Those who can afford to pay can enjoy faster access. It is, according to Dr Day, a right enjoyed by citizens in most countries of the world. The case is likely to end up at the Supreme Court of Canada.

---

1. In April 2013, the Harper government announced plans to discontinue funding to the Health Council of Canada, an independent body responsible for monitoring implementation of the 2004 Health Accord, effective 2014.

2. This hearing has been delayed, with a possible hearing date of September 2016.

Various coalition groups including Canadian Doctors for Medicare, the Canadian Health Coalition, the BC Health Coalition, the Canadian Federation of Nurses Unions, and the Council of Canadians argue that private, for-profit health care advocated by Dr Day will undermine the fundamental values on which Medicare was founded, namely that health care is a public good—a moral enterprise based on values of equity, fairness, and solidarity. Their concern is that if Dr Day's Charter challenge is successful, then access to public health care will decline. It is "the most serious threat to the principles of equality and universality that most Canadians support" (Fuller, 2015). In the words of Dr Dutt, "What the experiences of countries around the world have shown is that when for-profit care is allowed to flourish, both costs and wait times increase without improving quality of care" (Raso, 2015). In Ontario, concerns were raised when one in seven private health-care clinics failed provincial safety inspections, including hepatitis C outbreaks at three colonoscopy clinics (Devaney, 2014). Although there is resistance to for-profit health companies in Canada, private entrepreneurs continue to flourish. Centric Health, a large US-based for-profit conglomerate, has numerous clinics throughout Canada and registered before-tax profits of $43 million in 2012 (Blackwell, 2014).

Just over 50 years since Medicare was first introduced in Saskatchewan, the tensions, acrimonious relations, and confrontations between governments and special interest groups is as present now as it was when Medicare was born. Now, as was the case then, the debate is not based purely on reason or facts. It is an ideological one between adherents to **neo-liberalism** and those who defend social democratic values.

neo-liberalism
A political ideology that advocates the market as the best vehicle for the production and distribution of various resources and an enhanced role for the private sector.

For the most part, Canadians hold on to a vision of a universal publicly funded health-care system. For example, a recent poll by Nanos Research found that 94 per cent of Canadians support public—not private, for-profit—solutions as the way to make Canada's health-care system stronger (Canadian Health Coalition, 2011). As well, a report commissioned by the Health Action Lobby (HEAL) suggests a majority favour renewed government support to ensure the long-term sustainability of Medicare: "our most significant finding is that Canada's health-care system is as sustainable as we want it to be . . ." if there "is the political will to make the changes that will let that happen" (Tholl & Bujold, 2012, p. iv).

Conclusion

Canada's universal health-care program was implemented during a period that saw the continual growth of a social welfare state. However, in the 1980s, neo-liberalism became the operative model and earlier priorities of social and economic equality were shelved. The economics and ideology of neo-liberalism includes the following: promoting free enterprise as the means of increasing economic growth; cutting public expenditures for social services, such as health care; promoting privatization of public enterprises, such as hospitals; promoting the deregulation of labour and financial markets. As well, it replaces the concept of "the common good" and instead encourages individualism and consumerism (Navarro, 2007). During the 1990s, the Canadian government slashed billions of dollars from social programs, including expenditures for health care (Broadbent, 2009). Despite the principles outlined in the Canada Health Act, the government did little to stop the growth of for-profit health clinics and private surgical facilities.

In the past two decades, income inequality in Canada has grown dramatically (Broadbent Institute, 2012). Canada's reduced spending on social programs as a percentage of its GDP (now around 16 per cent) dropped it down to twenty-second place out of 30 OECD countries (Finn, 2012). This is bound to have major consequences for people's health: numerous studies have shown that inequality and poverty are decisive factors determining the health of populations. Research by Wilkinson and Pickett (2009), shows that not only are poor people less healthy, but inequality harms everyone in society. This suggests that reducing social spending even further will result in greater health inequalities.

It is within this context of neo-liberalism and reduced spending on social programs that the current debate about the future of Canada's universal health program is taking place. And, the future of Canadian health care hangs in the balance. Supporters of Medicare believe that universal and accessible health care for all is a fundamental right of citizenship. Those who advocate for a greater role of the private sector see health care in more individualistic terms; that is, those who can afford private care should have the right to purchase it.

As it was 50 years ago when Tommy Douglas first introduced his plan for government-funded health insurance, the struggle today involves a fundamental conflict over values. It is about power, ideology, and the role of the state in promoting economic equality and social rights.

Summary

- As with most Western European countries, a government-funded health-insurance plan in Canada was the result of public pressure and a coalition of progressive forces.
- A universal health-care program was first established in 1961 by the CCF government of Tommy Douglas in Saskatchewan with popular support from farm and labour groups.
- The Saskatchewan Medical Association strongly opposed "socialized medicine" and government involvement in health services, which culminated in a bitter 23-day doctors' strike. However, some 30 doctors supportive of the government worked with citizen groups to establish the Saskatoon Community Clinic as an alternative to private practice.
- In 1966, the federal government introduced the Medical Care Act modelled on the Saskatchewan plan: it set the five basic principles as universality, comprehensiveness, public administration, portability, and accessibility, later enshrined in the Canada Health Act.
- Funding for Medicare was originally cost-shared 50–50 by the federal government and the provincial/territorial governments. Subsequent funding agreements placed greater financial responsibility on the provinces/territories.
- In 1980, Justice Emmett Hall expressed concern that extra-billing and user fees practised by some doctors violated a basic principle of equal access. In response the federal government unanimously passed the Canada Health Act in 1984 that prohibited these practices.

- The Canadian Medical Association strongly opposed the government's decision to ban extra-billing. In 1986, the Ontario Medical Association launched a 25-day strike in opposition.
- In 1994, then Prime Minister Jean Chrétien established the National Forum on Health to advise on ways to improve Canada's health-care system. Both the Forum and the subsequent (2001) Romanow Commission on the Future of Health Care endorsed the basic principles of Medicare and recommended universal health coverage for currently uninsured medical services, such as pharmaceuticals and home care.
- Just over 70 per cent of Canada's expenditures on health care come from public-sector funds, below the OECD average of 73.3 per cent.
- Canada's health-care spending costs as a percentage of GDP rank eighth among OECD countries.
- Canada is the only country in the world with a universal health-care plan that doesn't provide universal coverage for prescription drugs.
- Canada's publicly funded universal health care is contested by those who favour increased privatization of health care. The debate is shaped by two opposing sets of values concerning the role of the state in promoting social equality and health equity for all.

Key Terms

allopathic medicine
extra-billing
Canada Health Act
gross domestic product
  (GDP)

Human Development Index
  (HDI)
ideology
Medicare
neo-liberalism

primary health care
unalienable human right
welfare state/social welfare
  state
values

Sociological Reflection: Public or Private Health Care?

Consider and outline the arguments for and against privatizing health-care services.

- What is the root of these differences?
- What are the implications of each position for the individual and society?
- Are there ethical concerns?
- If you were asked to appear before a commission reviewing health care, what position would you take and why?

Discussion Questions

1. Saskatchewan's model of publicly funded health insurance laid the foundations for Canadian Medicare. What key principles did it establish?
2. In what ways did the Canada Health Act (1984) enhance universal health care in Canada?
3. It has been suggested that the establishment of Medicare affected the position and power of the medical profession. Discuss.

4. What are some reasons that Canada developed a universal health-care plan and that the United States has so far failed to do so?
5. Why do the overwhelming majority of Canadians support public rather than private solutions as a way to strengthen the health-care system?
6. Are Canada's health-care expenditures reasonable compared to other OECD countries? Explain.

Further Investigation

1. Critically evaluate the role of values and ideology in the development of health policy. Illustrate your answer with examples of specific health policies.
2. Compare the Canadian model of a publicly funded universal health-care system with the predominantly private health-care system currently in the United States. What inequities, if any, result from a private, for-profit system?

Further Reading

Armstrong, P., & Armstrong, H. (2003). *Wasting away: The undermining of Canadian health care* (2nd ed.). Toronto, ON: Oxford University Press.

Badgley, R., & Wolfe, S. (1967). *Doctors' strike*. Toronto, ON: Macmillan of Canada.

Hall, Justice E. (1980). *Canada's national-provincial health program for the 1980s: A commitment for renewal*. Ottawa, ON: Government of Canada.

Health Council of Canada. (2013). *Better health, better care, better value for all: Refocusing health care reform in Canada*. Toronto: Health Council of Canada. September. Available at: www.cahspr.ca/web/uploads/conference/2014-02-14_Better_Health_Better_Care_Better_Value_For_All.pdf

National Forum on Health. (1997). *Canada health action: Building on the legacy: The final report*. Ottawa, ON: Government of Canada.

Romanow, R. (2002). *Building on values: The future of health care in Canada*. Ottawa, ON: Government of Canada.

Web Resources

Canada Health Act
http://laws.justice.gc.ca/en/c-6/index.html

Canada's Health Care System
www.hc-sc.gc.ca/hcs-sss/alt_formats/hpb-dgps/pdf/pubs/2005-hcs-sss/2005-hcs-sss-eng.pdf

Canadian Doctors for Medicare (CDM)
www.canadiandoctorsformedicare.ca/

Canadian Health Coalition
www.healthcoalition.ca/

Canadian Institute for Health Information (CIHI)
www.cihi.ca

Commission on the Future of Health Care in Canada
www.hc-sc.gc.ca/hcs-sss/hhr-rhs/strateg/romanow-eng.php

Health Council of Canada
www.healthcouncilcanada.ca/en/

Organisation for Economic Co-operation & Development Health Statistics
www.oecd.org/els/health-systems/health-data.htm

CHAPTER 14
The Pharmaceutical Industry and Health Canada: Values in Conflict?

Joel Lexchin, MD

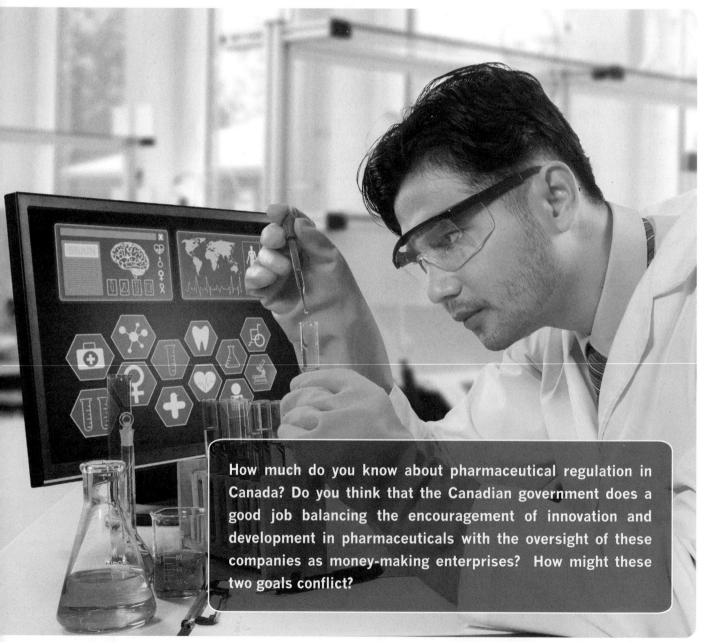

How much do you know about pharmaceutical regulation in Canada? Do you think that the Canadian government does a good job balancing the encouragement of innovation and development in pharmaceuticals with the oversight of these companies as money-making enterprises? How might these two goals conflict?

Overview

- How do pharmaceutical companies operate within a market economy?
- What is the relationship between the pharmaceutical industry and Health Canada?
- What are the values that guide Health Canada?

Pharmaceuticals are an essential element in modern health care but they are produced by companies operating within a capitalist market economy. This chapter explores how the profit motive affects the operation of the pharmaceutical industry while functioning within a regulatory structure set by the state. As a result, there are significant interactions between Health Canada and the industry. The values of Health Canada and how they are reflected in Health Canada's interactions is the subject of the second part of this chapter. Finally, the chapter ends with an exploration of whether the relationship between the industry and the government is compatible with democratic values.

Introduction: The Pharmaceutical Industry and the Canadian State

Pharmaceuticals are an essential element of modern medicine and when used appropriately can be of great value in maintaining and restoring health. Medicines for HIV/AIDS have turned what used to be a fatal illness into a chronic one, and drugs have revolutionized the care for some forms of cancer and heart disease. In 2012, there were about 559 million prescriptions dispensed in Canada (Canadian Generic Pharmaceutical Association, 2013) at a cost of $27.7 billion (CIHI, 2013b).

The importance of pharmaceuticals to health, along with the amount of money being spent on them, makes it imperative to understand the dynamics of the pharmaceutical industry. However, the industry does not stand in isolation; it is intimately intertwined with the **state** through a number of relationships: The public sector does much of the **basic research** that leads to the development of new medicines (United States Senate, 2000). The government has established a set of elaborate regulations that must be met before new medicines are allowed onto the market. A large share of all of the money spent on prescription medicines comes from the public sector (in Canada about 44.5 cents out of every dollar, or $12.3 billion, is spent by governments) (CIHI, 2013b). And, finally, legislation means that only select groups of professionals (doctors, dentists, and in some cases pharmacists, optometrists, nurse practitioners, podiatrists, and midwives) can prescribe medicines, and another professional, a pharmacist, has to dispense them.

Although the pharmaceutical industry is generally not considered a social determinant of health, it nevertheless has an important impact on the health status of Canadians. As we saw in Chapter 13, the cost of prescription medications is not generally covered

state
A term used to describe a collection of government and government-controlled institutions within a country.

basic research
The research phase where the basic discoveries are made about how cells function and about human physiology.

by provincial and territorial publicly funded health-insurance plans. Individuals who are unable to afford the cost of prescription drugs either do not fill their prescriptions or compromise their efficacy by not adhering to directions prescribed by their doctor. For example, some may take their medications every second day rather than every day so that prescriptions are refilled less frequently. Some people may cut a prescribed pill in half for the same reason. Affordability of prescription drugs is a growing concern for more Canadians as the cost of drugs escalates. This chapter opens with a description of some of the main characteristics of the pharmaceutical industry and then looks at the interaction between the industry and the state in four key areas: (1) **user fees** in drug regulation, (2) **postmarketing surveillance**, (3) **transparency** in the regulatory system, and (4) regulation of company **promotional activities**. Much of the information in this chapter is based on Canadian data, but in some cases it will be necessary to refer to information from the United States and other countries.

Characteristics of the Pharmaceutical Industry

The pharmaceutical industry is no different from any other enterprise in a capitalist economy; the primary motivation for making drugs is profit. The mission statement from **Canada's Research-Based Pharmaceutical Companies (Rx&D)** emphasizes the "social responsibilities and role to improve the health and social environments that Canadians enjoy" that its members take on (*Code of Ethical Practices—2012*, 2012). However, that quotation needs to be balanced against one from a former president of the association, who said "The pharmaceutical industry has never claimed to be motivated by altruism, but rather by profit for survival" (Garton, May 26, 1980, personal communication).

Profits and Public Values

A couple of Canadian examples (Lexchin, 2010a) show that when profits and the public interest conflict, companies put their financial interests first. The Canadian Coordinating Office for Health Technology Assessment (CCOHTA, now the Canadian Agency for Drugs and Technologies in Health) prepared an assessment regarding the comparability of the statin group of drugs, drugs used to lower cholesterol. The report concluded that all of the then available statins were equivalent in their benefits. Bristol-Myers Squibb, makers of Pravachol (pravastatin), took CCOHTA to court to stop the release of the report. Although the case was thrown out when it finally was heard by a judge, it delayed the release of the report by a full year and cost CCOHTA 13 per cent of its annual budget on lawyers' fees (Hemminki, Hailey, & Koivusalo, 1999).

Dr Anne Holbrook of McMaster University was hired by the government of Ontario to produce a report on **gastrointestinal medications**. Her report concluded that AstraZeneca's drug, Losec (omeprazole), was no better than two less expensive products in the same drug class. As a consequence of her conclusion, she received a letter from a law firm representing AstraZeneca claiming that if her report was released she would be contravening Canadian federal law and that "In the event that you proceed notwithstanding this warning you should assume that our client will take appropriate steps including the commencement of appropriate legal proceedings in order to protect its interests and

user fees
With respect to pharmaceuticals, it means that when companies apply to have a new drug approved they must pay a fee to Health Canada. Those fees form part of the revenue that is used to operate the part of Health Canada that deals with medications.

postmarketing surveillance
Refers to all of the activities that are undertaken to monitor the safety and effectiveness of drugs once they have been approved for marketing.

transparency
In the context of drug regulation, refers to how much input the public and health-care practitioners have in the decision to approve a new drug and how much public access there is to the clinical information that companies have to submit to Health Canada when they apply to get a drug approved.

promotional activities
All of the methods undertaken by pharmaceutical companies to increase the sales of their products.

Canada's Research-Based Pharmaceutical Companies (Rx&D)
The association that represents the Canadian subsidiaries of the brand-name multinational companies operating in Canada.

gastrointestinal medications
Drugs for stomach and bowel problems.

to obtain compliance with the law" (Shuchman, 1999). AstraZeneca quickly apologized to Dr Holbrook and claimed that the letter had been misdirected to her and should have instead been sent to the Ontario government (Rx&D, 2002).

This vigorous defence of profits has not gone unrewarded. For over 30 years profit levels in the pharmaceutical industry have outstripped profits in other industries by a wide margin, and that gap has been growing. During the 1970s, drug companies averaged 8.9 per cent profit as a percentage of revenue compared to 4.4 per cent for all Fortune 500 industries. In the 1980s, drug companies increased their margin by earning 11.1 per cent compared to 4.4 per cent for all Fortune 500 companies, and during the 1990s, the gap grew to 15.1 per cent compared to just 4.1 per cent (Public Citizen's Congress Watch, 2002). In the past couple of years, the pharmaceutical industry has fallen from first place in the Fortune 500 rankings but it still outpaces nearly all other industries in profitability (The Henry J. Kaiser Family Foundation, 2009). Profits for Canadian subsidiaries are more difficult to obtain since many of them are wholly owned by the parent company and do not publicly release much information. However, Statistics Canada reports indicate that except for a period in the late 1990s when industry profits were exceptionally low, drug companies operating in Canada earn about twice what all manufacturing industries do (Lexchin & Wiktorowicz, 2008).

The pharmaceutical industry uses two main arguments to justify its high profit levels. First, it claims that discovering new drugs is a highly risky venture where only 1 in 10,000 chemicals that are initially screened ever makes it to market (Rx&D, 2004). Given this level of risk, so the argument goes, high profits are necessary in order to convince investors to put their money into drug companies as opposed to companies where the risk is much lower. However, while the overall failure rate cited by the industry may be true, it does not mean that developing drugs is risky. Most of the chemicals that fail to make it to market do so very early on in the process when costs are minimal. By the time that prospective drugs enter the later stages of **human testing**, where 75 per cent of the costs are incurred, the failure rate is much lower—in the order of 1 in 2 or 1 in 3 (Light, Andrus, & Warburton, 2009). Finkelstein and Temin have analyzed the risk involved in drug R&D since 1970 and have concluded that

> the risk that large drug companies would have diverse fortunes, so evident in the 1970s, disappeared completely after 1980. They *all* do well. . . . And this trend of doing well appears to continue today. . . . The largest drug companies can mitigate the risk at the company level by diversifying it. . . . It's the difference between saying that any one house might burn down and saying that the company itself is risky. Investing at the drug company level is a good, solid, and basically *riskless* proposition [emphasis in original]. (Finkelstein & Temin, 2008)

The second argument brought forward by the industry is the cost of developing a new drug. Industry spokespeople cite a figure of over $800 million (US) as the amount it takes to bring a single new drug to market (DiMasi, Hansen, & Grabowski, 2003). This figure is heavily debated for a number of reasons, detailed in a critique by Light and Warburton (2005). Among other things they point out the following:

- The data used in calculating the $800 million figure came directly from the companies involved and could not be independently verified.

human testing
Drugs must go through three stages of human testing before they can be approved for marketing in Canada (and virtually all other industrialized countries). In Phase One they are tested in health volunteers to determine the metabolic and pharmacological actions of the drug in humans, the side effects associated with increasing doses, and, if possible, to gain early evidence of effectiveness. Phase Two testing takes place in several hundred people and consists of controlled clinical studies conducted to obtain some preliminary data on the effectiveness of the drug for a particular indication or indications in patients with the disease or condition. Phase Three testing usually involves several hundred to several thousand patients and is intended to gather the additional information about effectiveness and safety that is needed to evaluate the overall benefit-risk relationship of the drug.

- Although 24 companies were originally asked for information, only 12 responded, and data from 2 of those 12 was not usable.
- The criteria used to select the drugs being studied meant that the sample represented less than one-quarter of all new drug approvals.
- Estimates of company spending on drug development are presented without deducting (or at least identifying) government subsidies, including taxpayer funding from the US National Institutes of Health and other public agencies.
- Amounts are not adjusted for tax deductions and credits for doing research and development, which reduce the final costs by nearly 50 per cent.

DiMasi and colleagues (2005) have vigorously defended their work (using 11 pages to respond to a 4-page critique), but acceptance of their calculations is far from universal.

Research Priorities

patents
Medicines typically have two different types of patents—a patent on the process used to make them and a patent on the product itself. While a patent is valid, the company owning the product has the exclusive right to sell it.

For the past few decades, the research priorities of the industry have been driven by a blockbuster mentality whereby, in order to deliver the type of returns investors have come to expect, the industry needs to produce medicines that will sell in excess of $1 billion annually worldwide. What this approach translates into in terms of research and development (R&D) is that companies are almost exclusively focused on products that can be **patented** and that will be used by large numbers of people with chronic diseases who live in First World countries. Most people in these countries either have the ability to purchase medicines on their own or, as is more often the case, the cost of medicines is covered publicly. (However, in Canada it is estimated that 13 per cent of the Canadian population is either uninsured or underinsured for prescription drug costs and people with no drug coverage and paying out of pocket are usually people with minimum wage jobs (Applied Management in association with Fraser Group Tristat Resources, 2000).) Under these circumstances, most drugs are likely to be profitable with companies that are willing to invest in the necessary R&D.

market failure
The failure of the free-market system to produce results that are socially desirable due to the absence of a sufficient profit motive.

neglected diseases
Diseases that occur in small numbers of people or in people with little to no purchasing power. In these cases, the absence of sufficient sales (in dollar value) means that drugs for these illnesses will not be developed by profit-seeking companies.

Evidence of **market failure**, that is, the lack of medicines for unprofitable diseases, is not hard to document. In spring 2001, the 20 top-grossing pharmaceutical companies in the world were surveyed about recent drug development activity for five neglected diseases: Chagas disease, leishmaniasis, malaria, sleeping sickness, and tuberculosis. Eleven companies responded; eight had spent nothing on Chagas disease, leishmaniasis, and sleeping sickness; seven had spent less than 1 per cent of their total R&D budget on any of the five diseases (Drugs for Neglected Diseases Working Group & Campaign for Access to Essential Medicines, 2001). In the ensuing years, little changed with respect to industry-initiated R&D for neglected diseases; five out of twelve of the top multinational companies were not conducting any research, and these companies were unwilling to enter this area regardless of any incentives offered to them (Moran, Ropars, Guzman, Diaz, & Garrision, 2005). Of 850 new therapeutic products marketed from 2000 to 2011, just 37 (4 per cent) were indicated for **neglected diseases** and of 148,445 clinical trials registered on December 31, 2011, only 2016 (1.4 per cent) were for neglected diseases (Pedrique et al., 2013). Furthermore, many of the (few) drugs that the industry had developed were of low overall value to developing countries because they were poorly suited to situations in these countries, for example, they needed to be administered within a hospital setting, were not affordable, or had poor efficacy or a poor safety profile (Moran et al., 2005).

The blockbuster mentality also means that companies tend to copy already successful medicines in the hopes of obtaining a share of the market and the profit for themselves. The end result is that the bulk of these new drugs do not offer any significant therapeutic gain over what is already available. The **Patented Medicine Prices Review Board (PMPRB)** and the French drug bulletin *La revue Prescrire* evaluate the therapeutic advances of new medicines. Between 2000 and 2012, out of 336 new medicines marketed in Canada, the conclusion from these two sources was that 31 (9.2 per cent) were major therapeutic gains (Prescrire Editorial Staff, 2014). (See Table 14.1 for a breakdown of the results from *La revue Prescrire*.)

The majority of the drugs that the companies introduce are considered "superfluous" because they do not add to the clinical possibilities offered by already available products and a substantial number have potential or real disadvantages. Garattini and Bertele (2002) examined 12 new anticancer drugs approved in Europe between 1995 and 2000 that contained new molecular entities or known active principles with new indications and concluded that none of the 12 offered any significant improvement in action. Of the 61 new biotechnology products introduced in Europe between 1995 and 2003 for therapeutic purposes, only two were approved on the basis that they were superior to existing therapies using hard clinical endpoints (Joppi, Bertele, & Garattini, 2005).

Patented Medicine Prices Review Board (PMPRB)
A federal Canadian agency that sets a maximum introductory price for any new patented medicine that is marketed in Canada and also limits the rise in the price of patented medicines to the annual rate of inflation.

Value of Research Done in Canada

The research that the pharmaceutical industry conducts in Canada is largely comprised of **clinical drug trials**, considered the development aspect of R&D. Out of the $865.6 million that companies spent here in 2012, $520.9 million (60.2 per cent) went to clinical trials versus $114.6 million (13.2 per cent) on basic research (Annual report, 2012, Patented Medicine

clinical drug trials
Testing of drugs on humans. (See *human testing*.)

Table 14.1   Value of New Drugs and New Indications for Existing Drugs Introduced into the French Market, 2004–2013

Category	Number (% of total)
Major therapeutic innovation in an area where previously no treatment was available.	2 (0.2)
Important therapeutic innovation but has limitations.	6 (0.6)
Some value but does not fundamentally change the present therapeutic practice.	56 (5.5)
Minimal additional value and should not change prescribing habits except in rare circumstances.	190 (18.7)
May be new molecule but is superfluous because does not add to clinical possibilities offered by previously available products.	538 (53.0)
Without evident benefit but with potential or real disadvantages.	165 (16.3)
Decision postponed until better data and more thorough evaluation.	58 (5.7)
Total	1015

Source: Adapted from Prescrire Editorial Staff. (2014). New drugs and indications in 2013: Little real progress but regulatory authorities take some positive steps. *Prescrire International*, *23*, 107–10.

Prices Review Board, 2013). One attempt to explore the value of this clinical research was carried out in 1990 through a survey of 40 key medical figures engaged in pharmaceutical research in Canada (Lexchin & Wiktorowicz, 2008). They were happy about the availability of funding from pharmaceutical companies, but they also expressed a number of misgivings about drug industry funding: 90 per cent foresaw a likely conflict of interest, 80 per cent deemed pharmaceutical clinical research "me too" research (research on drugs that are very similar to those already on the market), while 75 per cent saw it as "might as well" research (research that is not interesting but since money is available and the researcher is capable of doing it, he or she might as well do it), and 40 per cent were worried about a potential delay in the publication of unfavourable results (Taylor, 1991).

Research funded by the pharmaceutical industry may leave many questions untouched. Dr Patricia Baird, former chair of the Royal Commission on New Reproductive Technologies, noted that in the area of infertility, drug companies were only likely to fund research that would lead to a new patentable drug, ignoring topics such as behavioural factors involved in the cause and prevention of infertility (Baird, 1996). This research bias described by Baird has important consequences. It focuses the attention of researchers in a particular direction—at therapies directed at the individual rather than looking more broadly at the social causes of many problems. For instance, in the case of infertility much of that is due to sexually acquired diseases that result from unsafe sexual practices; unsafe sexual practices are strongly related to socio-economic class. However, if there is little research funding available to look at the socio-economic construction of sexual practices then researchers will ignore this area.

Drug Promotion

According to data from the US National Science Foundation, in 2004, pharmaceutical companies operating in the US spent $31.4 billion (US) on R&D (National Science Foundation, 2006) but that figure pales beside the $57.5 billion (US) spent on promotion in that same year (Gagnon & Lexchin, 2008). Exact figures for promotion in Canada are not available but estimates are that companies spend between $2.4 and $4.8 billion here annually (CAM Corp International, 2005) or between $35,000 and $70,000 for every doctor in the country. The bulk of that money is spent on the medication samples left behind in doctors' offices and the visits that pharmaceutical company sales representatives make to doctors. There are approximately 5200 sales representatives in Canada (*2002 detailing survey*, 2003). In 2000, Merck left behind over 1 million samples of Vioxx (rofecoxib), a drug used for pain and inflammation, with Canadian doctors; there were over 77,000 visits to doctors' offices to promote Celebrex (celecoxib), another drug for pain and inflammation (see Table 14.2. Sales representatives give doctors minimally adequate safety information in only 1.7 per cent of promotions (Mintzes et al., 2013).

Besides visiting doctors' offices and leaving samples behind, pharmaceutical companies engage in a variety of other forms of direct and indirect promotion. Direct promotion involves advertising in medical journals and providing hospitality to doctors "in order to facilitate greater interaction around [the company's] business." Although the "hospitality should not be utilized as the primary access to" health-care professionals, it can be used "as an opportunity to expand the business discussions." Indirectly, companies will, under certain circumstances, be able to "provide financial support for a maximum of

Table 14.2   Promotional Activity in Canada, 2000

Name of Drug	Company Making Drug	Used in Treatment of	Promotional Expenditure ($000)	Number of Advertisement Pages in Medical Journals	Number of Visits by Sales Representatives (000)	Number of Samples Left with Doctors (000)
Vioxx	Merck	Pain and inflammation	6286	1090	48	1060
Celebrex	Pharmacia & Upjohn	Pain and inflammation	6064	613	77	988
Effexor	Wyeth	Depression	5262	974	48	410
Lipitor	Pfizer	High cholesterol	4385	559	65	513
Baycol	Bayer	High cholesterol	3952	361	54	281

Source: Adapted from CBC News. (2002, March 5).Targeting doctors. Graph: Top 50 drugs by promotion dollars. *Disclosure.* CBC.

ten . . . individuals to [attend an] international CHE [continuing health education] event" (*Code of Ethical Practices—2012*, 2012). In addition to paying doctors to travel outside Canada to attend medical conferences, between 2000 and 2004, 70 per cent of all the continuing medical education programs accredited by the College of Family Physicians of Canada had some funding from the pharmaceutical industry (B. Marlow, 2010, personal communication).

When new drugs are marketed, they are promoted extremely heavily in order to start generating revenue for the company involved. Although the available literature on the effects of promotion can only demonstrate an **association**, the vast majority of the studies that have been done show that the more doctors rely on promotion from drug companies as their source of information, the less likely they are to **prescribe appropriately** (Spurling et al., 2010). The extensive promotion and its negative influence on prescribing means that drugs are prescribed to a far wider range of people than the group who were exposed to them during the clinical trials. Furthermore, relatively little is known about the overall safety profile of these new drugs compared to drugs that have been on the market for a number of years, meaning that many people are exposed to potentially unsafe products.

Two of the most heavily prescribed drugs in Canada in 2000 (Vioxx and Baycol) were subsequently removed from the market due to safety problems. In the US, Graham and colleagues estimate that in the five years (1999–2004) that rofecoxib was on the market there were between 88,000 and 140,000 excess cases of serious coronary heart disease with 44 per cent of these people dying as a consequence of their heart problems (Graham et al., 2005).

User Fees in Drug Regulation and Their Consequences

Health Canada has traditionally been under-resourced for the activities it is required to undertake with respect to prescription and non-prescription medicines. As a result, it

association
In statistical terms, means there is a relationship between two items; however, the presence of an association does not prove a cause and effect.

appropriate prescribing
Means only using medications when they are the best type of treatment, selecting the correct medication, understanding and informing patients about the harms and benefits associated with the medication, prescribing it in the correct dose and for the right period of time, and monitoring patients to ensure that the drug is having a beneficial effect.

Health Canada
The federal department responsible for helping the people of Canada maintain and improve their health. Within Health Canada, the Therapeutic Products Directorate (TPD) approves and monitors prescription and non-prescription drugs derived from chemical manufacturing and medical devices. The TPD also is responsible for making the decision to remove drugs for safety reasons. The Marketed Health Products Directorate (MHPD) deals with the safety of products already approved for marketing.

clientele pluralism
A term that describes the relationship between an agency of the state and the industry that it is charged with regulating, whereby some of the authority of the state is transferred to the industry.

operates through a system known as **clientele pluralism** (Atkinson & Coleman, 1989). In such a system the state has a high degree of concentration of power in one agency—Health Canada—but a low degree of autonomy. With respect to pharmaceuticals, the Canadian government regulation of drug safety, quality, and efficacy is almost solely the responsibility of Health Canada (Lexchin, 2007a). But the state does not possess the wherewithal to undertake the elaborate clinical and pre-clinical trials required to meet the objective of providing safe and effective medications. Nor is the state willing or able to mobilize the resources that would be necessary to undertake these tasks. Therefore, a tacit political decision is made to relinquish some authority to the drug manufacturers, especially with respect to information that forms the basis on which regulatory decisions are made. In clientele pluralism, the state relinquishes some of its authority to private-sector actors, who, in turn, pursue objectives with which officials are in broad agreement. Not only does the state turn over some of its authority, but the objectives that are being pursued are ones that are often jointly developed between Rx&D and the relevant state bureaucracy, in this case, Health Canada.

Since the early 1990s, the relationship between the industry and the regulatory agencies has, if anything, intensified, driven by user fees from industry and an atmosphere of deregulation (Lexchin, 2007a; see Figure 14.1). In Canada in the early 1990s, the federal government, committed to an ideology of neo-liberalism, focused its attention on the budgetary deficit that was running more than $40 billion annually and, in the process,

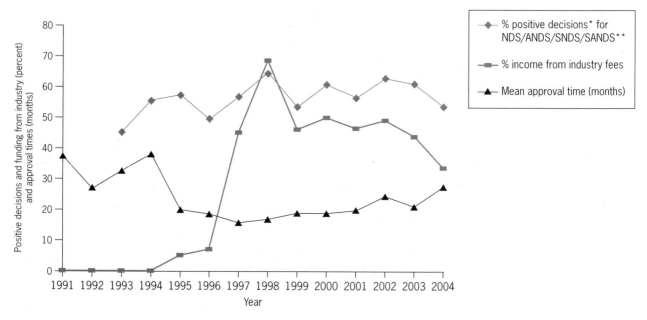

Figure 14.1 Relationship between User Fees and Positive Decisions about New Drugs and Approval Times in Canada

Note: *NDS = new drug submission, ANDS = abbreviated new drug submission, SNDS = supplementary new drug submission, SANDS = supplementary abbreviated new drug submission.

Source: Lexchin, J. (2006). Relationship between pharmaceutical company user fees and drug approvals in Canada and Australia: a hypothesis-generating study. *Annals of Pharmacotherapy, 40,* 2216–22.

cut funding to many government departments (see Chapters 4 and 13). To make up for the shortfall in revenue, departments, including the TPD, turned to user fees to fund their activities. Pharmaceutical companies are charged a fee for every application that they submit to market a new product, and in addition, pay an annual amount for each drug they have on the market. At present, about one-half of the revenue required to deal with medicines (run the operations of the TPD that involve drug regulation) comes from industry (Health Canada, 2011c). In 1994, before money came from industry, it took on average 38 months to approve a new drug and about 50 per cent of applications received a positive decision. Within one year of industry money coming into the TPD, approval times were cut in half; by the late 1990s, between 60 and 70 per cent of applications were being approved (Lexchin, 2006).

Both of these changes are favourable to the pharmaceutical industry and are consistent with **principal–agent theory**. Prior to the introduction of user fees, the principal was the Canadian public and the agent was Health Canada. However, since 1994, a new principal has been added—the pharmaceutical industry, which is now providing a substantial fraction of the money needed to run the drug regulatory system. In the case of the approval times, the industry, through its primary organization Rx&D, has consistently emphasized that these need to be faster (Canada's Research-Based Pharmaceutical Companies, 2002) and Health Canada has adopted this goal (Therapeutic Products Directorate, 2004).

> **principal–agent theory**
> Proposes that there is a relationship between a principal, who has a task that needs to be performed, and an agent, who is contracted to do the task in exchange for compensation.

Major figures within the drug regulatory system have also made statements in the past indicating that cost recovery has shifted the notion of who is regarded as the principal. For example, Dann Michols, director general of the Therapeutic Products Programme (TPP, one of the predecessors of the TPD), circulated an internal bulletin in which he discussed the question of who the TPP's client is. With regard to cost recovery, he advised staff that "the client is the direct recipient of your services. In many cases this is the person or company who pays for the service." This one-page bulletin focused on service to industry, relegating the public to the secondary status of "stakeholder" or "beneficiary" (Michols, 1997).

Regulatory agencies' dependency on user fees may also be compromising drug safety. Carpenter and colleagues looked at the safety of drugs approved by the US **Food and Drug Administration (FDA)**, specifically those drugs approved on the cusp of the approval deadline clock (Carpenter, 2008; Carpenter, Zucker, & Avorn, 2008). The FDA has a statutory requirement to complete its review of 90 per cent of new drug applications within specific periods of time. If the FDA fails to meet that obligation, then renewal of legislation that allows it to collect user fees from industry may be endangered. The conclusion reached by Carpenter et al. was that if the deadline is imminent, the FDA does a less thorough job of reviewing drugs in order to avoid crossing the deadline and potentially jeopardizing its revenue from drug companies.

> **Food and Drug Administration (FDA)**
> The US equivalent of Canada's Health Products and Food Branch.

Similarly, revenue to the TPD will also suffer if service standards (completion of reviews of new drug applications within the targeted time) are not met (Lexchin, 2009). If the TPD takes too long to review applications for new drugs in one year, then in the next year, it will be forced to reduce user fees. For example, if review times are 20 per cent over time in 2012, then fees will drop by 20 per cent in 2013 (Health Products and Food Branch, 2007b). Faced with the prospect of penalties, it is possible that the TPD might follow the pattern set by the FDA and rush to approve new drugs that are approaching the deadline in order to avoid incurring a financial loss in the next year.

Postmarketing Surveillance

Food and Drugs Act
The federal legislation dealing with medicines.

According to the **Food and Drugs Act**, Health Canada can order the withdrawal of any medication without first consulting with the company that makes it. However, the only recent situation where this power was actually exercised concerned Adderall XR™, a product used in treating attention deficit hyperactivity disorder (ADHD) in children (Health Canada, 2005a). (Adderall XR™ was subsequently allowed back on the market.) In all other situations Health Canada has preferred to negotiate with drug companies prior to removing drugs from sale (Lexchin, 2009).

Negotiating instead of acting can have tragic consequences. Companies are often extremely reluctant to lose products, especially if they are ones that are generating large sales revenue (Lexchin, 2009). In the US, instead of withdrawing the antidiabetic drug Rezulin (troglitazone) from the market as the British did, the FDA and Warner-Lambert, the company marketing the drug, went through a protracted series of negotiations over a period of 29 months that resulted in four labelling changes to the information about troglitazone. When the drug was finally withdrawn, there had been more than 60 deaths due to liver failure. Had the FDA acted when the British did, there would have been fewer than half a dozen deaths. Over the time when the drug was sold, Warner-Lambert made $2.1 billion (Willman, 2000). (Troglitazone was approved in Canada but never marketed because the company and the Patented Medicine Prices Review Board could not reach an agreement about the pricing of the drug.)

The most serious deficiency in Health Canada's powers is its lack of the authority to require the manufacturer to undertake any new studies into the product's safety once a drug is on the market (Lexchin, 2009). It can request this type of study but experience in the US indicates that many such requests may never be acted on. In the US, between 2002 and 2005, there were a total of 743 unique postmarketing commitments made by companies. By the end of 2007, just over a third were completed, 91 were delayed, and 200 had not yet started (Booz, Allen, Hamilton, 2008). (Some of the 200 that were pending were not considered delayed since they had not yet passed the original projected beginning date but an unspecified number also did not have FDA-imposed deadlines.) Companies are also required to submit annual reports to the FDA documenting the status of their commitments, but 35 per cent of the 336 reports that were or should have been filed in 2004 were missing entirely or contained no useful information on postmarketing commitments; 39 per cent were missing one or more items of required information (Office of Inspector General, 2006).

In the past five or six years, Health Canada has embraced a concept known as **smart regulation.** (Smart regulation is not unique to Health Canada; this approach to regulation is being widely used within the federal and provincial governments in Canada.) Smart regulation means that Canada should "regulate in a way that enhances the climate for investment and trust in the markets" and "accelerate reforms in key areas to promote health

Do government and industry work together for public health or for private profit? Do you think that the tug-of-war between government and industry is productive or destructive for public health goals? *Source:*

and sustainability, to contribute to innovation and economic growth, and to reduce the administrative burden on business" (Government of Canada, 2002). While health is not ignored, the emphasis is clearly on creating a business-friendly environment. The federal External Advisory Committee on Smart Regulation explicitly states that **risk management**, as an element of smart regulation, has an essential role in building public trust and business confidence in the Canadian market and regulatory system (External Advisory Committee on Smart Regulation, n.d.). For a discussion of risk management as it applies to the environment, see Chapter 8.

When applied to drug regulation, risk management means weighing potential negative effects against potential advantages. Potential negative effects are adverse health effects that might occur under reasonably foreseeable conditions (Health Canada, 2003b). The shift from the **precautionary principle** to risk management is subtle but unmistakable (Lexchin, 2010b). The precautionary principle says that if products cannot be shown to be safe, then they should either not be marketed or be marketed but with significant restrictions; risk management allows products on the market unless they are shown to be harmful. Realigning regulation to conform to the principles of smart regulation would not totally abandon the concept of precaution but would seem to imply that there would have to be a threat of serious or irreversible damage before risk management would come into play.

One indication of Health Canada's view of the importance of drug safety is in its allocation of personnel and money between the TPD, the arm that approves new drugs, and the MHPD, the part that monitors drug safety. In 2004, the TPD was already much more heavily resourced than the MHPD, having almost five times the number of staff and five times the operating budget (Progestic International Inc., 2004). By March 2010, the situation had improved but the TPD still had more than three times the budget and staff compared to the MHPD (Wiktorowicz, et al., 2010; see Table 14.3).

In the summer of 2008, Health Canada announced it was allocating $1 million to an independent research network, the Drug Safety and Effectiveness Network (DSEN), to

smart regulation
Regulating in a way that enhances the climate for investment and trust in the markets such that the administrative burden is reduced for businesses.

risk management
Taking the known risks and benefits of a drug into consideration before allowing it onto the market. Unless the product has serious known risks, the preference is to allow it to be sold.

precautionary principle
Means not only taking into account known risks of a drug but also potential risks even if the evidence for them is weak. In these circumstances, the precautionary principle would say that the product should either not be marketed or should be marketed under significant restrictions.

Table 14.3   Relative Funding of TPD Compared to MHPD, 2004 and 2010

	Annual Operating Cost Base ($ 000,000)		Number of Full-time Equivalent Employees	
	Year ending March 31, 2004	Year ending March 31, 2010	Year ending March 31, 2004	Year ending March 31, 2010
Therapeutic Products Directorate	38	44.9	423	514.5
Biologics and Genetic Therapies Directorate	22	29.7	228	312.2
Health Products and Food Branch Inspectorate	16	10.2	190	99.1
Marketed Health Products Directorate	8	23.6	90	213.9
Total	84	108.4	931	1139.7

Source: Wiktorowicz, M.E., Lexchin, J., Moscou, K., Silversides, A., & Eggertson, L. (2010). Keeping an eye on prescription drugs . . . Keeping Canadians safe: Active monitoring systems for drug safety and effectiveness in Canada and internationally. Toronto: Health Council of Canada.

study the safety of prescription drugs taken by Canadians. This was followed up in January 2009 with an additional $31 million over 4 years and $10 million per year after that. This investment is a much stronger commitment than Health Canada has previously made to drug safety but still falls short of what the new network may need (Silversides, 2008). As of mid-2014, Health Canada is continuing to fund research into drug safety and effectiveness, but there has not been any independent assessment of the impact of the research.

Regulatory Transparency

Another manifestation of the clientele pluralist relationship between the state and the pharmaceutical industry is the agreement between the industry and Health Canada that all of the information that companies submit as part of the regulatory approval process is deemed confidential and will not be released without the express consent of the company involved even if an Access to Information request has been filed (Lexchin, 2007a). There is a section of the Access to Information Act that would allow Health Canada to release information "if that disclosure would be in the public interest as it relates to public health . . . and, if the public interest in disclosure clearly outweighs in importance any financial loss or gain to, prejudice to the competitive position of or interference with contractual or other negotiations of a third party" (Government of Canada, 1985). Health Canada has never chosen to utilize this clause.

The level of secrecy in Health Canada has been criticized a number of times, including in a 2000 report by the ad hoc Committee on the Drug Review Process of Health Canada's own Science Advisory Board. The report stated that "in our view and that of many stakeholders, the current drug review process is unnecessarily opaque. Health Canada persists in maintaining a level of confidentiality that is inconsistent with public expectation and contributes to a public cynicism about the integrity of the process" (Science Advisory Board Committee on the Drug Review Process, 2000, p. 9).

There is no good evidence to show that the interests of companies would be harmed by the disclosure of information about safety and effectiveness (McGarity & Shapiro, 1980). On the other hand, non-disclosure has serious disadvantages for Health Canada, health professionals, and the public. If information submitted to regulatory agencies is never disclosed, then this data will never enter the normal peer-review channels and will not, therefore, be subject to scrutiny by independent scientists. Without this type of feedback, TPD reviewers may be more prone to misjudge the accuracy or usefulness of the data submitted; the scientific atmosphere in the agency may be stifled and the professional growth of its staff severely inhibited (McGarity & Shapiro, 1980). Deprived of any independent access to information, health professionals have to accept Health Canada's judgment about the safety and effectiveness of products. In the case of well-established drugs, this is probably not much of a concern, but it may be different with new drugs where experience is limited (Lexchin, 2010b).

Summary Basis of Decision
A document that is released by Health Canada after it has approved a new drug. It outlines the scientific and benefit/risk-based reasons for Health Canada's decision to grant market authorization for a product.

In response to repeated criticism about being overly secretive, in early 2004, Health Canada announced a new initiative termed the **Summary Basis of Decision (SBD)** (Lexchin, 2007b). The SBD is issued after a new drug or medical device is approved and explains the scientific and benefit/risk information that the TPD considered in making its decision (Health Canada, 2004b). As far as prescribers and consumers are concerned, the most important section of the SBD is the presentation of the clinical information on the product's safety and efficacy. Do the SBDs contain enough information to allow for the rational prescribing and use of new medications? This question is crucial because within the past few years there have been a number of instances where data held by regulatory agencies was significant in identifying problems with medications that were not apparent by just consulting the published literature. Examples of these problems include cardiovascular risks associated with hormone replacement therapy, safety issues with antidepressants in children and adolescents, and the gastrointestinal safety of Celebrex (celecoxib) versus traditional anti-inflammatory drugs (Lexchin & Mintzes, 2004). An analysis of all 161 SBDs released between January 1, 2005 and April 30, 2012 found that overall, clinical trial information in SBDs is presented in a haphazard manner, with no apparent method to its presentation. At least one-third of the potential information about patient trial characteristics and the benefits and risks of tested treatments was missing in the majority of SBDs (Habibi & Lexchin, 2014).

> The approach to releasing the clinical information that companies submit reflects a common understanding between officials in Health Canada and the pharmaceutical industry of medical information as a commodity with commercial value that must be protected. Such information can be "loaned" to the government for purposes of review but the companies do so with the expectation that the review will produce material gains through marketing of their products. This market based view stands in marked contrast to a view that data on health and safety is something that should be shared directly with the people most affected—those who prescribe and use the products. What we have instead is information filtered through, and protected by, the officials in Health Canada. (Lexchin, 2010b)

Regulation of Promotion

The Food and Drugs Act gives the Canadian government the theoretical ability to regulate all forms of drug promotion; however, under the model of clientele pluralism, the government has turned its authority over to the brand-name pharmaceutical industry (Rx&D) and the **Pharmaceutical Advertising Advisory Board (PAAB)**. The latter is an organization with membership from the medical and pharmacy professions, the generic and brand-name industry associations, consumer groups, and organizations representing both medical advertising agencies and medical publications. Rx&D has developed a Code of Conduct (*Code of Ethical Practices—2012*, 2012) that governs its members' activities with respect to visits by sales representatives, leaving medication samples with doctors, the sponsorship of continuing medical education activities for health professionals, and gift giving. PAAB also has a Code of Advertising Acceptance (*Code of Advertising Acceptance*, 2009) and **prescreens** all printed material that is either used in advertising of medicines or is produced by pharmaceutical companies and left with doctors. Of significant note, compliance with both codes is voluntary, although Rx&D has made adhering to the PAAB code a condition of membership in the organization.

As Lexchin and Kawachi (1996) point out, voluntary **self-regulation** seems an attractive option because, lacking government-industry adversariness, it is a flexible and cost-effective option. Government regulators also reason that in a highly competitive industry, the desire of individual companies to prevent competitors from gaining an edge can be

Pharmaceutical Advertising Advisory Board (PAAB)
An organization with membership from professional organizations, various industries, and consumer groups. PAAB evaluates all print advertising directed to medical professionals before it appears in print.

prescreen
Under this system, pharmaceutical companies submit their print advertising to PAAB and only use that advertising when PAAB has given its approval.

self-regulation
The process by which an industry is allowed to regulate its own behaviour.

harnessed to serve the public interest through a regime of voluntary self-regulation run by a trade association (Ayres & Braithwaite, 1992).

The problem with the foregoing analysis is that industry will always be tempted to exploit the privilege of self-regulation by producing a socially sub-optimal level of compliance with regulatory goals. Experience has repeatedly shown this to be the case in the marketing of pharmaceutical products (Kawachi, 1992). Effective industry control over its own promotional practices in the form of voluntary self-regulation is another reflection of a clientele pluralist relationship between the Canadian government and the pharmaceutical industry.

Under a system of voluntary self-regulation, few trade associations, such as Rx&D, vested with the authority to regulate drug promotion have made systematic efforts to either monitor the advertising practices of their members or to enforce compliance. The problem is that governments and pharmaceutical manufacturers' associations have different missions and goals. The mission of government is to protect public health by encouraging rational prescribing. The mission of trade associations is primarily to increase sales and profit. From the business perspective, self-regulation is mostly concerned with the control of anti-competitive practices. Therefore, when industrial associations draw up their codes of practice, they deliberately make them vague or do not cover certain features of promotion to allow companies a wide latitude. Self-regulation works well when anti-competitive promotional practices happen to coincide perfectly with government regulators' notions of misleading advertising. Most often, however, the fit is far from perfect because, far from being anti-competitive, many misleading advertising tactics are good for business. Therefore, from the public health perspective, the results of voluntary self-regulation are sub-optimal.

Both the PAAB and Rx&D codes demonstrate the inherent weaknesses in self-regulation. The Rx&D code operates under a reactive as opposed to a proactive style of regulation; that is, action is generally taken only upon receipt of complaints and there is no active monitoring of compliance with the code. Neither code has effective sanctions to levy when breaches have occurred. PAAB has no authority to impose monetary sanctions although it can require companies to pull offending advertisements, but by the time a complaint has been made and a ruling taken, the ad may be near to completing its run in any case. The penalty after a third violation of the Rx&D code in a single year is a $100,000 fine, an insignificant amount for a large pharmaceutical company, and the panel adjudicating whether or not a violation has taken place is composed of a majority of Rx&D officials. Neither code has a predefined period after which it needs to be reviewed nor any specific mechanism for revisions.

There is no requirement in the PAAB code for advertisements to devote as much space to safety information as they do to the benefits of the product being promoted, nor does the font size for safety information need to be as large as it is for benefit information. Similarly, the size of the font used for the generic name of the product does not have to be as large as that used for the brand name and the generic name does not have to be mentioned as frequently as the brand name. Furthermore, detailed information about products does not have to be placed directly beside the main display part of the advertisement but can appear at the back of the medical journal.

The Rx&D code does not specifically require sales representatives to provide doctors with information about risks, contraindications, and warnings, and sales representatives do not have to leave a copy of the government-approved official product monograph, which provides detailed information about the drug. Rx&D does not have any system in place to ensure that company sales representatives are following the minimal requirements of its code.

Health Canada has continued its policy of deregulating promotion by drug companies.

> An example of how Health Canada has abdicated its responsibilities in the area of controlling promotion is the case of direct-to-consumer promotion of prescription drugs. Regulations issued under the Food and Drugs Act only allow companies to advertise prescription drugs to the extent that the name, quantity and price of the product can be displayed. Policy statements in 1996 and 2000 reinterpreted this regulation to mean that companies were allowed to run "disease awareness" ads as long as the name of a product was not mentioned or firms could name a medication as long as its use was not discussed. The only type of advertising that remained prohibited was one where both a product was named and its use was given. (Michols, 1996; Rowsell, 2000, cited in Lexchin, 2010b)

Health Canada has been reluctant to enforce even this loose reinterpretation of its own regulations. An article in the *Canadian Medical Association Journal (CMAJ)* notes that "Response to complaints tends to be slow, probably reflecting Health Canada's undercapacity to regulate DTCA, and, arguably, ineffectual" (Gardner, Mintzes, & Ostry, 2003, p. 425). The authors go on to describe how a television advertisement promoting Zyban (bupropion) for smoking cessation was allowed to run for months, even though Health Canada had deemed that it violated the regulations. No penalty of any type was imposed on GlaxoSmithKline, the company responsible for the advertisement (The battle over a drug ad, 2001).

Conclusion

No one should be under any doubt that when properly prescribed and used medicines are an enormous benefit in helping us stay healthy. Similarly, no one should be under any illusion that pharmaceutical companies' primary purpose is not to make the maximum rate of return for their investors. To that end, the companies have developed their research strategy, defend their products against perceived threats, and devote billions of dollars to making sure that their new and expensive medicines are prescribed as widely as possible. All of these actions are perfectly understandable in a market economy.

What should cause us the utmost concern is that when there is a conflict between private profit and public health, Health Canada seems to be increasingly siding with the pharmaceutical industry:

> Private values are antithetical to democracy; they speak to the need to earn a profit, not to protect public health. While the two can at times be synonymous, that happens mostly by coincidence rather than by design. Within the private sector competition and the profit motive may be the best way to get newer and better computers or washing detergent. However, medications are not ordinary consumer products and government is intimately and necessarily involved with almost all aspects of medications because of their importance in health care. When government adopts

the values of private industry in drug regulation, it is in essence telling its people that the needs and values of the private sector take precedence over their health. Democracy is not just the right to vote in an election; it means the ongoing and active participation of the citizenry in determining the policies of the government with an expectation that government will acknowledge the views being put forward and incorporate them into its actions. (Lexchin, 2008)

Summary

- Pharmaceuticals are a key component of modern medicine if prescribed and used appropriately.
- The pharmaceutical industry exists in a market economy and is motivated by profit. Over the past few decades, it has been one of the most profitable industries in the world.
- Explanations offered by the industry for the need for large profits—high risk and costs in developing new drugs and low success rates in bringing new drugs to market—do not hold up under analysis.
- In order to enhance its profitability the pharmaceutical industry engages in a variety of activities, including trying to suppress unfavourable opinions about its products, gearing its research activities to areas where the market is largest, not necessarily where the medical need is greatest. As a result, most new medicines do not offer any advantages over existing therapies. Finally, companies heavily promote new drugs in order to start to generate return on investment quickly. The degree of promotion means that people are exposed to potentially risky medicines early on and the potential for harm is high.
- Health Canada and the pharmaceutical industry exist in a relationship termed "clientele pluralism," whereby Health Canada turns over some of its authority to the industry.
- Since the mid-1990s, the industry has been paying for an increasing share of the operating costs of Health Canada; as a result, the relationship between Health Canada and the industry has become closer over the past few decades with Health Canada adopting some of the industry's values as opposed to those of public health. This shift in Health Canada's values can be seen in its approach to drug approvals, postmarketing surveillance, regulatory transparency, and the way that promotion is controlled.

Key Terms

appropriate prescribing
association
basic research
Canada's Research-
   Based Pharmaceutical
   Companies (Rx&D)

clientele pluralism
clinical drug trials
Food and Drug
   Administration (FDA)
Food and Drugs Act
gastrointestinal medications

Health Canada
human testing
market failure
neglected diseases
Patented Medicine Prices
   Review Board (PMPRB)

patents
Pharmaceutical Advertising
  Advisory Board (PAAB)
postmarketing surveillance
precautionary principle
prescreen

principal–agent theory
promotional activities
risk management
self-regulation
smart regulation
state

summary basis of decision
  (SBD)
transparency
user fees

Sociological Reflection: Smart Regulation

There is an ongoing debate in regulatory theory between those who argue for a command-and-control approach and those who argue that government should set the rules but leave the day-to-day regulation to the industry. Under the first approach, the government would not only establish the regulations but would also employ people to ensure that the regulations are being followed. Under the second model, industry would be responsible for monitoring its own behaviour by filing periodic reports on its activities; the main task of the government would be to review the reports filed by industry. Those arguing in favour of the first approach maintain that industry cannot be trusted to regulate its own activities if such regulations put its profits at risk. Those arguing in favour of the second approach note that it is less expensive and that industry has a far greater level of expertise than government inspectors and therefore is able to catch problems that would escape government inspection.

*   With respect to postmarketing surveillance, discuss which model would better serve to identify new safety problems with medicines and minimize the risk from these problems.

Discussion Questions

1. All countries finance part or all of their drug regulatory system from user fees. Why should Canada be any different?
2. There is a trade-off between studying a drug for a long time before it is marketed in order to identify as many safety problems as possible and getting promising new drugs onto the market quickly so that patients can benefit from them. Where do you fall in this debate and why?
3. How should the government try to ensure that research into new drugs is directed to those areas where the medical need is the highest? What role do companies operating in a free market economy have to play in this regard?
4. How much profit should drug companies be allowed to earn provided that they don't do anything illegal in earning their profits? Is there any limit that should be imposed, and if so, how should that limit be determined?
5. Explain what your position is on whether or not direct-to-consumer advertising of prescription drugs should be legal in Canada.
6. Drugs can never be absolutely safe in every person. What kind of risk is tolerable when drugs are put on the market? Does the level of risk vary depending on what condition is being treated?

Further Investigation

1. The drug regulatory system in the United Kingdom is set up differently than the one in Canada. Analyze the UK system and contrast it to the Canadian one.
2. Discuss the pros and cons of risk management versus the precautionary principle as a basis for drug regulation.
3. Look at the history of the patent system in Canada for pharmaceuticals since 1969 and discuss how the changing use of patents has affected the cost of drugs in this country.

Further Reading

Abramson, J. (2004). *Overdosed America: The broken promise of American medicine.* New York: Harper Collins.

Angell, M. (2005). *The truth about the drug companies: How they deceive us, and what to do about it.* New York: Random House.

Avorn, J. (2005). *Powerful medicines: The benefits, risks, and costs of prescription drugs.* New York: Knopf.

Braithwaite, J. (1984). *Corporate crime in the pharmaceutical industry.* London: Routledge & Kegan Paul.

Brody, H. (2007). *Hooked: Ethics, the medical profession and the pharmaceutical industry.* Lanham: Rowman & Littlefield.

Cassel, A. (2012). *Seeking sickness: medical screening and the misguided hunt for disease.* Vancouver: Greystone Books.

Cohen, J.C., Illingworth, P., & Schüklenk, U. (Eds.). (2006). *The power of pills: Social, ethical & legal issues in drug development, marketing & pricing.* London: Pluto Press.

Davis, C., & Abraham, J. (2013). *Unhealthy pharmaceutical regulation.* Hampshire: Palgrave Macmillan.

Davis, P. (Ed.). (1996). *Contested ground: Public purpose and private interest in the regulation of prescription drugs.* New York: Oxford University Press.

Elliott, C. (2011). *White coat, black hat. Adventures on the hard side of medicine.* Boston: Beacon Press.

Finkelstein, S., & Temin, P. (2008). *Reasonable Rx: Solving the drug price crisis.* Upper Saddle River, NJ: FT Press.

Goldacre, B. (2012). *Bad pharma: How drug companies mislead doctors and harm patients.* Hammersmith: Fourth Estate.

Goozner, M. (2003). *The $800 million pill: The truth behind the cost of new drugs.* Berkeley: University of California Press.

Healy, D. (2012). *Pharmageddon.* Berkeley: University of California Press.

Kassirer, J. (2005). *On the take: How medicine's complicity with big business can endanger your health.* New York: Oxford University Press.

Medawar, C., & Hardon, A. (2004). *Medicines out of control? Antidepressants and the conspiracy of goodwill.* Amsterdam: Askant.

Mundy, A. (2001). *Dispensing with the truth: The victims, the drug companies, and the dramatic story behind the battle over fen-phen.* New York: St. Martin's Press.

O'Donovan, O., & Glavanis-Grantham, K. (Eds.). (2008). *Power, politics and pharmaceuticals*. Cork: Cork University Press.

Rochon Ford, A., & Saibil, D. (Eds.). (2009). *The push to prescribe: Women and Canadian drug policy*. Toronto: Women's Press.

Shah, S. (2006). *The body hunters: Testing new drugs on the world's poorest patients*. New York: The New Press.

Temple, N.J., & Thompson, A. (Eds.). (2007). *Excessive medical spending: Facing the challenge*. Oxford: Radcliffe Publishing.

Young, T. (2009). *Death by prescription: A father takes on his daughter's killer—the multi-billion-dollar pharmaceutical industry*. Toronto: Key Porter Books.

Web Resources

Canada's Research-Based Pharmaceutical Companies (Rx&D)
www.canadapharma.org/

Canadian Generic Pharmaceutical Association (CGPA)
www.canadiangenerics.ca/

Canadian Health Coalition
www.healthcoalition.ca

Health Action International
www.haiweb.org

Health Canada: Drug Products
www.hc-sc.gc.ca/dhp-mps/prodpharma/index-eng.php

Healthy Skepticism Inc.
www.healthyskepticism.org/

Hooked: Ethics, Medicine and Pharma
http://brodyhooked.blogspot.com/

IMS Health Inc.
www.imshealth.com/portal/site/imshealth?CURRENT_LOCALE=en_ca

International Federation of Pharmaceutical Manufacturers & Associations (IFPMA)
www.ifpma.org/

Patented Medicine Prices Review Board (PMPRB)
www.pmprb-cepmb.gc.ca/

PharmaWatch Canada
http://pharmawatchcanada.wordpress.com

PharmedOut
www.pharmedout.org/

Public Citizen: Drug Projects
www.citizen.org/Page.aspx?pid=4374

RxISK
www.rxisk.org/Default.aspx

Women and Health Protection (WHP)
www.whp-apsf.ca/en/index.html

CHAPTER 15
Nursing in the Twenty-First Century

Jennie Hornosty & Deidre Wicks

Current restructuring of our medical system threatens the emotional care provided by nurses that can't be quantified. In what ways might emotional care improve health outcomes?

Overview

- How has nursing changed historically?
- How did nursing develop in Canada?
- What are some of the major challenges faced by nurses today?
- What has been the impact of financial constraints and downsizing on nurses and nursing practice?

This chapter begins by looking at some of the sociological and theoretical approaches to nursing. It then turns to an examination of the role of nursing in the Canadian health-care system and some of the factors that affect nursing education, recruitment, and retention. This chapter provides a brief history of nursing and analyzes nursing reforms in Canada through a sociological lens. This analysis will also focus on the tension between the values of nursing care and the increasing tendency toward **rationalization** and control of labour in the health-care system.

rationalization
Refers to the standardization of social life through rules and regulations.

Introduction: The Changing Role of Nursing

Many would argue that nurses are the face of contemporary health care. They play a critical role in the management, delivery, and research of health-care services. They do the majority of caring work in hospitals, nursing/long-term care homes, and community health. Nurses today comprise the largest group of health-care providers in Canada. In 2013, there were 408,093 nurses (including registered nurses, registered psychiatric nurses, licensed practical nurses, and nurse practitioners) as compared to 77,674 physicians (excluding residents) (CIHI, 2014e).

Since the first formal training school for nurses in Canada opened in 1874 in St. Catharines, Ontario, nursing has undergone a number of changes. Then, nursing, traditionally seen as women's work, centred on care; nurses were to provide compassion and comfort for the sick and dying. Unlike physicians, their approach was more holistic. Today, health-care restructuring, managerial ideology, fiscal constraints, and nursing shortages have changed the face of nursing.

Sociological Approaches to Nursing

Post–World War II, nursing training in Canada was broadened to include both the technological and clinical advances that had occurred as a result of nursing experiences in war. Further expansion of nursing curricula occurred during the 1970s and 1980s to include input from the social sciences, namely psychology and sociology. This was based on a view of nursing that held that nurses needed an understanding of the social context of health-care delivery as well as of their patients' individual psychological needs and perceptions.

The dominant view in sociology was concerned with roles and role relationships, such as "the role of the doctor and nurse in health-care delivery" and "the role of the patient in hospital care." While mainstream sociological theories legitimated existing social relationships and acceptance of hierarchies of power and authority, sociology also had the effect of encouraging nursing students to think about social relationships and the impact of those relationships on nursing work and patient care. As the 1970s progressed, more radical approaches within sociology influenced nursing education. New interpretations of nursing history and practice, based on feminist theory in particular, began to appear, especially in the new diploma and later degree courses within universities. These courses encouraged a more critical examination of nursing history and practice, as well as a more critical interpretation of the relationship of nursing with other health occupations, especially medicine.

As well as broadening the understanding of nursing, these new approaches had the unintended effect of presenting nursing in a much more negative light—so much so that in the 1980s sociological writings about nursing presented an almost uniformly negative picture. Repeatedly, nursing was portrayed as a subordinated occupation and nurses themselves, as passive victims of medical power. While there have been differences in the way that various sociological perspectives viewed nursing, there has been a consistent theme running through all the interpretations, from social histories of nursing through to more radical feminist accounts. In the historical accounts, it is argued that many of the enduring characteristics of nursing have their roots in nineteenth-century gender relations and associated ideas regarding the appropriate behaviour for women in Victorian society. These "[assumptions] replicated within the hospital the existing gender relationships of Victorian society, and did not challenge prevailing male notions of womanly behaviour. Deference to doctors and acceptance of the 'handmaiden role' was a cornerstone of this strategy" (Beardshaw & Robinson, 1990). This argument has been a legend in nursing history.

There is, however, a theoretical and logical flaw in many of the accounts and analyses, which assumed that the political strategy of those in charge and the real-life behaviour of the nurses in question were one and the same. Victorian doctors and administrators may well have desired the nurse to be "restrained, disciplined and obedient, [carrying] out the orders of doctors in a suitably humble and deferential way" (Davies, 1977). But this did not mean that matrons, nurses, and sisters always co-operated; indeed, there is ample evidence that they frequently did not. For instance, in the earliest era of modern nursing in London, there was an important dispute at Guy's Hospital between Mrs Burt (the matron) and the doctors (Abel-Smith, 1960), and there were also disputes at St Thomas's Hospital over the timing of medical rounds (The Doctors versus the Nurses, 1962). In addition, labour history has documented various forms of industrial action taken collectively by nurses over the past century. Finally, **ethnographic** studies have revealed numerous examples of negotiation, disagreement, subversion, and open conflict as constant elements of nurse–doctor interactions within hospital settings (Game & Pringle, 1983; Hughes, 1988; Porter, 1995; Svensson, 1996; Wicks, 1999). Against this evidence, an orthodoxy has developed within both mainstream and more radical approaches that has focused on the power of doctors, hospitals, and medicine more generally. Nurses were thought to have inherited a tradition of passivity and powerlessness and, worse, a tendency to engage in **horizontal violence** (Roberts, 1983). Indeed, given these characteristics and the twin edifices of class and gender, the position of nurses was considered to be all but hopeless (Short & Sharman,

ethnography
A research method that is based on direct observation of a particular social group's social life and culture—of what people actually do.

horizontal violence
A concept derived from Paolo Freire that describes a behaviour common to all oppressed groups, whereby, because of their powerlessness, the oppressed are unable to direct their anger toward their oppressor and, as a result, turn it toward each other, with various degrees of violence and negativity.

1995). The common thread running through these accounts has focused on the power of **social structure** to shape and control nurses' work, identity, and behaviour and has ignored human **agency**.

Feminist Approaches

Since the 1990s, theoretical developments in feminist theory, and within sociology more generally, have promoted a re-examination of the **structure–agency debate**—that is, the degree to which individual choice (agency) is determined by outside forces (structure)—and of the need to understand an issue that has such important implications for politics and social life. With the influence of **post-structuralism**, there has been a re-emphasis on individual choice and action in the making and re-making of **social institutions**. While some authors think that this trend has gone too far (Walby, 1992), others see it as liberating in its challenges to the grand narratives that characterized groups such as women as being oppressed by strong and unchanging social structures (Barrett, 1991).

In the early 1970s, two writers from the US—Barbara Ehrenreich and Deirdre English—turned conventional theories on their head with their pamphlet *Witches, Midwives and Nurses: A History of Women Healers* (1973). Their work, with its strong feminist perspective, was a breath of fresh air in a field dominated by conventional histories of medicine. And yet its widespread influence in the decades since its publication has also had a detrimental effect on feminist sociological analyses of nursing. This stems from the way that Ehrenreich and English view the struggle within health care as something that took place in an earlier period between traditional women healers and formal male practitioners. According to their analysis, the defeat of the women healers ushered in an epoch of widespread subordination to organized, scientific male medicine. For instance, they are critical of middle-class reformers, such as Florence Nightingale, and of nineteenth-century feminists who "did not challenge nursing as an oppressive female role" (1973, p. 38). This analysis overlooks much that is crucial to a dynamic analysis of the historical relationship between nursing and medicine. By viewing the nineteenth-century formation of modern nursing only in terms of capitulation and defeat, the work has had the unintended effect of devaluing contemporary nurses and nursing work.

An influential piece of writing on nursing and its relationship to medicine is Eve Gamarnikow's "Sexual Division of Labour: The Case of Nursing" (1978). In this important paper, Gamarnikow challenges accounts of the **sexual division of labour (SDL)** that are based on naturalism or biological determinism—that is, the idea that it is natural for women to be nurses in the same way that women are naturally maternal. She argues, rather, for a **materialist analysis**, which locates the SDL as a social relationship that is not inevitable or natural but that has been socially constructed. This was such a significant breakthrough, in an area typified by naturalist explanations, that sociological analysis to this day continues to refer to it to establish a position that runs counter to biological or naturalist accounts of the nurse–doctor relationship (see, for example, Game & Pringle, 1983; Hazleton, 1990; Russell & Schofield, 1986; Short & Sharman, 1995; Willis, 1983). This materialist analysis is still widely regarded as the necessary foundation on which any critical sociological account of nurse–doctor relations must be built.

However, upon closer examination, it is evident that Gamarnikow's account is located squarely within a modernist feminist theoretical model, with its tendency to generalize

social structure
The recurring patterns of social interaction through which people are related to each other, such as social institutions and social groups.

agency
The ability of people, individually and collectively, to influence their own lives and the society in which they live.

structure–agency debate
A key debate in sociology over the extent to which human behaviour is determined by social structure.

post-structuralism/ postmodernism
Often used interchangeably, these terms refer to a broad perspective that is opposed to the view that social structure determines human action, and instead emphasizes a pluralistic world view that explores the local, the specific, and the contingent in social life.

social institutions
Formal structures within society—such as health care, government, education, religion, and the media—that are organized to address identified social needs.

sexual division of labour (SDL)
Refers to the nature of work performed as a result of gender roles. The stereotype is that of the male breadwinner and the female homemaker.

materialist analysis
An analysis that is embedded in the real, actual, material reality of everyday life.

and universalize. In this case, Gamarnikow generalizes the structural oppression of all nurses by all doctors through a patriarchal ideological structure. While Gamarnikow's approach provides a crucial sense of the strength and pervasiveness of social structure in explanations of the SDL, both Robert W. Connell (1987) and, more recently, Anne Witz (1992) make the point that this approach ignores or at least minimizes the importance of patriarchal practices within the labour market and the workplace itself. The effect of Gamarnikow's emphasis on patriarchal ideology and structure, and that same emphasis in other accounts derived from this analysis, has been the representation of nurses as an undifferentiated bloc of subordinated women. Individual or collective acts of resistance have either been ignored or minimized, being characterized as insignificant or as yet another variant of complaint among nurses (Turner, 1986b). The emphasis on an all-pervasive ideological structure has also had the effect of denying nurses subjectivity (their own identity) because, in accounts based on the power and pervasiveness of structure, the voices of nurses were rarely heard.

Gamarnikow's contribution was pivotal, however, for a critical reassessment of the conventional literature on nurse–doctor relations. Indeed, the emphasis on power relationships in general, and on **patriarchy** in particular, opened up the traditional nurse–doctor relationship to a sophisticated and long overdue sociological critique. Nevertheless, an emphasis on structural oppression and on an inferred passivity on the part of nurses also runs the danger of indirectly contributing to the status quo by suggesting that the situation is inevitable and hopeless.

Over the past few decades, there has been somewhat of a "paradigm shift" within the founding theoretical principles of modern **feminism** (Barrett & Phillips, 1992). Central to this shift has been a questioning of at least three basic assumptions of 1970s feminism: (1) the notion of women's oppression; (2) the assumption that it is possible to specify a cause for the oppression; and (3) consensus that the cause lies at the level of social structure, be it patriarchy, class, ethnicity, or a combination of any or all of the above (Barrett & Phillips, 1992). The new emphasis focuses on how different women experience different types and degrees of oppression in specific circumstances. This general approach has been heavily influenced by the philosopher and social theorist Michel Foucault. Sociologist Rosemary Pringle (1995) argues that Foucault's emphasis on power as productive (and not merely coercive) has opened up the space for a view of women as active agents rather than as passive recipients of orders from above.

This and other similar approaches have not been without their critics. Feminist theorist Sylvia Walby, for example, has argued that the shift away from structure and toward **discourse** has resulted in a conceptualization of power as highly dispersed rather than as concentrated in identifiable places and groups. She argues further that the concepts of "woman" and "patriarchy" are, in fact, essential if we are not to lose sight of the power relations involved and if we are to understand the gendered nature of the social world. In particular, she points out that an analysis of the new international division of labour shows clearly the need to maintain the use of the structural concepts of patriarchy, class, and **racism** (Walby, 1992). While Walby agrees that there were problems with the old **meta-narratives** based solely on class, she holds that the answer is not to discard the concept of social structure. Rather, the answer is to develop better, theoretically richer concepts that are more capable of catching and explaining the theoretical and practical complexities of the operation of power in the social world.

patriarchy
A system of power through which males dominate households. It is used more broadly by feminists to refer to society's domination by patriarchal power, which functions to subordinate women and children.

feminism/feminist
A broad social and political movement based on a belief in equality of the sexes and the removal of all forms of discrimination against women. A feminist is one who makes use of, and may act upon, a body of theory that seeks to explain the subordinate position of women in society.

discourse
A domain of language use that is characterized by common ways of talking and thinking about an issue (for example, the discourses of medicine, madness, or sexuality).

racism
Beliefs and actions used to discriminate against a group of people because of their physical and cultural characteristics.

meta-analysis/ meta-narratives
The big-picture analysis that frames and organizes observations and research on a particular topic.

The important point about these theoretical developments and debates is not that there are disagreements, but that feminist theory in the twenty-first century is marked not by orthodoxy and homogeneity but, rather, by debate and openness. Directly or indirectly, these developments have encouraged a revival in sociological analyses of nursing and of the division of labour within medicine. Rather than accept old-style assumptions about patriarchal oppression and medical dominance that are implicit in the **doctor/nurse game**, recent writers, working from a variety of sociological perspectives, have re-examined nurses' and doctors' working relationships and have come up with new and important findings.

doctor/nurse game
A concept coined by Stein (1967) to refer to the so-called game played out between doctors and nurses, whereby a nurse can be assertive and make suggestions about a patient without appearing to do so, so that nurses' suggestions are provided as prompts for doctors, who can act on them as though they were their own ideas.

Development of Nursing in Canada

David Coburn (1988b) analyzes the development of nursing in Canada in terms of three different time periods. The first period, the emergence of lay nursing, including organization and registration, spans the time period 1870–1930. While some form of nursing care had always been done, it was largely carried out by family members or religious nursing orders. The second era of nursing (1930–50) saw a move from private nursing to hospital nursing, while the third period of nursing began at the end of the Second World War and brought major changes for nurses and the profession.

The Canadian Encyclopedia (Nursing, n.d.) credits Marie Rollet Hébert as the first person to provide nursing care to the sick after arriving in Quebec in 1617 with her surgeon-apothecary husband. Subsequently, as members of religious orders immigrated to what is now Canada, "nursing sisters" took on the role of providing nursing care. These nurses, however, were quite different from nurses today; they often served as doctors, making medicines and undertaking surgery; helped establish hospitals; and served as administrators. The Sisters of Charity, more commonly known as the Grey Nuns, were a non-cloistered order, founded in 1737 by a Quebec widow, Marguerite d'Youville. From the outset, they provided free health care and concentrated their work on home visits to the sick. This predominant group of nursing sisters played an important historical role in the development of health care in the country. Recognizing the importance of segregating the sick, especially during periods of epidemic outbreaks, they spearheaded the creation of a network of hospitals across Canada in the eighteenth and nineteenth centuries, including an orphanage and a home for the aged. Caring for the sick was practised as a devotion to God.

The Emergence of Lay Nursing

The rise and professionalization of nursing is tied to the emergence of hospitals. The formal training of nurses began in the 1870s to provide hospital personnel who would be able to carry out doctors' orders (Wotherspoon, 2009). As new hospitals were established, more nurses were needed to provide care to the sick: "With a nursing force at hand, public hospitals could shift their image and emphasis from providing a repository for the terminally ill to serving as a centre for treatment and recovery" (p. 105). At the time, nursing was viewed as a supporting occupation concerned primarily with caring and hygiene as compared to that of the curative powers of physicians. In the view of Wotherspoon (p. 105), this medical division of labour reproduced a patriarchal structure whereby men were doctors and women were nurses.

Nightingale tradition
The view that nursing was a natural extension of women's role as caregivers; nurses were expected to be altruistic and to act with selfless dedication.

As in Britain, Australia, and the United States, nursing in Canada emerged within the **Nightingale tradition**. Florence Nightingale, born in 1820, was a pioneer in nursing in England who laid the foundation for professional nursing for decades to come. Her impact on the practice of nursing, however, is viewed equivocally. On the one hand, her determination to make nursing a high status profession for women, her holistic approach to health, and her commitment to promoting health rather than simply to nursing illness are viewed as significant achievements. Her prototype for nursing schools, which resulted in a strong female hierarchy in the hands of one female trained head nurse to protect exploitation, is also considered an important contribution. On the other hand, her strategy to reinforce the status of nursing by promoting an ethos of service had the effect of subordinating nurses, who became viewed as "handmaidens" to doctors. Indeed, the motto of the first Canadian training school for nurses (1874) founded on Nightingale's principles was "I see and I am Silent." It became the watchwords for nurses for the next hundred years (Growe, 1991, p. 47). Summing up Nightingale's legacy, US nurse Marlene Grissum wrote that "Florence Nightingale may well be given the credit for establishing nursing as we know it—including low pay, long hours, and subservience to men" (cited in Growe, 1991, p. 51).

Hospital administrators quickly recognized the value of nurses in providing inexpensive labour. The number of hospital schools of nursing in Canada grew from 1 in 1874 to 170 in 1909 and to approximately 220 in 1930 (Wotherspoon, 2009, p. 105). The newly trained nurses were taught complete subordination, unquestioning obedience, and loyalty to doctors. A nursing training program accomplished contradictory functions: "it dampened the hostilities of doctors who scorned nurses as unskilled and uneducated" (Wotherspoon, 2009, p. 105); at the same time, doctors who saw the trained nurse as a potential threat to their livelihood found that they could advance their own interests by getting involved in the nursing training programs. Public health nurses who worked semi-independently in the community were viewed as a special threat. Physicians opposed the founding in 1895 of the Victorian Order of Nurses (VON) and public health nursing in general—and wherever they saw nurses doing work that they believed could be done more profitably by doctors (Coburn, 1988b).

By the end of the nineteenth century, trained nurses striving to increase their own status and distinguish themselves from untrained nurses began to lobby and organize: "Through registration and licensing regulations, nurses sought to obtain a monopoly over the provision of nursing services and to gain higher fees and salaries for themselves. . . ." (Coburn, 1988b, p. 443). Opposition came from both hospital administrators, who feared such

© iStock.com/traveler1116

Florence Nightingale: "I see and I am silent."

power, and doctors. In 1908, the Canadian National Association of Trained Nurses was established; in 1924, with 52 affiliated member organizations, this became the Canadian Nurses Association (CNA) (Wotherspoon, 2009, p. 106). The group focused its energies on establishing registries of trained nurses and by 1922 received legislative recognition in all nine provinces.[1] This institutionalization of nursing, however, Coburn (1988b) argues, was gained at the price of subordination to medicine and to hospital administrators and marked the end of the first era of nursing. Nurses did not attain a monopoly over nursing but only the exclusive right to use the title of nurse or RN (registered nurse). Nursing associations focused on raising standards of care rather than on improving working conditions or pay, but they had no control over who could actually practise nursing. The equation of nursing with qualities of women and motherhood persisted well into the twentieth century: "Becoming professional meant an altruistic orientation of selfless dedication, the ever-higher education credentialing of nursing, and the placing of as much distance as possible between nurses and lower level hospital workers and between nurses and working-class organizations such as unions" (Coburn, 1988b, p. 445).

Move to Hospital Nursing

The second era of nursing (1930–50) saw a move from private nursing to hospital nursing. The Depression of the 1930s brought with it high unemployment and economic hardship for a vast number of Canadians. Private-duty nurses, who at the time were in the majority, had a hard time surviving as the demand for their services declined; they faced increased periods of unemployment and meager wages. While some left nursing, many moved to the hospitals, which provided more secure employment and better wages, despite poor working conditions. The shift is evident in the following statistics: in 1930, 60 per cent of nurses were in private duty and 25 per cent worked in hospitals or nursing schools; by 1948, 67 per cent were in hospitals or nursing schools, and only 15 per cent were private-duty nurses (Coburn, 1988b).

The Depression also took its toll on hospitals: occupancy rates declined and there was pressure to close schools of nursing and decrease the number of nurse graduates. However, things began to change with World War II, when a large number of nurses went into active service. After the war, improved economic conditions generally meant greater hospital utilization and an increased demand for more nurses. By the end of the war, there was a shortage of nurses in the country. Coburn (1988b) argues that the 1940s and 1950s saw a major shift in the orientation of nursing from a care model rooted in the Nightingale tradition to a more instrumental view that saw nursing as no different from other occupations. There was a growing disparity between the views of the nursing elite, whose interests were in enhancing nurses' professional status through increased education and training, and the majority of ordinary nurses, that is, the "rank and file,"[2] who were more concerned with their working conditions and wages.

After some success in pressing for regulation and licensing, nursing associations focused on improving nursing education and increasing standards. In 1932, Dr George Weir, who

---

1. Newfoundland did not join Canada as its tenth province until 1949.
2. The term *rank and file* is frequently used in the labour context to refer to ordinary members who constitute the majority of workers in a group.

had been jointly appointed by a committee of the Canadian Medical Association and the CNA, released a report that called for sweeping changes in nursing education, and he recommended that nursing schools be removed from hospital control and instead be integrated with provincial educational systems (Wotherspoon, 2009). He argued that nurses needed a liberal as well as a technical education. Although there were various external pressures to move the training of nurses away from hospitals, according to Growe (1991), nursing education remained largely under hospital control for another 45 years.

Post-WWII Changes to the Profession

The third period of nursing, beginning at the end of the Second World War, brought major changes for nurses and the profession, including unionization, rationalization of health care, a new managerialism in hospitals, and a move from hospital-based nurse training to colleges and universities. Following the war, there was an expansion of the social welfare state and a growth of the health-care sector in Canada. In 1947, Saskatchewan established the first government-financed hospital-insurance plan; a year later, the federal government provided incentives for new hospital construction. By the early 1950s, about one-third of Canadians had private hospital insurance and over one-quarter had some coverage for medical procedures. And in 1958, a federally financed hospital-insurance plan was put into place. All these initiatives increased the demand for nurses: between 1941 and 1961, the number of nurses increased from 25,826 to 70,647 (Wotherspoon, 2009, p. 107).

By the 1950s and 1960s, nurses and nursing associations became more concerned with pay and working conditions. Nurses no longer embraced earlier notions of female obedience and self-sacrifice. Although nursing leaders took a cautious approach to collective bargaining and unionization, the majority of nurses became more vocal about their rights. The fact that most nurses were now employed in hospitals and shared similar experiences also made organizing easier. The move toward union certification and collective bargaining, however, occurred at different times throughout the country. The first group of nurses to negotiate an employment contract was through a professional organization in Quebec in 1939. In 1946, the British Columbia Nursing Association endorsed collective bargaining and the first hospital was certified in that year in Vancouver. However, Ontario nurses did not certify until 1966 (Nursing, n.d.; Coburn, 1988b). In 1973, a Saskatchewan court decision ruled that provincial associations could not act as bargaining agents for nursing employees because management nurses controlled it. This led to a separation between all-nurse unions and professional associations; the former engaged in collective bargaining for better wages and working conditions while the latter managed registration, discipline, and standards of practice (Growe, 1991, p. 105).

In Canada, over 80 per cent of employed nurses belong to unions. Of those who work in the public sector, 87 per cent are unionized (Canadian Federation of Nurses Unions, 2013a). The Canadian Federation of Nurses Unions (CFNU) was founded in 1981 and is seen as the national voice for unionized nurses. With a membership of close to 200,000, it represents nurses unions in eight provinces: Quebec and British Columbia have their own union organizations. The CFNU is an active member of the Canadian Health Coalition, protesting against extra-billing, user fees, health cuts, privatization, and the move to a two-tier health-care system. Unlike doctors, nurses from the very beginning supported the creation of government-financed hospital and medical insurance. In 1998, the CFNU joined the Canadian Labour Congress (CLC) and works in solidarity with other labour unions to improve the social and economic well-being of workers and defend Canada's social programs. The CFNU has also expanded its ties internationally, for example, with nurses' unions in other countries, most of whom are facing similar, and sometimes worse, threats to their occupation and to their health-care systems (Canadian Federation of Nurses Unions, 2012).

Another significant milestone for nurses and nursing in Canada was the move away from hospital-based training first advocated in the 1930s. Change began only after a Royal Commission on Health Services in Canada in the 1960s indicted the nursing education system of the time as educationally unsound and inadequate for the needs of nurses and the health-care system. Besides recommending that nurse training be separated from hospitals, the Royal Commission's report suggested there be coordinated nursing education programs integrated with higher education systems in Canada. In 1964, with the co-operation of the Ontario government, a nursing diploma program was established at Ryerson Polytechnic Institute.[3] Just over a decade later, full-time enrolment in community college nursing programs increased dramatically. University-degree nursing programs were gradually established. Although the pace of nursing educational reform, particularly at the university level, was initially slow, in part due to the limited commitments by governments and educational institutions, such reform was accelerated by the 1990s through extensive lobbying by the CNA (Canadian Nurses Association, 2000; Wotherspoon, 2009). Today, the educational concerns raised by the Royal Commission have been addressed, and nurses are making significant advances in becoming a university-trained workforce. Colleges and universities across Canada now have a series of collaborative agreements to deliver joint nurse training programs. Today, all provinces and territories, except Quebec and the Yukon, require a baccalaureate in nursing (BN or BSCN) to enter the profession (Canadian Nurses Association, 2014). In 2011, 38.8 per cent of practising registered nurses had baccalaureate degrees and an additional 3.9 per cent had either a master's or doctorate degree (CIHI, 2012b, p. 7). Currently, there are 32 master's programs and 15 doctoral programs in nursing available in Canadian universities (Canadian Nurses Association, 2014).

Although the attainment of a university degree represents an increased professional status for nursing, "it does not guarantee that nurses will gain greater decision-making authority and autonomy" (Wotherspoon, 2009, p. 112). Cutbacks in health-care budgets, restructuring of hospitals to increase efficiency, and a new managerial style committed to applying industrial techniques to the health-care sector have had a significant impact on nursing today (Armstrong & Armstrong, 2003; Coburn, 1988b). Cost-cutting measures have increased managerial control; new scientific techniques based on **time and motion principles** were put into place to monitor care and force nurses to carry out more work in less time. As a means of saving money, nurses' time is rationalized, forcing nurses to give fewer and fewer services to more and more patients faster and faster (Growe, 1991, p. 75; Berry & Curry, 2012). In the words of a nurse from Saskatchewan, "I worked the unit for four months before quitting. Looking back, I realize I was having ethic/moral distress in not being able to provide nursing care at the level my patients deserved. I was going home feeling horrible that half of my patients didn't get bathed that day" (Berry & Curry, 2012, p. 16). As Austin (2011, p. 158) explains, "corporate and commercial values

time and motion principles Introduced by F.W. Taylor in the second decade of the twentieth century to improve industrial efficiency. This involved breaking a job into component parts and measuring the length of time each task would take. It would become the benchmark for how long a particular activity should take.

---

3. Now called Ryerson University.

are inducing some healthcare organizations to prescribe a customer service model that reframes the provision of nursing care." The caring, comforting, and nurturing aspects of their job, which most nurses value highly, are being undermined. Nursing work has become routinized and increasingly fragmented into discrete tasks that can be allocated to those with fewer qualifications who are paid lower wages. In talking about the impact of new managerial strategies on nursing practice, one nurse put it this way: "You hit that ward at a run, and you're always having to say to people, 'I haven't got time to do that. I'm sorry sir.' And it's a horrible way to nurse" (cited in Armstrong et al., 2000, p. 91). Another nurse, explaining why she left hospital nursing, said that "I was losing that human kind of touch and being able to hold someone's hand and give them that TLC that they need when they're going through a rough time, which you can't do 'cause you're running doing all the tasks" (pp. 95–6). Wendy Austin (2007) in her article, "The McDonaldization of Nursing?", expressed the frustrations of nurses: "This is not nursing; it's crowd control. It's like running a marathon, you have very little time to ever stop and breathe. There's not enough time for each person usually. There's never any time to stop either and just talk to the people and treat them like people instead of tasks" (p. 265).

The Nursing Workforce Today

As discussed in the previous section, nursing underwent major changes from the 1970s through the 1990s. Unionization spread rapidly; nurses went on strike; nursing professional associations actively promoted enhanced credentials and university education as the standard for nurses; nurses opposed medical hegemony and succeeded in gaining occupational autonomy; nurses condemned the 1986 doctors' strike in Ontario and lobbied in favour of the Canada Health Act; the CFNU along with other labour groups joined the Canadian Health Coalition to lobby in support of preserving and enhancing Medicare. Today, Coburn (1988b) argues, nursing is marked by both professional and instrumental orientations. Nursing is now viewed by many nurses as any other service job, and is largely approached in an **instrumental** manner. While a professional orientation based on altruism and dedicated service is still present in nursing, professionalization "is clearly part of the struggle by nurses to escape hospital and physician control over the nursing labour process" (Coburn, 1988b, p. 452). A look at the nursing labour force today illustrates some of the current challenges that nurses face.

As of 2013 in Canada, the largest group of paid health-care professionals is regulated nurses with a total workforce of 408,093[4] (CIHI, 2014e). In 2011, they accounted for 42.7 per cent of the Canadian health-care workforce (CIHI, 2013a, p. 11). This group is comprised of 296,029 (72.5. per cent) **registered nurses (RNs)**, including **nurse practitioners (NPs)**; 106,447 (26.1 per cent) **licensed practical nurses (LPNs)**; and 5617 (1.4 per cent) **registered psychiatric nurses (RPNs)** (CIHI, 2014e). Since 2009, there has been an 8 per cent increase in the number of regulated nurses licensed to practice in Canada (see Figure 15.1). However, the Canadian Federation of Nurses Unions (2014) notes that there are fewer RNs per capita today than in the early 1990s. The ratio of practising nurses to

instrumental approach
One in which a job is valued as a means to an end, not for its intrinsic worth.

registered nurses (RNs)
Nurses who coordinate health care, deliver direct services, and support patients in their self-care decisions.

nurse practitioners (NPs)
RNs with additional education qualifications and experience. They may order and interpret diagnostic tests, as well as prescribe medications and other therapies.

licensed practical nurses (LPNs)
Nurses who assess patients and work in health promotion and illness prevention. This group is called RPNs (registered practical nurses) in Ontario.

registered psychiatric nurses (RPNs)
Nurses who provide services to patients whose primary-care needs relate to mental and development health. They plan, implement, and evaluate therapies and programs on the basis of psychiatric nursing assessments. They are regulated separately from other nursing professionals in four provinces.

---

4. This is the number of regulated nurses eligible to practise in Canada. However, there were 378,768 nurses working as nurses in 2013 (Canadian Federation of Nurses Unions, 2014).

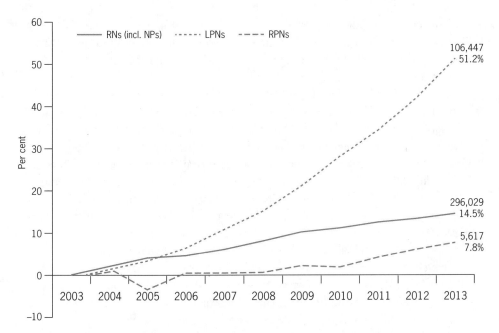

Figure 15.1 Percentage Growth in the Supply of Regulated Nurses in
Canada, 2003–2013

Source: CIHI. (2014). Figure 1: Percentage growth in the supply of regulated nurses, 2003 to
2013 *Regulated Nurses, 2013: Report*, p. 9. Reproduced from Public Health Agency of Canada
(2014). Retrieved at: https://secure.cihi.ca/free_products/Nursing-Workforce-2013_EN.pdf.

practising physicians in the country in 2009 was 4.4, the same as that of Japan but higher
than the United States (4.2) (OECD, 2011b, p. 73).

A report by the Canadian Institute for Health Information (CIHI, 2012b) indicates that
nursing remains overwhelmingly a female-dominated profession. In 2011, 93.4 per cent
of registered nurses (RNs) in the country were female, a figure that hasn't changed significantly over the past five years. Male nurses were overrepresented in Quebec, Manitoba,
and the territories. Overall, registered psychiatric nurses had the highest proportion of
males (22 per cent). Recent enrolments (2011) in nursing at the University of Calgary suggest, however, there will be an increase in the number of male nurses down the road:
13 per cent of those enrolled in first-year nursing were males, and male transfer students
into the nursing program totalled 21 per cent (UToday, 2011).

The nursing workforce is aging, with an average age in the mid-forties (45.1 for RNs)
in 2013. Those in the 40–60 age group constitute the majority of the workforce (52.3 per
cent of the RN workforce) (CIHI, 2014e, Table 11). This is of some concern since there is
already a shortage of nurses in the country and the situation is predicted to get worse as
more nurses retire. Budget restraints led to restrictions in enrolments in nursing programs such that currently, there are not enough nurses graduating to keep up with the
projected demand. The shortage is especially serious in northern, rural, and remote
regions in Canada as well as in Aboriginal communities (Canadian Federation of Nurses
Unions, 2013b). The Aboriginal Nurses Association of Canada (ANAC) points to the projected shortfall of Aboriginal nurses in the coming years and advocates a "more intensive

effort" to increase the number of Aboriginal nursing students. A firm belief of the ANAC is "that increasing the number of Aboriginal nurses can and will result in increasing the overall health status of our Aboriginal communities" (Aboriginal Nurses Association of Canada, n.d.).

A large majority of regulated nurses (approximately 70 per cent) work in public sector health care[5] as compared with the private sector. Recent changes in funding to the health-care system have had a major impact on nurses' working conditions. Increased workload is one consequence of the government budgetary cutbacks and downsizing, beginning in the 1990s, which reduced the number of nurses graduating and the monies available to hospitals and community services for operating expenses. In an effort to control costs, hospital administrators hired more part-time and casual workers. In 2013, only 58.4 per cent of registered nurses were employed full-time. In some cases, nurses who worked part-time or in casual positions (41.6 per cent) did so by choice, but in other cases, nurses were unable to obtain full-time work. For those with young children, the lack of affordable child care or limited flexibility in the workplace also made full-time employment impossible. In our society, women remain predominantly responsible for family life. Nurses need flexible and innovative schedules that allow a female-dominated workforce to balance home and working lives and to meet unpredictable family-care needs (Canadian Nursing Advisory Committee, 2002). It is perhaps not surprising that female RNs were less likely than male RNs to have full-time employment (58.3 per cent versus 72.6 per cent, respectively). A substantial number of nurses, especially those employed in part-time or casual positions, work for multiple employers. In many cases the number of hours that part-time nurses work exceed the number of hours full-time nurses work; however, part-time nurses are unlikely to receive overtime rates or the same benefits that full-time nurses receive (Canadian Federation of Nurses Unions, 2013b). Rather than creating permanent jobs in response to the nursing shortage, employers are expecting nurses to work more hours (Armstrong & Armstrong, 2003, p. 108). In fact, a survey of Canadian nurses in 2005 found that nearly half of those surveyed reported that they usually worked unpaid overtime, for an average of four hours per week (Shields & Wilkins, 2006). More recently, a study completed for the Canadian Federation of Nurses Unions (2013a) found that in 2012, public-sector health-care nurses worked an estimated overtime equivalent to 11,900 full-time jobs.

Reports and studies indicate that the working conditions of nurses today are stressful (Armstrong & Armstrong, 2003; Austin, 2007; Berry & Curry, 2012; Canadian Nursing Advisory Committee, 2002; Health Canada, 2007a; Shields & Wilkins, 2006). Reasons cited for this include the shortage of nurses, the intensity and complexity of patient-care environments, government funding cutbacks, increased workload, fragmentation of nursing work, the increasing use of part-time and casual workers, application of time and motion principles to nursing care, and violence and abuse in the workplace:

> Nurses are working harder, caring for more individuals, and spending less time with each person. What has shrunk in this changing environment is the amount of time they have to assess, monitor and provide appropriate nursing care as well as

---

5. This figure is derived from information put out by the Canadian Federation of Nurses Unions.

be teachers, comforters and communicators. (Ontario Nursing Task Force Report 2000, quoted in Canadian Nursing Advisory Committee, 2002, p. 12)

New managerial strategies, "propelled by the increasingly dominant global forces of corporatism and commercialism" (Austin, 2011, p. 159) require nurses to do more in less time or to do more than one thing at a time. As a result, nurses end up working long shifts without breaks or working overtime in order to complete their work, which leads to stress and burnout. Over half (54 per cent) of nurses in a Canadian study reported that they often arrived at work early or stayed late in order to get their work done, and 62 per cent reported working through breaks (Shields & Wilkins, 2006). The need to work overtime results in fatigue, a major problem for nurses who work 12-hour shifts. Constant pressures in the job have an impact on nurses' physical and psychological health: the result is high absenteeism, burnout, turnover, and inefficiency. The rate of absenteeism among nurses due to illness and injury is 80 per cent higher than the Canadian average. Nurses are at a particularly high risk for illness, emotional exhaustion, and musculoskeletal injuries (Greenslade & Paddock, 2007). Over a one year period (2012), the cost of absenteeism due to illness or disability among publicly employed nurses was $734 million (Canadian Federation of Nurses Unions, 2014). Violence on the job (physical and sexual assault, verbal aggression, or emotional abuse) is of increasing concern to nurses: nurses are more at risk for assault than prison guards or police officers, with female nurses considered the most vulnerable, although male nurses were much more likely than female nurses to face physical assaults (Shields & Wilkins, 2006; Canadian Federation of Nurses Unions, 2014). Twenty-five per cent of all workplace violence occurs in the health-care sector, affecting 50 per cent of all health-care workers (Canadian Federation of Nurses Unions, 2014). For example, Fernandes et al. (1999) found that over half of the staff at a Vancouver emergency department had been physically assaulted in a year and 90 per cent had been verbally abused at least once a week. Furthermore, 68 per cent reported an increased frequency of violence over time, and 60 per cent reported an increased severity. This increase in frequency and severity may be attributed to government funding cuts to hospitals, which has meant fewer doctors and nurses working in emergency departments. As a result, many patients have long waits to see a doctor or to receive treatment, sometimes leading to frustration and hostility. For example, in Fredericton, New Brunswick, it is not unusual to wait eight to ten hours to be seen by a doctor (except in acute situations, such as heart attacks and strokes).

A system-wide fiscal restraint that has restructured health care has meant fewer nurses to do more nursing; at the same time, they are expected to perform non-nursing tasks (Canadian Nursing Advisory Committee, 2002), all of which affects patient care. In a 2014 interview, Ann Tourangeau, associate dean of academic programs at the University of Toronto's Faculty of Nursing stated that workload and inadequate staffing across all sectors was the number one issue facing Ontario's nursing profession (Ogilvie, 2014). In a comparative study that included nurses in Canada, 42.9 per cent of Canadian nurses reported doing housekeeping duties; 43.6 indicated that they were unable to speak with and comfort patients because of time restraints (Aiken et al., 2001). As mentioned previously, these pressures have an impact on nurses' well-being. However, a reduced nursing staff and time pressures also have a negative impact on patient care. In their report on nursing workload and patient care, Berry & Curry (2012) note that two decades of national and international research shows a direct relationship between inadequate nurse staffing, and poor patient outcomes, including increases in mortality rates, hospital-acquired infections, and medication errors. The data from a Canadian survey in 2005 (Shields & Wilkins, 2006) showed that nearly one-fifth of RNs acknowledged that in the year prior, errors in medication for patients in their care had occurred "frequently" or "occasionally." The likelihood of error increased with the level of work overload. Similar findings are reported in an American study (Rogers et al., 2004).

According to an interview with Dr Judith Shamian, past-president of the Canadian Nurses Association and the newly elected president of the International Council of Nurses, there was a shift in ideology away from making health care a major priority when the Harper government came into power. Her fear is that "there [was] a larger political agenda to take health off the table so provinces can quietly invest less and get out of various health-care services they offer" (Gottlieb, 2009, p. 22). There is little reason for optimism that things can turn about quickly in the near future. The dominance of neo-liberal discourse advocating fiscal restraint makes federal and provincial governments reluctant to find the necessary additional monies and resources needed for the public health-care sector. On the positive side, however, the newly elected federal Liberal government has promised to address some glaring public-health needs as soon as possible.

Ongoing Tensions

The problems confronting Canadian nurses are not unique. The current shortage of hospital nurses in Western countries is expected to get worse as a result of job dissatisfaction and an aging workforce. A national study reported that the turnover rate for nurses is close to 20 per cent (cited in Canadian Federation of Nurses Unions, 2014). Although the CIHI (2014e) report indicates that the growth in the supply of regulated nurses continues to outpace the Canadian population growth, the Canadian Nurses Association is predicting a shortfall of 60,000 full-time equivalent nurses by 2022 (cited in Canadian Federation of Nurses Unions, 2013a). In a national study of nurses in Canada, about 12 per cent of both female and male nurses reported overall job dissatisfaction, compared to 8 per cent in the general employed population. Older nurses were more likely to be dissatisfied than younger nurses (Shields & Wilkins, 2006). A comparison of nurses' work in five countries—Canada, United States, England, Scotland, and Germany—indicates that nurses report similar systems of distress (Aiken et al., 2001). In every country except Germany, at least one-third of nurses reported that they were dissatisfied with their job; a significant percentage (29.4 per cent in Canada) of nurses under 30 were planning to leave their job within the year. A clear majority of nurses in Canada (63.6 per cent) and the United States (83.2 per cent) reported that a major problem, as a result of restructuring in hospitals, was the increased number of patients assigned to them combined with a rise in patient acuity levels. Over 60 per cent of nurses in all five countries reported that there were not enough registered nurses to provide high-quality care. Deterioration in patient care was most frequently reported in Canada and the United States—related, it appears, to the extensive hospital restructuring in both countries. As Aiken et al. (2001) conclude, the re-engineering and restructuring (to emulate industrial models of productivity) that have occurred in the health-care sector have negative outcomes for both nurses and patients.

Conclusion

> Restructuring, lack of human and structural resources, altered work environments,
> increased patient acuity with off-loading of care to families . . . have created a sig-
> nificant level of moral chaos in the nursing profession. (Storch et al., 2013, p. 190,
> quoted in Berry & Curry, 2012, p. 38)

Nurses are the cornerstone of our health-care system. However, nursing practice today
is shaped by a **new managerialism** and a market model of care that has reduced nurses'
autonomy, and narrowly conceptualizes care as quantifiable tasks that can be counted
and measured (Day, 2013, p. 27). The restructuring taking place puts an emphasis on
efficiency, accountability, quantification, and cost-driven decision-making. This results
in cutbacks to nursing staff and other hospital workers, impedes nurses' everyday work,
and reduces the quality of patient care. In the view of Bernice Carter (2007), "Nursing is
subtly and insidiously being reformatted, re-engineered, processed to become something
which may be efficient and effective in a managerial, commercial and business sense but
which is unrecognizable as something nurses or patients genuinely wish to engage with"
(p. 270). What is being lost with the restructuring is the emotional aspect of nursing care
(Weinberg, 2006, cited in Day, 2013, p. 26).

A Canadian study by Varcoe et al. (2004, cited in Beagan & Ells, 2009) found that nurses
struggled to enact their personal and professional values in a context where they were
required to document and account for their work in a way that discounted those aspects of
care that were not quantifiable. As one frustrated nurse commented, "How do you measure emotional support? . . . that's ridiculous" (Beagan & Ells, 2009, p. 99). This institutional
emphasis on efficiency forces nurses to ration their time and their care; it is a constant source
of ethical tension as they are unable to provide the kind of care that compelled them to go into
nursing in the first place (Beagan & Ells, 2009, p. 99). The inability to engage with patients
in a meaningful way dehumanizes nurses, making their work robotic (Austin, 2011). As a
result, nurses, unable to live up to their expectations of ethical practice, are experiencing
what Storch et al. (2013) refer to as moral distress that threatens the well-being and safety of
nurses and their patients (cited in Berry & Curry, 2012, p. 38). A new study (Spenceley et al.,
2015) found that 75 per cent of nurses in Southern Alberta who provide care to residential
dementia patients reported situations that caused at least a moderate degree of moral distress
once a week; the two most frequently mentioned concerns were seeing care suffer because of
inadequate staff to do the work and having to rush the care because of lack of time.

Critics have referred to the reorganization that is taking place within nursing as the
McDonaldization of nursing (Austin, 2007, 2011). It is argued that such a system trans-
forms individualized health care into a commodity. It "requires that nurses, who are educated and committed to care for *people*, are expected to nurse the hospital *organization*"
(Austin, 2007, p. 266). The corporatization of the hospital entails the transfer of the culture
of business to the hospital (Fried et al., 1987, cited in Beardwood et al., 1999, p. 367). There
is even a new business language that frames patient satisfaction as "customer service,"
and the chief administrator is now called a CEO. Importantly, this new language reflects
a change in the conception of rights: from health care as a social right—that is, based on
the collective right of citizenship—to health care as a consumer right (Beardwood et al.,
1999, p. 367).

new managerialism
A term that arose in the
1980s to describe a shift in
the transfer of power from
professionals (i.e., doctors) to
management. It encouraged
the implementation of
industrial techniques that
emphasized continuous
evaluation of performance
against defined objectives,
rationing of resources
using effectiveness criteria,
and surveillance of health
professionals (Beardwood
et al., 1999).

McDonaldization
A term coined by George
Ritzer to expand Weber's
notion of rationalization;
defined as the standardization
of social life by rules and
regulations, such as increased
monitoring and evaluation of
individual performance, akin
to the uniformity and control
measures used by fast-food
chains. These principles are
now applied to other sectors,
both locally and globally.

The situation of nursing in Canada must be viewed within this broader socio-economic and political context. The politics of economic restraint and neo-liberalism beginning in the 1980s have meant a reduction in social spending, including cuts to health care. The paradigm shift in health-care environments to a marketplace model has the potential to radically change nursing as a profession (Austin, 2011). In the words of Austin (2011, p. 192), "customer service can neither encompass authentic relationship nor the intimacy of caring."

Summary

- Nurses today comprise the largest group of health-care providers in Canada.
- Early sociological interpretations emphasized the influence of social structure and portrayed nurses as lacking agency. More recent developments within sociology and feminist theory have shifted the focus toward nursing agency and resistance.
- Nursing emerged within the Nightingale tradition that promoted an ethos of service and subordination.
- The development of nursing in Canada can be analyzed in terms of three time periods: the emergence of lay nursing (1870–1930); the move from private nursing to hospital nursing (1930–50); and developments post–Second World War that brought about major changes, including unionization, university and college-based educational requirements, and a new managerialism in hospitals.
- The Canadian Nurses Association played a key role in promoting professionalization and higher credentials for nurses.
- By the 1960s, nurses became increasingly concerned with working conditions and pay; today, over 80 per cent of employed nurses belong to unions.
- Cutbacks in health-care budgets in the 1980s led to a decline in nursing enrolments and hospital restructuring that led to increased workload for nurses and the fragmentation of nursing work.
- New managerialism and a market model of care, referred to by critics as the "McDonaldization" of nursing, emphasizes efficiency, quantification, and cost-driven decision-making at the expense of the emotional aspect of nursing care.
- The shortage of nurses, reduced autonomy, heavy workloads, and stress on the job has negative impacts on both nurses' well-being and patient safety.
- Nursing remains a female-dominated profession.

Key Terms

agency
discourse
doctor/nurse game
ethnography
feminism/feminist
horizontal violence
instrumental approach

licensed practical nurses (LPNs)
materialist analysis
McDonaldization
meta-analysis/ meta-narratives
new managerialism

Nightingale tradition
nurse practitioners (NPs)
patriarchy
post-structuralism/ postmodernism
racism
rationalization

registered nurses (RNs)
registered psychiatric
  nurses (RPNs)

sexual division of labour
  (SDL)
social institutions

social structure
structure–agency debate
time and motion principles

Sociological Reflection: The Reorganization of Nursing Work

Some have suggested that the way nursing is organized today can be compared to the fast-food industry—i.e., what is referred to as the McDonaldization of nursing.

- Do you think that this is an appropriate analogy? If so, in what ways is it appropriate? Think of some empirical examples from your own experience or from the experience of others.
- If you do not think it is appropriate, why not? What do you think would be a more appropriate analogy?

Discussion Questions

1. How do you understand the term *agency* in the context of nursing work?
2. What social forces affect nursing today?
3. What are the major organizational challenges faced by nurses today?
4. How and why has nursing education changed over the past century?
5. Why is nursing such a stressful profession?
6. What factors led to the rapid unionization of nurses?
7. What factors explain the rise of a new managerialism and a restructuring of nursing care in hospitals?
8. What are some specific ways that nurses' workloads have an impact on patients' health?

Further Investigation

1. In what other areas of health care, besides nursing, has there been a rationalization of health-care resources? Provide some empirical examples.
2. Why does nursing remain a female-dominated profession? Why might men be reluctant to become nurses?

Further Reading

Armstrong, P., Armstrong, H., & Scott-Dixon, K. (2008). *Critical to care: The invisible women in health services*. Toronto, ON: University of Toronto Press.

Armstrong, P., & Braedley, S. (Eds). (2013). *Troubling care: Critical perspectives on research and practices*. Toronto: Canadian Scholars' Press Inc.

Armstrong, P., Choiniere, J., & Day, E. (1993). *Vital signs: Nursing in transition*. Toronto, ON: Garamond Press.

Austin, W. (2011). The incommensurability of nursing as a practice and the customer service model: An evolutionary threat to the discipline. *Nursing Philosophy, 12*, 158–66.

Ehrenreich, B., & English, D. (1973). *Witches, midwives and nurses*. New York, NY: Old Westbury Feminist Press.

Growe, S.J. (1991). *Who cares: The crisis in Canadian nursing*. Toronto, ON: McClelland & Stewart Inc.

Rankin, J., & Campbell, M. (2006). *Managing to nurse: Inside Canada's health care reform*. Toronto, ON: University of Toronto Press.

Web Resources

Aboriginal Nurses Association
www.anac.on.ca

Canadian Federation of Nurses Unions
https://nursesunions.ca

Canadian Health Coalition
www.healthcoalition.ca

Canadian Institute for Health Information
www.cihi.ca/CIHI-ext-portal/internet/EN/ Theme/spending+and+health+workforce/ cihi010658

Canadian Nurses Association (CNA)
www.cna-nurses.ca/cna/

Health Canada
www.hc-sc.gc.ca (see Nurses site)

CHAPTER 16
Complementary and Alternative Health Care

Jennie Hornosty, Gary Easthope & Alex Broom

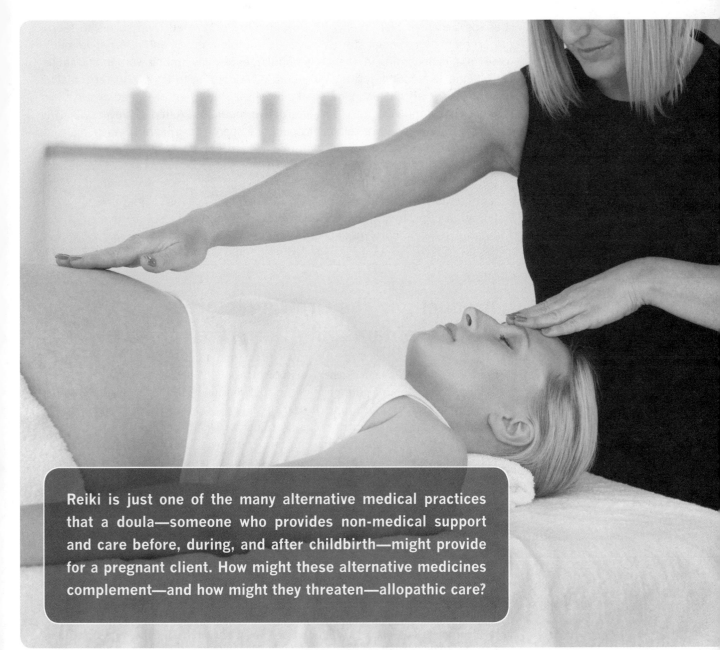

Reiki is just one of the many alternative medical practices that a doula—someone who provides non-medical support and care before, during, and after childbirth—might provide for a pregnant client. How might these alternative medicines complement—and how might they threaten—allopathic care?

Overview

- How does complementary and alternative medicine (CAM) differ from conventional medicine?
- Why is CAM increasingly popular?
- What are the benefits and limitations of CAM?

Conventional (i.e., allopathic) medicine is the dominant form of medicine in Canada because, historically, its practitioners organized themselves to lobby governments for special status. However, complementary and alternative medicine (CAM) is becoming increasingly popular, especially among women and those with higher education and higher incomes. According to Dr Konigsberg, a clinical professor at McMaster medical school, "73 per cent of Canadians in their lifetime use complementary and alternative medicine" (cited in Deveau, 2010). Reasons for CAM use are related to people's search for meaning, their distrust of science, the preponderance of chronic rather than acute illness, the personal relationship between healers and their clients, and the search for control over one's life. However, most users of alternative therapies and medicines do not reject conventional medicine but use both. Today we are seeing an increasing integration of CAM with conventional medicine, leading to what is being called "integrative health care" (IHC) (Possamai-Inesedy & Cochrane, 2013).

Introduction: The Growing Interest in Complementary and Alternative Health Care

There has been a growing awareness and acceptance of complementary and alternative health care among both health practitioners and consumers. Recently, for example, the community health centre Anishnawbe Health Toronto (AHT) incorporated naturopathic medicine, traditional Aboriginal practices (through healers, elders, medicine people), and conventional practices with physicians and nurses to provide health services to Aboriginal peoples. Naturopathic medicine is seen to be especially appropriate due to its emphasis on holistic treatment, a central component of the Aboriginal tradition (Walji et al., 2010). In Western industrialized countries, estimates of CAM use among the general population vary widely from 10 per cent to 84 per cent (Metcalfe et al., 2010; Thomson et al., 2014). Yet there are also many skeptics of CAM. A central question is: how does CAM differ from conventional medicine? Is one "quackery" and the other "scientific" as some would suggest? As we will see in this chapter, such a simplistic distinction is inaccurate. Rather the difference has a lot to do with ideology and the relative political power and organizational structures of the two.

There are three questions that are frequently asked by anyone—layperson, doctor, or sociologist—who is at all interested in alternative medicine. The first question—why is alternative medicine considered alternative?—explores what distinguishes

complementary and alternative medicine from **conventional medicine**.[1] The answer provides a historical and political explanation rather than an explanation in terms of modes of treatment. The next question—why is CAM increasingly popular?—is answered by looking at empirical research on the clients of CAM practitioners and at the market for CAM in the context of changes in society and the nature of illness today. An answer to the last question—does CAM work?—requires a discussion of what it means for a treatment to work.

How Does Alternative Medicine Differ from Conventional Medicine?

As we saw in Chapter 12, conventional medicine is a recent social invention. In the early twentieth century, it was only one among a range of medical practices. Its theoretical base was that disease is a result of an imbalance in the body; to restore balance, something must be given or taken away. To decide on a course of action, the doctor observed the symptoms and prescribed something to produce an opposite effect to those symptoms (a process known as **allopathy**). For example, up until 1884 a patient whose face was suffused with blood would be bled to reduce the blood in the body.

Conventional Medicine

Allopathy received a great boost in the mid-nineteenth century when Louis Pasteur discovered micro-organisms, thereby vindicating allopathic theory: namely that, toxic organisms invaded the body, upsetting its balance and causing symptoms that needed to be treated by attacking the invaders. Following Pasteur's lead, the application of laboratory science to medical practice was an outstanding feature of the development of conventional medicine in the latter half of the nineteenth century and during the early twentieth century. The practice base of conventional medicine was developed in the clinic or hospital where doctors observed large numbers of patients and began to develop classificatory schemes that grouped sets of symptoms into categories. In the nineteenth century, after Koch formulated a set of rules for determining conclusively whether a particular bacterium was the cause of a particular disease, such classifications became more sophisticated, and symptoms were used as indicators of underlying theoretical entities called "diseases." Modern medicine was thus created from a combination of allopathic theory, a focus on the body, empirical clinical experience, and laboratory science. This scientific, clinical, allopathic **biomedicine** (**biomedical model**) became the conventional medicine only in the late nineteenth and early twentieth century. When Canada became a nation in 1867, for example, most people relied on home remedies or sought help from the more affordable and respected homeopaths, chemists, Chinese herbalists, and spiritual leaders.

Conventional medicine did not become the dominant model because it had a better cure rate than other forms of medicine; rather, its practitioners were better organized and

complementary and alternative medicine (CAM)
A broad term used to describe both alternative medical practitioners and practices that may stand in opposition to conventional medicine and also those who complement or collaborate with conventional medical practice.

conventional medicine
The medical practices and institutions developed in Europe during the nineteenth and twentieth centuries that are legally recognized by the state.

allopathy
A descriptive name often given to conventional medicine. Allopathy is the treatment of symptoms by opposites.

biomedicine/biomedical model
The conventional approach to medicine in Western societies, based on the diagnosis and explanation of illness as a malfunction of the body's biological mechanisms. This approach underpins most health professions and health services, which focus on treating individuals, and generally ignore the social origins of illness and its prevention.

---

1. In the literature the term *conventional medicine* often is used interchangeably with orthodox medicine, allopathic medicine, and biomedicine. In this chapter, conventional medicine will be the term generally used.

Simon Kneebone, reproduced with permission.

Is Canada's support of the medical health model over other models of medicine due to its proven superiority or to cultural conditioning?

state
A term used to describe a collection of institutions, including the Parliament (government and opposition political parties), the public-sector bureaucracy, the judiciary, the military, and the police.

apothecary
A historical name for a pharmacist, that is, someone who specialized in compounding and distributing medicines and herbs.

homeopath/homeopathy
Homeopathy is a system of natural medicine that uses micro-doses of natural remedies from the plant, animal, and mineral kingdom to stimulate the body's self-healing abilities. (What Is Homeopathy? 2009).

more politically astute than practitioners in other forms of medicine, such as homoeopathy. Through the implementation of various policies, acts, regulations, and laws, biomedicine—to a large extent—ensured the exclusion of certain other health practices from **state** legitimation. In other words, conventional practitioners successfully restricted or suppressed the activities of the more popular healers, such as **apothecaries** and **homeopaths** and, through their affiliation with elite educational institutions, gained increased respectability that allowed them to restrict entry to the profession. As such, the dominance of conventional medicine has been as much about political manoeuvring and achievement of self-regulation as it has been about effectiveness.

Attempts by conventional physicians to restrict who could legally practise medicine began in Canada as early as 1795. However, it was not until the beginning of the twentieth century that medicine consolidated its power over licensing, admittance to medical schools, and educational curriculum. The degree to which conventional doctors were able to control the work of other health practitioners varies among countries, but in most countries only conventional doctors can formally diagnosis disease, recommend medical treatment, and sign birth and death certificates. And generally only certified doctors are able to verify illness for work absence or insurance purposes; directly or indirectly, then, doctors affect the work of other health professionals.

The status of conventional medicine was further boosted by the improved morbidity and mortality rates of the twentieth century. Conventional medicine took credit for these improvements, although we know now that in countries like Canada these were primarily the result of clean drinking water, improved sewerage, and better nutrition rather than due to medical intervention (Butler-Jones, 2008).

The dominance of conventional medicine brought with it a specific set of understandings about the body, the nature of disease, and the patient/provider relationship; what we generally refer to as the biomedical model. This includes the assumptions that the roots of illness are primarily biological, that the body is analogous to a machine, that the physician is the authority and expert, and that all procedures and medications have been scientifically proven to be efficacious. When it is accepted that disease is reducible to the organ, cellular, or genetic levels, (that it is not connected to such things as the mind, spirit, or social environment), then more is spent on technologies that focus on organ, cell, and gene-specific problems. Medical technologies, interventions, and practices significantly frame how we make sense of illness—they effectively render some things treatable and others untreatable. It is precisely such assumptions of conventional medicine and its treatment practices that bring it into conflict with CAM practitioners and consumers.

Alternative Medicine

Complementary and alternative medicine encompasses a wide spectrum of therapeutic practices, approaches, and beliefs. Broadly defined, CAM refers to the diagnosis, treatment, and/or prevention that complements mainstream medicine, satisfies a demand not met by conventional approaches, and is not generally reimbursed by health benefit plans (Health Policy Research Bulletin, 2003; Millar, 2001). Further, CAM refers to "healing resources that encompasses all health systems, modalities, and practices and their accompanying theories and beliefs" that are not intrinsic to the dominant health system of a society (cited in York University Centre for Health Studies, 1999, p. 24). It has also been argued that CAM is ultimately a socially constructed and dynamic entity that is historically and culturally variable, suggesting that our understanding of CAM varies over time. Although our definition of CAM is fluid, there are some characteristics that are unique to CAM:

- It is **holistic**, meaning that all aspects of an individual—physical, emotional, mental, social, spiritual, lifestyle—are interrelated; therefore, treatment requires treating the whole person.
- CAM assumes healing is innate to the human body because it contains self-healing mechanisms; the role of a CAM practitioner is to stimulate this natural healing process.
- The patient is considered an active participant in the management of illness and needs to take personal responsibility for health.
- The patient–practitioner relationship is an intimate one that aids healing through intentionality and awareness of multiple factors that lead to illness.

holistic/holism
An approach to health that considers all aspects of an individual—physical, emotional, mental, social, spiritual, and lifestyle—as interrelated and must be treated as such.

The central focus in CAM is on disease prevention and fostering well-being (Smith & Simpson, 2003; York University Centre for Health Studies, 1999, pp. 25–7).

According to Health Canada, there are as many as 4000 different practices, disciplines, or areas catalogued as complementary and alternative health-care approaches (Smith & Simpson, 2003). Other sources suggest there are 200 to 300 different CAM therapies and practices (York University Centre for Health Studies, 1999). These range from complete systems of medicine, such as traditional Chinese medicine and Ayurvedic medicine, to specific interventions, such as acupuncture, aromatherapy, chiropractic, craniosacral therapy, homeopathy, massage, naturopathy, osteopathy, reiki, and herbalism.

A helpful way to understand CAM is the classificatory approach to CAM therapies favoured by the US National Center for Complementary and Alternative Medicine (now the National Center for Complementary and Integrative Health [NCCIH]) that divides the modalities into five major categories (Hilbers & Lewis, 2013, p. 52). See Table 16.1.

Such diversity makes it difficult to measure CAM usage in a definitive manner since studies sometimes use different definitions and measures, posing a methodological

Table 16.1 Categories of CAM

CAM Type	Description
Alternative medical systems	Alternative medical systems are built upon complete systems of theory and practice. Often, these systems have evolved apart from and earlier than the conventional medical approach used in the US. Examples of alternative medical systems that have developed in Western cultures include homeopathic medicine and naturopathic medicine. Examples of systems that have developed in non-Western cultures include traditional Chinese medicine and Ayurveda.
Mind–body interventions	Mind–body medicine uses a variety of techniques designed to enhance the mind's capacity to affect bodily function and symptoms, including meditation, prayer, mental healing, and therapies that use creative outlets such as art, music, or dance.
Biologically based therapies	Biologically based therapies in CAM use substances found in nature, such as herbs, foods, and vitamins. Some examples include dietary supplements, herbal products, and the use of other so-called natural therapies (for example, using shark cartilage to treat cancer).
Manipulative and body-based methods	Manipulative and body-based methods in CAM are based on manipulation and/or movement of one or more parts of the body. Some examples include chiropractic or osteopathic manipulation, and massage.
Energy therapies	Energy therapies involve the use of energy fields. They are of two types: (1) Biofield therapies are intended to affect energy fields that purportedly surround and penetrate the human body. The existence of such fields has not yet been scientifically proven. Some forms of energy therapy manipulate biofields by applying pressure and/or manipulating the body by placing the hands in, or through, these fields. Examples including qigong, reiki, and therapeutic touch. (2) Bioelectromagnetic-based therapies involve the unconventional use of electromagnetic fields, such as pulsed fields, magnetic fields, or alternating-current or direct-current fields.

Source: National Center for Complementary and Integrative Health (NCCIH), U.S. Department of Health & Human Services.

challenge for researchers (Andrews & Boon, 2005; Hilbers & Lewis, 2013). Nevertheless, the general consensus is that CAM use is on the increase. In 2006, Canadians are said to have spent about $7.84 billion on CAM (Fallis, 2012, p. E454).

Natural health products (NHPs) are a large and generally increasing part of the Canadian health-care reality (Simpson, 2003). A 2001 survey found that 75 per cent of Canadians regularly take natural health products, such as nutritional supplements like vitamins and minerals, herbal products, homeopathic medicines, and the like (cited in de Bruyn, 2002, p. 6). Use of NHPs varies depending on the region of the country: it is highest in British Columbia, where 41 per cent of respondents reported using three or more NHPs in the previous six months, as compared with 15 per cent of respondents in the Atlantic provinces (Simpson, 2003). This finding may be partially explained by the ethnic composition of the two regions. Many more people from Asian and South Asian countries, where there is greater receptiveness to complementary and alternative therapies, make British Columbia their home. Women, findings suggest, make greater use of NHPs than men (Simpson, 2003). Concerns with appearance among young people, which can promote dieting and body-building, may be a factor that explains the finding that people aged 18 to 24 appear more likely to use natural health products.

Whereas CAM practices are regulated individually and by each Canadian province, NHPs are regulated at the federal level.[2] As a result of federal regulations that came into

2. The Natural Health Products Directorate (NHPD) has changed its name to the Natural and Non-prescription Health Products Directorate (NNHPD) (Health Canada, 2014).

effect in Canada on January 1, 2004, the manufacture, sale, and importation of NHPs is subject to regulation if they are sold in Canada (Andrews & Boon, 2005). This was a critical development since many consumers and even some practitioners believe that NHPs are always safe, no matter how they are used (Smith & Marles, 2003).

The recognition of the growing use of CAM and NHPs has led policy-makers and conventional health-care practitioners to define these therapies and practices as an important issue for health-care systems. Among the concerns are how to regulate CAM professions and natural health products, how best to incorporate CAM treatments with conventional medicine, and how to protect the public from a wide range of possible CAM-conventional medicine interactions (Boon et al., 2006).

Who Uses CAM?

CAM use varies by factors such as gender, age, education, income, and number of chronic illnesses (de Bruyn, 2002; McFarland et al., 2002; Millar, 2001; Park, 2005). Surveys suggest that women are more likely to consult CAM practitioners even when other factors are taken into account (Keshet & Simachai, 2014; Kristoffersen et al., 2014). There is also a gender difference in terms of which types of practitioners are consulted: holistic spiritualities and mind-body interventions, for example, are more frequently sought out by women consumers (Keshet & Simachai, 2014). While both women and men were equally likely to have visited a chiropractor, a much greater percentage of women report consulting other alternative practitioners (Millar, 2001; Park, 2005). This gender difference in CAM use may be explained in part by women's unique physiology and reproductive roles. A significant number of pregnant women, for example, use CAM modalities such as massage, herbal medicine, and relaxation therapies (Hall et al., 2011). However, Keshet and Simachai suggest that gender differences in usage reflect gender patterns of health behaviour in general. Women have been taught to be more health-conscious and are likely to read more health-care magazines where CAM and NHPs are discussed. In general, many users of CAM do not discuss their use with their primary care physicians (Metcalfe et al., 2010; Thomson et al., 2014).

Besides gender, other variables that differentiate CAM users are education, income, age, geographic location, and the existence of a chronic condition. People between the ages of 25 and 64, with a university education and in the highest income groups, are more likely to consult CAM practitioners (Park, 2005). This group of people are more likely to be in the paid labour force and therefore have some disposable income or a supplementary private medical plan that would cover some of the costs of CAM. This can be a critical determinant in CAM use, since, in Canada, provincial health plans do not cover the cost of most CAM treatments.[3] In 2003, for example, 26 per cent of individuals in the highest income groups compared to only 13 per cent in the lowest income group saw a CAM practitioner (Park, 2005). Use is much higher in Western provinces—British Columbia, Alberta, Saskatchewan, and Manitoba—than in the Atlantic region. Between 3 and 9 per cent of people in the Atlantic region consulted complementary and alternative health-care practitioners compared to 21 to 25 per cent in the Western provinces (Millar, 2001). Different

---

3. There is variation among the provinces as to which, if any, CAM services are covered by public health insurance (CIHI, 2005, p. 117).

regulatory policies and different provincial health-care plans as well as ethnocultural factors may account for some of the difference (Millar, 2001; Park, 2005).

Conventional medicine is successful in dealing with acute illness, but it does not have cures or solutions for most chronic conditions, including chronic pain. Thus, it is not surprising that individuals with chronic conditions are more likely to be frequent users of CAM (Millar, 2001, p. 17). A Toronto study, for example, found that 78 per cent of people with HIV/AIDS had used some form of complementary therapy (Canadian AIDS Society, 1995, cited in Pawluch et al., 2000). There is also increasing use of CAM among cancer patients (Hilbers & Lewis, 2013). And, a recent Canadian survey found that CAM use was significantly higher for those with asthma and migraine than the general population (Metcalfe et al., 2010). Research by Fries (2014) indicates that older people may turn to CAM as a way of dealing with what is often considered "age-related" health issues, including various chronic conditions. His work supports the findings of other research that "baby boomers' self-care behaviour includes the use of CAM therapies" (p. 2).

Conventional Medicine's Response

Conventional medicine has responded in various ways to the growing popularity of CAM. Although historically biomedical doctors were skeptical of CAM practitioners—labelling them as poorly trained quacks—physicians today in Western countries are increasingly both tolerant of and interested in CAM. A systematic review of 25 surveys, for example, found that roughly half of physicians believe in the value of at least one modality of CAM. The study revealed that 43 per cent of physicians make referrals for acupuncture, 40 per cent for chiropractic, and 21 per cent for massage (Hirschkorn & Bourgeault, 2005). A recent study of American hospitals found that 42 per cent offered at least one complementary or alternative therapy in 2010 (Fallis, 2012). In 2007, 83 per cent of American health-care workers used CAM to deal with their own health problems (Fallis, 2012). Although not quite to the same degree, the situation in Canada is also changing; for example, some physicians in British Columbia include acupuncture as part of their treatment. The Association of Canadian Medical Colleges has agreed to include CAM content in Canadian undergraduate medical education programs (Caron & Simpson, 2003). A survey of 16 Canadian medical schools in 1999 showed that most schools included CAM in their curricula via lectures as part of a required course (Huang, 2004); as well, recent interviews with academic and community physicians from five regions across Canada all indicated their support for including CAM instruction in medical schools as being important in training competent doctors (Mulkins et al., 2006). Since 2003, the medical school at Queen's University in Kingston, Ontario, has implemented a CAM Symposium, a full-day program with a series of lectures covering a range of CAM modalities (Huang, 2004). McMaster University in Hamilton incorporates on-site visits to alternative practitioners as part of its core curriculum (Deveau, 2010). The fact that a number of provinces in Canada have passed laws protecting physicians who practise alternative forms of medicine will increase the likelihood that more doctors will become involved with alternative therapies. The College of Physicians and Surgeons of Alberta has already created a system to register doctors who use alternative therapies if they have the required proof of proper training and education in the therapies (Silversides, 2002). New models of integrative health care that combine conventional medicine with CAM are being developed at two Canadian medical clinics (Boon & Kachan, 2008).

CAM's Search for Legitimacy

Some CAM associations are emulating the strategy of conventional doctors to achieve a recognized professional status. Chiropractic has been particularly successful in this: it has set up colleges to train and certify its practitioners and practises usurpatory **social closure** by limiting chiropractic to these certified chiropractors, which it has achieved with the support of private health insurers and the state (Dew, 2000; O'Neill, 1994, 1995). Today, there are over 8400 practising chiropractors in Canada, comprising one of the largest primary-contact health-care professions in the country. Chiropractic treatment is reimbursed generally by private health-insurance plans although there is some provincial health-plan coverage in two provinces: Manitoba and Saskatchewan. Like medicine, chiropractic is a self-regulating profession. Each province and the Yukon Territory have a Chiropractic Act that establishes a self-regulatory process, including extensive testing for licensure (Canadian Chiropractic Association, 2015). There are two accredited chiropractic schools in Canada, one in Ontario and one in Quebec, as well as five post-graduate speciality colleges where chiropractors can further advance their skills; most Canadians wishing to become a Doctor of Chiropractic attend schools in the United States. Increasingly, chiropractors are working complementarily as part of health-care teams in community centres and hospitals.

social closure
A term first used by Max Weber to describe the way that power is exercised to exclude outsiders from the privileges of social membership (in social classes, professions, or status groups).

Naturopathic medicine is also striving for professional recognition through social closure by working to formalize education and qualification standards and thereby limit access to a restricted group of eligible practitioners. Naturopaths, however, are trained in a wide range of therapeutic modalities, which makes it problematic for them to create clear professional boundaries, an important step in the professionalization process (Verhoef et al., 2006). Nonetheless, naturopathic medicine has gained formal recognition, including provincial/territorial regulation, in six Canadian provinces: British Columbia, Alberta, Saskatchewan, Manitoba, Ontario, and Nova Scotia. Other provinces and territories are actively pursuing regulation (Canadian Association of Naturopathic Doctors, 2015). Currently there are over 1876 licensed naturopathic doctors in Canada. While some private health-insurance companies reimburse patients a limited amount for naturopathic care, naturopathic treatment is not covered by provincial health plans. One of the challenges for naturopaths is to protect their profession from the services of lay natural practitioners and from a powerful biomedical system that is attempting to incorporate aspects of holistic health—e.g., acupuncture and biofeedback—into its own practice (Verhoef et al., 2006, p. 415).

naturopathic medicine
A form of alternative medicine that uses natural methods and substances, such as nutritional supplements, exercise, and homeopathy, to support the natural power of the body to establish, maintain, and restore health.

In a recent study, Canadian researchers (Toupin April & Gaboury, 2013) looked at the extent to which regulated Canadian CAM schools provided education and training that would be valued by conventional medicine. Their interviews with curriculum and program directors from schools in chiropractic, naturopathy, massage therapy, and acupuncture indicate that, although variable by school, CAM schools did offer traditional research methods courses, evidence based health-care training as well as opportunities for collaborative work with biomedical peers. Directors expressed interest in fostering inter-professional collaboration and working with academic researchers to "conduct high quality research" in order "to improve the quality of care they provide and facilitate the development and recognition of their profession" (p. 6).

Why Is Complementary and Alternative Medicine Increasingly Popular?

A simple survey of any undergraduate class is likely to find that a large majority of students have used some form of complementary and alternative health care or taken a natural health product in the past few years to treat an illness or injury or to promote well-being. You may have gone to a chiropractor or osteopath, had a massage or acupuncture, consulted a homeopath or naturopath, practised yoga or tai chi, or taken vitamins, herbal medicines, or nutritional supplements. CAM's popularity is indexed by the increasing number of people who are using alternative therapies, the increasing number of CAM therapists, the growing market for natural health products and medicines, and the increasing number of tertiary institutions offering training in various CAM therapies. It has been suggested for example that nearly 75 per cent of Canadians will use CAM in their lifetime and over 80 per cent of American health workers already do so (Deveau, 2010; Fallis, 2012). For a comparison of Canadian usage of CAM therapies, see Figure 16.1. A population-based survey in Australia found that nearly 20 per cent of people would try CAM *before* conventional medicine (Thomson et al., 2014). (For a survey of CAM usage in different countries, see Ernst & White, 2000).

Various explanations have been posited for the growing number of people who use complementary and alternative medicine: that it is a search for meaning, that people distrust science, that there is a dissatisfaction with conventional medicine, that healers offer a more personal relationship than doctors, that CAM gives people a feeling of control, and that many illnesses today are not easily treated by conventional medicine because they are chronic or terminal. However, there is no one single reason that can explain why people choose CAM.

The Search for Meaning

Health and illness are fundamental issues that all societies face. However, conventional medicine has no developed theory to explain illness except allopathy and the theory of germs. In Western society today, in which few become seriously ill through germs but in which many suffer from heart attack or cancer, such conventional explanations have little appeal. Even within the germ theory, there is no clear explanation of personal misfortune—for why one person gets ill in a flu epidemic and another stays healthy. Under these circumstances, alternative medical theories that explain illness in terms of spiritual forces (spiritualism), the balance of elements in the body (yin and yang, naturopathy), or the development of life force (homeopathy) have great appeal. Research shows that individuals who rate themselves as being "spiritual" are more predisposed to use CAM (Thomson et al., 2014).

Because of its holistic approach to health, CAM therapies can provide individuals with emotional and psychological support as well as give attention to physical concerns. Patients

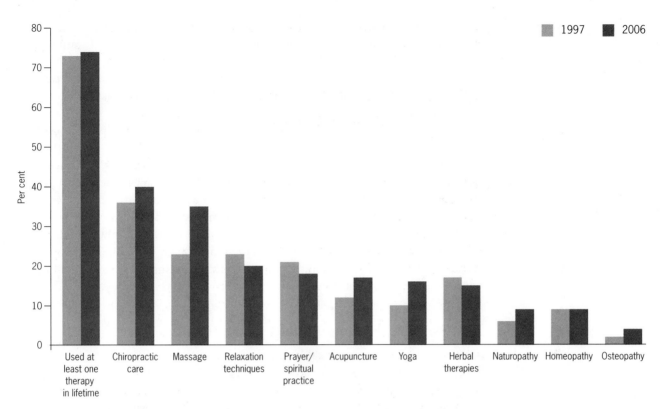

Figure 16.1 Percentage Use of Selected CAM Therapies in Canada in an Individual's Lifetime, 1997 and 2006

Source: Adapted from Esmail, N. (2007). Complementary and alternative medicine in Canada: Trends in use and public attitudes, 1997–2006. *Public Policy Sources, 87,* 16. Available at: www.fraserinstitute.org/uploadedFiles/fraser-ca/Content/research-news/research/publications/complementary-alternative-medicine-in-canada-2007.pdf

who are chronically ill speak of their positive experience with CAM in helping them heal emotionally and spiritually, an important dimension of well-being. This is well illustrated in Pawluch et al.'s (2000) research with AIDS patients. Patients told the researchers that their experience with CAM had been transformative and had led to personal growth. As a result, they embraced more philosophical and metaphysical concerns about the meaning of life and death rather than focusing on everyday survival. One patient put it this way: "It [AIDS] has saved my life. . . . My priorities are different. My whole life is different. I'm pretty sure I would have taken a different route if it hadn't been for this gift of AIDS in my life" (Pawluch et al., 2000, pp. 255–6). One explanation for why more women favour CAM practices is that "engagement with holistic spiritualities validates women's traditional work of relational care, and legitimates the work of emotional care" (Keshet & Simachai, 2014, p. 81).

Distrust of Science

Science has lost its gloss, and scientific medicine has declined in status along with it (Gray, 1999). Science is no longer seen as the solution but instead is frequently seen as part of

risk society
A term coined by Ulrich Beck (1992) to describe the centrality of risk calculations in people's lives in Western society.

the problem. The **risk society** (Beck, 1992) is obsessed with the risks created by scientific actions; the environment is seen to be under constant threat from global warming, oil spills, nuclear radiation, and acid rain, all of which are blamed on science and technology. Scientific medicine, moreover, has produced thalidomide as well as the bionic ear. The technological fix is increasingly mistrusted. For example, Fuschia Sirois and Mary Gick (2002) found that dissatisfaction with conventional medicine was one of the best predictors of overall and initial CAM use. Many pregnant women use CAM therapies because they are considered to be safe alternatives to pharmaceuticals (Hall et al., 2011, p. 823). Pawluch et al. (2000) found that their respondents described Western medicine as "dangerous," "powerful," and "toxic" (p. 257). They saw complementary therapies as less likely to have

iatrogenesis/iatrogenic
A concept popularized by Ivan Illich that refers to any adverse outcome or harm as a result of medical treatment.

iatrogenic consequences and fewer debilitating side-effects. Similarly, Fries (2014) found older adults' concern with the iatrogenic risk of biomedicalized health care—"Big Pharma and the medical industrial complex, which they viewed as antithetical to healthy aging care"—was an important factor in their decision to use CAM (p. 6). In other words, the increased popularity of CAM can be seen as a backlash against the perceived failings of science and biomedical interventions.

The Personal Healer–Patient Relationship

An important dimension of CAM is that its practitioners provide a personalized service. They spend time listening to their clients, obtain diverse information regarding diet, lifestyle, and social and personal relationships, and tailor their treatment to the individual client (Easthope, 1985; Lowenberg & Davis, 1994; Keshet & Simchai, 2014). CAM practitioners generally spend more time with patients and provide emotional support unlike conventional physicians. This is in keeping with their underlying philosophy of holism, which requires treating the whole person (York University Centre for Health Studies, 1999). The patient is also considered an active participant in the management of illness and the healing process, which potentially reduces power asymmetries between patient and practitioner (Nissen, 2011, cited in Keshet & Simchai, 2014, p. 82). For consumers, CAM's holistic approach to health is a welcome alternative to what is perceived as the more "dehumanized" approach of conventional medicine (Fries, 2014, p. 7). "Research indicates that feelings of trust, acceptance, empowerment, and being supported and cared for are key qualities that consumers feel distinguish CAM care from conventional care" (Williams-Piehota et al., 2011, p. 28).

The Search for Control over One's Life

postmodern society/ postmodernity
A disputed term in sociology that broadly refers to a society or social condition following modernity that is more fragmented, as tradition is replaced by a high level of social differentiation and cultural diversity.

In what is described as today's **postmodern society**, much of life is felt to be outside the control of the individual. In response, people often search for areas of control. The individualized and subjective understandings of health and disease promoted by CAM are congruent with postmodernity. People are exhorted to live a healthy lifestyle—that is, to manage and control their physical and spiritual bodies through physical activity, relaxation therapies, healthy eating, using natural herbal supplements or other alternative therapies. Sirois & Gick (2002) found, for example, that the most frequently endorsed reason for people using CAM is that it allowed them to take a more active role in their health

(p. 1032). It has been suggested that this emphasis on self-care and individual responsibility for health—what some have termed "healthism"—is consistent with neo-liberal strategies for the governance of population health (Fries, 2014, p. 9). CAM practitioners help people to manage their own disease by giving them the ability to reconstruct themselves. For example, Fries (2014) found that a primary reason older adults seek out CAM is to gain individual control over their aging bodies and health. The potential of CAM to help people transform their lives is clearly illustrated in the interviews Pawluch et al. (2002) conducted with AIDS patients. For some CAM users, self-care is a central means for the expression of one's embodied identity (Fries, 2013). One of Fries' interviewees, a 50-year-old, university educated female CAM user summarized her experience this way: in addition to improved health "I feel like I'm more in control of my health and life" (Fries, 2013, p. 46). In other words, using CAM becomes for some a lifestyle choice and a form of identity.

The Nature of Illness

People with certain chronic conditions are more likely to consult CAM practitioners than those without (Simpson, 2003; Sirois & Gick, 2002). The success of environmental controls over sewage and water—coupled with immunization, vaccination, and antibiotics—has meant that most illness in modern societies is either chronic or terminal. However, the knowledge base and organizational structure of conventional medicine is generally not well suited to treat chronic illnesses, which require long-term, intermittent intervention rather than one-stop cures. Having comorbid chronic conditions is a key factor in motivating individuals to use CAM (Sirois, 2008a). See Table 16.2 for an example of CAM usage among those with different conditions. In a comparison of consumers who used CAM, Sirois (2008b) found that two-thirds of survey respondents in 2005 (both those with chronic conditions and those without) reported that they felt that conventional treatments were not effective for treating their health problem. Respondents in a Swedish study indicated they turned to CAM to treat their bowel disease because of their concerns with the side effects of pharmaceuticals and because conventional treatment failed to produce the desired effect (Lindberg et al., 2014, p. 3). The plethora of research studies that examine CAM use among individuals with specific chronic conditions, including cancer, diabetes, arthritis, asthma, Crohn's disease, hypertension, and heart disease, clearly indicate a growing interest in CAM use among those with a chronic illness as suggested by Lindberg et al. (2014). This is hardly surprising given that those with chronic conditions generally have more health problems and more unmet health needs.

As we have seen, users of CAM cannot be treated simply as a homogenous group with similar beliefs, motivations, and needs. In the words of Pawluch et al. (2000), "there is no simple explanation for the appeal of complementary therapies. The picture is too complex and varied. . . . Individuals are attracted to these therapies for a variety of reasons" (p. 262). Some worry about the dangers of medical interventions and prefer alternative medicine because it is seen as drug-free and natural; some are attracted to the individualized nature of CAM; others may be seeking control over their health-care and treatment decisions. Still others look to CAM as a positive choice that offers a natural, holistic approach and a sense of individual responsibility. The meanings that individuals ascribe to CAM are shaped by individuals' social character and change over time.

Table 16.2 Use of Alternative Therapy for the 10 Most Frequently Reported Principal Medical Conditions, 2006

Condition	Per cent Reporting Condition	Per cent Using Alternative Therapy in Past 12 Months*	Per cent Who Saw a Provider in Past 12 Months*	3 Most Commonly Used Alternative Therapies
Allergies	29	62	34	Massage Therapies, Prayer, Relaxation Techniques
Back or Neck Problems	28	71	47	Massage Therapies, Chiropractic Care, Prayer
Arthritis or Rheumatism	21	61	31	Prayer, Massage Therapies, Chiropractic Care
Difficulty with Routine Walking	17	64	39	Prayer, Massage Therapies, Chiropractic Care
Frequent Headaches	14	70	41	Prayer, Massage Therapies, Relaxation Techniques
Lung Problems	13	63	33	Prayer, Relaxation Techniques, Massage Therapies
Digestive Problems	11	64	39	Prayer, Massage Therapies, Relaxation Techniques
Gynecological Problems	9	66	40	Massage Therapies, Relaxation Techniques, Prayer
Anxiety Attacks	9	72	45	Relaxation Techniques, Prayer, Massage Therapies
Heart Problems or Chest Pain	7	60	30	Prayer, Relaxation Techniques, Massage Therapies

*Percentages are of those who reported the condition. Provider denotes a provider of care who is not a medical doctor.

Source: Adapted from Esmail, N. (2007). Complementary and alternative medicine in Canada: Trends in use and public attitudes, 1997–2006. *Public Policy Sources, 87,* 24. Available at: www.fraserinstitute.org/uploadedFiles/fraser-ca/Content/research-news/research/publications/complementary-alternative-medicine-in-canada-2007.pdf

Does Alternative Medicine Work?

The question of whether CAM works is much more complex than it would at first appear. An intervention by a practitioner can be said to work in three analytically distinct ways (although these ways often overlap empirically):

1. It changes the relationship of individuals to their afflictions so that they feel more comfortable, suffer less pain, and are able to manage their normal daily lives.
2. It produces a clinically observable change in a set of symptoms.
3. It produces a change in a set of symptoms that is scientifically demonstrated to be a function of the intervention.

These three ways of working can be observed in both alternative and conventional medicine. Only a small proportion of conventional medical interventions—estimated as 15 per cent (Coleman, 1994)—have been scientifically tested via **randomized control trials (RCTs)**, and the Cochrane collaboration (Berman et al., 2000) reports that only 21 per cent of conventional medicine's practices have a clearly positive effect. However, an even smaller proportion of complementary and alternative practices have been scientifically tested. Let us look at each of these three ways of working in turn, focusing solely on CAM, and speculate on how CAM works in each instance.

With regard to the first measure, that is, whether the individual's relationship to his or her affliction is changed, there are clear indications that CAM can be effective. Emerging evidence suggests that CAM users report feelings of empowerment, body awareness, improved quality of life, and better coping strategies for dealing with their illness (Eaves et al., 2015). Pawluch et al. (2000), for example, found that AIDS patients' experience with CAM had been transformative, providing them with the tools to re-frame the meaning of their life. It is also argued that CAM therapies are instrumental in helping individuals become aware of the interconnections among body, mind, and lifestyle, thus leading individuals to change their health behaviours. In this respect, CAM providers are considered agents of health-behaviour change (Williams-Piehota et al., 2011).

There is little doubt that, in terms of clinical efficacy, many CAM healing practices work. Why they work is sometimes unclear, but that is equally true of many conventional healing practices. Two possible explanations of such clinical efficacy have been advanced: the **placebo effect** and the operation of social support (including the activation of the immune response through such support).

The placebo effect is any therapeutic practice that has no clear physiological effect but that nevertheless has an effect on the patient: pain and other symptoms go away (Sugaring the Pill, 1996). Work on the placebo response has demonstrated that the key features that produce a placebo effect are a feeling of uncertainty in the patient coupled with trust in the authority of the healer. People go to a health-care provider—conventional or alternative—when they are uncertain of their own diagnosis and prognosis and are seeking expert advice and aid. When that individual presents as an authoritative person who gives them personal attention and who is, therefore, someone that patients feel they can trust, a placebo response is very likely. Most alternative practitioners, and many conventional practitioners, present themselves in precisely this way (Easthope, 1985). However, meta-analyses of clinical interventions using acupuncture, herbal remedies, manual therapies, and nutritional therapies have found they are more effective for certain conditions than placebos are—for example, echinacea for relief of cold symptoms (Barrett et al., 1999) and acupuncture for post-operative nausea (Berman et al., 2000). A recent large study of cardiovascular in-patients found that using certain CAM treatments (bodywork, mind–body and energy therapies, traditional Chinese medicine) as part of integrative medicine showed statistically significant decreases in pain and anxiety (Johnson et al., 2014). A placebo response is consequently not an adequate explanation for the success of some CAM therapies.

Social support has been proven to be an important variable in illness. It has been implicated in the sociological view of the *causes* of affliction since Émile Durkheim (1951/1897) demonstrated in 1897 that apparently individual acts of suicide produced suicide rates that varied according to the levels of such support (what he called "social solidarity"). A similar finding was made in a comparative analysis of modern societies (Wilkinson, 1996), which found that social cohesion is a central factor in producing good health for populations. An extensive summary of the literature argued that "social

randomized control trials (RCTs)
A biomedical research procedure used to evaluate the effectiveness of particular medications and therapeutic interventions that privileges biomedical over social responses to illness.

placebo/placebo effect
Any therapeutic practice that has no clear clinical effect. In practice, it usually means giving patients an inert substance to take as a medication.

social support
The support provided to an individual by being part of a network of kin, friends, or colleagues.

risk factors
Conditions that are thought to increase an individual's susceptibility to illness or disease, such as abuse of alcohol, poor diet, and smoking.

relationships, or the relative lack thereof, constitute a major **risk factor** for health—rivaling the effects of well-established risk factors such as cigarette smoking, blood pressure, blood lipids, and lack of physical activity" (House et al., 1988, p. 541). It is now also becoming clear that social support may be implicated in the *relief* of affliction. A recently completed meta-analysis of 87 studies on the associations of perceived social support, network size, and marital status with cancer survival concluded that high levels of perceived social support and large social networks reduced the risk for mortality in cancer patients (Pinquart & Duberstein, 2010). Other studies of the survival rates of women with breast cancer also report that social support is an important variable (Maunsell et al., 1995; Waxler-Morrison et al., 1991). David Ornish, an American physician, uses social support (along with diet and exercise) in a regimen that produces changes in the hearts of his patients, which are demonstrable in angiograms (Ornish, 1990; Ornish et al., 1990). A biomedical, rather than a sociological, explanation of these effects is provided by **psychoneuroimmunology** (PNI) (see Vijoen et al., 2003). What the theory of PNI does is to reduce the social to the biological. Proponents of PNI argue that social effects cause changes in the immune system of individuals, and that these changes mean that people are less likely to become ill and more likely to recover when they are ill (see, for example, the study of HIV-positive men by Persson et al., 2002).

psychoneuroimmunology (PNI)
A study of the interaction between psychological (mental) processes and the body's nervous and immune systems, using an interdisciplinary approach that incorporates a number of scientific and medical disciplines.

As we have seen earlier in this chapter, an important feature of CAM for many users is precisely the intimate patient-practitioner relationship and the strong emotional support, caring, and encouragement that its practitioners are seen to provide.

To date, there have been few scientific tests of alternative medicine. One reason for this is the different world view held by many CAM practitioners. Many are not concerned with cure but, rather, with healing and thus do not accept the scientific criteria of cure. Further, their strong emphasis on a holistic approach to illness and health means they are unwilling to treat groups of people in exactly the same way; this means that a treatment group cannot be compared with a control group to test a treatment's efficacy. However, the Research Council on Complementary Medicine in the United Kingdom has argued that conventional randomized control trial methodologies can be used to assess alternative therapies (Berman et al., 2000; Mason et al., 2002); some such trials have been undertaken. The journal *Focus on Alternative and Complementary Therapies* (FACT) is using similar methods to the Cochrane collaboration to assess the clinical effectiveness of alternative therapies and medications. Recently, a randomized clinical trial in Canada to evaluate the effectiveness of naturopathic medicine in reducing the risk of cardiovascular disease showed that compared with a control group, participants who received naturopathic care had a statistically significant reduced adjusted 10-year cardiovascular risk (Seely et al., 2013). The authors conclude that the addition of naturopathic care to enhanced usual care may reduce the risk of cardiovascular disease among high risk patients. Now that "integrative medicine (IM)" models are increasingly being employed in various health-care settings, it is possible there will be more "scientific" evidence about the efficacy of CAM.

Integrative Medicine

Among both conventional and CAM practitioners, attention has shifted away from separating therapeutic practices into being either biomedical or alternative toward a focus on merging diverse modalities into a new integrative health system (Boon & Kachan,

2008; Hollenberg, 2006). This is in keeping with a shift in contemporary health-care practice towards a more holistic view of health such that medicine and/or therapies combine approaches to support physical, social, psychological, and spiritual well-being (Hilbers & Lewis, 2013, p. 52). This growing trend, which is occurring globally, has led to the creation of a hybrid, termed **integrative medicine** or **integrative health care** (Possamai-Inesedy & Cochrane, 2013, p. 65). The move towards integrative health care is especially strong in Canada, the US, and the UK, particularly within oncology services (Hilbers & Lewis, 2013, p. 58). According to Johnson et al. (2014, p. 2), integrative medicine includes the use of CAM therapies, such as massage, acupuncture, and mind-body therapies, in conjunction with conventional medicine with a focus on healing and treating the "whole person." Fundamental to integrative medicine "is the concept of a health-care model that aspires to be client-centred and holistic, with focus on health rather than disease as well as mutual respect among peer practitioners" (Templeman & Robinson, 2011, p. 84). See Seely et al. (2013); Walji et al. (2010); and Johnson et al. (2014) for some recent examples of integrative health care.

> **integrative medicine/ integrative health care**
> Generally refers to health practitioners with different backgrounds and training working together, although the precise meaning is contested.

In Canada, as elsewhere, examples of integrative health care are evidenced in various institutional health-care settings (Deveau, 2010; Walji et al., 2010; Boon & Kachan, 2008; Seely et al., 2013). Both patients and clinicians feel that integrative medicine is the best way to provide optimal health care (Boon & Kachan, 2008; Deveau, 2010). Furthermore, research at different integrative health-care clinics in Canada suggests that despite some problems and limitations, integrative medicine does work (Boon & Kachan, 2008; Hollenberg, 2006; Walji et al., 2010). The success of this approach depends on a number of factors, including having credible champions to facilitate programs at an institutional level, having staff members who are receptive to different approaches, and developing trust and respect between the practitioners (Boon & Kachan, 2008). Yet, underlying tensions remain. In his study of two recently established integrative health-care clinics in Canada, Hollenberg (2006) found that biomedical physicians used exclusionary closure techniques and demarcationary strategies to maintain dominance in health care; similarly, CAM practitioners used usurpatory strategies by evoking esoteric knowledge and credentialism to increase their status.

Important questions are being raised, however, about the epistemological incompatibilities between CAM and conventional medicine and the underlying motives for integration. As sociologists have noted, integration may in fact be more about strategic co-option of certain CAM procedures and technologies than the coming together of CAM and biomedicine. Questions are raised about the extent of the integration as well as the impact on CAM—such as appropriation and marginalization (Possamai-Inesedy & Cochrane, 2013, p. 66). Drawing on an anti-colonial analysis of integrative health-care settings in Canada, Hollenberg and Muzzin (2010) suggest that the continued dominance of the biomedical paradigm results in the devaluing of other knowledges and paradigms, which poses a major challenge for achieving an equitable integrative medicine. As Kaptchuk and Miller (2005, p. 289, cited in Hollenberg & Muzzin, 2010, p. 35) ask, "Whose worldview is expressed in 'integrative medicine'? Whose worldview is excluded? . . . Who decides? On what basis are decisions made between competing worldviews and standards of evidence?" Hollenberg and Muzzin suggest that what is in fact happening in integrative medicine is paradigm appropriation and assimilation by biomedicine: CAM modalities are adopted in a piecemeal way, with disregard for the healing systems or traditions on which these modalities rest. For example, the technique of medical acupuncture is widely practised by biomedical practitioners without understanding or appreciating the paradigm on which it is based. "Acupuncture, understood in traditional Chinese medicine as stimulating the flow of Qi along the body's meridians to resolve Qi obstruction and to promote healing, becomes instead in biomedicine as the stimulation of cells to release pain-relieving endorphins" (p.49). It is argued, in other words, that certain individual aspects of CAM are appropriated from their original context in a way that increases their compatibility with the biomedical model.

Conclusion

CAM remains an important issue for the health-care system. The high rates of CAM use among a diverse group of people attest to its growing popularity. It has also been suggested that consumers are driving the growth of integrative medicine. More biomedically trained doctors are incorporating alternative treatment modalities into their practice of medicine, referring patients to CAM practitioners, or working with CAM practitioners in integrative ways to manage chronic illness. In response to this interest, most medical schools in Canada incorporate education about CAM into their curriculum. "Canada is home to some of the path-breaking researchers of CAM" and increasingly more researchers are using a variety of disciplinary perspectives and methods to study CAM in the medical, health professional, and social sciences (Andrews & Boon, 2005, p. 25). The recent establishment of the Canadian Interdisciplinary Network for Complementary and Alternative Medicine Research (IN-CAM), funded by the Canadian Institutes for Health Research (CIHR), reflects both government support and priorities.

Questions remain as to the primary motives for medical integration. Some have suggested that conventional doctors are looking to CAM therapies to re-establish their role, which is being eroded by increased competition for patients and the development of corporate medicine backed by the state (Strasser, 1992; White, 2000). In the marketplace for medical treatment, as in the commercial marketplace, one way to deal with the opposition is to mount a takeover bid (Saks, 1994). Nurses, too, have seen advantages in adopting CAM modalities: the emphasis on care rather than cure, which is a major aspect of CAM, is a means of extending their professional role (Adams & Tovey, 2004). Where the market is the primary driving force, there has been considerable convergence, with most natural health products/alternative medicines now produced by conventional pharmaceutical companies (Collyer 2004).

Sociologists have increasingly explored the lived experiences of CAM users and the complexities of CAM usage in a range of disease contexts. There is still a need for more research examining the role of gender, class, and ethnicity in shaping experience of CAM, but it seems clear that CAM achieves certain things often not "done well" in biomedicine. This includes recognizing the subjectivity of health and illness, the importance of the therapeutic relationship, and the utility of allowing people to have a sense of agency and control over their illness. It is also important to acknowledge and interrogate the limitations of CAM as well as conventional medicine. Equally we need to critically analyze integrative medicine.

Summary

- Conventional medicine is dominant as a result of better organization, its exclusionary practices, and ability to gain state legitimation.
- Different epistemologies inform CAM and conventional medicine.
- From a sociological perspective, CAM is a constructed entity that varies historically and culturally.
- Key characteristics of CAM modalities are its holistic approach, the intimate nature of the patient-practitioner, an emphasis on agency, the promotion of well-being, and acknowledgement of subjectivity.
- CAM usage varies by factors such as gender, age, geographic location, income, and the presence of chronic illness.
- Many conventional doctors are incorporating some CAM modalities in their practices, although a significant number continue to resist CAM as being "unscientific."
- The popularity of CAM is related to people's search for meaning, its congruence with postmodernity, the emphasis on agency in health care, the growing skepticism of science, CAM's holistic approach, and the failure of conventional medicine to adequately deal with chronic illness.
- There is a growing movement towards integrative medicine, which combines conventional and alternative modalities, although questions are being raised about the possibility of this happening in an equitable manner, given biomedical dominance.

Key Terms

allopathy

apothecary

biomedicine/biomedical model

conventional medicine

complementary and alternative medicine (CAM)

holistic/holism

homeopath/homeopathy

iatrogenesis/iatrogenic

integrative medicine/ integrative health care

naturopathic medicine

placebo effect

postmodern society/ postmodernity

psychoneuroimmunology

randomized control trials (RCTs)

risk factors

risk society

social closure

social support

state

Sociological Reflection: Alternative, Conventional, or Integrative?

- Have you ever used CAM therapies? Why or why not?
- Are there certain CAM therapies that you would never use? Why or why not?
- Are there any health-related issues for which you would only consult a biomedical doctor? Why or why not?
- Would you choose to go to an integrative health clinic over more traditional options if one were available? Why or why not?

- Is the process of convergence between conventional medicine and CAM an example of social closure to protect medical dominance or an indication of a more patient-focused medical practice?

Discussion Questions

1. To what extent does CAM individualize notions of health and illness by promoting self-care and healthy lifestyles? What are the implications of this?
2. CAM therapies are used more frequently by people who have good incomes and, therefore, can afford to pay the fees. Should the government subsidize some CAM practices so that people on low incomes can use them? If so, which practices should be subsidized, and why?
3. Why are natural health products so popular today? Is the Canadian government doing an adequate job of regulation?
4. Should treatments be provided to patients only if there is scientific evidence of their efficacy? What constitutes "evidence" and who should decide this?
5. Does CAM provide therapies that could be adopted by nurses or other health workers to improve their practice? If so, which therapies would be most useful?
6. Why are more people using CAM therapies today? Will its popularity continue?
7. Do integrative health-care clinics provide better patient care than either conventional medicine or CAM used alone? Why?

Further Investigation

1. Compare any one complementary and alternative medical therapy (e.g., acupuncture) with any one conventional therapy (e.g., fixing a broken wrist). When making your comparison, examine the mode of diagnosis, the role of technology in treatment, the types of therapists involved in treatment, and the institutions in which treatment occurs.
2. Compare and contrast the way conventional medicine and CAM are portrayed in the media. Make comparisons in only one type of media (television, radio, newspapers, or magazines).

Further Reading

Adams, J., Magin, P., & Broom, A. (Eds.). (2013). *Primary care and complementary and integrative medicine: Contemporary practice and research.* London: Imperial College Press.

Collyer, F. (2004). The corporatisation and commercialisation of CAM. In P. Tovey, G. Easthope, & J. Adams (Eds.), *The mainstreaming of complementary and alternative medicine.* London, UK: Routledge.

Hollenberg, D. (2006). Uncharted ground: Patterns of professional interaction among complementary/alternative and biomedical practitioners in integrative health care settings. *Social Science & Medicine, 62*, 731–44.

Hollenberg, D., & Muzzin, L. (2010). Epistemological challenges to integrative medicine: An anti-colonial perspective on the combination of complementary/alternative medicine with biomedicine. *Health Sociology Review, 19*(1), 34–56.

Kelner, M., Wellman, B., Boon. H, & Welsh, S. (2004). Responses of established health-care to the professionalization of complementary and alternative medicine in Ontario. *Social Science & Medicine, 59*, 915–30.

Keshet, Y., & Simchai, D. (2014). The "gender puzzle" of alternative medicine and holistic spirituality: A literature review. *Social Science & Medicine, 113*, 77–86.

Sirois, F. (2008). Motivations for consulting complementary and alternative medicine practitioners: A comparison of consumers from 1997–8 and 2005. *BMC Complementary and Alternative Medicine, 8*(16) www.biomedcentral.com/content/pdf/1472-6882-8-16.pdf

Williams-Piehota, P., Sirois, F., Bann, C., Isenberg, K., & Walsh, E. (2011). Agents of change: How do complementary and alternative medicine providers play a role in health behavior change? *Alternative Therapies in Health and Medicine, 17*(1), 22–30.

York University Centre for Health Studies. (1999). *Complementary and alternative health practices and therapies—A Canadian overview*. Prepared for Health Promotion and Programs Branch, Health Canada.

Web Resources

CAM Networks: Research Council for Complementary Medicine
www.rccm.org.uk/node/204

Canadian College of Naturopathic Medicine (CCNM)
www.ccnm.edu

Canadian Interdisciplinary Network for Complementary & Alternative Medicine Research (IN-CAM)
www.incamresearch.ca/index.php?home &lng=en

International Society for Complementary Medicine Research (ISCMR)
www.iscmr.org

Canadian Chiropractic Association (CCA)
www.chiropractic.ca/

National Center for Complementary and Integrative Health (NCCIH)
http://nccih.nih.gov/

Health Canada: Natural Health Products
www.hc-sc.gc.ca/dhp-mps/prodnatur/index-eng.php

The Society of Homeopaths
www.homeopathy-soh.org/

CONCLUSION

Jennie Hornosty

> Freedom is not merely the chance to do as one pleases; neither is it merely the opportunity to choose between set alternatives. Freedom is, first of all, the chance to formulate the available choices, to argue over them—and then, the opportunity to choose. . . . The future is what is to be decided—within the limits, to be sure, of historical possibility. But this possibility is not fixed. . . .
>
> —C. Wright Mills, *The Sociological Imagination* (1959, p. 174)

Issues of health, illness, and health care are of central concern to Canadians, both at an individual and a societal level. In this book, we have provided you with an introduction to health sociology and with a sample of the diversity of topics and approaches that comprise the general field. The three introductory chapters introduced you to the social model of health, including the social determinants and different theoretical approaches, concepts, and methodologies sociologists use to study health, illness, and health care. The first chapter set the foundation for understanding and applying a sociological analysis to health-related issues; we introduced you to what C. Wright Mills (1959) calls "the sociological imagination," an analytical framework for understanding the relationships between individual experience, social structure, and history. The interrelationship between structure and agency as components of human life is emphasized. This entails a critical approach that looks at how our health and health-care systems are influenced by factors outside our immediate control, that is, social, economic, and political forces, yet does not lose sight of the fact that human beings, acting collectively, construct society.

Understanding how various types of social inequalities perpetuate health inequalities for individuals and social groups is the focus in the five chapters that comprise Part 1. The approach taken here shows the importance of the social model of health as an alternative to conventional understandings of health and illness drawn from biomedical approaches. Many of the questions raised in this section have been guided by a critical political economy analysis that seeks to understand how our society is organized, and how it distributes material resources among its members, in order to explain how health inequalities are produced.

It is suggested that structured inequality produces inequality of conditions and differential opportunities and life chances, which in turn determines one's health status. The focus is on understanding the complexity of illness-inducing and health-enhancing environments by considering the social determinants of health, social contexts, environments, and social relations. The intersectionality of various social determinants—including social class, income, education, employment, early childhood, gender, Aboriginal status, racialization and social exclusion, as well as the environment in which one lives—are explored as having significant impacts on health.

In making the case that social inequality is a determinant in health status and experiences of health and illness, sociologists focus on socio-structural factors to explain why some groups in society live longer and healthier lives than others. However, this is not to suggest a type of social determinism whereby individuals are viewed as puppets. While a critical sociological perspective places individual behaviour, beliefs, and experiences in a social context, it acknowledges equally that it is people who bring about changes in society. The structure–agency debate introduced in Chapter 1 makes us aware of the interdependence of individuals and their social environments. To paraphrase Karl Marx, "people make their own history, but they do not make it as they please; they do not make it under self-selected circumstances, but under circumstances existing already, given and transmitted from the past" (Marx, 1869/1959, p. 320). The important message is that our social structures and institutions are human creations that are produced, reproduced, and changed by our actions or inactions.

In the three chapters that comprise Part 2, we looked at how aspects of human life are socially constructed; that is, the ways people actively make the societies in which they live and the ways they give meaning to their actions. Social determinants remain important but the focus is on the role of human agency in everyday life and how people perceive, understand, and respond to health- and illness-related events. Issues discussed in this part include the concept of medicalization, that is, how non-medical problems or behaviours once considered part of everyday life come to be defined and treated as medical issues; how disability and chronic illness are socially constructed; and how aging and dying are social processes.

In the final part of the book, we focused on questions related to the social organization and delivery of health care, and considered the role that values, power, and ideology have played in shaping our health-care systems and options. In each of the five chapters our aim was to understand why our health system is organized in a particular way and how it could be otherwise. The dominant influence of the medical profession on health policy, other health professions, and on health-care delivery is seen in four of the chapters. The power and influence of the pharmaceutical industry on health policy and drug approvals is explored in a separate chapter. While this section focused primarily on socio-structural factors in shaping health care, it also highlights the importance of human agency in bringing about institutional change. Canada's health-care system today is a product of individuals and groups challenging the hegemonic control of medicine over health-care delivery.

Future Trends

Health and health-care delivery remain an enduring societal concern. A great deal of health research in Canada today is funded by the Canadian Institute for Health Research (CIHR), a government agency created in 2000 that reports to the minister of health. An indication of CIHR's health research priorities is apparent in the 13 research networks (institutes) it has created to work on particular health issues. In addition to institutes with a biomedical focus, for example, genetics, cancer research, and circulatory and respiratory health (the three leading causes of death in Canada), there are research networks to address the societal, cultural, and environmental dimensions of health: for example, Aboriginal people's health, gender, and population and public health. Some concerns, however, have been raised that CIHR has pulled social health research toward neo-positivism and that social determinants of health research will become a form of epidemiology, lacking a critical social dimension. There is reason to believe that future research in health sociology will be influenced to a large degree by government priorities. Cutbacks in federal government funding for basic scientific research[1] and the targeting of new funding for projects considered "strategic" or that show commercial promise skews the direction of social science and health research; for example, away from fundamental explorations of illness and prevention (CAUT, 2013). While we already know about the importance of the social determinants of health in addressing health and illness issues, the challenge remains how to translate that knowledge into government priorities and action so as to address structural health inequalities. In Canada, we have seen a progressive dismantling of the social welfare state and the emergence of neo-liberal policies and priorities which are likely to produce greater health inequalities while putting the onus on individuals to take responsibility for their health. The potential effect of globalization and international trade agreements on health and illness is also of concern. The impact of these social forces in perpetuating inequalities and inequities, and their affect on health and health-care delivery as well as the Medicare debate will continue to be of major interest to critical health researchers working within a political economy tradition. Additional research is needed on the intersectionality of social determinants, especially within the context of racialized and other marginalized peoples. The dismal status of Aboriginal people's health needs serious attention, including a focus on how Aboriginal peoples can have greater input and control in health-care delivery that honours their cultural values and traditions. Environmental degradation and the health effects of such will continue to be an important research focus. Other important issues include the need to better understand the impact of an aging population, both in terms of provision of health services as well as building communities that allow the elderly to age at home. Given Canada's cultural and ethnic diversity, health sociology will need to explore further questions of meaning and different people's subjective experiences of illness. The role of technology and biomedicalization in health care is likely to be of increasing concern to health researchers. Importantly, to adequately understand and address health inequities future research needs to continue to move beyond the biomedical paradigm and expand the social model of health.

Critical Thinking and Developing Your Sociological Analysis Skills

As we have shown in our consideration of various health-related topics, thinking sociologically requires us to challenge beliefs that are taken for granted, as well as common-sense understandings of reality. The beginning point for a critical sociology is to ask the question "Why?" It is to wonder whether things could be otherwise; it frequently requires that we detach ourselves from the prevailing attitudes of the dominant groups to gain a level of understanding that goes beyond conventional perspectives. In other words, critical thinking asks us to engage with "the sociological imagination."

Much of government policy and funding priorities focuses on promoting lifestyle changes and making healthy choices to address what has been labelled the "obesity

---

1. Basic research refers to experimental and theoretical work where the primary aim is to acquire new knowledge rather than having as its primary focus a particular application for commercial purposes (CAUT, 2013, p. 6).

epidemic." Recent initiatives include proposed changes to nutrition labelling on packaged foods, new mobile education apps to help people follow suggested dietary intake and make healthy food choices, and an online initiative targeted at men to promote healthy habits. What will such programs *really* accomplish? What sorts of assumptions are being made in the above-mentioned initiatives about the reasons for poor health? Thinking critically, how might you tackle problems of poor nutritional health and unhealthy lifestyles? One might consider how social determinants of health such as food security, poverty, employment, social exclusion, and social environments generally affect individual behaviours. One could ask questions about whether all people have the same degree of choice about the foods they eat or the leisure and fitness activities in which they participate. We might equally ask if addressing issues of structured inequality might be a better (more effective) solution to address the health of populations. As C. Wright Mills (1959) argued, when something affects only one or two people, it is a "personal trouble" that can be addressed by individualistic approaches; however, when large groups of people are involved we need to look at the structure of society—its economic and political institutions—to find solutions. Looking at the issue differently, we might also ask whether there is indeed an "obesity epidemic", or whether part of what is occurring in the discourse is a particular framing of the "ideal body."

Another example where critical thinking would be helpful is in framing the current debate about privatization and for-profit health care. According to Dr Day, the owner of a privately owned surgery centre in Vancouver and a major spokesperson for private health care "There is nothing unethical about spending your own money on your own health care . . ." (Mickleburgh, 2010, p. A13). Supporters of Medicare, on the other hand, argue that the right to health care is an inalienable human right: that universal, publicly funded health care is a "moral enterprise, not a business venture" (The Honourable Roy Romanow, 2002). Using sociological analysis, how might you make sense of this debate? Are there underlying social factors—power, ideology, values, economic resources, etc.— that are driving the debate? Are there particular interests at stake? Can sociology be useful in helping you decide where you stand and what actions you will take in response to this controversy?

Final Thoughts

This second Canadian edition has introduced you to some of the key health issues that concern Canadians in the twenty-first century. It has also shown you how to think sociologically about health issues and social life in general. In a world where we are constantly bombarded with media images and simplistic slogans, we believe that the sociological perspective provides a sounding board for a critical analysis of health issues. By studying inequities and inequalities in health status and health care, a critical sociology helps us envision a different set of social arrangements. Using the sociological imagination helps us understand how we can construct the world differently to ultimately produce a qualitatively better and healthier life for all. Your task now is to use your newly acquired analytical skills to create this future.

Glossary

Aboriginal people Indigenous people in North America and their descendants generally.

acculturation A process by which newcomers to a country take on the values and behaviours of their host country.

acute illness An illness that develops quickly and is short-lived.

ageism A term, as with *sexism* and *racism*, that denotes discrimination but based on age.

agency The ability of people, individually and collectively, to influence their own lives and the society in which they live.

agribusiness Farming today is part of an integrated larger system that not only includes produce growers but also suppliers, distributors, and food manufacturers.

allopathic medicine Conventional biomedicine. Treatment of diseases is by drugs which have effects opposite to the symptoms.

allopathy Conventional medicine. Allopathy is the treatment of symptoms by opposites.

andropause An age-related decline in testosterone levels. It is often considered the male equivalent of menopause.

apothecary A historical name for a pharmacist, that is, someone who specialized in compounding and distributing medicines and herbs.

appropriate prescribing Favourable prescribing practices that include using medications only when they are the best type of treatment, selecting the correct medication, understanding the harms and benefits associated with the medication, prescribing it in the correct dose and for the right period of time, informing patients about the nature of their treatment, and monitoring patients to ensure that the drug is having a beneficial effect.

assimilate/assimilation Refers to the expectation that Aboriginal peoples and immigrants will give up their culture and become indistinguishable from the dominant Canadian majority.

assisted living Where individuals live somewhat independently in apartment units but receive assistance with meals, housekeeping, and personal health care.

association In statistical terms, means that there is a relationship between two items; however, the presence of an association does not prove a cause and effect.

autoethnography An ethnography that focuses on the experience of the researcher.

basic research The research phase where the basic discoveries are made about how cells function and about human physiology. This type of research lays the groundwork for further work in developing new molecules (drugs) that affect these functions.

biological determinism An unproven belief that individual and group behaviour and social status are an inevitable result of biology.

biomedicalization Increasingly complex, multi-sited, and multi-directional processes of medicalization.

biomedicine/biomedical model The conventional approach to medicine in Western societies, based on the diagnosis and explanation of illness as a malfunction of the body's biological mechanisms. This approach underpins most health professions and health services, which focus on treating individuals, and generally ignores the social origins of illness and its prevention.

biopsychosocial model An extension of the biomedical model. It is a multifactorial model of illness that takes into account the biological, psychological, and social factors implicated in a patient's condition. As with the biomedical model, it focuses on the individual patient for diagnosis, explanation, and treatment.

bodies Material constructs, usually talked about as physically separate from the environment but are here understood as shaped by the environment.

Canada Health Act An act passed by Parliament in 1984, which outlined the five principles of Canada's universal, government-funded health-care system.

Canada's Research-Based Pharmaceutical Companies (Rx&D) The association that represents the Canadian subsidiaries of the brand-name multinational companies operating in Canada.

capitalism An economic and social system based on the private accumulation of wealth.

Cartesian dualism Also called mind/body dualism and named after the philosopher Descartes, it refers to a belief that the mind and body are separate entities. This assumption underpins medical approaches that view disease in physical terms and thus ignore the psychological and subjective aspects of illness.

chronic illness An illness that is ongoing, often lasts a lifetime, and has no known cure.

class (or social class) A position in a system of structured inequality based on the unequal distribution of power, wealth, income, and status. People who share a class position typically share similar life chances.

clientele pluralism The relationship between an agency of the state and the industry that it is charged with regulating, whereby some of the authority of the state is transferred to the industry.

clinical drug trials Testing of drugs on humans. (See *human testing.*)

colonization/colonialism A process by which one nation imposes itself economically, politically, and socially upon another.

commodification of health Treating health as an object or commodity that can be purchased or marketed.

commodification of health care Treating health care as a commodity to be bought and sold in the pursuit of profit maximization.

complementary and alternative medicine (CAM) Refers to the diagnosis, treatment, and/or prevention that complements mainstream medicine and that satisfies a demand not met by conventional approaches and is not generally reimbursed by health benefit plans. *Complementary medicine* refers to forms of care that are not in opposition to, and often are provided together with, conventional medicine. *Alternative medicine* refers to care used instead of conventional medical care.

context Refers to the social, political, physical, and economic environment.

conventional medicine The medical practices and institutions developed in Europe during the nineteenth and twentieth centuries that are legally recognized by the state. Central to these practices is the teaching hospital, where all new doctors are inducted into laboratory science, clinical practice, and allopathic biomedicine. These practices and institutions are now dominant in all parts of the world. Conventional medicine is also referred to as orthodox medicine or allopathic medicine.

critical race theory A theoretical framework that posits racialization as a key structuring mechanism in society. Focuses on how socially constructed racial and ethnic categories are used to order groups in a way that disenfranchises and oppresses people. Goal is to not only understand inequities but to develop strategies to eliminate them.

culturally competent health care Delivery of health-care services in a way that recognizes the cultural beliefs and needs of those they serve.

deinstitutionalization A policy of moving patients in mental institutions out into community-based living arrangements and health centres. In theory, such policies are meant to be supported by extensive community resources to "break down barriers" and better integrate the mentally ill into the community.

demedicalization The reverse of medicalization—that is, when a behaviour once defined in medical terms is no longer defined as such.

deviance Behaviour or activities that violate social expectations about what is normal.

Diagnostic and Statistical Manual of Mental Disorders (DSM-IV) A manual published by the American Psychiatric Association that lists all mental health disorders for both children and adults. It also indicates causes, types of treatment, and prognosis.

dichotomies The distinctions made between two parts that are understood to be distinct and quite different.

diminished self The term that Charmaz (1983) uses to refer to the loss of a previously valued identity.

disabilities The social model of disabilities understands physical and mental limitations as primarily the result of social conditions while the medical model understands these limitations as primarily the result of bodies.

discourse A domain of language use that is characterized by common ways of talking and thinking about an issue (for example, the discourses of medicine, madness, or sexuality).

disease Refers to a biophysical condition diagnosed by a medical practitioner.

doctor/nurse game A concept coined by Stein (1967) to refer to the so-called game played out between doctors and nurses, whereby a nurse can be assertive and make suggestions about a patient without appearing to do so, so that nurses' suggestions are provided as prompts for doctors, who can act on them as though they were their own idea.

ecological model Derived from the field of human ecology, and when applied to public health, it suggests that an understanding of health determinants must consider the interaction of social, economic, geographic, and environmental factors.

economic rationalism/economic liberalism Terms used to describe a political philosophy based on small-government and market-oriented policies, such as deregulation, privatization, reduced government spending, and lower taxation.

education Formal schooling.

embodiment The lived experience of both being a body and having a body.

emotional labour Refers to the use of feelings by employees as part of their paid work. In health care, a key part of nursing work is caring for patients, often by providing emotional support.

empirical Describes observations or research that is based on evidence drawn from experience. Such research is, therefore, distinguished from something based only on theoretical knowledge or on some other kind of abstract thinking process.

endocrine disruptors They mimic natural hormones circulating in the body, either enhancing or blocking the production of these hormones.

environmental racism The notion that disadvantaged communities are disproportionately exposed to dangerous environmental health factors and disasters brought about by government and/or industrial policies.

epidemiology/social epidemiology The statistical study of patterns of disease in the population. Originally focused on epidemics, or infectious diseases, it now covers non-infectious conditions, such as stroke and cancer. Social epidemiology is a subfield aligned with sociology that focuses on the social determinants of illness.

ethnic group A group of people who not only share an ethnic background but also interact with each other on the basis of their shared ethnicity.

ethnicity Sociologically, the term refers to a shared cultural background, which is a characteristic of all groups in society. As a policy term, it is used to identify immigrants who share a culture that is markedly different from that of Anglo-Canadians. In practice, it often refers only to immigrants from non-English-speaking backgrounds.

ethnography A research method that is based on direct observation of a particular social group's social life and culture—of what people actually do.

euthanasia Meaning "gentle death," the term is used to describe voluntary death, often medically assisted, as a result of incurable and painful disease.

evidence-based medicine (EBM) An approach to medicine that maintains all clinical practice should be based on evidence from randomized control trials (RCTs) to ensure treatment effectiveness and efficacy.

extra-billing An arrangement that allowed doctors to charge patients over and above the set payment schedule for which the patient was not reimbursed.

feminism/feminist A broad social and political movement based on a belief in equality of the sexes and the removal of all forms of discrimination against women. A feminist is one who makes use of, and may act upon, a body of theory that seeks to explain the subordinate position of women in society.

feminization A shift in the gender base of a group from being predominantly male to being increasingly female.

First Nations Refers to all those people called "Indian."

Food and Drug Administration (FDA) The US equivalent of the Health Products and Food Branch.

Food and Drugs Act The federal legislation dealing with medicines.

food security A state that "exists when all people, at all times, have physical and economic access to sufficient, safe and nutritious food to meet their dietary needs and food preferences for an active and healthy life" (Agriculture and Agri-Food Canada, 1996).

functional prerequisites A debated concept based on the assumption that all societies require certain functions to be performed for them to survive and maintain social order. Also known as functional imperatives.

gastrointestinal medications Drugs for stomach and bowel problems.

gender Most frequently understood as "a multidimensional social construct that is culturally based and historically specific, and thus constantly changing" (Johnson, Greaves, & Repta, 2009, p. 6).

gender/sex Refers to the socially constructed categories of feminine and masculine (the cultural values that dictate how men and women should behave), as opposed to the categories of biological sex (female or male).

globalization Political, social, economic, and cultural developments—such as the spread of multinational companies, information technology, and the role of international agencies—that result in people's lives being increasingly influenced by global, rather than national or local, factors.

gross domestic product (GDP) The market value of all goods and services that have been sold during a year.

grounded theory Usually associated with qualitative methods, it refers to any social theory that is derived from (or grounded in) empirical research of social phenomena.

growth imperative Economic growth that is long term and sustained, supported by government policies that promote free markets.

Health Canada The federal department responsible for helping the people of Canada maintain and improve their health. Within Health Canada, the Health Products and Food Branch (HPFB) is responsible for drug, food, and consumer product safety. In the HPFB, there are four directorates dealing with medicines. The Therapeutic Products Directorate (TPD) approves and monitors prescription and non-prescription drugs derived from chemical manufacturing and medical devices. The TDP also is responsible for making the decision to remove drugs for safety reasons. The Biologics and Genetic Therapies Directorate (BGTD) is responsible for biological and radiopharmaceutical drugs, including blood and blood products, viral and bacterial vaccines, genetic therapeutic products, tissues, organs, and xenografts. The Marketed Health Products Directorate (MHPD) deals with the safety of products already approved for marketing. Finally, the Natural Health Products Directorate (NHPD) approves natural health products.

health promotion Any combination of education and related organizational, economic, and political interventions designed to promote individual behavioural and environmental changes conducive to good health, including legislation, community development, and advocacy. Draws attention to a variety of social determinants. See also *primary health care* and *public health*.

healthy immigrant effect The concept that newly arrived immigrants appear to have a health advantage but after a period of time their health status tends to converge toward that of the host population.

hegemony/hegemonic Dominance or power of one social group, idea, or discourse over another.

holistic/holism An approach to health that considers all aspects of an individual—physical, emotional, mental, social, spiritual, and lifestyle—as interrelated and must be treated as such.

homeopath/homeopathy Homeopathy is a system of natural medicine that uses micro-doses of natural remedies from the plant, animal, and mineral kingdom to stimulate the body's self-healing abilities. (What Is Homeopathy? 2009).

horizontal violence A concept derived from Paolo Freire that describes a behaviour common to all oppressed groups, whereby, because of their powerlessness, the oppressed are unable to direct their anger toward their oppressor and, as a result, turn it toward each other, with various degrees of violence and negativity.

Human Development Index (HDI) Provides a composite measure of three dimensions of human development: living a long and healthy life (measured by life expectancy), being educated (measured by adult literacy and gross enrolment in education), and having a decent standard of living (measured by purchasing power parity and income).

human testing The testing that a drug must go through before it can be approved for marketing in Canada (and virtually all other industrialized countries). In the first stage, drugs are tested in a small number of healthy people to determine the mechanism by which the drug works and to look at whether the number of side effects increases with higher doses. In the second stage, the drugs are tested in about 100–3000 people who have the disease in question in order to evaluate how well the drugs work and to determine side effects and risks. Finally, in stage three the drug is used in several hundred to several thousand people to gather the additional information about its efficacy and safety to more accurately determine the drug's harm-to-benefit ratio.

iatrogenesis/social iatrogenesis A concept popularized by Ivan Illich that refers to any adverse outcome or harm as a result of medical treatment.

ideal type A concept originally devised by Max Weber to refer to the abstract or pure features of any social phenomenon.

ideology In a political context, refers to those beliefs and values that relate to the way in which society should be organized, including the appropriate role of the state.

illness The subjective response to a disease.

immigrants First-generation immigrants are those who were born outside of Canada. Second generation refers to those who are Canadian-born and have at least one parent who was born outside Canada. Third generation or more are the offspring of Canadian-born parents (Statistics Canada, 2003).

Indian Act Sets out certain federal government obligations and regulates the management of Indian reserve lands, Indian monies, and other resources. The act defines an Indian as "a person who, pursuant to this Act, is registered as an Indian or is entitled to be registered as an Indian."

Indigenous peoples Used interchangeably with the term *Aboriginal peoples*.

individualism/individualization A belief or process supporting the primacy of individual choice, freedom, and self-responsibility.

inequities A term used instead of *inequality* because it implies injustice and because it does not imply the objective of treating everyone the same, as is implied by *equality*. Equitable treatment or conditions require recognizing differences and addressing them in ways that are socially just.

infant mortality Refers to the number of infants who die in the first year after birth per 1000 births.

institutional ethnography (IE) A feminist research strategy associated with Dorothy Smith combining theory and method. It begins from the standpoint of people in the actualities of their everyday world to show how people's social relations are organized by forces outside of them.

instrumental approach One in which a job is valued as a means to an end, not for its intrinsic worth.

integrative medicine/integrative health care Generally refers to health practitioners with different backgrounds and training working together, although the precise meaning is contested.

intersectionality A term coined by American critical race scholar, Kimberlé Chrenshaw in 1989 to examine how race and sex/gender were mutually constituted for African-American women. The idea that one needs to examine how various biological, cultural, and social categories interact on multiple (and often simultaneous) levels that lead to oppression and inequality.

Inuit Replaces the term *Eskimo* and refers to Aboriginal people who live primarily in Arctic Canada.

labelling theory Focuses on the effect that social institutions and professions (such as the police, the courts, and psychiatry) have in labelling (defining and socially constructing) behaviours and activities as deviant.

licensed practical nurses (LPNs) Nurses who assess patients and work in health promotion and illness prevention.

life chances Derived from Max Weber, the term refers to people's opportunity to realize their lifestyle choices, which are often assumed to differ according to their social class.

lifestyle choices/factors The decisions people make that are likely to impact on their health, such as diet, exercise, smoking, alcohol, or drug use. The term implies that people are solely responsible for choosing and changing their lifestyle.

lifetime risk of maternal death The probability that a 15-year-old female will die eventually from a maternal cause assuming that current levels of fertility and mortality (including maternal mortality) do not change in the future.

McDonaldization A term coined by George Ritzer to expand Weber's notion of rationalization; defined as the standardization of social life by rules and regulations, such as increased monitoring and evaluation of individual performance, akin to the uniformity and control measures used by fast-food chains. These principles are now applied to other sectors, both locally and globally.

manufacturers of illness Corporations who not only manufacture material goods and services—their products can also produce illness and death.

market failure The failure of the free-market system to produce results that are socially desirable due to the absence of a sufficient profit motive.

materialist analysis An analysis that is embedded in the real, actual, material reality of everyday life.

medical dominance The power of the medical profession in terms of its control over its own work, over the work of other health workers, and over health resource allocation, healthy policy, and the way that hospitals are run.

medical-industrial complex The growth of profit-oriented medical companies and industries, whereby one company may own a chain of health services, such as hospitals, clinics, and radiology and pathology services.

medicalization The process by which non-medical problems become defined and treated as medical issues, usually in terms of illnesses, disorders, or syndromes.

Medicare Canada's universal health-care program, which is funded and administered by federal, provincial, and territorial governments.

meta-analysis/meta-narratives The "big-picture" analysis that frames and organizes observations and research on a particular topic.

Métis People of mixed Aboriginal and European ancestry.

morbidity Rates of illness.

mortality Rates of death.

naturopathic medicine A form of alternative medicine that uses natural methods and substances, such as nutritional supplements, exercise, and homeopathy, to support the natural power of the body to establish, maintain, and restore health.

neglected diseases Diseases that occur in small numbers of people or in people with little to no purchasing power. In these cases the absence of sufficient sales (in dollar value) means that drugs for these illnesses will not be developed by profit-seeking companies.

neo-liberalism Economic policies and ideology that advocate a free market for the production and distribution of resources, an enhanced role for the private sector, and a reduction of government involvement in the economy.

new managerialism A term that arose in the 1980s to describe a shift in the transfer of power from professionals (i.e., doctors) to management. It encouraged the implementation of industrial techniques that emphasized the achievement of measurable objectives, continuous evaluation of performance against defined objectives, rationing of resources using effectiveness criteria, and surveillance of health professionals (Beardwood, 1999).

Nightingale tradition The view that nursing was a natural extension of women's role as caregivers; nurses were expected to be altruistic and to act with selfless dedication.

nurse practitioners (NPs) RNs with additional education qualifications and experience. They may order and interpret diagnostic tests, prescribe medications and other therapies.

Ottawa Charter for Health Promotion A 1986 document produced by the World Health Organization. It was launched at the first international conference for health promotion, held in Ottawa, Canada.

Participation and Activity Limitation Survey (PALS) A national survey designed to collect information on people whose activities are limited because of a condition or health problem.

participatory action research (PAR) A more activist approach to research whereby researchers work with local communities, social groups, or individuals to empower the group or its representatives. Often involves participants in formulating the research questions.

Patented Medicine Prices Review Board (PMPRB) A federal Canadian agency that sets a maximum introductory price for any new patented medicine that is marketed in Canada and also limits the rise in the price of patented medicines to the annual rate of inflation. The PMPRB has authority over prices as long as the medication has a valid patent.

patents Medicines typically have two different types of patents—a patent on the process used to make them and a patent on the product itself. While a patent is valid, the company owning the product has the exclusive right to sell it. Patents are granted for a 20-year term from the date when the patent application is filed. Patent terms are the same worldwide except for a group of very poor countries.

patriarchy/patriarchal A system of power through which males dominate households. The term is used more broadly by feminists to refer to society's domination by patriarchal power, which functions to subordinate women and children.

Pharmaceutical Advertising Advisory Board (PAAB) An organization with membership from the medical and pharmacy professions, the generic and brand-name industry associations, consumer groups, and organizations representing both medical advertising agencies and medical publications. PAAB evaluates all print advertising directed to medical professionals before it appears in print.

pharmaceuticalization A complex socio-technical process whereby health "problems" are constructed as having pharmaceutical solutions which includes the successful mobilization of consumers wanting access to drugs.

placebo/placebo effect Any therapeutic practice that has no clear clinical effect. In practice, it usually means giving patients an inert substance to take as a medication. When a patient reacts to a placebo in a way that is not clinically explicable, this is called the "placebo effect."

political economy Focuses on how political, economic, and ideological factors influence the distribution of power and other resources in a society, which in turn shapes individual experience and state policies.

positivist research methodologies Research methods that attempt to study people in the same way that physical scientists study the natural world—by focusing on quantifiable and directly observable events. Such research methods focus on the collection of statistical data.

postmarketing surveillance All of the activities that are undertaken to monitor the safety and effectiveness of drugs once they have been approved for marketing.

postmodern society/postmodernity A disputed term in sociology that broadly refers to a society or social condition following modernity in which many of the key social institutions, including the state, unions, and professions, have lost their power to determine social outcomes as tradition is replaced by a high level of social differentiation and cultural diversity.

post-structuralism/postmodernism Often used interchangeably, these terms refer to a broad perspective that is opposed to the view that social structure determines human action, and instead emphasizes a pluralistic world view that explores the local, the specific, and the contingent in social life.

precautionary principle The principle of taking into account not just known risks, but also potential risks, even if the evidence for those potential risks is weak. In these circumstances, (e.g., a drug) the precautionary principle would say that the product should either not be marketed or should be marketed under significant restrictions.

prescreen A system where pharmaceutical companies submit their print advertising to PAAB and only use that advertising when PAAB has given its approval.

primary health care Both the point of first contact with the health-care system and a philosophy for delivery of that care.

principal–agent theory Proposes that there is a relationship between a principal, who has a task that needs to be performed, and an agent, who is contracted to do the task in exchange for compensation.

promotional activities All of the methods undertaken by pharmaceutical companies to increase the sales of their products. These include, but are not limited to, advertisements in medical journals, visits by pharmaceutical sales representatives to doctors' offices, medication samples left behind in doctors' offices, and television advertisements about diseases.

prove harm Scientific proof that a product is harmful.

Prozac A new type of medication (selective serotonin reuptake inhibitor [SSRI]) introduced in 1987 to treat depression.

psychoneuroimmunology (PNI) A study of the interaction between psychological (mental) processes and the body's nervous and immune systems, using an interdisciplinary approach that incorporates a number of scientific and medical disciplines.

public care Health care provided by health-care professionals in a public setting, such as a doctor's office or hospital. Public care is part of Canada's publicly funded, universal health-care insurance policy.

public health-care system Canada's universal, publicly funded health-care system.

public health/public-health infrastructure Policies, programs, and services designed to keep citizens healthy and to improve the quality of life. The focus is on enhancing the health status and well-being of the general population rather than just looking at the health of individual persons. *Public-health infrastructure* refers specifically to the institutions, buildings, and equipment necessary to ensure healthy living conditions for the population.

purposive sampling The selection of units of analysis to ensure that the processes involved are adequately studied, and where statistical representativeness is not required.

qualitative research Research that focuses on the meanings and interpretations of the participants.

quantitative research Research that focuses on the collection of statistical data.

"race" A term without scientific basis that uses skin colour and facial features to describe allegedly biologically distinct groups of humans. It is a social construction that is used to categorize groups of people and usually implies assumed (and unproven) intellectual superiority or inferiority.

racialized groups The term preferred by those who work with immigrants and refugees when talking about visible minorities.

The term captures the fact that certain groups are treated as inferior by the dominant group.

racism/racist *Racism* refers to a set of false beliefs that one racial group is naturally superior to another group based on biological differences. It perpetuates notions of cultural superiority and inferiority and is one basis for social exclusion and discriminatory practices against a group of people because of their physical and cultural characteristics.

randomized control trials (RCTs) A biomedical research procedure used to evaluate the effectiveness of particular medications and therapeutic interventions. Random refers to the equal chance of participants being in the experimental or control group (the group to which nothing is done and is used for comparison), and trial refers to the experimental nature of the method. It is often mistakenly viewed as the best way to demonstrate causal links between factors under investigation, but it privileges biomedical over social responses to illness.

rationalization The standardization of social life through rules and regulations. See *McDonaldization*.

reductionism The belief that all illnesses can be explained and treated by reducing them to biological and pathological factors.

refugees Individuals who flee their country of origin because of a fear of persecution for reasons of gender, sexual orientation, ethnicity, religion, political opinion, nationality, or membership in a particular social group.

registered nurses (RNs) Nurses who coordinate health care, deliver direct services, and support patients in their self-care decisions.

registered psychiatric nurses (RPNs) Nurses who provide services to patients whose primary-care needs relate to mental and development health. They plan, implement, and evaluate therapies and programs on the basis of psychiatric nursing assessments. They are regulated separately from other nursing professionals in four provinces.

relations of ruling A concept used by Dorothy Smith to refer to a complex of organized practices, including government, law, bureaucracy, professional organizations, educational institutions and discourses in texts, and objectified social relations with their gender subtext, that coordinate and organize the lives of individuals. In this mode of ruling, the particular actualities of peoples' everyday lives are abstracted and objectified into standardized forms of knowledge that in turn regulate, guide, and control their lives (Smith, 1987).

research methods Procedures used by researchers to collect and investigate data.

rigour A term used by qualitative researchers to describe trustworthy research that carefully scrutinizes and describes the meanings and interpretations given by participants.

risk assessment The process governments use to assess a chemical's potential for injury on humans and on the environment.

risk factors Conditions that are thought to increase an individual's susceptibility to illness or disease, such as abuse of alcohol, poor diet, and smoking.

risk management Taking the known risks and benefits of a drug into consideration before allowing it onto the market. Unless the product has serious known risks, the preference is to allow it to be sold.

risk/risk discourse *Risk* refers to "danger"; *risk discourse* is often used in health-promotion messages warning people that certain actions involve significant risks to their health.

risk society A term coined by Ulrich Beck (1992) to describe the centrality of risk calculations in people's lives in Western society, whereby the key social problems today are unanticipated hazards, such as the risks of pollution, food poisoning, and environmental degradation.

Royal Commission on Aboriginal Peoples (RCAP) Created by the Canadian government in 1991 to address economic, social, and political issues related to First Nations, Métis, and Inuit peoples in Canada. The commissioners held 178 days of public hearings, visited 96 communities, consulted dozens of experts, and commissioned research studies. They came up with hundreds of recommendations to address the inequities faced by Aboriginal peoples.

ruling class This is a hotly debated term used to highlight the point that the upper class in society has political power as a result of its economic wealth. The term is often used interchangeably with *upper class*.

self-regulation The process by which an industry is allowed to regulate its own behaviour.

sex Most frequently understood as "a multidimensional biological construct that encompasses anatomy, physiology, genes, and hormones, which together affect how we are labelled and treated in the world" (Johnson, Greaves, & Repta, 2009, p. 5); however, this book challenges the possibility of separating gender from sex.

sexual division of labour The nature of work performed as a result of gender roles. The stereotype is that of the male breadwinner and the female homemaker.

sickness The actions a sick individual takes, including taking on the sick role.

sick role A concept used by Talcott Parsons to describe the social expectations of how sick people should act and of how they are meant to be treated.

smart regulation Regulating in a way that enhances the climate for investment and trust in the markets such that the administrative burden is reduced for businesses.

social capital Social relations, networks, norms, trust, and reciprocity between individuals that facilitate co-operation for mutual benefit.

social closure A term first used by Max Weber to describe the way that power is exercised to exclude outsiders from the privileges of social membership (in social classes, professions, or status groups).

social cohesion The social ties that are the basis for group behaviour and integration. See *social capital*.

social construction/constructionism The socially created characteristics of human life based on the idea that people actively construct reality, meaning it is neither natural nor inevitable. Therefore, notions of normality/abnormality, right/wrong, and health/illness are subjective human creations that should not be taken as natural or universal.

social control Mechanisms that aim to induce conformity or at least to manage or minimize deviant behaviour.

social Darwinism The incorrect application of Charles Darwin's theory of animal evolution to explain social inequality by transferring his idea of "survival of the fittest" among animals to explain human inequality.

social death The marginalization and exclusion of elderly people from everyday life, resulting in social isolation.

social determinants of health The social and economic environments in which people live and determine their health. Examples of social determinants include housing, food security, job security, employment, working conditions, education, early life, income, "race," social class, gender, disability, Aboriginal status, health services, and the social safety net. The quality of these determinants is a reflection of how society is organized and how it distributes its economic and social resources.

social exclusion A process whereby some groups in society are denied access to material and social resources, thereby excluding their full participation in society. It produces inequality in outcomes.

social iatrogenesis *Iatrogenesis* is a concept popularized by Ivan Illich that refers to adverse effects caused by, or resulting from, medical treatment. *Social iatrogenesis* refers to the process by which biomedicine extends its domain over every stage of life. Illich talked about three dimensions of iatrogenesis: clinical, social, and cultural.

social institutions Formal structures within society—such as health care, government, education, religion, and the media—that are organized to address identified social needs.

social justice A belief system that gives high priority to the interests of the least advantaged.

social model of health Focuses on social determinants of health, such as the social production, distribution, and construction of health and illness, and the social organization of health care. It directs attention to the prevention of illness through community participation and social reforms that address living and working conditions.

social support The support provided to an individual by being part of a network of kin, friends, or colleagues.

social structure The recurring patterns of social interaction through which people are related to each other, such as social institutions and social groups.

socialism/communism *Socialism* is a political ideology with numerous variations but generally refers to the creation of societies in which private property and wealth accumulation are replaced by state ownership and distribution of economic resources. *Communism* represents a vision of society based on communal ownership of resources, co-operation, and altruism to the extent that social inequality and the state no longer exist. Both terms are often used interchangeably.

socialization The process of learning the culture of a society (its language, values, and customs), which shows us how to behave and communicate.

sociological imagination A term coined by C.W. Mills to describe the sociological approach to analyzing issues. We see the world through a sociological imagination, or think sociologically, when we make a link between personal troubles and public issues.

specific etiology The idea that there is a specific cause or origin for each specific disease.

state A collection of government and government-controlled institutions within a country, including parliament (government and opposition political parties), public-sector bureaucracy, judiciary, military, and police.

stigma A physical or social trait, such as a disability or a criminal record, that results in negative social reactions, such as discrimination and exclusion.

structure–agency debate A key debate in sociology over the extent to which human behaviour is determined by social structure.

Summary Basis of Decision A document that is released by Health Canada after it has approved a new drug. It outlines the scientific and benefit/risk-based reasons for Health Canada's decision to grant market authorization for a product.

systemic discrimination A form of discrimination that arises from the way that organizational structures, policies, practices, and procedures operate (unrelated to the requirements of the job), which, while appearing neutral, have a discriminatory effect on certain groups of people.

the self A concept used by George Herbert Mead to refer to a core identity. For Mead the self is a social product that emerges through our interaction with others.

time and motion principles Introduced by F.W. Taylor in the second decade of the twentieth century to improve industrial efficiency. This involved breaking a job into component parts and measuring the length of time each task would take. It would become the benchmark for how long a particular activity should take.

total institutions A term used by Erving Goffman to refer to institutions such as prisons and asylums in which life is highly regulated and subjected to authoritarian control to induce conformity.

transparency In the context of drug regulation, the extent of input from the public and health-care practitioners in the decision to approve a new drug and the degree of public access to the clinical information that companies have to submit to Health Canada when they apply to get a drug approved.

trickle-down theory The theory that everyone benefits by allowing the upper class to prosper relatively unfettered. If wealthy capitalists are allowed and encouraged to maximize their profits, it is believed that this increased wealth will eventually "trickle down" to the workers.

Truth and Reconciliation Commission (TRC) Established in 2005 to reveal the truth and document the individual and collective harms perpetrated against Aboriginal peoples by church-run residential schools, and to guide a process leading toward reconciliation with Aboriginal families and between Aboriginal peoples and non-Aboriginal communities.

unalienable human right A right considered to inhere in a person as a human being and that cannot be relinquished by government; sometimes referred to as "natural rights."

unemployment rate Estimates the proportion of people who are not employed but who are actively looking for work.

user fees A general term applied when an individual, group, company, or organization that benefits from a public service is required to pay part of the cost of that service. With respect to pharmaceuticals, it means that when companies apply to have a new drug approved they must pay a fee to Health Canada. Those fees form part of the revenue that is used to operate the part of Health Canada that deals with medications.

values Important beliefs and ideals shared by members of a culture or society.

verstehen A process of interpretative and empathetic understanding.

victim blaming The process whereby social inequality is explained in terms of individuals being solely responsible for what happens to them in relation to the choices they make and their assumed psychological, cultural, and/or biological inferiority.

visible minorities A term used by Statistics Canada and other government bodies "to refer to persons, other than Aboriginal peoples, who are non-Caucasian in race or non-white in colour," as defined by the Employment Equity Act.

welfare state/social welfare state A system whereby the government assumes primary responsibility for the welfare of its citizens through programs designed to protect and promote the economic and social well-being of its citizens.

women's health movement In Canada, includes both formal and informal organizations of women that addressed issues ranging from birth control to poverty. The movement did not have a single voice or leader but, rather, encompassed a variety of groups and activities, collectively known as the women's health movement.

References

2002 detailing survey. (2003). IMH Health Canada.

Abella, R. (1984). *Report of the commission on equality in employment.* Ottawa, ON: Minister of Supply and Services.

Abel-Smith, B. (1960). *A history of the nursing profession.* London, UK: Heinemann.

Aboriginal Healing Foundation. (n.d.). Mission statement. Retrieved from www.ahf.ca/about-us/mission.

Aboriginal Nurses Association of Canada (n.d.) *Fact sheet.* Retrieved from www.moraldistress.ca/edit/userfiles/files/Moral%20 Distress%20in%20Residential%20Care_Final%20Report.pdf.

Abraham, J. (2010). Pharmaceuticalization of society in context: Theoretical, empirical and health dimensions. *Sociology, 44*(4), 603–22.

Abramson, B. (2009). Women and health: Taking the matter to heart. In P. Armstrong & J. Deadman (Eds.), *Women's health intersections of policy, research, and practice* (pp. 53–60). Toronto, ON: Women's Press.

A Brief History of the Medical Reform Group of Ontario 1979–1994. Retrieved from www.connexions.org/CxLibrary/Docs/CX5209 -MRGHistory-1979-1994.htm.

Access Alliance. (2005). Racialized groups and health status: A literature review. Retrieved from http://accessalliance.ca/sites/acces-salliance/files/documents/Literature%20Review_Racialized%20 Groups%20and%20Health%20Status.pdf.

———. (2007). Racialization and health inequalities: Focus on children. Retrieved from http://accessalliance.ca/sites/accessalliance/files/ documents/RacializationandHealthInequalities.pdf.

Acharya, M., & Northcott, H.C. (2007). Mental distress and the coping strategies of elderly Indian immigrant women. *Transcultural Psychiatry, 44*(4), 614–36.

Adams, J., & Tovey, P. (2004). CAM and nursing: From advocacy to critical sociology. In P. Tovey, G. Easthope, & J. Adams (Eds.),*The mainstreaming of complementary medicine.* London, UK: Routledge.

Adelson, N. (2005, Mar/Apr). The embodiment of inequity: Health disparities in Aboriginal Canada. *Canadian Journal of Public Health, 96*, s45–s60.

AFB. (2007, April). Does the 2007 federal budget address inequality and poverty? *Canadian Centre for Policy Alternatives.*

Agnew, H. (1933). The mental institutions of Canada. Editorial Comments. *The Canadian Medical Association Journal, 29*(1), 73–4.

Agnew, V. (Ed.). (2009). *Racialized migrant women in Canada. Essays on health, violence and equity.* Toronto, ON: University of Toronto Press.

Agriculture and Agri-Food, Canada. (1998). *Canada's action plan for food security.* Retrieved from www.agr.gc.ca/index_e. php?s1=misb&s2=fsec-seca&page=action.

———. (2006). Next generation of agriculture and agri-food policy. Retrieved from www5.agr.gc.ca/resources/prod/doc/pol/consult/ econom/pdf/structure_e.pdf.

Agricultural Crop Rotation Act. (2002). Government of Prince Edward Island. Retrieved from www.canlii.org/en/pe/laws/regu/pei-reg-ec166-02/63581/pei-reg-ec166-02.pdf.

Ahmad, F., Driver, N., McNally, M-J, & Stewart, D. (2009). Why doesn't she seek help for partner abuse? An exploratory study with South Asian immigrant women. *Social Science & Medicine, 69* (4), 613–622.

Ahmad, F., Shik, A., Vanza, R., Cheung, A., George, U., & Stewart, D. (2004). *Voices of South Asian Women: Immigration and Mental Health, 40*(4),113–130.

Aiken, L., Clarke, S., Sloane, D., Sochalski, J., Busse, R., Clarke, H., & Shamian. (2001, May/June). Nurses' reports on hospital care in five countries. *Health Affairs, 20*(3), 43–53.

Alasuutari, P. (1995). *Researching culture: Qualitative method and cultural studies.* London, UK: Sage.

Albritton, R. (2009). *Let them eat junk: How capitalism creates hunger and obesity.* Winnipeg, MB: Arbeiter Ring Publishing.

Alexander, J.C. (Ed.). (1985). *Neofunctionalism.* Beverly Hills, CA: Sage.

Alexander, J.C. (1998). *Neofunctionalism and after.* Oxford, UK: Blackwell.

Alford, R. (1975). *Health care politics: Ideological and interest group barriers to reform.* Chicago, Illinois: Chicago University Press.

Ali, J.S., McDermott, S., & Gravel, R.G. (2004, May–June). Recent research on immigrant health from Statistics Canada's population survey. *Canadian Journal of Public Health*, 9–13.

Allan, B., & Smylie, J. (2015). *First peoples, second class treatment: The role of racism in the health and well-being of Indigenous peoples in Canada.* Toronto, ON: Wellesley Institute. Retrieved from www. wellesleyinstitute.com/wp-content/uploads/2015/02/Report-First-Peoples-Second-Class-Treatment-Final.pdf.

Allotey, P., Manderson, L., & Grover, S. (2001). The politics of female genital surgery in displaced communities. *Critical Public Health, 11*(3), 189–201.

American Psychiatric Association (APA). (2013). *Diagnostic and statistical manual of mental disorders* (5th ed.). Arlington, VA: APA.

AMSSA. (2013). Info Sheet (May 17). Refugees: Statistics & trends in Canada and BC. Retrieved from www.amssa.org/files/Info_Sheet/ AMSSA%20Info%20Sheet%20Issue%208%20-%20Final.pdf.

Anderson, J. (1991). Immigrant women speak of chronic illness: The social construction of the devalued self. *Journal of Advanced Nursing, 16*, 710–17.

Anderson, L., Scrimshaw, S., Fullilove, M., Fielding, J., Normand, J., and the Task Force of Community Preventive Services. (2003). Culturally competent healthcare systems: A systematic review. *American Journal of Preventative Medicine, 24*(3S), 68–79.

Andersen, R., & McIvor, M. (2013). Growing inequalities and their impacts in Canada. *GINI Country Report Canada.* Retrieved from http://gini-research.org/system/uploads/507/original/Canada. pdf?1373493076.

Andrews, G., & Boon, H. (2005). CAM in Canada: Places, practices, research. *Complementary Therapies in Clinical Practice, 11*, 21–7.

Andrews, M. (1999). The seductiveness of agelessness. *Ageing and Society, 19*, 301–18.

Aneshensel, C.S., Rutter, C., & Lachenbruch, P.A. (1991). Social structure, stress, and mental health: Competing conceptual and analytic models. *American Sociological Review, 56*(2), 166–78.

Angus, M. (2009, Winter). To benefit us all: Childcare in Canada. *The Catalyst 32*(1), 1–4. Retrieved from www.cpj.ca/en/content/benefit-us-all-childcare-canada.

Annandale, E. (2004). *Feminist theory and the sociology of health and illness.* London, UK: Routledge.

Annandale, E., & Clarke, J. (1996). What is gender? Feminist theory and the sociology of human reproduction. *Sociology of Health and Illness, 18*(1), 17–44.

Annandale, E., & Hunt, K. (Eds.). (2000). Gender inequalities and health. Buckingham, UK: Open University Press.

Annual Report, 2012. (2013). Ottawa, ON: Patented Medicine Prices Review Board.

Applied Management in association with Fraser Group Tristat Resources. (2000). *Canadian's access to insurance for prescription medicines: Volume 2: The uninsured and the under-insured.* Ottawa.

Ariès, P. (1981). *The hour of our death.* (H. Weaver, Trans.). New York, NY: Knopf Publishers.

Armstrong, D. (1983). *Political anatomy of the body: Medical knowledge in Britain in the twentieth century.* Cambridge: Cambridge University Press.

Armstrong, P. (2013). Unpaid healthcare work: An indicator of equity. Pan American Health Organization. Retrieved from http://new.paho.org/hq/index.php?option=com_content&view=article&id=2680&Itemid=4017.

Armstrong, P., Amaratunga, C., Bernier, J., Grant, K., Pederson, A. and Willson, K. (Eds.) (2002). *Exposing privatization: Women and health care reform.* Aurora, ON: Garamond Press.

Armstrong P., & Armstrong, H. (2003). *Wasting away: The undermining of Canadian health care* (2nd ed.). Don Mills, ON: Oxford University Press.

——— & ———. (2008). *Health care: About Canada.* Halifax, NS: Fernwood Publishing.

——— & ———. (2010a). Conceptual guide to the health care module. Retrieved from www.genderwork.ca/gwd/page-id=20.

——— & ———. (2010b). *The double ghetto: Canadian women and their segregated work.* (Updated 3rd ed.). The Wynford Project. Toronto, ON: Oxford University Press.

Armstrong, P., Armstrong, H., Bourgeault, I., Choiniere, J., Mykhalovskiy, E., & White, J. (2000). *"Heal thyself": Managing health care reform.* Aurora, ON: Garamond Press.

Armstrong, P., Armstrong, H., & Coburn, D. (Eds.). (2001). *Unhealthy times: Political economy perspectives on health and care in Canada.* Don Mills, ON: Oxford University Press.

Armstrong, P., Armstrong, H., & Scott-Dixon, K. (2008). *Critical to care: The invisible women in health services.* Toronto, ON: University of Toronto Press.

Armstrong, P., Blow B., Grant K., et al. (2012). *Thinking women and health care reform in Canada.* Toronto ,ON: Women's Press.

Armstrong, P., & Braedley, S. (Eds.). (2013). *Troubling care: Critical perspectives on research and practices.* Toronto: Canadian Scholars' Press Inc.

Armstrong, P., Choiniere, J., & Day, E. (1993). *Vital signs: Nursing in transition.* Toronto, ON: Garamond Press.

Armstrong, P., Clow, B., Grant K., Haworth-Brockman, M., Jackson, B., Pederson, A., & Seeley, M. (2012). *Thinking women and health care reform in Canada.* Toronto: Women's Press.

Armstrong, P., Laxer, K., & Armstrong, H. (2010). Conceptual guide to the health care module. Retrieved from www.genderwork.ca/gwd/page-id=20.

Armstrong, P., Laxer, K., & Armstrong, H. (2014). Nurses unions: Where knowledge meets know-how. M. McIntyre and C. McDonald (Eds.), *Realities of Canadian nursing: Professional, practice and power issues* (4th ed.) (pp. 158–80). New York, NY: Walters Kluwer/Lippincott Williams and Wilkins.

Ashton, J., & Seymour, H. (1988). *The new public health: The Liverpool experience.* Open University Press, Milton Keynes.

Assembly of First Nations. (2002, May). Fact sheet: Top misconceptions about Aboriginal peoples. Retrieved from http://tricitiesecd.citysoup.ca/NR/rdonlyres/DBF1E6EF-66A7-4357-A3A5-50E1473FD3DE/68643/FACTSandMisconceptions.pdf.

———. (2009). Background. Retrieved from http://64.26.129.156/article.asp?id=2845.

Association of Faculties of Medicine of Canada. (2012). *The future of medical education in Canada (FMEC): A collective vision for MD education.* March. Retrieved from http://www.afmc.ca/fmec/pdf/collective_vision.pdf.

———. (2013a). Enrolment in MD programs in Canadian. faculties of medicine. *Canadian Medical Education Statistics 2013.* Retrieved from www.afmc.ca/pdf/Cmes2013_Enrolment-Attrition-2014-05-09.pdf.

———. (2013b). Graduates of MD programs in Canadian faculties of medicine. *Canadian Medical Education Statistics 2013.* Retrieved from www.afmc.ca/pdf/Cmes2013_MDGraduates.pdf.

Athabasca Chipewyan First Nation. (2014, July 15). Athabasca Chipewyan First Nation pulls out of Grand Rapids hearings: Citing prejudiced process that favors industry (ACFN). Athabasca Chipewyan First Nation and the Tar Sands. Retrieved December 22, 2015 https://acfnchallenge.wordpress.com/.

Atkinson, M.M., & Coleman, W.D. (1989). *The state, business, and industrial change in Canada.* Toronto, ON: University of Toronto Press.

Au, W.W., Lane, R.G., Legator, M., Whorton, E.B, Wilkinson, G.S., & Gabehart, G.J. (1995). Biomarker monitoring of a population residing near uranium mining activities. *Environmental Health Perspectives,103*(5), 466–70.

Auger, J. (2000). *Social perspectives on death and dying.* Halifax, NS: Fernwood.

Auger, N., & Alix, C. (2009). Income, income distribution, and health in Canada. In D. Raphael (Ed.). *Social determinants of health* (2nd ed.) (pp. 61–73). Toronto, ON: Canadian Scholars' Press.

Auger, J., & Tedford-Litle, D. (2002). *From the inside looking out: Competing ideas about growing old.* Halifax, NS: Fernwood.

Austin, W. (2007). The McDonaldization of nursing. *Health: An Interdisciplinary Journal for the Social Study of Health, Illness and Medicine, 11*(2), 265–72.

———. (2011). The incommensurability of nursing as a practice and the customer service model: An evolutionary threat to the discipline. *Nursing Philosophy, 12*, 158–66.

Ayres, I., & Braithwaite, J. (1992). *Responsive regulation: transcending the deregulation debate.* New York, NY: Oxford University Press.

Badgley, R., & Wolfe, S. (1967). *Doctors' strike.* Toronto, ON: Macmillan of Canada.

Baggott, R. (2000). *Public health: Policy and politics.* Basingstoke, UK: Palgrave.

Baird, P.A. (1996). Funding medical and health-related research in the public interest. *Canadian Medical Association Journal, 155,* 299–301.

Ballon, D. (2011). Looking back: Reflections on community mental health in Ontario. *Network: Framing the Future.* Canadian Mental Health Association. Spring 2011, *27*(1), 17–20. Retrieved from http://ontario.cmha.ca/files/2013/04/spring_2011.pdf.

Barsky, A., & Boros, J. (1995). Somatization and medicalization in the era of managed care. *Journal of the American Medical Association, 274,* 1931–4.

Barrett, B., Kiefer, D., & Rabago, D. (1999). Assessing the risks and benefits of herbal medicine: An over-view of scientific evidence. *Alternative Therapies in Health and Medicine, 5*(4), 40–50.

Barrett, M. (1991). *The politics of truth: From Marx to Foucault.* Cambridge, UK: Polity Press.

Barrett, M., & Phillips, A. (1992). *Destabilizing theory: Contemporary feminist debates.* Cambridge, UK: Polity Press.

Barrett, M., & Roberts, H. (1978). Doctors and their patients. In C. Smart & B. Smart (Eds.), *Women, sexuality and social control* (pp. 41–52). London, UK: Routledge.

Bartky, S.L. (1998). Foucault, femininity, and the modernization of patriarchal power. In R. Weitz (Ed.), *The politics of women's bodies: Sexuality, appearance and behavior.* New York, NY: Oxford University Press.

Battiste, M., & Henderson, J.Y. (2012). Oppression and the health of Indigenous peoples. In E. McGibbon (Ed.), *Oppression: A social determinant of health.* Halifax & Winnipeg: Fernwood Publishing.

Bauer, G. (2014). Incorporating intersectionality theory into population health research methodology: Challenges and the potential to advance health equity. *Social Science and Medicine, 110,* 10–17.

Baum, F. (2002). *The new public health* (2nd ed.). Melbourne: Oxford University Press.

Baum, F., MacDougall, C., & Smith, D. (2006). Participatory action research. *Journal of Epidemiology and Community Health, 60,* 854–7

Beagan, B., & Ells, C. (2009). Values that matter, barriers that interfere: The struggle of Canadian nurses to enact their values. *Canadian Journal of Nursing Research, 41*(1), 86–107.

Beardshaw, V., & Robinson, R. (1990). *New for old: Prospects for nursing in the 1990s.* London, UK: King's Fund.

Beardwood, B., Walters, V, Eyles, J., & French, S. (1999). Complaints against nurses: A reflection of "the new managerialism" and consumerism in health care. *Social Science & Medicine, 48,* 363–74.

Beattie, A. (1991). Knowledge and control in health promotion: A test case for social policy and social theory. In J. Gabe, M. Calnan, & M. Bury (Eds.), *The sociology of the health service.* London, UK: Routledge.

Beck, U. (1992). *Risk society: Towards a new modernity.* London, UK: Sage.

Becker, H.S. (1963). *Outsiders: Studies in the sociology of deviance.* New York, NY: Free Press.

Beiser, M. (2005, Mar/Apr). The health of immigrants and refugees in Canada. *Canadian Journal of Public Health, 96,* s30–s44.

Bell, C. (2010). Is disability studies actually white disability studies? In L. Davis (Ed.), *The Disability Studies Reader* (3rd ed.) New York: Routledge.

Bell, K. (2012). Cochrane reviews and the behavioural turn in evidence-based medicine. *Health Sociology Review, 21*(3), 313–21.

Bell, S. (1987). Changing ideas: The medicalization of menopause. *Social Sciences and Medicine, 24,* 535–42.

Bell, S., & Figert, A. (2012). Medicalization and pharmaceuticalization at the intersections: Looking backward, sideways and forward. *Social Science & Medicine, 75,* 775–83.

Belle, D. (1990, March). Poverty and women's mental health. *American Psychologist, 45*(3), 385–9.

Bennett, C., & Shearman, R. (1989). Maternity services in New South Wales: Childbirth moves towards the 21st century. *Medical Journal of Australia, 150,* 673–6.

Berenson, C., Miller, L., & Findlay, D. (2009). Through medical eyes: The medicalization of women's bodies and women's lives. In S. Bolaria & H. Dickinson (Eds.), *Health, illness, and health care in Canada* (4th ed.). Toronto, ON: Nelson Education Ltd.

Berger, P.L., & Luckmann, T. (1967). *The social construction of reality.* Harmondsworth, UK: Penguin.

Berlin, I. (1963). *Karl Marx: His life and environment* (3rd ed.). New York: Oxford University Press.

Berman, B.M., Swyers, J.P., Hartnoll, M., Sigh, B.B., & Bausell, B. (2000). The public debate over alternative medicine: The importance of finding a middle ground. *Alternative Therapies in Health and Medicine, 6*(1), 98–101.

Berry, L., & Curry, P. (2012). *Nursing workload and patient care: Understanding the value of nurses, the effects of excessive workload, and how nurse-patient ratios and dynamic staffing models can help.* Ottawa: CFNU.

Bertell, R. (1999). A pollution primer. In M. Wyman (Ed.), *Sweeping the earth: Women taking action for a healthy planet.* Charlottetown, PEI: Gynergy Books.

Bierman, A. (2007, December 4). Sex matters: Gender disparities in quality and outcomes of care. *Canadian Medical Association Journal, 177*(12). Retrieved from www.cmaj.ca/cgi/content/full/177/12/1520.

Bierman, A.S., Angus, J., Ahmad, F., Degani, N., Vahabi, M., Glazier, . . . Manuel, D. (2010). Access to health care services (Ch. 7). POWER Study, ECHO. Retrieved from www.powerstudy.ca/the-power-report/the-power-report-volume-1/access-to-health-ca.

Biggs, B., & Skull, S.A. (2003). Refugee health: Clinical issues. In P. Allotey (Ed.), *The health of refugees: Public health perspectives from crisis to settlement.* Melbourne: Oxford University Press.

Birch, L. (1999). Development of food preferences. *Annual Review of Nutrition, 19,* 41–62.

Biringer, A., & Carroll, J. (2012). What does the feminization of family medicine mean? *CMAJ, 184*(15), 1752.

Bischoff, A., Bovier, P.A., Isah, R., Francoise, G., Ariel, E., & Loutan, L. (2003). Language barriers between nurses and asylum seekers: Their impact on symptom reporting and referral. *Social Science & Medicine, 53*(3), 503–12.

Bissonnette, F., Cohen, J., Collins, J., Cowan, L., Dale, S., Dill, S., . . . Canadian Fertility and Andrology Society. (2007, June 14). Incidence and complications of multiple gestation in Canada: Proceedings of an expert meeting. *Reproductive Biomedecine Online, 6,* 773–90. Retrieved from www.ncbi.nlm.nih.gov/pubmed/17582911.

Black, D. (2014, July 4). Court strikes down Conservatives' cuts to refugee health-care coverage. Retrieved from www.thestar.com/news/canada/2014/07/04/court_rules_against_conservative_governments_refugee_health_cuts.html.

Blackwell, T. (2014, March 21). For-profit health company Centric health faces resistance as it spreads across Canada. *National Post*. Retrieved from http://news.nationalpost.com/2014/03/21/for-profit-health-company-centric-health-faces-resistance-as-it-spreads-across-canada/#__federated=1.

Blight Alert, A Simple Decision Support System for Prince Edward Island Potato Farmers. (2008). Agriculture and Agri-Food Canada. Retrieved from www.agr.gc.ca/eng/?id=1299091214522.

Blishen, B. (1991). *Doctors in Canada: The changing world of medical practice*. Toronto, ON: University of Toronto Press.

Block, S. (2010). *Ontario's growing gap: The role of race and gender*. Ottawa: Canadian Centre for Policy Alternatives.

Bloom, S. (2002). *The word as scalpel: A history of medical sociology*. New York, NY: Oxford University Press.

Bocking, S. (2012). Schindler's pissed: Freshwater science pioneer David Schindler fires back about tar sands development, closing the Experimental Lakes Area, and why researchers should speak out. *Alternatives Journal: Canada's Environmental Voice*. Retrieved from www.alternativesjournal.ca/people-and-profiles/schindlers-pissed.

Bolaria, S., & Dickinson, H. (Eds.). (2009). *Health, illness, and health care in Canada* (4th ed.). Toronto, ON: Nelson Education Ltd.

Boon, H., & Kachan, M. (2008). Integrative medicine: A tale of two clinics. Biomed Central, BMC complementary and alternative medicine (pp. 1–8). Retrieved from www.biomedcentral.com/content/pdf/1472-6882-8-32.pdf.

Boon, H., Verhoef, M., Vanderheyden, L., & Westlake, K. (2006). Complementary and alternative medicine: A rising healthcare issue. *Healthcare Policy, 1*(3), 19–30.

Booz, Allen, & Hamilton. (2008). *Postmarketing commitments study final report*. Washington, DC: Food and Drug Administration.

Bordo, S. (1993). *Unbearable weight: Feminism, western culture, and the body*. Berkeley, CA: University of California Press.

Borland, R., Donaghue, N., & Hill, D. (1994). Illnesses that Australians most feared in 1986 and 1993. *Australian Journal of Public Health, 18*, 366–9.

Boscoe, M., Basen, G., Alleyne, G., Bourrier-Lacroix, B., & White, S. (2004). The women's health movement in Canada. Looking back and moving forward. *Canadian Women's Studies, 24*(1), 7–14.

Boston, P. (1999). Cultural responsive cancer care in a cost-contained work-classification system. *Journal of Cancer Education, 14*(3), 148–53.

Bougie, E., Finès, P., Oliver, L., & Kohen, D. (2014, February). Unintentional injury hospitalizations and socio-economic status in areas with a high percentage of First Nations identity residents. *Health Reports, 25*(2), 3–12. Ministry of Industry. Statistics Canada.

Bourdieu, P. (1986). The forms of capital. In J. Richardson (Ed.), *Handbook of theory and research for the sociology of education* (pp. 241–58). New York, NY: Greenwood Press.

Bourgeault, I. (2006). Sociological perspectives on health and health care. In D. Raphael, T. Bryant, & M. Rioux (Eds.), *Staying alive, critical perspectives on health, illness, and health care* (pp. 35–57). Toronto, ON: Canadian Scholars' Press Inc.

Bowie, A. (2010, November 19). Changing bad habits critical for NBers' health-minister. *The Daily Gleaner*, p. A6.

Boyd, M., & Vickers, M. (2009). The ebb and flow of immigration in Canada. In E. Grabb & N. Guppy (Eds.), *Social inequality in Canada* (5th ed.) (pp. 237–52). Toronto, ON: Pearson Prentice Hall.

Boyer, Y. (2014). *Moving Aboriginal health forward*. Saskatoon, SK: Purich Publishing Limited.

Braedley, S., & Luxton, M. (Eds.). (2010). *Neoliberalism and everyday life*. Montreal: McGill-Queen's University Press.

Braithwaite, J. (1984). *Corporate crime in the pharmaceutical industry*. London, UK: Routledge & Kegan Paul.

Braun, L., Fausto-Sterling, A., Fullwiley, D., Hammonds, E., Nelson, A., Quivers, W., Reverby, S., & Shields, A. (2007). Racial categories in medical practice: How useful are they? PLoS *Medicine, 4*(9), 1423–8. Retrieved from www.plosmedicine.org.

Brewer, J. (2004). Imagining *The Sociological Imagination*: the biographical context of a sociological classic. *British Journal of Sociology, 55*, 317–33.

Briar, Celia. (Ed.). (2009). *Health hazards in women's work*. Wellington: Dunmore Publishing.

Broadbent, E. (2009, May 1). Barbarism lite. *The Monitor, Canadian Centre for Policy Alternatives*.

Broadbent Institute. (2012). *Towards a More Equal Canada: A Report on Canada's Economic & Social Inequality*. Ottawa: Broadbent Institute. Retrieved from www.broadbentinstitute.ca/sites/default/files/documents/towards_a_more_equal_canada.pdf.

Broom, A. (2014). The sociology of complementary and alternative medicine. In J. Germov (Ed.), *Second opinion: An introduction to health sociology* (5th ed.). Australia: Oxford University Press.

Broom, D. (1991). *Damned if we do: Contradictions in women's health care*. Sydney: Allen & Unwin.

Broom, D.H., & Woodward, R.V. (1996). Medicalisation reconsidered: Toward a collaborative approach to care. *Sociology of Health and Illness, 18*(3), 57–78.

Brophy, J., Keith, M., Watterson, A., Park, R., Gilbertson, M., Maticka-Tyndale, E., Beck, M., Abu-Zahra, H., Schneider, K., Reinhartz, A., DeMatteo, R., &Luginaah, I. (2012). Breast cancer risk in relation to occupations with exposure to carcinogens and endocrine disruptors: A Canadian case-control study. Environmental Health. Retrieved from www.ehjournal.net.

Brown, K., Kenny, S., & Turner, B.S. (2000). *Rhetorics of welfare: Uncertainty, choice and voluntary associations*. Basingstoke, UK: Macmillan.

Brown, P. (1995). Naming and framing: The social construction of diagnosis and illness. *Journal of Health and Social Behavior,* extra issue, 34–52.

———. (Ed.). (2000a). *Perspectives in medical sociology* (3rd ed.). Illinois: Waveland Press Inc.

———. (2000b). Naming and framing: The social construction of diagnosis and illness. In P. Brown (Ed.), *Perspectives in medical sociology* (3rd ed.) (pp. 74–103). Illinois: Waveland Press.

Brown, P., & Mikkelsen, E.J. (1997). *No safe place: Toxic waste, leukemia and community action*. Berkeley, CA: University of California Press.

Browne, J., Varcoe, C., & Fridkin, A. (2011). Violence and pain: Research on health services for women at the intersections of history and economics. In O. Hankivsky (Ed.), *Health Inequities in Canada*.

Brownridge, D.A., & Halli, S.S. (2002). Double jeopardy: Violence against immigrant women in Canada. *Violence and Victims, 17*, 455–71.

Brunner, E., & Marmot, M.G. (2006). Social organization, stress, and health. In M.G. Marmot & R.G. Wilkinson (Eds.), *Social Determinants of Health* (2nd ed.). Oxford: Oxford University Press.

Bryant, T. (2009). *An introduction to health policy.* Toronto, ON: Canadian Scholars' Press Inc.

Bryant, T., Raphael, D., & Rioux, M. (Eds.). (2010). *Staying alive: Critical perspectives on health, illness and health care* (2nd ed.). Toronto: Canadian Scholars' Press Inc.

Bryant, T., Raphael, D., Schrecker, T., & Labonte, R. (2010). Canada: A land of missed opportunity for addressing the social determinants of health. *Health Policy.* doi:10.1016/j.healthpol.2010.08.022.

Buhler, S. (2008, Summer). Gender, poverty and HIV/AIDS among women in Ontario: Exploring intersections across three sectors. OWHN E-Bulletin, 1–14. Retrieved from www.owhn.on.ca/ebulletin.htm#a.

Burton, K., & Wong, I. (2004, April 27). A force to contend with: The gender gap closes in medical schools. *Canadian Medical Association Journal, 170*(9), 1385–6.

Bury, M. (1982). Chronic illness as biographical disruption. *Sociology of Health and Illness, 4*(2), 167–82.

———. (2004). Defining and researching disability. In M. Bury & J. Gabe (Eds.), *The sociology of health and illness* (pp. 266–76). London, UK: Routledge Press.

Butler, J. (1990). *Gender trouble: Feminism and the subversion of identity.* London, UK: Routledge Press.

Butler-Jones, D. (2008). *The chief public health officer's report on the state of public health in Canada.* Ottawa, ON: Minister of Health.

———. (2010). *The chief public health officer's report on the state of public health in Canada 2010: Growing older—Adding life to years.* Retrieved from http://publichealth.gc.ca/CPHOreport.

———. (2012). *The chief public health officer's report on the state of public health in Canada: Influencing health—The importance of sex and gender.* Ottawa. ON. Retrieved from http://publichealth.gc.ca/CPHOreport.

Bytheway, B. (1995). *Ageism.* Buckingham, UK: Open University Press.

CAM Corp International. (2005). *Worldwide pharmaceutical promotion overview.* New Jersey.

Campbell, B., & Marchildon, G. (2007, November 19). *Completing Tommy's vision.* Ottawa, ON: Canadian Centre for Policy Alternatives.

Canada Health Act. (1984). Retrieved from http://laws.justice.gc.ca/PDF/Statute/C/C-6.pdf.

Canada's Aboriginal Action Plan. (1998). Gathering strength: Canada's Aboriginal action plan. Retrieved from www.ahf.ca/downloads/gathering-strength.pdf.

Canada's Research-Based Pharmaceutical Companies. (2002). *Improving health through innovation: a new deal for Canadians.* Ottawa, ON.

Canadian AIDS Society. (1995). *The complementary therapies project: HIV treatment project report.* Canadian AIDS Society, Ottawa, Ontario.

Canadian Association of Community Health Centres. (2015). *About community health centres.* Retrieved from www.cachc.ca/about/about-community-health-centres/.

Canadian Association of Naturopathic Doctors. (2015). Retrieved from www.chiropractic.ca.

Canadian Association on Gerontology. (2011). Home care in Canada. Retrieved from www.cagacg.ca/publications/552_e.php.

Canadian Cancer Society's Advisory Committee on Cancer Statistics. (2014). *Canadian Cancer Statistics 2014.* Toronto, ON: Canadian Cancer Society. Available at cancer.ca/statistics.

Canadian Cancer Statistics. (2013). Special Topic: Liver Cancer. Statistics Canada. Retrieved December 22, 2015 www.cancer.ca/~/media/cancer.ca/CW/cancer%20information/cancer%20101/Canadian%20cancer%20statistics/canadian-cancer-statistics-2013-EN.pdf.

Canadian Chiropractic Association. (2015). Retrieved from www.chiropractic.ca.

Canadian Community Health Survey. (2010). Retrieved from www.statcan.gc.ca/cgi-bin/imdb/p2SV.pl?Function=getSurvey&SDDS=3226&lang=en&db=imdb&adm=8&dis=2.

Canadian Council for Refugees. (2013 December). New refugee system–one year on. Retrieved from http://ccrweb.ca/files/refugee-system-one-year-on.pdf.

———. (2014). Refugee health care cuts: A quick review of the Federal Court decision. Retrieved from http://ccrweb.ca/en/refugee-health-care-cuts-quick-review-federal-court-decision.

Canadian Council of Social Development. (2010). Employment and persons with disabilities in Canada. In D. Raphael (Ed.), *Health promotion and quality of life in Canada.* Toronto, ON: Canadian Scholars' Press Inc.

Canadian Council on Learning. (2009, October 7). Strategies for overcoming barriers to training and education for Canadians with disabilities. Retrieved from www.ccl-cca.ca/pdfs/LessonsInLearning/10_07_09.pdf.

Canadian Council on Social Development. (2010, November 15). Equality, inclusion and the health of Canadians. Ottawa, ON: CCSD.

Canadian Diabetes Association. (2012, October 11). *Diabetes and urban Aboriginal populations in Canada: exploring the problem, finding solutions.* Retrieved from www.diabetes.ca/newsroom/search-news/diabetes-and-urban-aboriginal-populations-in-canada.

Canadian Doctors for Medicare. (n.d.). The case for Medicare. Retrieved from www.canadiandoctorsformedicare.ca/the-case-for-medicare.html.

———. (2011). The myth of health care unsustainability fact sheet: March 2011. Available at www.canadiandoctorsformedicare.ca/publications/resources.

Canadian Encyclopedia, The. (n.d.). Medical education. Retrieved from www.thecanadianencyclopedia.com/index.cfm?PgNm=TCE&Params=A1ARTA0005196.

Canadian Environmental Law Association. (2008, September 3). Press release: Environmental organizations issue criticism of Federal government for refusal to phase out cancer causing substances. Retrieved from www.cela.ca/newsevents/media-release/environmental-organizations-issue-criticism-federal-government-refusal-phas.

Canadian Federation of Nurses Unions (CFNU). (2012). *About us.* Retrieved from https://nursesunions.ca/about-us.

———. (2013a). *Trends in own illness or diability-related absenteeism and overtime among publicly-employed registered nurses: Quick facts.*

Informetrica Limited. Retrieved from https://nursesunions.ca/sites/default/files/cfnu_quick_facts_2013.pdf.

——. (2013b). *The nursing workforce: Canadian federation of nurses unions backgrounder.* January 2013.

——. (2014). *The nursing workforce. Canadian federation of nurses unions backgrounder.* Retrieved from https://nursesunions.ca/sites/default/files/2014_september.backgrounder.nursing_workforce.en_.pdf.

Canadian Generic Pharmaceutical Association. (2013). The value of generic prescription medicines. Retrieved from www.canadiangenerics.ca/en/advocacy/docs/ValueofGenericPrescriptionMedicine2013.pdf.

Canadian Health Coalition. (2004, October). Canadian healthcare manager: The verdict on Medicare. Retrieved from www.healthcoalition.ca/archive/chm.pdf.

——. (2008, October 6). Eroding public Medicare: Lessons and consequences of for-profit health care across Canada. Retrieved from www.healthcoalition.ca/archive/OHCPCR.pdf.

——. (2011). Support for public health care soars: 94% of Canadians–including Conservatives–choose public over for-profit solutions. Retrieved from www.newswire.ca/en/story/884001/support-for-public-health-care-soars-94-of-canadians-including-conservatives-choose-public-over-for-profit-solutions.

——. (2014). Homepage. Retrieved from http://healthcoalition.ca.

Canadian Health Human Resources Research Network (CHHRN). (2013, May). *Feminization of the physician workforce: Implications for health human resource planning.* Ottawa: Canadian Health Human Resources Research Network. Retrieved from www.hhr-rhs.ca/images/stories/docs/features/chhrn_feminization_one_pager.pdf.

Canadian Medical Association. (2013). Physicians and health equity: Opportunities in practice. Ottawa: Health Care Transformation in Canada. Retrieved from http://healthcaretransformation.ca/wp-content/uploads/2013/03/Health-Equity-Opportunities-in-Practice-Final-E.pdf.

——. (2014). Number and percent distribution of physicians by specialty and sex, Canada 2014. *Canadian physician statistics.* Retrieved from www.cma.ca/En/Pages/canadian-physician-statistics.aspx.

Canadian Nurses Association. (2000). Strengthening the voice: The ninth decade of the Canadian Nurses Association. Retrieved from www.cna-aiic.ca/cna/documents/pdf/publications/ninth_decade_e.pdf.

——. (2014). *Education.* Retrieved from www.cna-aiic.ca/en/becoming-an-rn/education.

Canadian Nursing Advisory Committee. (2002). Final report: Our health, our future: Creating quality workplaces for Canadian nurses. Retrieved from www.hc-sc.gc.ca/hcs-sss/alt_formats/hpb-dgps/pdf/pubs/2002-cnac-cccsi-final/2002-cnac-cccsi-final-eng.pdf.

Canadian Press. (2008). Walkerton study finds sharply higher risk of kidney disease. *CBC Online.* Retrieved from www.cbc.ca/health/story/2008/10/16/walkerton-study.html.

Canadian Public Health Association. (1996). *The health impact of unemployment: Discussion paper.* Retrieved from www.cpha.ca/uploads/resolutions/1996-dp1_e.pdf.

Caplan, P. (1995). *They say you're crazy: How the world's most powerful psychiatrists decide who's normal.* MA: Perseus Books.

Capra, F. (1982). *The turning point: Science, society and the rising culture.* New York, NY: Simon & Schuster.

Carlson, K., & Mahoney, J. (2014, August 22). PM rejects inquiry calls after girl's death. *The Globe and Mail,* p. A1.

Caron, I., & Simpson, J. (2003, November). Who's doing what? *Health Policy Research Bulletin, 7,* 28–9.

CARP. (2010, June10). *Open letter to Canada's finance ministers.* Retrieved from www1.carp.ca/PDF/Pension%20Open%20Letter%20Final%20June%2010%20Finance%20Ministers.pdf.

Carpenter, D. (2008). Drug-review deadlines and safety problems. *New England Journal of Medicine, 359,* 96–8.

Carpenter, D., Zucker, E.J., & Avorn, J. (2008). Drug-review deadlines and safety problems. *New England Journal of Medicine, 358,* 1354–61.

Carroll, W. (1984). The individual, class and corporate power in Canada. *Canadian Journal of Sociology, 9,* 245–68.

——. (2004). *Corporate power in a globalizing world: A study in elite social organization.* Toronto, ON: Oxford University Press.

——. (2009). Corporate Canada, globalization, and neoliberal democracy. In E. Grabb & N. Guppy (Eds.), *Social inequality in Canada: Patterns, problems and policies* (5th ed.) (pp. 29–43). Toronto, ON: Pearson Prentice Hall.

——. (2010). You are Here. *Socialist Studies* 6(2). Fall 2010.

Carson, R. (1962). *Silent spring.* Cambridge, MA: The Riverside Press.

Carter, B. (2007). Reformatting nursing: The invidious effects of the growth of managerialism. *Health: An Interdisciplinary Journal for the Social Study of Health, Illness and Medicine, 11*(2), 265–72.

Cash, T.F. (2001). The psychology of hair loss and its implications for patient care. *Clinic in Dermatology, 19,* 161–6.

Cashman, P. (1989). The Dalkon shield. In P. Grabosky & A. Sutton. (Eds.), *Stains on a white collar.* Sydney: Hutchinson.

CAUT. (2013). Federal funding of basic research. *CAUT Education Review, 13*(1). October. Retrieved from www.caut.ca/docs/default-source/education-review/educationreview13-1-en.pdf?sfvrsn=2.

CBC. (2004). Top ten greatest Canadians. Tommy Douglas: The greatest of them all. Retrieved from www.cbc.ca/10th/timelineContent/20041129_greatest.html.

CBC. (2008, May 12). A Miramichi pathologist under the legal microscope. Retrieved from www.cbc.ca/news/canada/new-brunswick/story/2008/05/12/f-pathologist-inquiry.html.

——. (2009). Dr. Charles Smith: The man behind the public inquiry. Retrieved from www.cbc.ca/news/canada/story/2009/12/07/f-charles-smith-goudge-inquiry.html.

——. (2010). Windsor hospital probes other cases of concern. Retrieved from www.cbc.ca/canada/windsor/story/2010/02/24/windsor-second-mastectomy-100224.html'ref=rss).

——. (2011, January). Canadians not as healthy as they think: Poll. Retrieved from www.cbc.ca/health/story/2010/12/31/canada-weighs-in-poll-health-myths.html.

CBC News. (2015, February 6). Doctor-assisted suicide a therapeutic service, says Canadian Medical Association. Retrieved from www.cbc.ca/news/health/doctor-assisted-suicide-a-therapeutic-service-says-canadian-medical-association-1.2947779.

Chapman, A. (2014). The impact of reliance on private sector health services on the right to health. *Health and Human Rights Journal, 16*(1), 122–33.

Chappell, N., & Penning, M. (2009). *Understanding health, health care, and health policy in Canada*. Don Mills, ON: Oxford University Press.

Charmaz, K. (1983). Loss of self: A fundamental form of suffering in the chronically ill. *Sociology of Health and Illness, 5*(2), 168–95.

———. (1993). *Good days, bad days: The self in chronic illness*. New Brunswick, NJ: Rutgers University Press.

———. (1995). The body, identity, and self: Adapting to impairment. *The Sociological Quarterly, 36*(4), 657–80.

Chatterjee, P. (1996). Who is stealing our future: Industry's toxic addiction to estrogen mimickers & endocrine disruptors. *CAQ, 15,* 16–23.

Chaufan, C., Hollister, B. Nazaareno, J., & Fox, P. (2012). Medical ideology as a double-edged sword: The politics of cure and care in the making of Alzheimer's disease. *Social Science & Medicine, 74,* 788–95.

Chernobyl: Assessment of Radiological and Health Impact. (2002). *Update of Chernobyl: Ten years on*. Retrieved from www.oecd-nea.org/rp/chernobyl/c01.html.

Chernomas, R., & Hudson, I. (2013). *To live and die in America: Class, power, health and healthcare*. Halifax & Winnipeg: Fernwood Press

Chivers, S. (2011). *The silvering screen: Old age and disability in cinema*. Toronto: University of Toronto Press.

CIHI. (2004). *Giving birth in Canada: Providers of infant and maternity care*. Ottawa, ON: CIHI.

———. (2005). *Exploring the 70/30 Split: How Canada's Health Care System is Financed*. Ottawa. Available at www.cihi.ca ISBN 1-55392-655-2 (PDF).

———. (2006a). *Health care in Canada*. Ottawa, ON: Statistics Canada.

———. (2006b). Child health. Retrieved from www.cihr-irsc.gc.ca/e/documents/child_health_mpkit_2005_e.pdf.

———. (2007a). *Health care in Canada*. Ottawa, ON: CIHI.

———. (2007b, August 14). Patient safety in Canada: An update. *Analysis in Brief*. Ottawa, ON: CIHI.

———. (2008a). Canada's health care providers 2008: Provincial profiles: A look at 24 health occupations. Retrieved from http://secure.cihi.ca/cihiweb/products/provincial_profiles_2010_e.pdf.

———. (2008b). Health care expenditures, health care in Canada. Ottawa, ON: CIHI.

———. (2011). *Health care in Canada, 2011: A focus on seniors and aging*. Ottawa: CIHI. Retrieved from www.cihi.ca.

———. (2012a). *Health care in Canada, 2012: A focus on wait times*. Ottawa: CIHI. Retrieved from https://secure.cihi.ca/free_products/HCIC2012-FullReport-ENweb.pdf.

———. (2012b). *Regulated nurses: Canadian trends, 2007 to 2011*. Ottawa: CIHI

———. (2013a). *Canada's health care providers, 1997 to 2011 – A reference guide: Overview and methodological notes*. Ottawa: CIHI. Retrieved from https://secure.cihi.ca/estore/productFamily.htm?locale=en&pf=PFC2161.

———. (2013b). *Drug expenditure in Canada, 1985 to 2012*. Ottawa.

———. (2014a). *Canada's health care providers: Provincial profiles 2012*. Ottawa: CIHI. Retrieved from https://secure.cihi.ca/estore/productFamily.htm?locale=en&pf=PFC2500.

———. (2014b). *National health expenditure trends: 1975-2014*. Retrieved from http://www.cihi.ca/web/resource/en/nhex_2014_report_en.pdf.

———. (2014c). *Physicians in Canada, 2013 Chartbook*. Ottawa. Retrieved from https://secure.cihi.ca/estore/productFamily.htm?locale=en&pf=PFC2676.

———. (2014d). *Prescribed drug spending in Canada, 2012: A focus on public drug programs*. Retrieved from https://secure.cihi.ca/free_products/Prescribed_Drug_Spending_in_Canada_EN.pdf.

———. (2014e). *Regulated nurses, 2013,* Ottawa: CIHI. Retrieved from https://secure.cihi.ca/free_products/Nursing-Workforce-2013_EN.pdf.

———. (2014g). *Supply, Distribution and Migration of Canadian Physicians, 2013*. Ottawa: CIHI.

———. (2015). *National Health Expenditure Trends: 1975–2015*. Available at https://secure.cihi.ca/free.../nhex_trends_narrative_report_2015_en.pdf.

CIHR. (2006). Research finding solutions to HIV/AIDS. Retrieved from www.cihr.ca/e/documents/wad_brochure2%281%29.pdf.

———. (2011). The facts: Research about Aboriginal health. Retrieved from www.cihr-irsc.gc.ca/e/43377.html.

———. (2012). *Aboriginal Health Research News, 1*(5). June. Retrieved from www.cihr-irsc.gc.ca/e/documents/iaph_06-2012-en.pdf.

———. (2014). Science fact or science fiction: Is depression in men overlooked? Issue 2. November. Retrieved from www.cihr-irsc.gc.ca/e/documents/igh_mythbuster_depression-en.pdf.

Clarke, A.E., Shim, J.K., Mamo, L., Fosket, J., & Fishman, J.R. (2010). *Biomedicalization: technoscience and transformation of health and illness in the United States*. Durham, N.C: Duke University Press.

Clarke, A., Shim, J., Mamo, L., Fosket, J., & Fishman, J. (2005). Biomedicalization: Technoscientific transformations of health, illness and U.S. biomedicine. In P. Conrad (Ed.), *The sociology of health and illness: Critical perspectives* (7th ed.) (pp. 442–55). New York, NY: Worth Publishers.

Clement, W. (1975). *The Canadian corporate elite*. Toronto, ON: McClelland and Stewart.

Cleveland, G., & Krashinsky, M. (1998). *The economic rationale for public investment in young children: A policy study*. Toronto, ON: Child Care Advocacy Association of Ontario.

——— & ———. (2003). *Fact and fantasy: Eight myths about early childhood education*. Toronto, ON: Childcare Resources and Research Unit, University of Toronto.

CMA. (2007). Projections of physician supply in Canada. Retrieved from www.cma.ca/Assets/assets-library/document/en/advocacy/Projections_paper.pdf.

Coburn, D. (1988a). Canadian medicine: Dominance or proletarianization. *The Milbank Quarterly, 66*(2), 92–116.

———. (1988b). The development of Canadian nursing: Professionalization and proletarianization. *International Journal of Health Services, 18*(3), 437–56.

———. (1998). State authority, medical dominance, and trends in the regulation of health professions: The Ontario case. In D. Coburn, C. D'Arcy, & G. Torrance (Eds.), *Health and Canadian society: Sociological perspectives* (3rd ed.) (pp. 332–46). Toronto, ON: University of Toronto Press.

———. (2000). Income inequality, social cohesion and the health status of populations: The role of neo-liberalism. *Social Science & Medicine, 51*(1), 135–46.

———. (2001). Health, health care, and neo-liberalism. In P. Armstrong, H. Armstrong, & D. Coburn (Eds.), *Unhealthy times: Political economy perspectives on health and care in Canada* (pp. 45–65). Toronto, ON: Oxford University Press.

———. (2004). Beyond the income inequality hypothesis: Globalization, class, and health inequalities. *Social Science and Medicine, 58*, 41–56.

———. (2006). Health and health care: A political economy perspective. In D. Raphael, T. Bryant, & M. Rioux (Eds.), *Staying alive: Critical perspectives on health illness, and health care* (pp. 59–84). Toronto, ON: Canadian Scholars' Press Inc.

———. (2010). Health and health care: A political economy perspective. In Bryant, T., Raphael, D., & Rioux, M. (Eds.), *Staying alive: Critical perspectives on health, illness, and health care* (2nd ed.) (pp. 65–91). Toronto: Canadian Scholars' Press.

Coburn, D., D'Arcy, C., & Torrance, G. (Eds.). (1998). *Health and Canadian society (sociological perspectives)* (3rd ed.). Toronto, ON: University of Toronto Press.

Coburn, D., Torrance, G., & Kaufert, J., (1983). Medical dominance in Canadian historical perspective: The rise and fall of medicine. *International Journal of Health Services, 13*, 407–32.

Coburn, E. (2010). Introduction to Carroll (2010). You are here. *Socialist Studies, 6*(2). Fall, 9.

Cockerham, W.C. (2004). *Medical sociology* (9th ed.). Englewood Cliffs, NJ: Prentice Hall.

Code of Advertising Acceptance. (2009). Pickering: Pharmaceutical Advertising Advisory Board.

Code of Ethical Practices—2012. (2012). Ottawa: Rx&D

Cohen, A.M., Stavri, P.Z., & Hersh, W. (2004). A categorization and analysis of the criticisms of evidence-based medicine. *International Journal of Medical Informatics, 73*, 35–43.

Cohen, M. (2014). *How can we create a cost-effective system of primary and community care built around interdisciplinary teams?* CCPA Submission to the Select Standing Committee on Health. Canadian Centre for Policy Alternatives – BC Office. December 18. Retrieved from www.policyalternatives.ca/publications/reports/ccpa-bc-submission-select-standing-committee-health.

Cohen, R. (1991). Women of color in white households: Coping strategies of live-in domestic workers. *Qualitative Sociology 14*(2), 197–215.

Colborn, T., Dumanoski, D., & Myers, J.P. (1996). *Our stolen future: Are we threatening our fertility, intelligence, and survival?* Dutton: Penguin

Coleman, J. (1988). Social capital in the creation of human capital. *American Journal of Sociology, 94*, 95–120.

Coleman, V. (1994). Betrayal of trust. *British Medical Journal, 42*, 9602.

Collins, M., Bradley, C.P., O'Sullivan, T., & Perry, I.P. (2009). Co-self-care coping strategies in people with diabetes: A qualitative exploratory study. *BMC Endocrine Disorders, 9*(6). doi: 10.1186/1472-6823-9-6.

Collins, P. (1993). Toward a new vision: Race, class, and gender as categories of analysis and connection. *Race, Sex & Class, 1*(1), 25–45.

———. (2000a). *Black feminist thought: Knowledge, consciousness, and the politics of empowerment* (2nd ed.). New York: Routledge.

———. (2000b). Gender, black feminism, and black political economy. *Annals of the American Academy of Political and Social Science, 568*, March, 41–53.

Collins, R. (1975). *Conflict sociology: Towards an explanatory science.* New York, NY: Academic Press.

Collyer, F. (2004). The corporatisation and commercialisation of CAM. In P. Tovey, G. Easthope, & J. Adams (Eds.), *The mainstreaming of complementary medicine.* London, UK: Routledge.

Commission on the Social Determinants of Health (CSDH). (2008). *Closing the gap in a generation: Health equity through action on the social determinants of health.* Final Report. Geneva: World Health Organization. Retrieved from www.who.int/social_determinants/thecommission/finalreport/en/.

Cone, M. (2008, November 10). Prescription drugs can deliver high doses of phthalates. *Environmental Health News.* Retrieved from www.environmentalhealthnews.org/ehs/news/prescription-drugs-can-deliver-high-doses-of-phthalates.

Conference Board of Canada. (2011). *Canadian income inequality (Is Canada becoming more unequal?)* Retrieved from http://www.conferenceboard.ca/hcp/hot-topics/caninequality.aspx.

———. (2013a). *Elderly poverty.* Retrieved from www.conferenceboard.ca/hcp/details/society/elderly-poverty.aspx?pf=tru.

———. (2013b). *Health.* Retrieved from www.conferenceboard.ca/hcp/details/health.aspx.

Connell, R.W. (1977). *Ruling class, ruling culture.* Cambridge, UK: Cambridge University Press.

———. (1988). Class inequalities and "just health." *Community Health Studies, 12*(2), 212–17.

———. (1987). *Gender and power.* Sydney: Allen & Unwin.

———. (1995). *Masculinities.* Berkeley, CA: University of California Press.

Conrad, P. (1992). Medicalization and social control. *Annual Review of Sociology, 18*, 209–32.

———. (Ed.). (2005). *The sociology of health & illness (critical perspectives)* (7th ed.). New York, NY: Worth Publishers.

———. (2007). *The medicalization of society.* Baltimore, MD: Johns Hopkins University Press.

Conrad, P., Mackie, T., & Mehrotra, A. (2010). Estimating the costs of medicalization. *Social Science & Medicine, 70*, 1943–7.

Conrad, P., & Potter, D. (2000). From hyperactive children to ADHD adults: Observations on the expansion of medical categories. *Social Problems, 47*, 559–82.

Conrad, P., & Schneider, J. (1992). *Deviance and medicalization: From badness to sickness* (2nd ed.). Philadelphia, PA: Temple University Press.

Conrad, P., & Schneider, J. (1983). *Having epilepsy: The experience and control of illness.* Philadelphia: Temple University Press.

Cooley, C.H. (1964/1906). *Human nature and the social order.* New York, NY: Scribner's.

Cooper, N., Stevenson, C., & Hale, G. (Eds.). (1996). *Integrating perspectives on health.* Buckingham, UK: Open University Press.

Council of Canadians with Disabilities. (2010). A call to combat poverty and exclusion of Canadians with disabilities. In D. Raphael (Ed.), *Health promotion and quality of life in Canada* (pp. 228–33). Toronto, ON: Canadian Scholars' Press Inc.

Covey, H. (2005). Western Christianity's two historical treatments of people with disabilities or mental illness. *The Social Science Journal, 42*(1), 107–14.

Coyne, A. (2014, August 26). Why a public inquiry of murders isn't justified. *Ottawa Citizen,* p. C5.

Craib, I. (1992). *Modern social theory* (2nd ed.). London: Harvester Wheatsheaf.

Cranswick, K., & Dosman, D. (2008). Eldercare: What we know today. *Canadian Social Trends.* Ottawa, ON: Statistics Canada.

Crawshaw, P. (2013). Public health policy and the behavioural turn: The case of social marketing. *Critical Social Policy, 33*(4), 616–37.

Creatore, M., Moineddin, R., Booth, G., Manuel, D., DesMeules, M., McDermott, S., & Glazier, R. (2010, May 18). Age-and sex-related prevalence of diabetes mellitus among immigrants to Ontario, Canada. *Canadian Medical Association Journal,* 781–91.

Crompton, S. (2000, Winter). Health. *Canadian Social Trends,* Statistics Canada, *59,* 12–17.

———. (2010). Living with disability series: Life satisfaction of working-age women with disabilities. *Canadian Social Trends,* Statistics Canada, 24–32.

———. (2011). What's stressing the stressed? Main sources of stress among workers. *Canadian Social Trends,* Statistics Canada, Catalogue no. 11-008, 44–51.

Currie, J. (2005). *The marketization of depression: The prescribing of SSRI antidepressants to women.* May. Toronto, ON: Women and Health Protection. Retrieved from www.whp-apsf.ca/pdf/SSRIs.pdf.

Curry-Stevens, A. (2009). When economic growth doesn't trickle down: The wage dimensions of income polarization. In D. Raphael (Ed.), *Social determinants of health* (2nd ed.) (pp. 41–60). Toronto, ON: Canadian Scholars' Press Inc.

Dahrendorf, R. (1959). *Class and class conflict in industrial society.* Stanford: Stanford University Press.

Daly, J., Kellehear, A., & Glicksman, M. (1997). *The public health researcher.* Melbourne: Oxford University Press.

Danzer, A.M., & Danzer, N. (2011). The long-run consequences of Chernobyl: Evidence on subjective well-being, mental health and welfare. Munich Discussion Paper No. 2014-25. Department of Economics University of Munich. Retrieved December 22, 2015 // epub.ub.uni-muenchen.de/20969/1/Danzer_Danzer_Chernobyl%2020140610_v2.pdf.

Dastjerdi, M., Olson, K., & Ogilvie, L. (2012). A study of Iranian immigrants' experiences of accessing Canadian health care services: a grounded theory. *International Journal for Equity in Health, 11*(55), 1–15.

Davidson, K. (1969). Conceptions of illness and health practices in a Nova Scotia community. *Canadian Journal of Public Health, 61,* 232–41.

Davidson, L., Shaw, J., Welborn, S., Mahon, B., Sirota, M., Gilbo, P., McDermid, M., Fazio, J., Gilbert, C., Breetz, S., & Pelletier, J-F. (2010). I don't know how to find my way in the world: Contributions of user-led research to transforming mental health practice. *Psychiatry, 73*(2), 101–13.

Davies, C. (1977). Continuities in the development of hospital nursing in Britain. *Journal of Advanced Nursing, 2,* 479–93.

Davis, D. (1996). The cultural construction of the premenstrual and menopause syndromes. In C. Sargent & C. Bertrell (Eds.), *Gender and health: An international perspective.* Toronto, ON: Pearson.

Davis, L. (Ed.). (2010). *The disability studies reader* (3rd ed.). New York: Routledge.

Davis, R. (2000). Refugee experiences and Southeast Asian women's mental health. *Western Journal of Nursing Research, 22*(2), 144–68.

Daw, J. (2002, October). Is PMDD real? *Monitor on Psychology, 33*(9), 58–9, American Psychological Association.

Day, B. (2012). The right to pay for private health care. *The Vancouver Sun.* July 23. Retrieved from www.brianday.ca/right-to-health-care.html.

Day, S. (2013). The implications of conceptualizing care. In P. Armstrong & S. Braedley (Eds.), *Troubling Care: Critical Perspectives on Research and Practices.* Toronto: Canadian Scholars' Press.

Dean, J.A., & Wilson, K. (2010). "My health has improved because I always have everything I need here…": A qualitative exploration of health improvement and decline among immigrants. *Social Science & Medicine, 70,* 1219–28.

De Bruyn, T. (2002). *A summary of national data on complementary and alternative health care. Current status and future development: A discussion paper.* Ottawa, ON: Health Canada.

Dei, G.J.S. (1999). The denial of difference: Refraining anti-racist praxis. *Race Ethnicity and Education, 2*(2), 17–38.

Delaney, J. (2006, March 23). Potato farms a hotbed for cancer. *The Epoch Times.* Retrieved from http://english.epochtimes.com/news/6-3-23/39627.html.

de Leeuw, S., & Greenwood, M. (2011). Beyond borders and boundaries: Addressing Indigenous health inequities in Canada through theories of social determinants of health and intersectionality. In O. Hankivsky (Ed.), *Health Inequities in Canada: Intersectional Frameworks and Practices* (pp. 53–70). Vancouver: UBC Press.

De Maio, F.G., & Kemp, E. (2010). The deterioration of health status among immigrants to Canada. *Global Public Health, 5*(5), 462–78.

Denton, M., & Kusch, K. (2006). *Well-being through the senior years.* Ottawa, ON: Social Development Canada.

Denzin, N. (1997). *Interpretive ethnography.* London, UK: Sage.

Department of Health and Social Security (DHSS). (1980). *Inequalities in health.* Report of a working group chaired by Sir Douglas Black. London, UK: Author. DHSS.

Depletion of the Ozone Layer and Its Impacts: Health and Environmental Effects. (2013). Retrieved from http://ec.gc.ca/ozone/default.asp?lang=En&n=3E8154B2-1.

Devaney, J. (2014). Private clinics are not the solution to health-care cuts. *Rabble.* November 18. Retrieved from rabble.ca/columnists/2014/11/private-clinics-are-not-solution-to-health-care-cuts.

Deveau, D. (2010, March 12). Integrated health services crossing the divide. *The Vancouver Sun.* Retrieved from www.vancouversun.com/sunrun/Integrated+health+services+crossing+divide/2676343/story.html.

Dew, K. (2000). Apostasy to orthodoxy: Debates before a commission of inquiry into chiropractic. *Sociology of Health and Illness, 22*(3), 310–30.

Dhalla, I., Kwong, J., Streiner, D., Baddour, R., Waddell, A., & Johnson, I. (2002, April 16). Characteristics of first-year students in Canadian medical schools. *Canadian Medical Association Journal, 166*(8).

Dhamoon, R., & Hankivsky, O. (2011). Why the theory and practice of intersectionality matter to health research and policy. In O. Hankivsky (Ed.), *Health inequities in Canada: Intersectional frameworks and practices* (pp. 16–50). Vancouver: UBC Press.

Diebel, L. (1997, September 28). Ground coffee practically enslaved workers in Guatemala, Workers in Guatemala pay a high price for coffee. *Toronto Star*, p. F1.

DiMasi, J.A., Hansen, R.W., & Grabowski, H.G. (2003). The price of innovation: New estimates of drug development costs. *Journal of Health Economics, 22*, 151–85.

DiMasi, J.A., Hansen, R.W., & Grabowski, H.G. (2005). Reply: Extraordinary claims require extraordinary evidence. *Journal of Health Economics, 24*, 1034–44.

Djuraskovic, I., & Arthur, N. (2009). The acculturation of former Yugoslavian refugees. *Canadian Journal of Counselling, 33*(1), 18–34.

DND denies blame for cancer in Shannon, Que. (2010, January 29). Retrieved from www.cbc.ca/news/canada/montreal/ dnd-denies-blame-for-cancer-in-shannon-que-1.869817.

Dossa, P. (2009). *Racialized bodies, disabling worlds: Storied lives of immigrant Muslim women*. Toronto, ON: University of Toronto Press.

Driedger, D., & Owen, M. (2008). Introduction. *Dissonant disabilities: Women with chronic illnesses explore their lives* (pp. 1–13). Toronto: Canadian Scholars' Press/Women's Press.

Drugs for Neglected Diseases Working Group, & Campaign for Access to Essential Medicines. (2001). Fatal imbalance: The crisis in research and development for drugs for neglected diseases. Geneva: Médecins Sans Frontières.

Dubos, R. (1959). *Mirage of health: Utopias, progress, and biological change*. New York, NY: Harper & Row.

Dunn, B. (2006). *LGTB health matters: An education & training resource*. LGTB Health Matters Project. Vancouver, January. Retrieved from www.sexualhealthcentresaskatoon.ca/pdfs/p_lgbt.pdf.

Durkheim, E. (1984/1893). *The division of labor in society* (W. Halls, Trans.). New York, NY: Free Press.

———. (1951/1897). *Suicide*. New York, NY: Free Press.

Dutt, M. (2014). *Affordable access to medicines: A prescription for Canada*. Canadian Doctors for Medicare—Canadian Centre for Policy Alternatives: Ottawa.

Duxbury, L., Higgins, C., & Shroeder, B. (2009). *Balancing paid work and caregiving responsibilities: A closer look at family caregivers in Canada* Ottawa: Human Resources and Skills Development Canada.

Dyck, R., Osgood, N., Hsiang, T., Gao, A., & Stang, M.R. (2010, January). Epidemiology of diabetes mellitus among First Nations and non-First Nations adults. *Canadian Medical Association Journal, 19*, 1–8.

Eastern European Communities. Retrieved from www.seniorscouncil. net/uploads/files/Issues/Mobilizing_Action_Report/EASTERN% 20EUROPEAN%20COMMUNITIES.pdf.

Easthope, G. (1985). Marginal healers. In K. Jones (Ed.), *Sickness and sectarianism* (pp. 51–71). Aldershot: Gower.

Eaves, E., Sherman, K., Ritenbaugh, C., Hsu, C., Nichter, M., Turner, J., & Cherkin, D. (2015). A qualitative study of changes in expectations over time among patients with chronic low back pain seeking four CAM therapies. *BMC Complementary and Alternative Medicine, 15*, 12. Available at: DOI 10.1186/s12906-015-0531-9.

Ebeling, M. (2011). "Get with the Program!": Pharmaceutical marketing, symptom checklist and self-diagnosis. *Social Science & Medicine, 73*, 825–32.

Egan, C., & Gardner, L. (1999). Racism, women's health and reproductive freedom. In E. Dua & A. Robertson (Eds.), *Scratching the surface: Canadian anti-racist feminist thought*. Toronto, ON: Women's Press.

Ehrenreich, B., & English, D. (1973). *Witches, midwives and nurses*. New York, NY: Old Westbury Feminist Press.

——— & ———. (1974). *Complaints and disorders: The sexual politics of sickness*. London, UK: Compendium.

——— & ———. (1979). *For her own good: 150 years of experts' advice*. London, UK: Pluto Press.

Elias, B., O'Neil, J.D., & Yassi, A. (1997). Wollaston Lake: The uranium mining industry and the perceptions of risk. Centre for Aboriginal Health Research. Retrieved from http://epub.sub.uni-hamburg.de/ epub/volltexte/2010/5159/pdf/WOLLASTON_LAKE.pdf

Ellis, C. (1995). *Final negotiations: A story of love, loss, and chronic illness*. Philadelphia, PA: Temple University Press.

———. (1998). Exploring loss through autoethnographic inquiry. In J. Harvey (Ed.), *Perspectives on loss: A sourcebook*. New York, NY: Brunner/Mazel.

Ellis, C., Adams, T., & Bochner, A. (2011, January). Autoethnography: An overview. *Forum: Qualitataive Social Research, 12*(1).

Elmslie, K. (n.d.). Against the growing burden of disease. Public Health Agency of Canada. Retrieved from www.ccgh-csih.ca/assets/ Elmslie.pdf.

Elston, M.A. (1991). The politics of professional power: Medicine in a changing health service. In J. Gabe, M. Calnan, & M. Bury (Eds.), *The sociology of the health service* (pp. 58–88). London, UK: Routledge.

Employment and Social Development Canada. (n.d.). Canadians in context: National Aboriginal populations. Retrieved from www4 .hrsdc.gc.ca/.3ndic.1t.4r@-eng.jsp?iid=36.

Engel, G.L. (1977). The need for a new medical model: A challenge for biomedicine. *Science, 196*, 129–36.

———. (1980). The clinical application of the biopsychosocial model. *American Journal of Psychiatry, 137*(5), 535–44.

Engels, F. (1958/1845). *The condition of the working class in England*. (W.O. Henderson & W.H. Chaloner, Trans.). Oxford, UK: Basil Blackwell.

Environment Canada. (2015). Drivers and Impacts of Air Pollution. Retrieved from http://ec.gc.ca/indicateurs-indicators/default. asp?lang=En&n=D189C09D-1.

Epp, J. (1986). *Achieving health for all: A framework for health promotion*. Ottawa, ON: Health and Welfare Canada.

Ernst, E., & White, A. (2000). The BBC survey of complementary medicine use in the UK. *Journal of Complementary Therapies in Medicine, 8*(1), 32–6.

Esmail, N. (2007). *Complementary and alternative medicine in Canada: Trends in use and public attitudes, 1997–2006*. Public Policy Sources, Number 87/May. www.fraserinstitute.org/uploadedFiles/fraser-ca/ Content/research-news/research/publications/complementary-alternative-medicine-in-canada-2007.pdf.

Este, D. (2007). Cultural competency and social work practice in Canada: A retrospective examination. *Canadian Social Work Review, 24*(1), 93–104.

Estroff, S. (1995). Whose story is it anyway? Authority, voice, and responsibility in narratives of chronic illness. In S. Toombs, D. Barnard, & R. Carson (Eds.), *Chronic illness: From experience to policy.* Bloomington, IN: Indiana University Press.

Ethno-Racial People with Disabilities Coalition of Ontario and the Ontario Women's Health Network. (2008). *Ten+ years later: We are visible.* Toronto, ON: OWHN.

Evans, M., Hole, R., Berg, L., Hutchinson, P., Sookraj, D. (2009). Common insights, differing methodologies: Towards a fusion of Indigenous methodologies, participatory action research, and white studies in an urban Aboriginal research agenda. *Qualitative Inquiry, 15*(5), 893–911.

External Advisory Committee on Smart Regulation. (n.d.). Risk management. Retrieved from www.smartregulation.gc.ca/en/05/01/i4-01.asp.

Ezzy, D. (2000a). Illness narratives: Time, hope and HIV. *Social Science & Medicine, 50*, 605–17.

———. (2000b). Fate and agency in job loss narratives. *Qualitative Sociology, 23*(1), 121–34.

———. (2001). *Qualitative analysis.* Sydney: Allen & Unwin.

Faid, P. (2013, September 27). *Older Canadians: Benefit or burden?* Grey Matters 2013 Seniors Services Conference, Lethbridge, AB. www.greymatters2013.ca/notes/Older%20Canadians%20Benefit%20or%20Burden.pdf.

Fallis, J. (2012). Patients driving alternative medicine boom. *Canadian Medical Association Journal, 184*(9), E453–E454.

Famous Canadian Physicians. (n.d.). Library and Archives Canada. Retrieved from www.collectionscanada.gc.ca/physicians/030002-2500-e.html.

Fausto-Sterling, A. (2005). The bare bones of sex: Part 1. *"Sex and Gender" Signs 30*(2), 1491–528.

———. (2008, October). The bare bones of race. *Social Studies of Science, 38*(5), 657–94.

Federal study confirms oilsands tailings found in groundwater, river. (2014, February 20). Retrieved December 22, 2015 from www.ctvnews.ca/canada/federal-study-confirms-oilsands-tailings-found-in-groundwater-river-1.1697050.

Feldberg, G., & Vipond, R. (2006). Cracks in the foundation: The origins and development of the Canadian and American health care systems. In D. Raphael, T. Bryant, & M. Rioux (Eds.), *Staying alive, critical perspectives on health illness, and health care* (pp. 220–39). Toronto, ON: Canadian Scholars' Press Inc.

Fenta, S., Hyman, I., & Noh, H. (2007). Health service utilization by Ethiopian immigrants and refugees in Toronto. *Journal of Minority Health, 9*, 349–57.

Fernandes, C., Bouthillette, F., Raboud, J., Bullock, L., Moore, C., Christenson, …Way, M. (1999, November 16). Violence in the emergency department: A survey of health care workers. *Canadian Medical Association Journal, 161*(10), 1245–8.

Ferrari, L., & Drew, L. (2005). *Different minds: Living with Alzheimer disease.* Fredericton, NB: Alzheimer Society of New Brunswick.

Findlay, D., & Miller, L. (2002). Through medical eyes: The medicalization of women's bodies and women's lives. In B.S. Bolaria & H.

Dickinson (Eds.), *Health, illness and health care in Canada* (3rd ed.). Scarborough, ON: Nelson Thomson Learning.

Finkelstein, S., & Temin, P. (2008). *Reasonable Rx: solving the drug price crisis.* Upper Saddle River, NJ: FT Press.

Finn, E. (2007). The fateful summer of '62. Canadian Centre for Policy Alternatives. Retrieved from www.policyalternatives.ca/publications/monitor/july-2007-fateful-summer-62.

———. (2012, July 1). Government's forgone income: Huge tax cuts, uncollected taxes starve our social programs. *The Monitor.* Ottawa: CCPA. Retrieved from www.policyalternatives.ca/publications/monitor/governments-forgone-income.

Firestone, S. (1979/1970). *The Dialectic of Sex; the case for feminist revolution.* Toronto, ON: Women's Press.

First Nations Regional Health Survey. (2012). The First Nations Information Governance Centre. *Phase 2 (2008/10) National Report on Adults, Youth and Children Living in First Nations Communities.* Ottawa: The First Nations Information Governance Centre.

Flavin, Christopher. (2006). Nuclear revival: Don't bet on it! *World Watch Magazine, 19*, 4. Retrieved from www.worldwatch.org/node/4107.

Flexner Report, The. (1910). Medical education in the United States and Canada.

Flicker, S., Maley, O., Ridgley, A., Biscope, S, Lombardo, C., & Skinner, H. (2008). e-PAR: Using technology and participatory action research to engage youth in health promotion. *Action Research, 6*(3), 285–303

Flood, C. (2014). Canada should look to Europe on health care, not the U.S. *The Globe and Mail.* July 22. Retrieved from www.theglobeandmail.com/globe-debate/canada-should-look-to-europe-on-health-care-not-the-us/article19706492/.

Food Banks Canada. (2010). Hunger count. Retrieved from www.foodbankscanada.ca/documents/HungerCount2010_.

———. (2013). *HungerCount 2013.* Retrieved from www.foodbankscanada.ca/FoodBanks/MediaLibrary/HungerCount/HungerCount2013.pdf.

Ford, C., & Airhihenbuwa, C. (2010a). Critical race theory, race equity, and public health: Toward antiracism praxis. *American Journal of Public Health.* Supplement 1, 100(S1).

——— & ———. (2010b). The public health critical race methodology: Praxis for antiracism research. *Social Science & Medicine, 71*, 1390–8.

Ford-Gilboe, M., Wuest, J., Varcoe, C., Davies, L., Merritt-Gray, M., Campbell, J., & Wilk, P. (2009). Modelling the effects of intimate partner violence and access to resources on women's health in the early years after leaving an abusive partner. *Social Science & Medicine, 68*(6), 1021–9.

Ford-Gilboe, M., Wuest, J., Varcoe, C., & Merritt-Gray, M. (2006). Developing an evidence based health advocacy intervention to support women who have left abusive partners. *Canadian Journal of Nursing Research, 38*(1), 147–68.

Foster, K. (2012). *Youth employment and un(der) employment in Canada: More than a temporary problem?.* Ottawa: Canadian Centre for Policy Alternatives. Retrieved from www.policyalternatives.ca.

Foster, K., McAllister, M., & O'Brien, L. (2005). Coming to autoethnography: A mental health nurse's experience. *International Journal of Qualitative Methods, 4*(4), 1–13.

Foucault, M. (1975). *The birth of the clinic: An archaeology of medical perception.* (A.M. Sheridan, Trans.). New York, NY: Vintage Books.

———. (1978). *The History of Sexuality.* New York: Pantheon Books.

———. (1979). *Discipline and punish.* Harmondsworth, UK: Penguin.

———. (1988). *Madness and civilization: A history of insanity in the age of reason.* (R. Howard, Trans.). New York, NY: Vintage Books.

Fowler, N. (1998). Providing primary health care to immigrants and refugees: The North Hamilton experience. *Canadian Medical Association Journal, 159,* 388–91.

Fox, M., Dwyer, D.J., & Ganster, D.C. (1993). Effects of stressful job demands and control on physiological and attitudinal outcomes in a hospital setting. *Academy of Management Journal, 36,* 289–318.

Frances, A. (2012). DSM-5 Is a guide, not a bible: Simply ignore its 10 worst changes. *Psychology Today.* December 2. Retrieved from www.psychologytoday.com/blog/dsm5-in-distress/201212/dsm-5-is-guide-not-bible-ignore-its-ten-worst-changes.

Frank, L. (2013). *Got milk?: The public policy relations of infant food insecurity in Canada.* Doctoral Dissertation. University of New Brunswick. December 2012.

Frankel, G., Speechley, M., & Wade, T. (1996). *The sociology of health and health care: A Canadian perspective.* Toronto, ON: Copp Clark.

Freidson, E. (1970). *Profession of medicine.* New York, NY: Harper & Row.

———. (1988). *Profession of medicine: A study of the sociology of applied knowledge.* Chicago, IL: University of Chicago Press.

———. (1994). *Professionalism reborn: Theory, prophecy and policy.* Cambridge, UK: Polity Press.

———. (2001). *Professionalism: The third logic.* Cambridge, UK: Polity Press.

French, S. (1993). Can you see the rainbow? The roots of denial. In J. Swaine, V. Finkelstein, S. French, & M. Oliver (Eds.), *Disabling Barriers—Enabling Environments* (pp. 81–6). London: Sage.

Freund, P., McGuire, M., & Podhurst, L. (2003). *Health, illness, and the social body: A critical sociology* (4th ed.). New Jersey: Prentice-Hall.

Fried, B.J., Deber, R.B., & Leatt, P. (1987). Corporatization and deprivatization of health services in Canada. *International Journal of Health Services, 17,* 567–84.

Friendly, M. (2009). Early childhood education and care as a social determinant of health. In D. Raphael (Ed.), *Social determinants of health* (2nd ed.) (pp. 128–42). Toronto, ON: Canadian Scholars' Press Inc.

Fries, C. (2013). Self-care and complementary and alternative medicine as care for the self: An embodied basis for distinction. *Health Sociology Review, 22*(1), 37–51.

———. (2014). Older adults' use of complementary and alternative medical therapies to resist biomedicalization of aging. *Journal of Aging Studies, 28,* 1–10.

Fuhrer, R., Stansfeld, S.A., Chemali, J., & Shipley, M.S. (1999). Gender, social relations and mental health: Prospective findings from an occupational cohort (Whitehall II study). *Social Science and Medicine, 48*(1), 77–87.

Fuller, C. (2015). *Cambie Corp. goes to court: The legal assault on universal health care.* Ottawa: Canadian Centre for Policy Alternatives.

Furlow, B. (2008, September). Special report: Cancer inquiry unveils Canada's troubled health system. *The Lancet,* 9. Retrieved from www.thelancet.com/ocology

Gaetz, S., Donaldson, J., Richter, T., & Gulliver, T. (2013). *The state of homelessness in Canada 2013.* Toronto: Canadian Homelessness Research Network

Gagnon, M.-A., & Lexchin, J. (2008). The cost of pushing pills: A new estimate of pharmaceutical promotion expenditures in the United States. *PLoS Medicine,* 5, e1.

Galabuzi, G.-E. (2001). Canada's creeping economic apartheid. Toronto, ON: CJS Foundation. Retrieved from www.socialjustics.org.

———. (2004). Social Exclusion. In D. Raphael (Ed.), *Social Determinants of Health: Canadian Perspectives* (pp. 235–51). Toronto: Canadian Scholars Press, Inc.

———. (2009). Social exclusion. In D. Raphael (Ed.), *Social determinants of health* (2nd ed.) (pp. 252–79). Toronto, ON: Canadian Scholars' Press Inc.

———. (2012, March 20). The persistence of racial inequality in Canada. Editorial Opinion. *The Toronto Star.* Retrieved from www.thestar.com/opinion/editorialopinion/2012/03/20/the_persistence_of_racial_inequality_in_canada.html.

Gamarnikow, E. (1978). Sexual division of labour: The case of nursing. In A. Kuhn & A.M. Wolpe (Eds.), *Feminism and materialism* (pp. 96–123). London, UK: Routledge & Kegan Paul.

Game, A., & Pringle, R. (1983). *Gender at work.* Sydney: Allen & Unwin.

Gamer, R., Carrière, C., Sanmartin, C. and the Longitudinal Health and Administrative Date Research Team. (2010). *The health of First Nations living off-reserve, Inuit, and Métis adults in Canada: The impact of socio-economic status on inequalities in health.* Ottawa: Ministry of Industry. Retrieved from www.statcan.gc.ca/pub/82-622-x/82-622-x2010004-eng.pdf.

Garattini, S., & Bertele, V. (2002). Efficacy, safety, and cost of new anti-cancer drugs. *BMJ, 325,* 269–71.

Gardner, D.M., Mintzes, B., & Ostry, A. (2003). Direct-to-consumer prescription drug advertising in Canada: Permission by default. *Canadian Medical Association Journal, 169,* 425–8.

Garfinkel, H. (1967). *Studies in ethnomethodology.* Englewood Cliffs, NJ: Prentice Hall.

Gathering strength: Canada's Aboriginal action plan. (1998). Minister of Indian Affairs and Northern government. Retrieved from www.ahf.ca/downloads/gathering-strength.pdf.

Gee, G., & Ford, C. (2011). Structural racism and health inequities: Old issues, new directions. *Du Bois Review: Social Science Research on Race, 8*(1), 115–32.

Germov, J. (1993, October). The waiting list bypass. *Health Forum, 27,* 23–4.

Germov, J., & Williams, L. (Eds.). (2004). *A sociology of food and nutrition: The social appetite* (2nd ed.). Melbourne: Oxford University Press.

Gesensway, D. (2001). Reasons for sex-specific and gender-specific study of health topics. *Annals of Internal Medicine, 135,* 935–8.

Giddens, A. (1986). *Sociology: A brief but critical introduction* (2nd ed.). London, UK: Macmillan.

———. (1991). *Modernity and self-identity: Self and society in the late modern age.* Stanford, CA: Stanford University Press.

———. (1997). *Sociology* (3rd ed.). Cambridge, UK: Polity Press.

———. (2006). *Sociology.* (5th ed.). Cambridge: Polity Press.

Gillespie, J.A. (1991). *The price of health: Australian governments and medical politics 1910–1960.* Melbourne: Cambridge University Press.

Gillespie, R., & Gerhardt, C. (1995). Social dimensions of sickness and disability. In G. Moon & R. Gillespie (Eds.), *Society and health: An introduction to social science for health professionals* (pp. 79–94). London, UK: Routledge.

Gilligan, C. (1993). *In a different voice.* Boston, MA: Harvard University Press.

Gionet, L. (2008, November 26). Inuit in Canada: Selected findings of the 2006 Census. *Canadian Social Trends.* Ottawa, ON: Statistics Canada.

———. (2009a, May 12). First Nations people: Selected findings of the 2006 Census. *Canadian Social Trends.* Ottawa, ON: Statistics Canada.

———. (2009b, January 20). Métis in Canada: Selected findings of the 2006 Census. *Canadian Social Trends.* Ottawa, ON: Statistics Canada.

Gionet, L., & Roshanafshar, S. (2013). *Select health indicators of First Nations people living off reserve, Métis and Inuit.* Ottawa: Statistics Canada.

Gitlin, T. (2000). Afterword. In C.W. Mills, *The Sociological Imagination* (40th Anniversary Edition) (pp. 229–40). New York. NY: Oxford University Press

Glaser, B., & Strauss, A. (2012). *The discovery of grounded theory: Strategies for qualitative research* (12th ed.).

Goar, C. (2009, September 9). Quebec shows the way on poverty. *Toronto Star.*

Goffman, E. (1961). *Asylums: Essays on the social situation of mental patients and other inmates.* Harmondsworth, UK: Penguin.

———. (1963). *Stigma: Notes on the management of spoiled identity.* New York, NY: Simon & Schuster.

Goldthorpe, J. (1996). Class and politics in advanced industrial societies. In D.J. Lee & B.S. Turner (Eds.). *Conflicts about class.* London, UK: Longman.

Goodley, D., Hughes, B., & Davis, L. (Eds.). (2012). *Disability and social theory: New development and directions.* London, England: Palgrave Macmillan.

Gottlieb, L. (2009). Putting health care during the past decade in context: An interview with Dr. Judith Shamian. *Canadian Journal of Nursing Research, 41*(1), 21–9.

Government of Canada. (1985). Access to information act.

Government of Canada. (2002). The Canada we want: speech from the throne to open the Second Session of the Thirty-Seventh Parliament of Canada 2002 [cited 2004 February 15]. Available from www.pco-bcp.gc.ca/sft-ddt/docs/sft2002.

———. (2014). *Action for seniors.* Available at www.seniors.gc.ca/build/theme-sc-ac/pdf/action_report_for_seniors.pdf.

Grabb, E. (2007). *Theories of social inequality* (5th ed.). Toronto, ON: Thomas Nelson.

———. (2009). Conceptual issues in the study of social inequality. In E. Grabb & N. Guppy (Eds.), *Social inequality in Canada: Patterns, problems and policies* (5th ed.) (pp. 1–16). Toronto, ON: Pearson Prentice Hall.

Grabb, E., & Hwang, M. (2009). Corporate concentration, foreign ownership, and state involvement in the Canadian economy. In E.

Grabb & N. Guppy (Eds.), *Social inequality in Canada: Patterns, problems and policies* (5th ed.) (pp. 19–28). Toronto, ON: Pearson Prentice Hall.

Graham, D.J., Campen, D., Hui, R., Spence, M., Cheetham, C., Levy, G.,...Ray, W.A. (2005). Risk of acute myocardial infarction and sudden cardiac death in patients treated with cyclo-oxygenase 2 selective and non-selective non-steroidal anti-inflammatory drugs: Nested case-control study. *Lancet, 365,* 475–81.

Grant, J., Angen, E., & Dyer, S. (2013, June). Forecasting the impacts of oilsands expansion: Measuring the land disturbance, air quality, water use, greenhouse gas emissions, and tailings production associated with each barrel of bitumen production. Pembina Institute. Retrieved December 22, 2015 at www.pembina.org/reports/oilsands-metrics.pdf.

Gray, J.A. (1999, October). Postmodern medicine. *Lancet, 354,* 153–5.

Green, J. (1998). Commentary: Grounded theory and the constant comparative method. *British Medical Journal, 316*(7137), 1064–5.

Green, R.J., Williams, P., Johnson, L., Shanthi, C., & Blum, I. (2008). Can Canadian seniors on public pensions afford a nutritious diet. *Canadian Journal on Aging, 27*(1), 69–79.

Greenberg, L., & Normandin, C. (2011). *Disparities in Life expectancy at birth.* Statistics Canada. April. Health at a glance. Retrieved from www.statcan.gc.ca/pub/82-624-x/2011001/article/11427-eng.htm.

Greenslade, M.V., & Paddock, K. (2007, February). Working conditions of nurses: A cause of concern. *Health Policy Research Bulletin, 13,* 13–16. Ottawa, ON: Health Canada.

Grills, S., & Grills, S. (2008). The social construction of doubt: Women's accounts of uncertainty and chronic illness. In D. Driedge & Owen, M. (Eds.), *Dissonant disabilities: Women with chronic illnesses explore their lives* (pp. 53–62). Toronto: Canadian Scholars' Press/Women's Press.

Growe, S.J. (1991). *Who cares: The crisis in Canadian nursing.* Toronto, ON: McClelland & Stewart Inc.

Guberman, N. (1999). *Caregivers and caregiving: New trends and their implications for policy.* Ottawa, ON: Health Canada.

Guimond, É., & Robitaille, N. (2008). When teenage girls have children: Trends and consequences. *Horizons Policy Research Initiative, 10*(1).

Gupta, S., & Ross, N. (2007, November). Under the microscope: Health disparities within Canadian cities. In Health Canada, People, place and health, *Health Policy Research Bulletin, 14,* 23–8. Retrieved from www.hc-sc.gc.ca/sr-sr/alt_formats/hpb-dgps/pdf/pubs/hpr-rps/bull/2007-people-place-gens-lieux/2007-people-place-gens-lieux-eng.pdf

Gurm, B.K., Stephen, J., MacKenzie, G., Doll, R., Barroetavena, M.C., & Cadell, S. (2008). Understanding Canadian Punjabi-speaking South Asian women's experience of breast cancer: A qualitative study. *International Journal of Nursing Studies, 45,* 266–76.

Habibi, R., & Lexchin, J. (2014). Quality and quantity of information in Summary Basis of Decision documents issued by Health Canada. *PLoS One, 9,* e92038.

Hall, H., Griffiths, D., & McKenna, L. (2011). The use of complementary and alternative medicine by pregnant women: A literature review. *Midwifery, 27,* 817–24.

Hall, Justice Emmett. (1964). *Report of the Royal Commission on Health Services*. Ottawa, ON.

———. (1980). *Canada's national-provincial health program for the 1980's: Commitment for renewal*. Ottawa, ON.

Halpern, S.A. (1992). Dynamics of professional control: Internal coalitions and crossprofessional boundaries. *American Journal of Sociology, 97*, 994–1021.

Halpin, B. (2009). Of the first water: The rights and roles of First Nations in source protection and water quality. *Canadian Water Treatment*, July/August: 18–21.

Hancock, T. (1985, November). The mandala of health: A model of the human ecosystem. *Family and Community Health*, 1–10.

Hankivsky, O. (Ed.), (2011). *Health inequities in Canada: Intersectional frameworks and practices*. Vancouver: UBC Press.

Hankivsky, O. (2011). Intersectionality and public policy: Some lessons from existing models. *Political Research Quarterly, 64*(1), 217–29.

Hankivsky, O., de Leeuv, S., Lee, J., Vissandjee, B., & Khanlou, N. (2011). Introduction: Purpose, Overview, and Contribution. In O. Hankivsky (Ed.), *Health inequities in Canada: Intersectional frameworks and practices*. Vancouver: UBC Press

Hankivsky, O., Reid, C., Cormier, R., Vaarcoe, C., Clark, N., Benoit, C., & Brotman, S. (2010). Exploring the promises of intersectionality for advancing women's health research. *International Journal for Equity in Health, 9*(5), 1–15.

Hansen, N. (2008). A Delicate Balance: Chronic Conditions and Workspace. In D. Driedger & M. Owen (Eds.), *Dissonant disabilities: Women with chronic illnesses explore their lives* (pp. 131–45). Toronto: Canadian Scholars' Press/Women's Press.

Hansson, E., Tuck, A., Lurie, S., & McKenzie, K. (2012). Rates of mental illness and suicidality in immigrant, refugee, ethnocultural, and racialized groups in Canada: A review of the literature. *Canadian Journal of Psychiatry, 57*(2), 111–21.

Harding, S. (1991). *Whose science? Whose knowledge?: Thinking from women's lives*. Ithaca, NY: Cornell University Press.

Harper, S., & Strumpf, E. (2012). Social Epidemiology: Questionable Answers and Answerable Questions. *Epidemiology, 23*(6), Web pdf.

Hazleton, M. (1990). Medical discourse on contemporary nurse education: An ideological analysis. *Australian and New Zealand Journal of Sociology, 26*(1), 107–25.

Health Canada. (1999a). *Canadian research on immigration and health: An overview*. Ottawa, ON: Author.

———. (1999 b). *Intersectoral action...towards population health: Report of the federal, provincial and territorial advisory committee on population health*. Ottawa, ON: Author.

———. (1999c). *Toward a healthy future. Second report on the health of Canadians*. Ottawa, ON: Author.

———. (2002a). *Canada's aging population, division of aging and seniors*. Ottawa, ON: Retrieved from http://dsp-psd.pwgsc.gc.ca/Collection/H39-608-2002E.pdf.

———. (2002b). *Health care system, "our health, our future": Creating quality workplaces for Canadian nurses*. Ottawa, ON: Author.

———. (2002c). *Income inequality as a determinant of health*. Retrieved from www.phac-aspc.gc.ca/ph-sp/oi-ar/pdf/02_income_e.pdf.

———. (2003a, March). Closing the gaps in Aboriginal health. *Health Policy Research Bulletin*, 5. Ottawa, ON: Author.

———. (2003b). *Improving Canada's regulatory process for therapeutic products: Building the action plan: Multistakeholder consultation: Public Policy Forum*. Ottawa, ON: Author.

———. (2003c, November). Who's doing what. *Health Policy Research Bulletin*, 7. Ottawa, ON: Author.

———. (2004a). *Health services review*. Retrieved from www.hc-sc.gc.ca/hcs-sss/com/fed/hs-ss-79-eng.php.

———. (2004b). *Issue analysis summary: Summary basis of decision-draft 7*. Ottawa, ON: Author.

———. (2005a). Health Canada important safety information on ADDERALL XR' (amphetamine salts). Retrieved from www.hc-sc.gc.ca/dhp-mps/medeff/advisories-avis/prof/_2005/adderall_xr_hpc-cps-eng.php.

———. (2005b, January). *First Nations comparable health indicators*. Ottawa, ON: Author.

———. (2005c). *First Nations, Inuit and Aboriginal health, health transfer*. Retrieved from www.hc-sc.gc.ca/fniah-spnia/pubs/finance/_agree-accord/10_years_ans_trans/3_transfert-eng.php.

———. (2005d). *Mandate and priorities, First Nations and Inuit health branch*. Retrieved from www.hc-sc.gc.ca/ahc-asc/branch-dirgen/fnihb-dgspni/mandat-eng.php.

———. (2006a). *Healthy Canadians–A federal report on comparable health indicators 2006*. Retrieved from www.hc-sc.gc.ca/hcs-sss/pubs/system-regime/2006-fed-comp-indicat/index-eng.php.

———. (2006b). *Healthy Canadians, measuring performance*. Retrieved from www.hc-sc.gc.ca/hcs-sss/alt_formats/hpb-dgps/pdf/pubs/2006-fed-comp-indicat/2006-fed-comp-indicat-eng.pdf.

———. (2007a). The working conditions of nurses: Confronting the challenges, 2005 national survey of the work and health of nurses. *Health Policy Research Bulletin*. Ottawa, ON: Author.

———. (2007b). *Indian health policy 1979*. Retrieved from www.hc-sc.gc.ca/ahc-asc/branch-dirgen/fnihb-dgspni/poli_1979-eng.php.

———. (2007c, November). People, place and health. *Health Policy Research Bulletin*, 14. Retrieved from www.hc-sc.gc.ca/sr-sr/alt_formats/hpb-dgps/pdf/pubs/hpr-rps/bull/2007-people-place-gens-lieux/2007-people-place-gens-lieux-eng.pdf.

———. (2008a). *Healthy Canadians, a federal report on comparable health indicators*. Ottawa, ON: Author.

———. (2008b). *Statistical profile on the health of First Nations in Canada, self-rated health and selected conditions, 2002–2005*. Retrieved from www.hc-sc.gc.ca/fniah-spnia/alt_formats/pdf/pubs/aborig-autoch/2009-stats-profil-vol3/2009-stats-profil-vol3-eng.pdf.

———. (2008c). *Fact sheet. First Nations and Inuit health branch (FNIHB)*. Retrieved from www.hc-sc.gc.ca/ahc-asc/branch-dirgen/fnihb-dgspni/index-eng.php.

———. (2009a). *A statistical profile on the health of First Nations in Canada: Determinants of health 1999 to 2003*. Ottawa, ON: Author.

———. (2009b). Delivery of palliative and end-of-life care services. Retrieved from www.hc-sc.gc.ca/hcs-sss/palliat/services/index-eng.php

———. (2011a). *Canada's food guide (2011)*. Ottawa: Health Canada Retrieved from: http://www.hc-sc.gc.ca/fn-an/food-guide-aliment/order-commander/index-eng.php#a1

———. (2011b). First Nations, Inuit and Aboriginal health. Retrieved from www.hc-sc.gc.ca.

———. (2011c). Cost recovery - frequently asked questions (FAQs).

Retrieved May 16, 2014, from www.hc-sc.gc.ca/dhp-mps/ prodpharma/activit/fs-fi/costfs_coutsfd-eng.php.

——. (2012a). *Canada's health care system.* Retrieved from www.hc-sc .gc.ca/hcs-sss/pubs/system-regime/2011-hcs-sss/index-eng.php#a5.

——. (2102b) *First Nations and Inuit health.* Retrieved from www. hc-sc.gc.ca/fniah-spnia/diseases-maladies/index-eng.php.

——. (2013a). *Better health, better care, better value for all: Refocusing health care reform in Canada.* Toronto: Health Council of Canada. September. Retrieved from www.cahspr.ca/web/uploads/conference/ 2014-02-14_Better_Health_Better_Care_Better_Value_For_All.pdf.

——. (2013b). *Harper Government and Retail Council of Canada bring health eating messages to Canadians where they shop – EAT WELL campaign delivers practical tips for busy families.* Retrieved from www.hc-sc.gc.ca/ahc-asc/media/nr-cp/_2013/2013-30-eng.php.

——. (2013c). *Healthy eating toolbox.* Retrieved from www.hc-sc.gc .ca/fn-an/nutrition/part/tb-bo/index-eng.php?utm_source=food_ nutrition-health_eating_tlbox&utm_medium=banner_en&utm_ campaign=theme_footer.

——. (2014). *Natural Health Products.* Modified April 24, 2014. Retrieved from www.hc-sc.gc.ca/dhp-mps/prodnatur/index-eng .php.

Health Council of Canada. (2005, January). *The health status of Canada's First Nations, Métis and Inuit peoples.* Toronto, ON: Author.

——. (2006). *Health care renewal in Canada: Clearing the road to quality.* Ottawa, ON: Author.

——. (2012). *Seniors in need, caregivers in distress: What are the home care priorities for seniors in Canada?* Retrieved from www.health-councilcanada.ca/rpt_det_gen.php?id=348.

——. (2013a). *Better health, better care, better value for all: Refocusing health care reform in Canada.* Toronto: Health Council of Canada. September. Retrieved from www.cahspr.ca/web/uploads/conference/ 2014-02-14_Better_Health_Better_Care_Better_Value_For_All.pdf.

——. (2013b). *Progress report 2013: Health care renewal in Canada.* Retrieved from www.healthcouncilcanada.ca/rpt_det.php?id=481.

Health Policy Research Bulletin. (2003, November 7). *Complementary and alternative health care: The other mainstream.* Ottawa: Health Canada.

Health Products and Food Branch. (2007a). *Cost recovery framework: Consultation document.* Ottawa, ON: Health Canada.

——. (2007b). *Cost recovery framework: Official notice of fee proposal for human drugs and medical devices.* Ottawa, ON: Health Canada.

Health Reports. (2007). *Physician consultations, 18*(1). Ottawa, ON: Statistics Canada.

Healthy U. (n.d.). Understanding health and wellness from the perspective of Aboriginal Peoples in Canada. Retrieved from http:// www.healthyalberta.com/699.htm.

Healy, D. (1997). *The anti-depressant era.* Cambridge Mass: Harvard University Press.

——. (2003). *Let them eat Prozac.* Toronto, ON: James Lorimer & Company Ltd.

Hedden, L., Barer, M., Cardiff, K., McGrail, K., Law, M., & Bourgeault, I. (2014). The implications of the feminization of the primary care physician workforce on service supply: A systematic review. *Human Resources for Health. 12*(32), 1–11. Retrieved from www.human -resources-health.com/content/12/1/32.

Hemminki, E., Hailey, D., & Koivusalo, M. (1999). The courts—A challenge to health technology assessment. *Science, 285,* 203–4.

Hepworth, M. (1995). Positive ageing: What is the message. In R. Bunton, S. Nettleton, & R. Burrow (Eds.), *The sociology of health promotion.* London, UK: Routledge.

Hertzman, C. (2000a). The case for an early childhood development strategy. *Isuma, 1*(2), 11–18.

Higginbottom, G., Hadziabdic, E., Yohani, S., & Paton, P. (2014). Immigrant women's experience of maternity services in Canada: A meta-ethnography. *Midwifery, 30,* 544–59.

Hilbers, J., & Lewis, C. (2013). Complementary health therapies: Moving towards an integrated health model. *Collegian, 20,* 51–60.

Hill Collins, P. (2000). *Black feminist thought: Knowledge, consciousness and the politics of empowerment* (2nd ed.). New York, NY: Routledge.

Hippocrates biography: His influence on modern medicine. (n.d.). Retrieved from www.allsands.com/science/hippocratesbiog _rtb_gn.htm.

Hirschkorn, K., & Bourgeault, I.L. (2005). Conceptualizing mainstream health care providers' behaviours in relation to complementary and alternative medicine. *Social Science and Medicine, 61,* 157–70.

History of Medicine. (n.d.). History of scientific medicine: The scientific revolution. Retrieved from www.planetseed.com/node/17132.

——. (n.d.). Renaissance medicine. Retrieved from www.planetseed. com/node/17101.

——. (n.d.). Shamanism: Healing by supernatural means. Retrieved from www.planetseed.com/node/17120.

——. (n.d.). The rise of scientific medicine: The nineteenth century. Retrieved from www.planetseed.com/node/17133.

Hollenberg, D. (2006). Uncharted ground: Patterns of professional interaction among complementary/alternative and biomedical practitioners in integrative health care settings. *Social Science & Medicine, 62,* 731–44.

Hollenberg, D., & Muzzin, L. (2010). Epistemological challenges to integrative medicine: An anti-colonial perspective on the combination of complementary/alternative medicine with biomedicine. *Health Sociology Review, 19*(1), 34–56.

Holloway, K. (2014). Uneasy subjects: Medical students' conflicts over the pharmaceutical industry. *Social Science and Medicine, 114,* 113–20.

Holmes, S., Greene, J., & Stonington, S. (2014). Locating global health in social medicine. *Global Public Health, 9*(5), 475–80.

hooks, b. (1984). *Feminist theory from margin to center.* Boston, MA: South End Press.

Hoover, M., & Rotermann, M. (2012). *Seniors' use of and unmet needs for home care, 2009.* Statistics Canada. Ottawa: Minister of Industry. Retrieved from: www.statcan.gc.ca/pub/82-003-x/2012004/article/ 11760-eng.htm.

Horkheimer, M. (1972). *Critical theory.* New York, NY: Herder and Herder.

Hornosty, J., & Doherty, D. (2003). Responding to wife abuse in farm and rural communities: Searching for solutions that work. In R. Blake & A. Nurse (Eds.), *The trajectories of rural life: New perspectives on rural Canada* (pp. 37–53). Regina, SK: Canadian Plains Research Centre.

——— & ———. (2004). Resistance and change: Building a framework for helping abused rural women. In B. Cheers, R. Clews, A.M. Powers,

& L. Carawan. (Eds.), Beyond geographical and disciplinary boundaries: Human services in rural communities. *Journal of Rural Social Work, 9*, 106–17.

Hossay, P. (2006). *Unsustainable: A primer for global environmental and social justice.* New York, NY: Zed Books.

Hothschild, A.R. (1979). Emotion work, feeling rules and social structure. *American Journal of Sociology, 85*(3), 551–75.

Hou, F., Balakrishnanen, T.R., & Jurdi, R. (2009). The economic integration of visible minorities in contemporary Canadian society: Revisited. In E. Grabb & N. Guppy (Eds.), *Social inequality in Canada* (5th ed.). Toronto, ON: Pearson Prentice Hall.

House, J.S., Landis, K.R., & Umberson, D. (1988). Social relationships and health. *Science, 241*, 121–4.

HRSDC – Health -Life Expectancy at Birth. (n.d.) Retrieved from www4.hrsdc.gc.ca/.3ndic.1t.4r@-eng.jsp?iid=3.

Huang, V. (2004, Spring). A brief overview of the teaching of complementary and alternative medicine in the undergraduate medical education curriculum. *Queen's Health Sciences Journal, 7*(2), 39–43.

Hughes, D. (1988). When nurse knows best: Some aspects of nurse/doctor interaction in a casualty department. *Sociology of Health and Illness, 10*(1), 51–63.

Hui, A. (2010, May 26). Nearly one-quarter of Canadians will be seniors by 2036. *The Globe and Mail.*

Human Development Report. (2014). *Sustaining human progress: Reducing vulnerabilities and building resilience.* United Nations Development Programme. Retrieved from http://hdr.undp.org/sites/default/files/hdr14-report-en-1.pdf.

Hylton, K. (2012). Talk the talk, walk the walk: Defining critical race theory in research. *Race Ethnicity and Education, 15*(1), 23–41.

Hyman, I. (2001). Immigration and health. Health Canada working paper 01–05. Canadian Research on Immigration and Health: An Overview. Ottawa, ON: Health Canada.

———. (2009). *Racism as a determinant of immigrant health.* Policy Brief for Strategic Initiatives and Innovations Directorate and the Public Health Agency of Canada. Retrieved from http://canada.metropolis.net/pdfs/racism_policy_brief_e.pdf.

Hyman, I., & Jackson, B. (2010). The healthy immigrant effect: A temporary phenomenon?. *Migration Health: Health Policy Research Bulletin, 17*, 17–21. Retrieved at www.hc-sc.gc.ca/sr-sr/pubs/hpr-rpms/bull/2010-health-sante-migr/index-eng.php.

ICPHR. (2013) *International collaboration for participatory health research position paper 1: What is participatory health research?* Version: Mai 20113. Berlin: International Collaboration for Participatory Health Research. Retrieved from http://communityresearchcanada.ca/res/download.php?id=4261.

Illich, I. (1976). *Limits to medicine.* Toronto, ON: McClelland & Stewart.

———. (1977). *Limits to medicine, medical nemesis: The exploration of health.* Harmondsworth, UK: Penguin.

IndexMundi. (2014). Canada Age Structure. Retrieved from www.indexmundi.com/canada/age_structure.html.

Indian Health Policy. (1979). Retrieved from www.hc-sc.gc.ca/ahc-asc/branch-dirgen/fnihb-dgspni/poli_1979-eng.php.

Innis, H. (1999/1930). *The fur trade of Canada.* Toronto, ON: University of Toronto Press.

Institute for Work & Health. (2009, August). *Issue briefing: Unemployment and mental health.* Available online at www.iwh.on.ca/briefings/unemployment-and-mental-health.

———. (2012). *At Work*, Issue 67. Retrieved from www.iwh.on.ca/wrmb/grounded-theory.

International Plastics Task Force. (2009). Retrieved from www.ecologycenter.org/iptf/.

Jackson, B., Pederson, A., & Bosco, M. (2006). Gender-based analysis and wait times: New questions, new knowledge. Research Paper. *Women and health care reform group.* Ottawa: Health Canada.

Jackson, B., Pederson, A., & Bosco, M. (2009). Waiting to wait. Improving wait times evidence through gender-based analysis. In P. Armstrong & J. Deadmaneds. *Women's health intersections of policy, research, and practice* (pp. 35–52). Toronto: Women's Press.

Jagger, A. (1983). *Feminist politics and human nature.* NJ: Rowman & Allanheld.

James, M. (2013). How to avoid phthalates (even though you can't avoid phthalates). *Gimme the good stuff: A conscious resource for conscious moms and healthy kids.* Retrieved from https://gimmethegoodstuff.org/scary-stuff-phenoxyethanol.

Johansen, B.E. (2002). The Inuit's struggle with dioxins and other organic pollutants. *American Indian Quarterly, 26*(3), 479–90.

Johnson, J., Crespin, D., Griffin, K., Finch, M., Rivard, R., Baechler, C., & Dusek, J. (2014). The effectiveness of integrative medicine interventions on pain and anxiety in cardiovascular inpatients: a practice-based research evaluation. *BMC Complementary and Alternative Medicine, 13*(486), 1–10. Retrieved from www.biomedcentral.com/1472-6882/14/486.

Johnson, J.L., Greaves, L., & Repta, R. (2009). Better science with sex and gender: Facilitating the use of a sex and gender-based analysis in health research. *International Journal of Health Equity.* Published on-line. 10.1186/1475-9276-8-14.

Joppi, R., Bertele, V., & Garattini, S. (2005). Disappointing biotech. *BMJ, 331*, 895–7.

Judge, K., Mulligan, J., & Benzenval, M. (1998). Income inequality and population health. *Social Science & Medicine, 46*(4–5), 567–79.

Kafele, K. (2004). *Racial discrimination and mental health in racialized and Aboriginal communities.* Ontario Human Rights Commission. Retrieved from www.ohrc.on.ca/en/book/export/html/8999.

Kaptchuk, T., & Miller, F. (2005). Viewpoint: What is the best and most ethical model for the relationship between mainstream and alternative medicine: Opposition, integration, or pluralism? *Academic Medicine, 80*(3), 286–90.

Katz, S. (2012). Book Review of Sally Chivers. (2011). *The silvering screen: Old age and disability in cinema. Canadian Journal of Aging, 31*(2), 254–5.

Kaufert, P., & Gilbert, P. (1987). Medicalization and the menopause. In D. Coburn, C. D'Arcy, G. Torrence, & P. New (Eds.), *Health and Canadian society: Sociological perspectives* (2nd ed.). Markham, ON: Fitzhenry & Whiteside.

Kawachi, I. (1992). Six case studies of the voluntary regulation of pharmaceutical advertising and promotion. In P. Davis (Ed.), *For health or profit* (pp. 269–87). Auckland: Oxford University Press.

Kellehear, A. (1993). *The unobtrusive researcher.* Sydney: Allen & Unwin.

Kelly, E.N., Short, J.W., Schindler, D.W., Hodson, P.V., Ma, M., Kwan, A.K., & Fortin, B.L. (2009). Oil sands development contributes polycyclic aromatic compounds to the Athabasca River and its tributaries. Proceedings of the National Academy of Sciences USA 106: 22346-22351.

Kelner, M., Wellman, B., Boon. H., & Welsh, S. (2004). Responses of established healthcare to the professionalization of complementary and alternative medicine in Ontario. *Social Science & Medicine, 59*, 915–30.

Keshet, Y., & Simchai, D. (2014). The "gender puzzle" of alternative medicine and holistic spirituality: A literature review. *Social Science & Medicine, 113*, 77–86.

Kirk, J. (1994). Gender inequality and medical education. In S. Bolaria & R. Bolaria (Eds.), *Women, medicine and health*. Halifax, NS: Fernwood.

Kirk, J., Muir, D., Gleason, et al. (2014). Atmospheric deposition of mercury and methylmercury to landscapes and waterbodies of the Athabasca oil sands region. *Environmental Science & Technology, 48*(13), 7374–83.

Kirk, M., Tomm-Bonde, L., & Schreiber, R. (2014). Public health reform and health promotion in Canada. *Global Health Promotion, 21*(2), 15–22.

Kirkey, S. (2013). Most Canadians doubt health care system prepared to handle "tsunami" of aging boomers, new poll shows. *National Post*. August 19. Available online at http://news.nationalpost.com/2013/08/19/most-canadiansdoubt-health-care-system-pre-pared-to-handle-tsunami-of-aging-boomers-new-poll-shows/.

Kirkey, S. (2014, January 19). Psychiatrist warns against trying to cure ordinary sadness as Canadians among top users of antidepressants. *National Post*. Retrieved at http://news.nationalpost.com/2014/01/19/psychiatrist-warns-against-trying-to-cure-ordinary-sadness-as-canadians-among-top-users-of-antidepressants.

Kirkey, S. (2014, August 20). MDs want right to opt out if assisted suicide legalized. *Ottawa Citizen*, p. A8.

Kirkey, S. (2014, October 9). Poll shows most Canadians support euthanasia rights. *Ottawa Citizen*, p. A11.

Kirmayer, L., Weingeld, M., Burgos, G., du Fort, G., Lasry, J-C., & Young, A. (2007). Use of health care services for psychological distress by immigrants in an urban multicultural milieu. *The Canadian Journal of Psychiatry, 52*(5).

Kittrie, N.N. (1971). *The right to be different: Deviance and enforced therapy*. Baltimore, MD: Penguin.

Kleinman, A. (1988). *The illness narrative: Suffering, healing and the human condition*. New York: Basic Books.

———. (2012). Culture, bereavement, and psychiatry. *The Lancet, 379*, 608–9.

Kleinman, A., & Seeman, D. (2000). Personal experience of illness. In G. Albrecht, R. Fitzpatrick, & S. Scrimshaw (Eds.), *The handbook of social studies in health & medicine* (pp. 230–42). London, UK: Sage.

Kobayashi, K. (2003). Do intersections of diversity matter: An exploration of the relationship between identity markers and health for mid-to later-life Canadians. *Canada Ethnic Studies, 35*(3), 85–98.

Kobayashi, K., & Prus, S. (2011). Adopting an intersectionality perspective in the study of the healthy immigrant effect in mid-to later life. In O. Hankivsky (Ed.), *Health inequities in Canada: Intersectional frameworks and practices* (pp. 180–97). Vancouver: UBC Press.

——— & ———. (2012). Examining the gender, ethnicity, and age dimensions of the healthy immigrant effect: Factors in the development of equitable health policy. *International Journal for Equity in Health, 11*(8), 1–6.

Kobayashi, K., Prus, S., & Lin, Z. (2008, April). Ethnic differences in self-rated and functional health: Does immigrant status matter. *Ethnicity & Health, 13*(2), 129–47.

Kondro, W. (2012). Health disparities among income groups becoming more pronounced. *Canadian Medical Association Journal, 184*(13), E695–E696.

Kopec, J., Williams, I., To, T., & Austin, P. (2001). Cross-cultural comparisons of health status in Canada using the health utilities index. *Ethnicity and Health, 6*(1), 41–50.

Kornelsen, J., & Grzybowski, S. with Anhorn, M., Cooper, E., Galvin, L., Pederson, A., & Sullivan, L. (2006). Rural women's experiences of maternity care: Implications for policy and practice. Retrieved from www.swc-cfc.gc.ca/pubs/pubspr/0662407997/index_e.html.

Kramer, B., & Thompson, E. (Eds.). (2005). *Men as caregivers*. Amherst, NY: Prometheus.

Krieger, N. (2001). Theories for social epidemiology in the 21st century: an ecosocial perspective. *International Journal of Epidemiology, 30*, 668–77.

Krieger, N. (2011). *Epidemiology and the people's health*. New York: Oxford University Press.

Kristoffersen, A., Stub, T., Salamonsen, A., Musial, F., & Hamberg, K. (2014). Gender differences in prevalence and associations for use of CAM in a large population study. *BMC Complementary and Alternative Medicine, 14*, 463. Retrieved from www.biomedcentral.com/1472-6882/14/463.

Krugman, P. (2009). *The conscience of a liberal*. New York: W.W. Norton & Co.

Laduke, W. (1999). *All our relations: Native struggles for land life*. Cambridge: South End Press.

La Follette, M.C. (1992). *Stealing into print: Fraud, plagiarism and misconduct in scientific publishing*. Berkeley, CA: University of California Press.

Lalonde, M. (1974). *A new perspective on the health of Canadians*. Ottawa, ON: Government of Canada.

Lam, R.W., Levitt, A., Levitan, R., Enns, M., Morehouse, R., Michalak. E., & Tam, E. (2006, May). The Can-SAD study: A randomized controlled trial of the effectiveness of light therapy and fluoxetine in patients with winter seasonal affective disorder. *American Journal of Psychiatry, 163*, 805–12.

Langston, N. (2008). The retreat from precaution: Regulating diethyl-stilbestrol (DES), endocrine disruptors and environmental health. *Environmental History, 13*(1). Retrieved from http://www.jstor.org/stable/pdf/25473193.pdf?acceptTC=true.

Larkin, G. (1983). *Occupational monopoly and modern medicine*. London, UK: Tavistock.

Larkin, J., Flicker, S., Mintz, S., Dagnino, M., Kolezar-Green, R., & Mitchell, C. (2007). HIV risk, systemic inequities and Aboriginal youth: Widening the circle for HIV prevention programming. *Canadian Journal of Public Health, 98*, 179–82.

Larkin, M. (1995). Estrogen: Friend or foe. *FDA Consumer, 29*(3), 25–9.

Larson, M.S. (1977). *The rise of professionalism: A sociological analysis.* Berkeley, CA: University of California Press.

Laslett, A. (1989). The demographic scene: An overview. In J. Eekelaar & D. Pearl (Eds.), *An aging world* (pp. 1–10). Oxford, UK: The Clarendon Press.

Leduc, N., & Proulx, M. (2004, January). Patterns of health services utilization by recent immigrants. *Journal of Immigration Health, 6,*(1), 15–27.

Lee, J., & Sum, A. (2011). Exploring health and identity through photo-voice, intersectionality, and transnational feminisms: Voices of racialized young women. In O. Hankivsky (Ed.), *Health inequities in Canada: Intersectional frameworks and practices* (pp. 147–165). Vancouver: UBC Press.

Lee, S., & Mysyk, A. (2004). The medicalization of compulsive buying. *Social Science & Medicine, 58*, 1709–18.

Lepofsky, D. (1985). Equality and disabled persons. In R. Abella & R. Rothman (Eds.), *Justice beyond Orwell* (pp. 309–32). Montreal, QC: Editions Y. Blais.

Levy, J., Ansara, D., & Stover, A. (2013). *Racialization and health inequities in Toronto.* Toronto Public Health. October. Retrieved from www.toronto.ca/health/reports.

Lewis, B. (2010). A mad fight: Psychiatry and disability activism. In L. Davis (Ed.), *The disability studies reader* (3rd ed.) (pp. 160–76). New York: Routledge.

Lexchin, J. (2001). Pharmaceuticals: Politics and policy. In P. Armstrong, H., Armstrong, & D. Coburn (Eds.), *Unhealthy times: Political economy perspectives on health and care in Canada* (pp. 31–44). Toronto, ON: Oxford University Press.

——. (2006). Relationship between pharmaceutical company user fees and drug approvals in Canada and Australia: A hypothesis-generating study. *Annals of Pharmacotherapy, 40*, 2216–22.

——. (2007a). Drug regulation: Two paradigms in conflict. In N.J. Temple & A. Thompson (Eds.), *Excessive medical spending: Facing the challenge* (pp. 53–62). Oxford, UK: Radcliffe Publishing.

——. (2007b). The secret thing belong unto the lord our god: Secrecy in the pharmaceutical arena. *Medicine and Law, 26*, 417–30.

——. (2008). New directions in Canadian drug regulation: Whose interests are being served. In O. O'Donovan & K. Glavanis-Grantham. (Eds.), *Power, politics and pharmaceuticals* (pp. 153–70). Cork: Cork University Press.

——. (2009). *Drug safety and Health Canada: Going, going, gone.* Ottawa, ON: Canadian Centre for Policy Alternatives.

——. (2010a). Medicines and money: The corruption of clinical information. In R. Burke, E. Tomlinson, & C. Cooper (Eds.), *Crime and corruption in organizations: Why it happens and what to do about it* (pp. 249–71). London: Gower.

——. (2010b). Pharmaceutical policy: The dance between industry, government and the medical profession. In D. Raphael, T. Bryant, & M. Rioux (Eds.), *Staying alive: Critical perspectives on health, illness, and health care* (2nd ed.) (pp. 371–93). Toronto, ON: Canadian Scholars' Press Inc.

——. (2014). Postmarket safety in Canada: are significant therapeutic advances and biologics less safe than other drugs? A cohort study. *BMJ Open, 4*, e004289.

——. (Forthcoming). Medicines and money: The corruption of clinical information. In R. Burke, E. Tomlinson, & C. Cooper (Eds.), *Crime and corruption in organizations: Why it happens and what to do about it.* London, UK: Gower.

Lexchin, J., & Kawachi, I. (1996). Voluntary codes of pharmaceutical marketing: Controlling promotion or licensing deception. In P. Davis (Ed.), *Contested ground: Public purpose and private interest in the regulation of prescription drugs* (pp. 221–35). New York, NY: Oxford University Press.

Lexchin, J., & Mintzes, B. (2004). Transparency in drug regulation: Mirage or oasis. *Canadian Medical Association Journal, 171*, 1363–5.

Lexchin, J., & Wiktorowicz, M. (2009). Profits first: The pharmaceutical industry in Canada. In B.S. Bolaria & H. Dickinson (Eds.), *Health, illness, and health care in Canada* (4th ed.) (pp. 437–57). Toronto, ON: Nelson.

Li, P.S. (2008). The market value and social value of race. In M.A. Wallis & S. Kwok (Eds.), *Daily struggles: The deepening racialization and feminization of poverty in Canada.* Toronto: Canadian Scholars' Press, Inc.

Lien, O. (1992). The experience of working with Vietnamese patients attending a psychiatric service. *Journal of Vietnamese Studies, 5*, 95–105.

Light, D.W., Andrus, J.K., & Warburton, R.N. (2009). Estimated research and development costs of rotavirus vaccines. *Vaccine, 27*, 6627–33.

Light, D.W., & Warburton, R.N. (2005). Extraordinary claims require extraordinary evidence. *Journal of Health Economcis, 24*, 1030–3.

Lincoln, Y. (1995). Emerging criteria for quality in qualitative and interpretive research. *Qualitative Inquiry, 1*, 275–89.

Lindberg, A., Fossum, B., Karlen, P., & Oxelmark, L. (2014). Experiences of complementary and alternative medicine in patients with inflammatory bowel disease—A qualitative study. *BMC Complementary and Alternative Medicine, 14*, 407. Retrieved from www.biomedcentral.com/1472-6882/14/407.

Living Lessons. (2007). Hospice palliative care fact sheet. Retrieved from www.living-lessons.org/main/hospice.asp.

Lloyd, G., & Norris, C. (1999). Including ADHD. *Disability & Society, 14*(4), 505–17.

——— & ———. (2000). Accounting for disease and distress: Morals of the normal and abnormal. In G. Albrecht, R. Fitzpatrick, & S. Scrimshaw (Eds.), *The handbook of social studies in health & medicine* (pp. 259–76). London, UK: Sage.

López-Abente, G., Aragonés, N., Pollán, M., Ruiz, M., & Gandarillas, A. (1999). Leukemia, lymphomas, and myeloma mortality in the vicinity of nuclear power plants and nuclear fuel facilities in Spain. Cancer *Epidemiology, Biomarkers and Prevention, 8*, 925–34.

López-Abente, G., Aragonés, N., & Pollán S. (2001). Solid-tumor mortality in the vicinity of uranium cycle facilities and nuclear power plants in Spain. *Environmental Health Perspectives, 109*(7), 721–9.

Lopez, J., & Scott, J. (2000). *Social Structure.* Buckingham, UK: Open University Press.

Loppie Reading, C., & Wien, F. (2009). *Health inequalities and social determinants of Aboriginal Peoples' health*. Prince George, B.C.: National Collaborating Centre for Aboriginal Health. Retrieved from www.nccah-ccnsa.ca/docs/social%20determinates/NCCAH-Loppie-Wien_Report.pdf.

Lorber, J. (2000). *Gender and the social construction of illness*. New York, NY: Altamira Press.

Lorber, J., & Moore, L. (2002). *Gender and the social construction of illness* (2nd ed.). New York, NY: AltaMira Press

Lowenberg, J.S., & Davis, F. (1994). Beyond medicalization/demedicalization: The case of holistic health. *Sociology of Health and Illness, 16*(5), 579–600.

Lupton, D. (1995). *The imperative of health: Public health and the regulated body*. London, UK: Sage.

———. (2012). M-health and health promotion: The digital cyborg and surveillance society. *Social Theory & Health, 19*(3), 229–44.

Luxton, M., & Maroney, J. (Eds.). (1987). *Feminism and political economy: Women's work, women's struggles*. Toronto, ON: Methuen Press.

Lynch, J. (2000). Income inequality and health: Expanding the debate. *Social Science & Medicine, 51*(3), 1001–5.

McBane, M. (2005). *Ill-health Canada: Putting food and drug company profits ahead of safety*. Ottawa, ON: Canadian Centre for Policy Alternatives.

McCoy, R. (2001). Employing an individual with a disability: Does this have an effect on employers' attitudes' (MA thesis). University of New Brunswick, Fredericton, NB.

McCrea, E. (1983). The politics of menopause: The discovery of a deficiency disease. *Social Problems, 31*(1), 111–23.

McCurdy, H. (2001). Africville: Environmental racism. In L. Westra & B. Lawson (Eds.), *Faces of environmental racism: Confronting issues of global justice* (pp. 95–112). Lanham, MD: Rowman & Littlefield Publishers.

McDaniel, S. (1986). *Canada's aging population*. Toronto, ON: Butterworths.

MacDonald, C. (2012). Understanding participatory action research: A qualitative research methodology option. *Canadian Journal of Action Research, 13*(2), 34–50.

Macdonald, D. (2014). *Outrageous fortune: Documenting Canada's wealth gap*. Ottawa: Canadian Centre for Policy Alternatives. Retrieved from www.policyalternatives.ca.

Macdonald, D., & Wilson, D. (2013). *Poverty or prosperity: Indigenous children in Canada*. Ottawa: Canadian Centre for Policy Alternatives.

McDonald, L., & Donahue, P. (2011). Retirement Lost?. *Canadian Journal of Aging, 30*(3), 401–22.

McDonald, T., & Kennedy, S. (2007). Cervical cancer screening by immigrant and minority women in Canada. *Journal of Immigrant Minority Health, 9*(4), 323–34.

McDonough, P. (2001). Work and health in the global economy. In P. Armstrong, H. Armstrong, & D. Coburn (Eds.), *Unhealthy times: Political economy perspectives on health and care in Canada* (pp. 195–222). Toronto, ON: Oxford University Press.

McFarland, B., Bigelow, D., Zani, B., Newsom, J., & Kaplan, M. (2002, October). Complementary and alternative medicine use in Canada and the United States. *American Journal of Public Health, 92*(10), 1616–18.

McGarity, T.O., & Shapiro, S. A. (1980). The trade secret status of health and safety testing information: Reforming agency disclosure policies. *Harvard Law Review, 93*, 837–88.

McGibbon, E. (2009). Health and health care: A human rights perspective. In D. Raphael (Ed.), *Social determinants of health* (2nd ed.) (pp. 318–35). Toronto, ON: Canadian Scholars' Press Inc.

McGibbon, E., & McPherson, C. (2011). Applying intersectionality & complexity theory to address the social determinants of women's health. *Women's Health & Urban Life, 10*(1), 59–86.

McGinty, Jo Craven. (2014, August 16). Much-criticized body mass index endures as a fatness guide. *Wall Street Journal*. Retrieved December 22, 2015 at www.wsj.com/articles/much-criticized-body-mass-index-endures-as-a-fatness-guide-1408148146.

McHugh, T., & Kowalski, K. (2009). Lessons learned: Participatory action research with young Aboriginal women. *Pimatisiwin: A Journal of Aboriginal and Indigenous Community Health, 7*(1), 117–31.

McIntosh, C., Fines, P., Wilkins, R., & Wolfson, M. (2009, November). Income disparities in health: Adjusted life expectancy for Canadian adults, 1991–2001. *Health Reports, 20*(4). Ottawa, ON: Statistics Canada.

Macintyre, C. (1999). From entitlement to obligation in the Australian welfare state. *Australian Journal of Social Issues, 34*(2), 103–29.

Macintyre, S. (1997). The Black report and beyond: What are the issues. *Social Science & Medicine, 44*(6), 723–45.

Mack, J. (2014). Neoliberalism and the rise of the a Parsonian medical encounter: An autopathography of injury recovery in the context of no doctor-patient relationship. Academia.edu. Retrieved from https://www.academia.edu/9660405/Neoliberalism_and_the_Rise_of_the_aParsonian_Medical_Encounter_An_autopathography_of_injury_recovery_in_the_context_of_no_doctor-patient_relationship.

McKay, A. (2006). Trends in teen pregnancy in Canada with comparisons to U.S.A. and England/Wales. *The Journal of Human Sexuality, 15*(3–4), 157–61.

McKeary, M., & Newbold, B. (2010). Barriers to care: The challenges for Canadian refugees and their health care providers. *Journal of Refugee Studies, 23*(4), 523–45.

McKeown, T. (1976). *The role of medicine: Dream, mirage or nemesis*. London, UK: Nuffield Hospital Trust.

———. (1979). *The role of medicine: Dream, mirage or nemesis*. Oxford, UK: Basil Blackwell.

———. (1988). *The origins of human disease*. Oxford, UK: Basil Blackwell.

Mackenzie, H. (2014). *All in a day's work? (CEO pay in Canada)*. Ottawa: Canadian Centre for Policy Alternatives. Retrieved from www.policyalternatives.ca.

Mackenzie, C.A., Lockridge, A., & Keith, M. (2005). Declining sex ratio in a First Nation community. *Environmental Health Perspectives, 113*(10), 1295–8.

McKinlay, J.B., & McKinlay, S.M. (1977). The questionable effect of medical measures on the decline of mortality in the United States in the twentieth century. *Milbank Memorial Fund Quarterly, 55*, 405–28.

McKinlay, J. (2005). A case for refocusing upstream: The political economy of illness. In P. Conrad (Ed.), *The sociology of health and illness* (7th ed.) (pp. 551–65). New York, NY: Worth Publishing.

MacKinnon, C. (1989). *Toward a feminist theory of the state.* Harvard University Press.

MacKinnon, M., & Howard., L. (2010). Affirming immigrant women's health: Building inclusive health policy immigrant women's health. In V. Zawilski (Ed.), *Inequality in Canada: A reader on the intersections of gender, race, and class* (2nd ed.) (194–210). Toronto, ON: Oxford University Press.

McLeod, K.S. (2000). Our sense of snow: The myth of John Snow in medical geography. *Social Science & Medicine, 50*, 923–35.

MacMahon, B., & Pugh, T.F. (1970). *Epidemiological principles and methods.* Boston, MA: Little Brown.

McMichael, A.J. (1991). Food, nutrients, health and disease: A historical perspective on the assessment and management of risks. *Australian Journal of Public Health, 15*, 7–13.

McMullin, J. (2010). *Understanding social inequality: Intersections of class, age, gender, ethnicity and race in Canada.* Toronto, ON: Oxford University Press.

Maggi, J., & Daly, T. (2006). Gender matters: Understanding the emotional and social support needs of women with HIV/AIDS. *Research Bulletin.* Retrieved from http://findarticles.com/p/articles/mi_6860/is_2_5/ai_n28426149/

Maheux, B., Dufort, F. Beland, F., Jacques, A., & Levesque, A. (1990, January). Female medical practitioners: More preventive and patient oriented. *Medical Care, 28*(1), 87–92.

Malacrida, C. (2004). Medicalization, ambivalence and social control: Mothers' descriptions of educatiors and ADD/ADHD. *Health: An Interdisciplinary Journal for the Social Study of Health, Illness and Medicine, 8*(1), 61–80.

Malthouse, M. (2011). An autoethnography on shifting relationships between a daughter, her mother and Alzheimer's dementia (in any order). *Dementia, 10*(2), 249–56.

Man, G. (2012). Racialization of gender, work, and transnational migration. In S. Hier & S. Bolaria (Eds.), *Race & racism in 21st-century Canada: Continuity, complexity and change* (pp. 235– 252). North York, ON: University of Toronto Press.

Manderson, L., & Mathews, M. (1981). Vietnamese attitudes towards maternal and infant health. *Medical Journal of Australia, 1*, 69–72.

Manning, N. (2000). Psychiatric diagnosis under conditions of uncertainty: Personality disorder, science and professional legitimacy. *Sociology of Health & Illness, 22*, 621–39.

Markens, S. (1996). The problematic of "experience": A political and cultural critique of PMS. *Gender and Society, 10*, 42–58.

Marmot, M. (1999). Introduction. In M. Marmot & R. Wilkinson (Eds.), *Social determinants of health.* Oxford, UK: Oxford University Press.

———. (2000, April 17). Social determinants of health: From observation to policy. *Medical Journal of Australia, 172*, 379–82.

———. (2004). *Status syndrome: How your social standing directly affects your health and life expectancy.* Oxford, UK: Bloomsbury.

Marmot, M., Bosma, H., Hemingway, H., Brunner, E., & Stansfeld, S. (1997, July 26). Contribution of job control and other risk factors to social variations in coronary heart disease incidence. *Lancet, 350*(9073), 235–9.

Marmot, M.G., Davey Smith, G., Stansfield, S., Patel, C., North, F., Head, J., . . . Feeney, A. (1991). Health inequalities among British civil servants: The Whitehall II study. *Lancet, 337*(8754), 1387–93.

Marmot, M.G., Siegrist, J., Theorell, T., & Feeney, A. (1999). Health and the psychosocial environment at work. In M. Marmot & R. Wilkinson (Eds.), *Social determinants of health.* Oxford, UK: Oxford University Press.

Marmot, M., & Wilkinson., R. (Eds.). (2006). *Social determinants of health* (2nd ed.). Oxford, UK: Oxford University Press.

Marshall, B. (2006). The new virility: Viagra, male aging and sexual function. *Sexualities, 9*(3), 345–62.

———. (2007). Climacteric redux? (Re)medicalizing the male menopause. *Men and Masculinities, 9*(4), 509–29.

Martin, E. (1987). *The woman in the body: A cultural analysis of reproduction.* Boston, MA: Beacon Press.

Martin, S. (2015, February 7). A just bittersweet victory. *Globe & Mail*, pp. A8–A9.

Marx, K. (1964/1844). *The economic & philosophic manuscripts of 1844.* New York, NY: International Publishers.

———. (1967/1867). *Capital, volume 1.* New York, NY: International Publishers.

———. (1970/1845). *The German ideology.* New York, NY: International Publishers.

———. (1959/1869). The eighteenth brumaire of Louis Bonaparte. In L. Feuer (Ed.), *Marx & Engels: Basic writings on politics & philosophy.* Garden City, NY: Anchor Books, Doubleday & Company.

Mason, S., Tovey, P., & Long, A.F. (2002). Evaluating complementary medicine: Methodological challenges of randomised controlled trials. *British Medical Journal, 325*, 832–4.

Maticka-Tyndale, E., McKay, A., & Barrett, M. (2001). Teenage sexuality and reproductive behavior in developed countries. *Occasional Report 4.* New York, NY: The Alan Guttmacher Institute.

Maunsell, E., Brisson, J., & Deschenes, L. (1995). Social support and survival among women with breast cancer. *Cancer, 76*(4), 631–7.

Maximova, K., & Krahn, H. (2010). Health Status of Refugees Settled in Alberta: Changes Since Arrival. *Canadian Journal of Public Health, 101*(4), 322–6.

Maxwell, D.M., MD. (2008). Cancer, genetic defects are uranium's legacy: An interview with Dr. David Maxwell. Environmental Health Association of Nova Scotia. Retrieved from www.environmentalhealth.ca/fall08legacy.html

May, M. (2012). RCTs: Not all that glitters is gold. Stanford Social Innovation Review. Retrieved from www.ssireview.org/blog/entry/rcts_not_all_that_glitters_is_gold.

McNamara, B., Waddell, C., & Colvin, M. (1994). The institutionalization of a good death. *Social Science & Medicine, 39*(11), 1501–9.

Mead, G.H. (1964/1934). *Mind, self and society.* Chicago, IL: University of Chicago Press.

Meadows, L.M., Thurston W.E., & Berenson C.A. (2001). Health promotion and preventive measures: Interpreting messages at midlife. *Qualitative Health Research, 11*(4), 450–63.

Meadows, L., Thurston, W., & Melton, C. (2001). Immigrant women's health. *Social Science & Medicine, 52,* 1451–8.

Mei, A., Eales, J., & Fast, J. (2013). *Older Canadians are volunteers and charitable donors.* Retrieved from www.mysage.ca/public/download/documents/4058.

Mendes, F. (2013). Active ageing: A right or a duty?. *Health Sociology Review.*

Mesley, W. (2006, March 5). *Chasing the cancer answer* [Television broadcast]. Toronto, ON: CBC Marketplace.

Meslin, E. (1987, August). The moral costs of the Ontario physicians' strike. *Hastings Center Report, 17*(4), 11–13.

Messing, K. (1998). *One-eyed science: Occupational health and women workers.* Philadelphia, PA: Temple University Press.

Metcalfe, A., Williams, J., McChesney, J., Patten, S., & Jetté. (2010). Use of complementary and alternative medicine by those with a chronic disease and the general population – results of a national population based survey. *BMC Complementary & Alternative Medicine, 10,* 58. Retrieved from www.ncbi.nlm.nih.gov/pmc/articles/PMC2967501/pdf/1472-6882-10-58.pdf.

Meyer, I.H. (2003). Prejudice, social stress, and mental health in lesbian, gay, and bisexual populations: Conceptual issues and research evidence. *Psychological Bulletin, 129*(5), 674–97.

Michols, D. (1996). *The distinction between advertising and other activities.* Ottawa, ON: Health Canada, Therapeutic Products Programme.

———. (1997). *Drugs and medical devices programme quality initiative bulletin #2.* Ottawa, ON: Health Protection Branch.

Mickleburgh, R., (2010, November 6). The outspoken surgeon Medicare advocates love to hate. *The Globe and Mail,* pp. A12–A13.

Mikkonen, J., & Raphael, D. (2010). Social determinants of health, the Canadian facts. Retrieved from www.thecanadianfacts.org/The_Canadian_Facts.pdf.

Milan, A., & Vézina, M. (2011). *Senior women.* Ottawa: Ministry of Industry. Retrieved from www.statcan.gc.ca/pub/89-503-x/2010001/article/11441-eng.htm.

Millar, W. (2001, December). Patterns of use: Alternative health care practitioners. *Health Reports, 13*(1). Ottawa, ON: Statistics Canada, Catalogue 82–003.

Mills, C.W. (1959). *The sociological imagination.* New York, NY: Oxford University Press.

Milner, N. (1989). The denigration of rights and the persistence of rights talk: A cultural portrait. *Law and Social Inquiry, 14,* 631–75.

Mintzes, B., & Jureidini, H. (2009, Spring). Exposure to SSRI antidepressants in pregnancy. *Women and Environments, 80/81,* 29–32.

Mintzes, B., Lexchin, J., Sutherland, J., Beaulieu, M.-D., Wilkes, M., Durrieu, G., et al. (2013). Pharmaceutical sales representatives and patient safety: a comparative prospective study of information quality in Canada, France and the United States. *Journal of General Internal Medicine, 28,* 1368–75.

Mitchinson, W. (1993). The medical treatment of women. In S. Burt, L. Code, & L. Dorney (Eds.), *Changing patterns: Women in Canada* (2nd ed.) (pp. 391–421). Toronto, ON: McClelland & Stewart Inc.

Mittlestaedt, M. (2006, December 6). Pesticides are what is killing our kids. *The Globe and Mail.* Retrieved from http://v1.theglobeandmail.com/servlet/story/RTGAM.20061206.wxcancerenviro06/BNStory/cancer/home

Mobilos, S., Chan, M., & Brown, J. (2008, September). Women in medicine: The challenge of finding balance. *Canadian Family Physician, 54,* 1285-6.e1–5

Montague, P. (2004). The chemical wars, part 1, 2 and 3. *Rachel's Environment & Health News, 798, 799, 780.*

Monture, P. (2012). Racing and erasing: Law and gender in white settler societies. In S. Hier & S. Bolaria (Eds.), *Race & racism in 21st-century Canada: Continuity, complexity and change* (pp. 197–216). North York, ON: University of Toronto Press.

Moran, J. (2009). History of madness and mental illness: A short history of care and treatment in Canada. Retrieved from http://historyofmadness.ca/index.php?option=com_content&view=article&id=80.

Moran, M., Ropars, A.-L., Guzman, J., Diaz, J., & Garrision, C. (2005). *The new landscape of neglected disease drug development.* London, UK: Wellcome Trust.

Morgan, S., & Cunningham, C. (2011). Population aging and he determinants of healthcare expenditures: The case of hospital, medical and pharmaceutical care in British Columbia, 1996 to 2006. *Healthcare Policy, 7*(1), 68–79.

Morgan, S., Daw, J., & Law, M. (2013). *Rethinking pharmacare in Canada.* C.D. Howe Institute. Commentary No. 384. Health Policy, June. Retrieved from www.cdhowe.org/pdf/Commentary_384.pdf.

Morgan, S., Martin, D., Gagnon, M-A., Mintzes, B., Daw, J., & Lexchin, J. (2015). *Pharmacare 2020: The future of drug coverage in Canada.* Vancouver, Pharmaceutical Policy Research Collaboration, University of British Columbia. Available at www.pharmacare2020.ca.

Morris, J. (1991). *Pride against prejudice.* London: Women's Press.

Morrow, M., Dagg, P., & Pederson, A. (2008). Is deinstitutionalization a "failed experiment"? The ethics of re-institutionalization. *Journal of Ethics in Mental Health, 3*(2), 1–7.

Moss P., & Dyck, I. (2003). *Women, body and illness.* Oxford, UK: Roman and Littlefield.

Moss, P., & Teghtsoonian, K. (Eds.). (2007). *Contesting illness processes and practices.* Toronto, ON: University of Toronto Press.

——— & ———. (2008). Power and illness: Authority, bodies, and context. In P. Moss & K. Teghtsoonian (Eds.), *Contesting illness: Processes and practices* (pp. 3–27). Toronto: University of Toronto Press.

Mulkay, M. (1993). Social death in Britain. In D. Clark (Ed.), *The sociology of death* (pp. 31–49). Cambridge, UK: Blackwell.

Mulkins, A., O'Beirne, M., Brundin-Mather, R., & Verhoef, M. (2006, May). Do academic and community physicians recognize a role for CAM in undergraduate medical education. *University of Toronto Medical Journal, 83*(3), 184–7.

Muntaner, C., & Gómez, M.B. (2003). Qualitative and quantitative research in social epidemiology: Is complementarity the only issue? *Gaceta Sanitaria, 17*(Supl 3), 53–7. Retrieved from www.scielosp.org/pdf/gs/v17s3/debates1.pdf.

Muntaner, C., & Lynch, J. (1999). Income inequality, social cohesion, and class relations: A critique of Wilkinson's neo-Durkheimian research program. *International Journal of Health Services, 29*(1), 59–81.

Muntaner, C., Lynch, J., & Davey Smith, G. (2001). Social capital, disorganized communities and the third way: Understanding the retreat from structural inequalities in epidemiology and public health. *International Journal of Health Services, 31*(2), 213–37.

Muzyka, D., Hodgson, G., & Prada, G. (2012). The inconvenient truths about Canadian health care. Retrieved from www.conferenceboard.ca/cashc/research/2012/inconvenient_truths.aspx.

Muzzin, L., Brown, G., & Hornosty, R. (1998). Professional ideology in Canadian pharmacy. In C. Coburn, C. D'Arcy, & G. Torrance (Eds.), *Health and Canadian society: Sociological perspectives* (3rd ed.) (pp. 379–98). Toronto, ON: University of Toronto Press.

Najman, J. (1980). Theories of disease causation and the concept of general susceptibility. *Social Science & Medicine, 14A*, 231–7.

NASA Earth Observatory. (2012, September 18). Retrieved from http://earthobservatory.nasa.gov/IOTD/view.php?id=79198.

National Council of Welfare. (2009). Retrieved from www.ncwcn-bes.net/documents/researchpublications/ResearchProjects/PovertyProfile/2009/Poverty Profile 1 2007 E.pdf.

———. (2012). *A snapshot of racialized poverty in Canada.* Poverty Profile: Special Edition. Retrieved from www.ncw.gc.ca.

National Forum on Health. (1997). Volume 1, Canada health action: Building on the legacy: The final report of the national forum on health. Ottawa, ON: Author. Retrieved from www.hc-sc.gc.ca/hcs-sss/pubs/renewal-renouv/1997-nfoh-fnss-v1/index-eng.php#tphp.

National Health Strategy (NHS). (1993). *Removing cultural and language barriers to health.* Issues Paper, No. 6, Canberra, AU: AGPS.

National Science Foundation. (2006). U.S. industrial R&D performers report increased expenditures for 2004. Retrieved from www.nsf.gov/statistics/infbrief/nsf07304/#notes.

National Seniors Council. (2011). *Report on the labour force participation of seniors and near seniors, and intergenerational relations.* Gatineau, Quebec: Human Resources and Skills Development Canada. Retrieved from www.seniorscouncil.gc.ca/eng/research_publications/labour_force/page00.shtml.

Navarro, N. (2004, June). Inequalities are unhealthy. *Monthly Review, 56*(2).

Navarro, V. (1976). *Medicine under capitalism.* New York, NY: Prodist.

———. (1986). *Crisis, health and medicine: A social critique.* London, UK: Tavistock.

———. (1988). Professional dominance or proletarianization: Neither. *The Milbank Quarterly, 66*, Supplement 2, 57–75.

———. (1998). Book review of private medicine and public health: Profits, politics and prejudice in the American health care enterprise by Lawrence D. Weiss. *Contemporary Sociology, 27*(4), 419–20.

———. (Ed.). (2004). *The political and social contexts of health.* Amityville, NY: Baywood Publishing Company, Inc.

———. (Ed.). (2007). *Neoliberalism, globalization and inequalities: Consequences for health and quality of life.* Amityville, NY: Baywood Publishing Company, Inc.

———. (2007). Neoliberalism as class ideology. In V. Navarro (Ed.), *Neoliberalism, globalization, and inequalities: Consequences for health and quality of life.* Amityville, NY: Baywood Publishing Company, Inc.

———. (2008). Neoliberalism and its consequences: The world health situation since Alma Ata. *Global Social Policy, 8*, 152–5.

———. (2009). What we mean by social determinants of health. *Global Health Promotion, 16*(1), 5–16.

Navarro, V., & Muntaner, C. (Eds.). (2004). *Political and economic determinants of population health and well-being: Controversies and developments.* Amityville, NY: Baywood Publishing Company, Inc.

Neff, J.A., McFall, S.L., & Cleaveland, T.D. (1987). Psychiatry and medicine in the US: Interpreting trends in medical specialty choice. *Sociology of Health and Illness, 9*(1), 45–61.

Nelson, S., & Gordon, S. (Eds.). (2006). *The complexities of care. Nursing reconsidered.* Ithica, NY: Cornell University Press.

Nesdole, R., Voigts, D., Lepnurm, R., & Roberts, R. (2014). Reconceptualizing determinants of health: Barriers to improving the health status of First nations peoples. *Canadian Journal of Public Health, 105*(3), 209–13.

Nestel, S. (2012). *Colour coded health care: the impact of race and racism on Canadians' Health.* Toronto: Wellesley Institute. Retrieved from www.wellesleyinstitute.com.

Newbold, K.B. (2005). Self-rated health within the Canadian immigrant population: Risk and the healthy immigrant effect. *Social Science & Medicine, 60*, 1359–70.

———. (2009). The short-term health of Canada's new immigrant arrivals: Evidence from LSIC. *Ethnicity & Health, 14*(3), 315–36.

Newbold, K.B & Danforth, J. (2003). Health status and Canada's immigrant population. *Social Science & Medicine, 57*, 1981–95.

Ng, E. (2011). The healthy immigrant effect and mortality rates. *Health Reports, 22*(4). December. Ottawa: Statistics Canada.

Ng, E., & the LHAD research team. (2011). Insights into the healthy immigrant effect: Mortality by period of immigration and birthplace. *Health Research Working Paper Series.* Health Analysis Division. Ottawa: Ministry of Industry. September.

Ng, E., Wilkins, R., Gendron, F., & Berthelot, J-M. (2005a). *Dynamics of immigrants' health in Canada: Evidence from the national population health survey.* Ottawa, ON: Statistics Canada.

Ng, E., Wilkins, R., Gendron, F., & Berthelot, J-M. (2005b, Autumn). The changing health of immigrants. *Canadian Social Trends.* Ottawa, ON: Statistics Canada.

Ngowi, A.V.F., Maeda, D.N., Wesseling, C., Partanen, T.J., Sanga, M.P., & Mbise, G. (2001). Pesticide-handling practices in agriculture in Tanzania: Observational data from 27 coffee and cotton farms. *International Journal of Occupational and Environmental Health, 7,* 326–32.

Nguyen, L. (2010, August 4). Patients should be "unafraid" to seek second opinion. Retrieved from www.canada.com/health/Patients+should+unafraid+seek+second+opinion/2640644/story.html.

———. (2010, August 24). Patients should be "unafraid" to seek second opinion: Top MD. *Times Colonist.* Retrieved from www.timescolonist.com/story_print.html'id=2640644&sponsor.

Nguyen, V.K. (2010). *The republic of therapy: Triage and sovereignty in West Africa's time of AIDS.* Durhan, NC: Duke University Press.

Niles, C. (2013). Examining the deinstitutionalization movement in North America. *Health Tomorrow, 1*, 54–83.

Nissen, N. (2011). Challenging perspectives: Women, complementary and alternative medicine, and social change. *Interface: A Journal for and about Social Movements, 3*(2), 75–91.

Noone, J., & Stephens, C. (2008). Men, masculine identities, and health care utilisation. *Sociology of Health & Illness, 30*(5), 711–25.

Northcott, H., & Petruik, C. (2011). The geographic mobility of elderly Canadians. In *Canadian Journal on Aging, 30*(3), 311–22.

Northcott, H., & Wilson, D. (2001). *Dying and death in Canada.* Aurora, ON: Garamond.

Nuckolls, C. (1997). Allocating value to gender in official American psychiatry, part I: The cultural construction of the personality disorder classification system. *Anthropology & Medicine, 4*, 45–66.

Nunavut News. (2013, March 12). Nunavut suffers lowest life expectancy of any province, territory: StatsCan. Retrieved from www .nunatsiaqonline.ca/stories/article/65674nunavut_lowest_life_ expectancy_of_any_province_territory_statscan/.

Nursing. (n.d.). In The Canadian Encyclopedia online. Retrieved from http://thecanadianencyclopedia.com/index. cfm?PgNm=TCE&Params=A1ARTA0005851.

Oakley, A. (1980). *Women confined.* Oxford, UK: Martin Robertson.

OECD. (2011a). *Divided we stand: Why inequality keeps rising.* OECD Publishing.

———. (2011b). Nurses. *Health at a Glance 2011: OECD Indicators.* OECD Publishing. Retrieved from http://dx.doi.org/10.1787/ health_glance-2011-26-en.

———. (2013). Pharmaceutical Consumption. *Health at a Glance 2013, OECD Indicators.* Retrieved from www.oecd-ilibrary.org/docserver/ download/8113161ec041.pdf?expires=1408998984&id=id&accname =guest&checksum=F58B61820334A5CBCAA36B8B03DF88A6.

———. (2014). *OECD Health Statistics 2014.* Retrieved from www.oecd. org/els/health-systems/health-data.htm.

Office of Inspector General. (2006). *FDA's monitoring of postmarketing study commitments.* Washington: Department of Health and Human Services.

Office of the Auditor General of Canada. (2011). *Status Report of the Auditor General of Canada to the House of Commons: Chapter 4 – Programs for First Nations on Reserves.* Ottawa: Minister of Public Works and Government Services. Retrieved from www.oag-bvg .gc.ca/internet/docs/parl_oag_201106_04_e.pdf.

Ogilvie, M. (2014). Why hasn't the nursing crisis improved since a 2008 story on Canada's shortage? *Toronto Star.* December 10. Retrieved from www.thestar.com/life/health_wellness/2014/04/16/ why_hasnt_the_nursing_crisis_improved_since_a_2008_story_ on_canadas_shortage.html.

Ogrodniczuk, J.S., & Oliffe, J.L. (2011). Men and depression. *Canadian Family Physician, 57*(2), 153–5.

Oliver, M. (1996). *Understanding disability.* London, UK: Macmillan Press.

———. (2004). Defining impairment and disability. In M. Bury & J. Gabe (Eds.), *The sociology of health and illness* (pp. 277–90). London, UK: Routledge Press.

———. (2009). The social model in context. In T. Titchkosky & R. Michalko (Eds.), *Rethinking Normalcy* (pp. 19–30). Toronto: Canadian Scholars' Press, Inc.

Oliver, V. (2010). Homesick: A political economy of the health experiences of homeless young women. (Doctoral thesis). York University, Toronto, Ontario.

O'Neill, A. (1994). *Enemies within and enemies without: Educating chiropractors, osteopaths, and traditional acupuncturists.* Melbourne: La Trobe University.

———. (1995). Daylight at noon: Alternative health battles. In H. Gardner (Ed.), *The politics of health* (2nd ed.) (pp. 482–452). Melbourne: Churchill Livingston.

Ontario Council of Agencies Serving Immigrants. (2005). Immigrant women and health. Retrieved from www.ocasi.org/index. php?qid=785&catid=115.

Ontario Women's Justice Network Workplace. (2013). Violence and Harassment: Occupational Health and Safety Act. Retrieved from http://owjn.org/owjn_2009/component/content/article/60 -discrimination-equality-harassment/336-workplace-violence -and-harassment-occupational-health-and-safety-act#2.

Organisation for Economic Co-operation and Development (OECD). (2001). Policy Brief. *OECD health at a glance: How Canada compares.* Retrieved from www.oecd.org/dataoecd/5/25/2465559.pdf.

Ornish, D. (1990). *Reversing heart disease.* London, UK: Century.

Ornish, D., Brown, S.E., Scherwitz, L.W., Billings, J.H., Armstrong, W.T. Ports, T.A.,...Gould, K.L. (1990). Can lifestyle changes reverse coronary heart disease. *Lancet, 336*, 129–33.

Ornstein, M. (2006). *Ethno-racial groups in Toronto, 1971–2001: A demographic and socio-economic profile.* Toronto, ON: Institute for Social Research, York University.

Orwell, G. (1945). *Animal farm.* London, UK: Secker & Warburg.

Osberg, L. (2006, Apr–May). Pulling apart—The growing gulfs in Canadian society. *Policy Options.*

———. (2008). *A quarter century of economic inequality in Canada: 1981–2006, Growing Gap.* Ottawa, ON: Canadian Centre for Policy Alternatives.

———. (2009). *Canada's declining social safety net: The case for EI reform.* Ottawa: Canadian Centre for Policy Alternatives.

Ottawa Charter for Health Promotion. (1986). WHO. Retrieved from www.phac-aspc.gc.ca/ph-sp/docs/charter-chartre/pdf/charter.pdf.

Our Voices. (2009). *Toolkit: Our voices: First Nations, Métis, and Inuit GBA.* Retrieved from: www.aboriginalgba.ca/category.aspx ?catid=136&rt=2.

Palpz. (2004). The honourable Thomas Clement Douglas, greatest Canadian of all time, 1904–1986. Retrieved from http://everything2 .com/user/Palpz/writeups/Tommy+Douglas.

Paltiel, F. (1997). State initiatives; Impetus and effects. In C. Andrew & S. Rogers (Eds.), *Women and the Canadian state* (pp. 27–51). Montreal, QC: McGill-Queens University Press.

Pan American Health Organization. (2007). Health in the Americas, volume 11, Countries, Canada. Retrieved from www.paho.org/hia/ archivosvol2/paisesing/Canada%20English.pdf.

Panitch, L. (1977). *The Canadian state: Political economy and political power.* Toronto, ON: University of Toronto Press.

Panitch, L., & Gindin, S. (2013). *The making of global capitalism: The political economy of American empire.* Brooklyn, NY: Verso Books.

Panitch, L., & Leys, C. (Eds.). (2009). *Morbid symptoms: Health under capitalism.* Socialist Register 2010. London: Merlin Press.

Paradies, Y. (2006). A systematic review of empirical research on self-reported racism and health. *International Journal of Epidemiology, 35*, 888–901.

Park, J. (2005, March). Use of alternative health care. *Health Reports, 16*(2). Ottawa, ON: Statistics Canada.

Parsons, T. (1951a). Illness and the role of the physician: A sociological perspective. American *Journal of Orthopsychiatry, 21*, 452–66.

———. (1951b). *The social system.* New York, NY: Free Press.

Patychuk, D. (2011). *Health equity and racialized groups: A literature review.* Toronto: Health Equity Council. Retrieved from www.healthequitycouncil.ca.

Pawluch, D., Cain, R., & Gillett, J. (2000). Lay constructions of HIV and complementary therapy use. *Social Science & Medicine, 51*, 251–64.

Pearce, T. (2014, March). Men doing more dishes, but women still take the lion's share. *Globe and Mail,* L3.

Pedrique, B., Strub-Wourgaft, N., Some, C., Olliaro, P., Trouiller, P., Ford, N.,...Bradol, J.-H. (2013). The drug and vaccine landscape for neglected diseases (2000–11): A systematic assessment. *Lancet Global Health, 1*, e371–e379.

Pembina Institute. Retrieved December 22, 2015 at www.pembina.org/oil-sands.

Pendergrast, M. (2010). *Uncommon grounds: The history of coffee and how it transformed our world.* (Rev. ed.). New York: Basic Books.

Penning, M.J., & Votova, K. (2009). Aging, health and health care: From hospital and residential care to home and community care. In S. Bolaria & H. Dickinson (Eds.), *Health, illness and health care in Canada* (4th ed.). Toronto, ON: Nelson.

Pérez, C. (2002). Health status and health behaviour among immigrants. Supplement to *Health Reports*, 13. Ottawa, ON: Statistics Canada.

Perfecto, I., Rice, R, Greenberg, R., & Van Der Voort, M.E. (1996). Shade coffee: A disappearing refuge for biodiversity. *Bioscience, 46*, 598–608.

Perkel, Colin, N. (2002). *Well of lies: The Walkerton water tragedy.* Toronto, ON: McClelland & Stewart Ltd.

Perspectives on Labour and Income. (2009, Summer). Work absences rates. *Perspectives on Labour and Income, 21*(2), 59–68.

Persson, L., Osgergren, P.O., Hanson, B.S., Lindgren, A., & Naucler, A. (2002). Social network, social support and the rate of decline of CD4 lymphocytes in asymptomatic HIV-positive homosexual men. *Scandinavian Journal of Public Health, 30*(3), 184–90.

Petersen, A. (1996). Risk and the regulated self: The discourse of health promotion as politics of uncertainty. *Australian and New Zealand Journal of Sociology, 32*, 44–57.

Petersen, A., & Lupton, D. (1996). *The new public health: Health and self in the age of risk.* Sydney: Allen & Unwin, and London: Sage.

Petersen, K. (2008). Boiling point. *The Dominion: News from the grassroots*, 53. Retrieved from www.dominionpaper.ca/articles/1944.

Pflugbeil, S., Claussen, A., and Schmitz-Feuerhake, I. (2011). Table: Thyroid cancer in the Gomel area (Belarus) for 13 years before and 13 years after the Chernobyl catastrophe. In *Health Effects of Chernobyl: 25 years after the reactor catastrophe.* German Affiliate of International Physicians for the Prevention of Nuclear War. Retrieved from www.chernobylcongress.org/fileadmin/user_upload/pdfs/chernob_report_2011_en_web.pdf.

Phillips, S., & Austin, E. (2009). The feminization of medicine and population health. *JAMA, 301*(8), 863–4.

Picard, A. (2014, August 20). CMA softens stance on assisted suicide. *The Globe and Mail,* A1.

Pickersgill, M. (2012). Standardising antisocial personality disorder: the social shaping of a psychiatric technology. *Sociology of Health & Illness, 34*(4), 544–59.

———. (2014). Debating DSM-5: Diagnosis and the sociology of critique. *Journal of Medical Ethics, 40*, 521–5.

Pinto, P.C. (2009). Women, disability and the right to health. In P. Armstrong & J. Deadman (Eds.), *Women's health. Intersections of policy, research and practice* (pp. 119–30). Toronto, ON: Women's Press.

Pinquart, M., & Duberstein, P. (2010, August). Associations of social networks with cancer mortality: A meta-analysis. *Critical Reviews in Oncology/Hematology, 75*(2), 122–137.

Pollock, F., Newbold, K.B, Lafrenière, G., & Edge, S. (2012). Discrimination in the doctor's office: Immigrants and refugee experiences. *Critical Social Work, 13*(2), 61–79.

Poole, M. (2014). Ageing, health, and the demographic revolution. In J. Germov (Ed.), *Second opinion: An introduction to health sociology* (5th ed.) (pp. 297–319). Melbourne, Australia: Oxford University Press.

Poovey, M. (1988). Feminism and deconstruction. *Feminist Studies, 14*(1), 52–65.

Porter, R. (1997). *The greatest benefit to mankind: A medical history of humanity from antiquity to the present.* London, UK: HarperCollins.

———. (1995). *Nursing's relationship with medicine.* Aldershot:, UK: Avebury.

Possamai-Inesedy, A., & Cochrane, S. (2013). The consequences of integrating complementary and alternative medicine: An analysis of impacts on practice. *Health Sociology Review, 22*(1), 65–74.

Power, E. (2008, March/April). Conceptualizing food security. *Canadian Journal of Public Health, 99*(2).

Prescrire Editorial Staff. (2014). New drugs and indications in 2013: Little real progress but regulatory authorities take some positive steps. *Prescrire International, 23*, 107–10.

Priest, N., Paradies, Y., Trenerry, B., Truong, M., Karlsen, S., & Kelly, Y. (2013). A systematic review of studies examining the relationship between reported racism and health and wellbeing for children and young people. *Social Science & Medicine, 95*, 115–27.

Prince, P. (2009). A population health approach to obesity in Canada: Putting the problem back into context. *Transdisciplinary Studies in Population Health Series, I*(I), 22–33.

Pringle, R. (1995). Destabilising patriarchy. In B. Caine & R. Pringle. (Eds.), *Transitions: New Australian feminisms* (pp. 198–211). Sydney: Allen & Unwin.

Progestic International Inc. (2004). *Final report for the financial models project.* Ottawa, ON: Health Canada.

Prudham, S. (2004). Poisoning the well: Neoliberalism and the contamination of municipal water in Walkerton, Ontario. *Geoforum, 35*, 343–59.

Public Citizen's Congress Watch. (2002). *America's other drug problem. A briefing book on the Rx drug debate.* Washington, D.C.: Public Citizen.

Public Health Agency of Canada. (2001). What determines health. Retrieved from www.phac-aspc.gc.ca/ph-sp/determinants/determinants-eng.php#healthychild.

———. (2005). Report: A public health agency for Canada—Working group. Retrieved from www.phac-aspc.gc.ca/publicat/phawg-aspgt-noseworthy/index-eng.php#toc.

———. (2006a). *The human face of mental health and mental illness in Canada 2006*. Chapter 11 Hospitalization and mental illness. Retrieved from www.phac-aspc.gc.ca/publicat/human-humain06/pdf/human_face_e.pdf.

———. (2006b). The state of the HIV/AIDS pandemic. Retrieved from www.phac-aspc.gc.ca/media/nr-rp/2006/2006_05bk1-eng.php.

———. (2008a). Chronic disease facts and figures. Retrieved from www.phac-aspc.gc.ca/cd-mc/facts_figures-faits_chiffres-eng.php.

———. (2008b). History. Retrieved from www.phac-aspc.gc.ca/about_apropos/history-eng.php.

———. (2008c). The social determinants of health. Retrieved from www.phac-aspc.gc.ca/ph-sp/oi-ar/index-eng.php.

———. (2009a). Aging & seniors. Retrieved from www.phac-aspc.gc.ca/seniors-aines/index-eng.php.

———. (2009b). Tracking heart and stroke disease in Canada. Retrieved from www.phac-aspc.gc.ca/publicat/2009/cvd-avc/pdf/cvd-avs-2009-eng.pdf.

———. (2009c). *What mothers say: The Canadian maternity experiences survey*. Ottawa, ON.

———. (2009d). Who are Canada's seniors. Retrieved from www.phac-aspc.gc.ca/seniors-aines/publications/public/various-varies/papier-fed-paper/fedreport1-eng.php.

———. (2011a). About the agency. Retrieved from www.phac-aspc.gc.ca/about_apropos/index-eng.php.

———. (2011b). *Healthy aging in Canada: A new vision, A vital investment*. Discussion Brief. Retrieved from www.phac-aspc.gc.ca/seniors-aines/publications/public/healthy-sante/vision/vision-bref/chap01-eng.php.

———. (2011c). *Fast facts about chronic obstructive pulmonary disease (COPD)*. Retrieved from www.phac-aspc.gc.ca/cd-mc/publications/copd-mpoc/ff-rr-2011-eng.php.

———. (2011d). *Fast facts about diabetes 2011*. Retrieved from www.phac-aspc.gc.ca/cd-mc/publications/diabetes-diabete/ff-rr-2011-eng.php.

———. (2011e). *Reducing health inequalities: A challenge for our times*. Ottawa: Public Health Agency of Canada. Retrieved from www.phac-aspc.gc.ca.

———. (2011f). *Summary: Estimates of HIV prevalence and incidence in Canada, 2011*. http://webqa.phac-aspc.gc.ca/aids-sida/publication/survreport/estimat2011-eng.php.

———. (2012). Age friendly communities. Retrieved from http://www.phac-aspc.gc.ca/seniors-aines/afc-caa-eng.php.

———. (2013). Preventing chronic disease strategic plan 2013–2016. Retrieved from www.phac-aspc.gc.ca/cd-mc/diabetes-diabete/strategy_plan-plan_strategique-eng.php.

———. (2014a). Aging and Seniors: info. Retrieved from www.phac-aspc.gc.ca/seniors-aines/index-eng.php.

———. (2014b). What determines health? Retrieved from www.phac-aspc.gc.ca/ph-sp/determinants/index-eng.php.

Putnam, R. (1993). *Making democracy work: Civic traditions in modern Italy*. Princeton, NJ: Princeton University Press.

Quan, D. (2014, August 27). Action better than inquiry into native women deaths, cops say. *Ottawa Citizen*, p. A10.

Radiation health effects. (2007). Radiation effects research foundation. A Cooperative Japan-US Research Organization. Retrieved from www.rerf.jp/radefx/index_e.html.

Raffensperger, C., & Tickner, J. (Eds.). (1999). *Protecting public health & the environment: Implementing the precautionary principle*. Washington, DC: Island Press.

Rainbow Health Ontario. (2011). Retrieved from www.rainbowhealthontario.ca/wp-content/uploads/woocommerce_uploads/2011/06/RHO_FactSheet_LGBTQMENTALHEALTH_E.pdf.

Rankin, J.M., & Campbell, M. (2006). *Managing to nurse: Inside Canada's health care reform*. Toronto, ON: University of Toronto Press.

——— & ———. (2009, May). Institutional ethnography (IE): Nursing work and hospital reform: IE's cautionary analysis. *Qualitative Social Research, 10*(2), 8.

Raphael, D. (2001). From increasing poverty to societal disintegration: How economic inequality affects the health of individuals and communities. In P. Armstrong, H. Armstrong, & D. Coburn (Eds.), *Unhealthy times: Political economy perspectives on health and care in Canada* (pp. 223–46). Don Mills, ON: Oxford University Press.

———. (2003). Barriers to addressing the societal determinants of health: Public health units and poverty in Ontario, Canada. *Health Promotion International, 18*(4), 397–405.

———. (2006). Social determinants of health: An overview of concepts and issues. In D. Raphael, T. Bryant, & M. Rioux (Eds.). (2006). *Staying alive: Critical perspectives on health, illness, and health care*. (pp. 115–38). Toronto, ON: Canadian Scholars' Press Inc.

———. (2008, December). Grasping at straws: A recent history of health promotion in Canada. *Critical Public health, 18*(4), 483–95

———. (Ed.). (2009a). *Social determinants of health* (2nd ed.). Toronto, ON: Canadian Scholars' Press Inc.

———. (2009b). Social determinants of health: An overview of key issues and themes. In D. Raphael (Ed.), *Social determinants of health* (2nd ed.) (pp. 2–19). Toronto, ON: Canadian Scholars' Press Inc.

———. (2009c). Social structure, living conditions and health. In D. Raphael (Ed.), *Social determinants of health* (2nd ed.) (pp. 20–36). Toronto, ON: Canadian Scholars' Press Inc.

———. (2009d). Escaping from the phantom zone: Social determinants of health, public health units and public policy in Canada. *Health Promotion International, 24*(2), 93–198.

———. (Ed.). (2010). *Health promotion and quality of life in Canada*. Toronto, ON: Canadian Scholars' Press Inc.

———. (2012a). Canadian Experiences. In D. Raphael (Ed.), *Tackling health inequalities: Lessons from International Experiences*. Toronto: Canadian Scholars' Press Inc.

———. (2012b). The importance of tackling health inequalities. In D. Raphael (Ed.), *Tackling health inequalities: Lessons from international experiences*. Toronto: Canadian Scholars' Press Inc.

———. (Ed.). (2012c). *Tackling health inequalities: Lessons from international experiences*. Toronto: Canadian Scholars' Press Inc.

———. (2014). Social determinants of children's health in Canada: Analysis and implications. *International Journal of Child, Youth and Family Studies, 5*(2), 220–39.

Raso, K. (2015). Canadian Doctors for Medicare. Private Correspondence.

Ratcliffe, J., Wallack, L., Fagnani, F., & Rodwin, V. (1984). Perspectives on prevention: Health promotion vs health protection. In J. de Kervasdoue, J.R. Kimberley, & G. Rodwin (Eds.), *The end of an illusion: The Future of health policy in western industrialized nations* (pp. 56–84). Berkeley, CA: University of California Press.

Raymond, É., & Grenier, A. (2013). Participation in policy discourse: New form of exclusion for seniors with disabilities?. *Canadian Journal on Aging, 32*(2), 117–29.

Reading, J. (2009). *A life course approach to the social determinants of health for Aboriginal Peoples'. Appendix A.* For the Senate Sub-Committee on Population Health. Retrieved from www.parl.gc.ca/Content/SEN/Committee/402/popu/rep/appendixAjun09-e.pdf.

Reardon J. (2008). Race and biology: Beyond the perpetual return of crisis. In S. Muller-Wille & H.-J. Rheinberger, *Race and geonomics. Old wine in new bottles? Documents from a Transdisciplinary Discussion* (pp. 373–7). Retrieved from http://download.springer.com/static/pdf/453/art%253A10.1007%252Fs00048-008-0301-6.pdf?auth66=1410824453_e933f9985d1826c2b142858a38e66a88&ext=.pdf.

Reid, R., Maag, J., & Vasa, S. (1993). Attention deficit hyperactivity disorder as a disability category: A critique. *Exceptional Children, 60*, 198–215.

Reid, S. (2014, August 23). Crime against aboriginal women is a systemic problem. *Ottawa Citizen*, p. D1.

Reinharz, S. (1992). *Feminist methods in social research.* New York, NY: Oxford University Press Inc.

Reitmanova, S., & Gustafson, D. (2012a). Coloring the white plague: a syndemic approach to immigrant tuberculosis in Canada. *Ethnicity & Health, 17*(4),403–18.

———. (2012b). Exploring the mutual constitution of racializing and medicalizing discourses of immigrant tuberculosis in the Canadian press. *Qualitative Health Research, 229*(7), 911–20.

Researchers find link between chemical, cancer in Shannon, Que. (2009). Retrieved from www.cbc.ca/news/health/story/2009/01/29/mtl-tce-shannon-researchers-0129.html.

Ricciardelli, R. (2011). Masculinity, consumerism, and appearance: A look at men's hair. *Canadian Review of Sociology, 48*(2), 181–201.

Rice, P.L. (Ed.). (1994). Asian mothers, Australian birth: Pregnancy, childbirth and childrearing: The Asian experience in an English-speaking country. Melbourne: Ausmed Publications.

Rice, P.L., & Ezzy, D. (1999). *Qualitative research methods: A health focus.* Melbourne: Oxford University Press.

Rice, P.L., Ly, B., & Lumley, J. (1994). Childbirth and soul loss: The case of a Hmong woman. *Medical Journal of Australia, 160*, 577–8.

Rice, R., & Ward, J. (1996). *Coffee conservation, and commerce in the western hemisphere: How individuals and institutions can promote ecologically sound farming and forest management in Northern Latin America.* Washington, DC: Natural Resources Defense Council and Smithsonian Migratory Bird Center.

Rich, P. (2008, January/February). The Canada Health Act. *Canadian Health Magazine.* Retrieved from www.canadian-health.ca/2_1/42_e.htm.

Richards, E. (1988). The politics of therapeutic evaluation: The vitamin C and cancer controversy. *Social Studies of Science, 18*, 653–701.

Richardson, L. (1994). Writing: A method of inquiry. In N. Denzin & Y. Lincoln. (Eds.), Handbook of qualitative research. Thousand Oaks, CA: Sage.

Richman, A., & Harris, P. (1983). Mental hospital deinstitutionalization in Canada: A national perspective with some regional examples. *International Journal of Mental Health, 11*(4), 64–83.

Riessman, C. (1983). Women and medicalization: A new perspective. *Social Policy, 14*(1), 3–18.

———. (1993). *Narrative analysis.* Newbury Park, CA: Sage.

Rioux, M. (1985). Labelled disabled and wanting to work. In R. Abella, *Research studies of the commission on equality in employment* (pp. 611–40). Ottawa, ON: Minister of Supply and Services Canada.

———. (2009). Bending towards justice. In T. Titchkosky & R. Michalko (Eds.), *Rethinking normalcy* (pp. 201–216). Toronto: Canadian Scholars' Press, Inc.

———. (2010). The right to health: Human rights approaches to health. In T. Bryant, D. Raphael, & M. Rioux (Eds.), *Staying alive: Critical perspectives on health, illness, and health care* (2nd ed.) (pp. 93–119). Toronto: Canadian Scholars' Press.

Rioux, M., & Daly, T. (2010). Constructing disability and illness. In T. Bryant, D. Raphael, & M. Rioux (Eds.), *Staying alive, critical perspectives on health illness, and health care* (2nd ed.) (pp. 347–69). Toronto: Canadian Scholars' Press Inc.

Ristovski-Slijepcevic, S., Bell, K., Chapman, G., & Beagan, B. (2010). Being "thick" indicates you are eating, you are healthy and you have an attractive body shape: Perspectives on fatness and food choice amongst black and white men and women in Canada. *Health Sociology Review, 19*(3), 317–29.

Ritzer, G. (1993). *The McDonaldization of society.* Thousand Oaks, CA: Pine Forge Press.

———. (1996). *Sociological theory* (4th ed.). New York, NY: McGraw-Hill.

———. (1997). *Postmodern social theory.* New York, NY: McGraw-Hill.

———. (2008). *The McDonaldization of society* (5th ed.). Los Angeles, CA: Pine Forest Press.

Roach Anleu, S.L. (1999). *Deviance, conformity, and control* (3rd ed.). Melbourne: Longman.

Robb, J.M., McGhie, B.T.M., & McPherson, A.L. (1934). *The hospitals in Ontario: A short history.* Department of Health, Hospitals Division.

Robb, N. (1999, April 6). Canada has its first female dean—170 years after first medical school opened. *Canadian Medical Association Journal, 160*(7), 1042.

Roberts, S.J. (1983). Oppressed group behaviour: Implications for nursing. *Advances in Nursing Science, 5*(4), 21–30.

Robinson, M. (2007). The value of a human rights perspective in health and foreign policy. *Bulletin of the World Health Organization.* March, *85*(3), 241–2.

Rochon Ford, A., & Saibil, D. (Eds.). (2010). *Push to prescribe. Women and Canadian drug policy.* Toronto, ON: Women's Press.

Rogers, A., Hwang, W., Scott, L., Aiken, L., & Dinges, D. (2004, July/August). The working hours of hospital staff nurses and patient safety. *Health Affairs, 23.*

Romanow, Honourable Roy. (2002). *Building on values: The future of health care in Canada.* Ottawa, ON: Government of Canada.

Rosen, G. (1972). The evolution of social medicine. In H.E. Freeman, S. Levine, & L.G. Reeder (Eds.), *Handbook of medical sociology* (2nd ed.) (pp. 30–60). Englewood Cliffs, NJ: Prentice Hall.

———. (1993). *A history of public health*. New York, NY: Johns Hopkins University Press.

Rosenberg, H. (1990). The home is the workplace: Hazards, stress and pollutants in the household. In M. Luxton & H. Rosenberg (Eds.), *Through the kitchen window*. Toronto, ON: Garamond.

Rosenhan, D.L. (1973). Being sane in insane places. *Science, 179*, 250–8.

Rothblum, E., & Solovay, S. (Eds.). (2009). *The fat studies reader*. New York: New York University Press.

Rowsell, L. (2000). *Advertising campaigns of branded and unbranded messages*. Ottawa, ON: Health Canada, Therapeutic Products Directorate.

Royal Commission on Aboriginal Peoples. (1996a). *Highlights from the report of the royal commission on Aboriginal peoples (People to people, nation to nation)*. Ottawa, ON: Indian and Northern Affairs. Retrieved from www.ainc-inac.gc.ca/ap/pubs/rpt/rpt-eng.asp.

———. (1996b). *Report of the royal commission on Aboriginal peoples*. Ottawa, ON: Indian and Northern Affairs.

Rusk, J. (2005, October 24). Conditions on reserve "atrocious," doctor says. *Globe and Mail*.

Russell, C., & Schofield, T. (1986). *Where it hurts: An introduction to sociology for health workers*. Sydney: Allen & Unwin.

Rx&D. (2002). Talking points re: Media reports—Dr. Holbrook and AstraZeneca. (2002). Retrieved March 1, 2003, from www.canadapharma.org/Media_Centre/Backgrounders/Holbrook99_e.html.

———. (2004). *Towards increasing research and development in Canada: A new innovative pharmaceutical strategy*. Ottawa, ON: Author.

Ryan, W. (1971) *Blaming the victim*. New York, NY: Vintage.

Sackett, D. (1981). How to read clinical journals, V: To distinguish useful from useless or even harmful therapy. *Journal of the Canadian Medical Association, 124*, 1156–62.

Sadakova, Y. (December 9, 2013). Retrieved from http://www.benefitscanada.com/benefits/disability-management/disabled-still-face-work-barriers-47144.

Saks, M. (1994). The alternatives to medicine. In J. Gabe, D. Kelleher, & G. Williams (Eds.), *Challenging medicine* (pp. 84–103). London, UK: Routledge.

Sampson, A. (2000, September 19). How the boomers are being skinned. *Sydney Morning Herald* (Insight), p. 7.

Sawyer, E. (2006). *Guarding Canada's health system: The history of the Canadian Healthcare Association, 1931 to 2006*. Ottawa, ON: CHA Press.

Sbaraini, A., Carter, S., Evans, R.W., & Blinkhom, A. (2011). How to do a grounded theory study: A worked example of a study of dental practices. *BMC Medical Research Methodology, 11*, 128. Retrieved from www.biomedcentral.com/1471-2288/11/128.

Schabas, R. (2002). Public health: What is to be done? *Canadian Medical Association Journal, 166*(10), 1282–3.

Schanfarber, L. (2007). Interview with Dr. Jay Wortman. Retrieved from www.alive.com/6201a15a2.php.

Schapiro, M. (2007). *Exposed: The toxic chemistry of everyday products and what's at stake for American power*. White River Junction, Vermont: Chelsea Green Publishing.

Scheff, T.J. (1966). *Being mentally ill: A sociological theory*. Chicago, IL: Aldine.

Schlosser, E. (2002). *Fast food nation: The dark side of the all-American meal*. New York, NY: Perennial.

Schneider, B. (2012). Participatory action research, mental health service user research, and the hearing (our) voices projects. *International Journal of Qualitative Methods, 11*(2), 152–65.

Schoen, C., Osborn, R., squires, D., Doty, M., Pierson, R., & Applebaum, S. (2010). How health insurance design affects access to care and costs, by income, in eleven countries. *Health Affairs, 29*(12), 2323–34.

Schrecker, T., Chapman, A., Labonté, R., & Vogli, R. (2010). Advancing health equity in the global marketplace: How human right can help. *Social Science and Medicine, 71*, 1520–6.

Schutz, A. (1972/1933). *The phenomenology of the social world*. London, UK: Heinemann.

Science Advisory Board Committee on the Drug Review Process. (2000). *Report to Health Canada*. Ottawa, ON.

Scott, S. (2006). The medicalization of shyness: From social misfits to social fitness. *Sociology of Health & Illness, 28*(2), 33–153

Scull, A.T. (1975). From madness to mental illness: Medical men as moral entrepreneurs. *Archives Européennes de Sociologie, 16*, 218–61.

———. (1977). Madness and segregative control: The role of the insane asylum. *Social Problems, 24*, 337–51.

Seale, C., & Pattison, S. (Eds.). (1994). *Medical knowledge: Doubt and certainty*. Buckingham, UK: Open University Press.

Sealy, P., & Whitehead, P. (2004). Forty years of deinstitutionalization of psychiatric services in canada: An empirical assessment. *Canadian Journal of Psychiatry, 49*(4), 249–57.

Seely, D., Szczurko, O., Cooley, K., Fritz, H., Aberdour, S., Herrington, C., Herman, P., Rouchotas, P., Lescheid, D., Bradley, R., Gignac, T. Bernhardt, B., Zhou, Q., & Guyatt, G. (2013). Naturopathic medicine for the prevention of cardiovascular disease: A randomized clinical trial. *Canadian Medical Association Journal*. June 11, *185*(9), E409–16.

Dei, G.J.S. (1999, September). Knowledge and politics of social change: The implication of anti-racism. *British Journal of Sociology of Education, 20*(3), 395–409.

Segall, A. (1997). Sick role concepts and health behaviour. In D. Gochman (Ed.), *Handbook of health behaviour research I: Personal and social determinants* (pp. 289–301). New York, NY: Plenum Press.

Segall, A., & Chappell, N. (2000). *Health and health care in Canada*. Toronto, ON: Prentice-Hall.

Senzilet, L. (2007, November). Health variations across Canada: A snapshot. In Health Canada, People, place and health. *Health Policy Research Bulletin, 14*. Retrieved from www.hc-sc.gc.ca/sr-sr/alt_formats/hpb-dgps/pdf/pubs/hpr-rps/bull/2007-people-place-gens-lieux/2007-people-place-gens-lieux-eng.pdf.

Service Canada. (n.d.) Services for Canada. Retrieved from www.servicecanada.gc.ca/eng/audiences/seniors/index.shtml

Shakespeare, T. (2010). The social model of disability. In L. Davis (Ed.), *The disability studies reader* (3rd ed.) (pp. 266–73). New York: Routledge.

Sharman, Z., & Johnson, J. (2012). Towards the inclusion of gender and sex in health research and funding: An institutional perspective. *Social Science and Medicine, 74,* 1812–16.

Sharpe, A. (2011). Income redistribution in Canada. In D. Carney (Ed.), *The Canada we want in 2020; Towards a strategic policy roadmap for the federal government* (pp. 95–101). Canada 2020: Canada's Progressive Centre.

Shaw, G.B. (1908). *The doctor's dilemma.* London, UK: Constable.

Shields, M., & Wilkins, K. (2006). *Findings from the 2005 national survey of the work and health of nurses.* CIHI, Ottawa, ON: Statistics Canada.

Short, S.D., & Sharman, E. (1995). The nursing struggle in Australia. In G.M. Lupton & J. Najman (Eds.), *Sociology of health and illness: Australian readings* (2nd ed.) (pp. 236–51). Melbourne: Macmillan.

Shuchman, M. (1999, November 17). Drug firm threatens suit over MD's product review. *The Globe and Mail,* p. A1.

Silverburg, R. (1966). *The dawn of medicine.* New York: G.P. Putnam's Sons.

Silversides, A. (2002, February 5). More provinces protecting MDs who practice alternative medicine. *Canadian Medical Association Journal, 166,* 367.

———. (2008). Health Canada's investment in new postmarket drug surveillance network a "pittance." *Canadian Medical Association Journal, 179,* 412–13.

Simic, M. (2012). A critical reading of *The spirit level: Why equality is better for everyone.* R. Wilinson & K. Pickett: What is the scientific content of the book? CERES department, pp. 1–30. January. Retrieved from www.environnement.ens.fr/IMG/file/stages/A%20critical%20reading%20of%20The%20Spirit%20Level_Milos%20Simic-2.pdf.

Simich. L., Beiser, M., Stewart, M., & Mwakarimba, E. (2005, October). Providing social support for immigrants and refugees in Canada: Challenges and directions. *Journal of Immigrant Health, 7*(4), 259–268.

Simon, R.W. (2002). Revisiting the relationships among gender, marital status and mental health. *American Journal of Sociology, 107*(4), 1065–96.

Simpson, J. (2003, November). Utilization patterns and trends. *Health Policy Research Bulletin, 7.* Ottawa, ON: Health Canada.

———. (2010, February 4). Playing a dirty game: Exporting asbestos. *The Globe and Mail,* p. A5.

———. (2014, June 11). Our hospitals are not ready for the grey tsunami. *The Globe and Mail,* p. A15.

Simpson, J.L., Genel, M., Carlson, A.S., Ferris, E., de la Chapelle, A., & Ehrhardt, A.A. (2000). Gender verification in the Olympics. *Journal of the American Medical Association, 284,* 1568–9.

Sinding, C. (2010, December). Using institutional ethnography to understand the production of health care disparities. *Qualitative Health Research, 20*(12), 1656–63.

Singer, P. (1980). *Marx.* Oxford: Oxford University Press.

Sinha, M. (2009). *An investigation into the feasibility of collecting data on the involvement of adults and youth with mental health issues in the criminal justice system.* Canadian Centre for Justice Statistics. Ottawa: Statistics Canada. Retrieved from www.statcan.gc.ca/pub/85-561-m/85-561-m2009016-eng.htm.

———. (2012). A Portrait of Caregivers. Retrieved from www.statcan.gc.ca/pub/89-652-x/89-652-x2013001-eng.htm.

Sirois, F. (2008a). Provider-based complementary and alternative medicine use among three chronic illness groups: Associations with psychosocial factors and concurrent use of conventional health-care services. *Complementary Therapies in Medicine, 16,* 73–80.

———. (2008b). Motivations for consulting complementary and alternative medicine practitioners: A comparison of consumers from 1997–8 and 2005. *BMC Complementary and Alternative Medicine,* 8(16). April 29. Retrieved from www.biomedcentral.com/content/pdf/1472-6882-8-16.pdf.

Sirois, F., & Gick, M. (2002). An investigation of the health beliefs and motivations of complementary medicine clients. *Social Science & Medicine, 55,* 1025–37.

Skinner, B., & Rovere, M. (2011). *Canada's Medicare bubble: Is government health spending sustainable without user-based funding?* Fraser Institute. Retrieved from www.fraserinstitute.org.

Smedley, B. (2012). The Lived Experience of Race and Its Health Consequences. *American Journal of Public Health, 102*(5), 933–5.

Smith, B., & Hutchinson, B. (2004). *Gendering disability.* New Brunswick, NJ: Rutgers University Press.

Smith, D. (1987/1974). Women's perspective as a radical critique of sociology. In S. Harding (Ed.), *Feminism and methodology.* Bloomington, IN: Indiana University Press.

———. (1987). *The everyday world as problematic: A feminist sociology.* Toronto, ON: University of Toronto Press.

———. (1993). *Texts, facts and femininity: Exploring the relations of ruling.* New York, NY: Routlege.

Smith, D.E., & David, S. (Eds.). (1975). *Women look at psychiatry.* Vancouver, BC: Press Gang.

Smith, M. (1993, October). The Rodriguez case: A review of the Supreme Court of Canada decision on assisted suicide. Ottawa, ON: Government of Canada, Law and Government Division. Retrieved from http://dsp-psd.pwgsc.gc.ca/Collection-R/LoPBdP/BP/bp349-e.htm.

Smith, M., & Marles, R. (2003, November). It's natural, so it can't hurt me—right? In *Health Policy Research Bulletin,* 7, Ottawa, ON: Health Canada.

Smith, M., & Simpson, J. (2003, November). Alternative practices and products: A survival guide. *Health Policy Research Bulletin,* 7. Ottawa, ON: Health Canada.

Smith, S. (2009). Social justice and disability: Competing interpretations of the medical and social models. In K. Kristiansen, S. Vehmas, & T. Shakespeare (Eds.), *Arguing about disability: Philosophical perspectives* (pp. 15–29). London: Routledge.

Smylie, J. (2009). The health of Aboriginal peoples. In D. Raphael (Ed.), *Social determinants of health* (2nd ed.) (pp. 281–99). Toronto, ON: Canadian Scholars' Press, Inc.

Smylie, J., Fell, D., Ohlsson, A., & the Joint Working Group on First Nations, Indian, Inuit, and Métis Infant Mortality of the Canadian Perinatal Surveillance System. (2010). A review of aboriginal infant mortality rates in Canada: Striking and persistent Aboriginal/Non-Aboriginal inequities. *Canadian Journal of Public Health, 101*(2), March/April, 143–8.

Snow, J. (1936/1855). *On the mode of communication of cholera* [reprinted as *Snow on cholera*]. New York, NY: Hafner.

Snyder, L., & Caplan, A. (Eds.). (2001). *Assisted suicide: Finding common ground.* Indianapolis, IN: Indiana University Press.

Spade, J.Z., & Valentine, C.G. (2008). *The kaleidoscope of gender. Prisms, patterns and possibilities.* Thousand Oaks, CA: Sage.

Sparling, D., & Laughland, P. (2008). Are large farms really different? Vista: On the agri-food industry and the farm community. Statistics Canada Catalogue 21-004-X. Retrieved from www.statcan.gc.ca/pub/21-004-x/21-004-x2007001-eng.pdf. (PDF Version, 123 kb).

Spenceley, S., Hagen, B., Hall, B., Awosoga, O., Witcher, C., & Ikuta, R. (2015). *Moral distress in the care of persons with dementia in residential care settings in southern Alberta.* May. Retrieved from www.moraldistress.ca/edit/userfiles/files/Moral%20Distress%20in%20Residential%20Care_Final%20Report.pdf.

Spills lead to fisheries Act convictions. (2000). *Toxic Chemicals Update: An Environment Canada Atlantic Region Newsletter, 4*(1). Retrieved from http://atlantic-web1.ns.ec.gc.ca/epb/newsletters/toxchem/Default.asp'lang=En&n=42EF7454-1#spills.

Spitzer, D. (2005). Engendering health disparities. *Canadian Journal of Public Health, 96*, March/April, S78–S96.

Spurling, G., Mansfield, P.R., Montgomery, B., Lexchin, J., Doust, J., Othman, N., et al. (2010). Information from pharmaceutical companies and the quality, quantity, and cost of physicians' prescribing: A systematic review. *PLoS Medicine, 7*, e1000352.

Starr, P. (1982). *The social transformation of American medicine: The rise of a sovereign profession and the making of a vast industry.* New York, NY: Basic Books.

Statistics Canada. (1995). *Earnings of women and men.* Ottawa, ON: Industry Canada.

———. (1996). *Earnings of women and men.* Ottawa, ON: Industry Canada.

———. (1999). *Statistical report on the health of Canadians.* Retrieved from www.statcan.gc.ca/pub/82-570-x/82-570-x1997001-eng.pdf.

———. (2002). Mental health of Canada's immigrants. Supplement to *Health Reports*, 13. Ottawa, ON.

———. (2003). *Ethnic diversity survey: Portrait of a multicultural society.* Ottawa, ON: Author.

———. (2006a). *Aboriginal Peoples highlight tables.* Retrieved from www12.statcan.ca/census-recensement/2006/dp-pd/hlt/97-558/index.cfm?Lang=E.

———. (2006b). *Disability rights in Canada: A virtual museum.* Retrieved from http://disabilityrights.freeculture.ca/index.php.

———. (2006c). *Participation and activity limitation survey, 2006 analytical report.* Retrieved from www.statcan.gc.ca/pub/89-628-x/89-628-x2007002-eng.pdf.

———. (2006d). *Women in Canada.* Ottawa, ON: Ministry of Industry.

———. (2007a). *The South Asian community in Canada.* Retrieved from www.statcan.gc.ca/pub/89-621-x/89-621-x2007006-eng.htm.

———. (2007b, February). Important health and healthcare issues in Canada. *Health Reports, 18*(1). Retrieved from www.statcan.gc.ca/ads-annonces/82-003-x/index-eng.htm.

———. (2007c). *A portrait of seniors.* Retrieved from www.statcan.gc.ca/pub/89-519-x/89-519-x2006001-eng.pdf.

———. (2008a). *Aboriginal peoples in Canada in 2006: Inuit, Métis and First Nations.* 2006 Census. Ottawa, ON: Author.

———. (2008b). *Canadian demographics at a glance.* Retrieved from www.statcan.gc.ca/pub/91-003-x/91-003-x2007001-eng.pdf.

———. (2008c). *Canada's ethnocultural mosaic.* 2006 Census. Retrieved from http://dsp-psd.pwgsc.gc.ca/collections/collection_2010/statcan/CS97-562-2006-1-eng.pdf.

———. (2008d). *2006 Census Canada. All occupations.* Ottawa, ON: Industry Canada.

———. (2009a). *Health care professionals and official minorities in Canada 2001 and 2006.* Ottawa, ON: Author.

———. (2009b). *Infant mortality rates.* Retrieved from www65.statcan.gc.ca/acyb02/1947/acyb02_19470143004a-eng.htm and www40.statcan.ca/l01/cst01/health21a-eng.htm.

———. (2009c). *Perspectives on Labour and Income, 10*(3). Ottawa, ON.

———. (2010a). Life expectancy at birth, by sex, by province. Retrieved from www40.statcan.ca/l01/cst01/health26-eng.htm.

———. (2010b). *Population projections for Canada, provinces and territories: 2009-2036.* Ottawa: Ministry of Labour. Available www.statcan.gc.ca/pub/91-520-x/91-520-x2010001-eng.pdf.

———. (2010c). *Projections of the diversity of the Canadian population; 2006–2031.* Ottawa: Ministry of Canada. Retrieved from www.statcan.gc.ca/pub/91-551-x/91-551-x2010001-eng.pdf.

———. (2011). CANSIM Table 202-07011, 6. Market, total and after-tax income, by economic family type and income quintiles, 2011 constant dollars. Retrieved from www5.statcan.gc.ca/cansim/a47.

———. (2012a). *Living arrangements of seniors. Families, households and marital status. Structural type of dwelling and collectives, 2011 Census of Population.* Ottawa: Ministry of Industry. Retrieved from www12.statcan.gc.ca/census-recensement/2011/as-sa/98-312-x/98-312-x2011003_4-eng.pdf.

———. (2012b). *The Canadian population in 2011: Age and sex.* Ottawa: Minister of Industry. Retrieved from www12.statcan.gc.ca/census-recensement/2011/as-sa/98-311-x/98-311-x2011001-eng.pdf.

———. (2013a). *Aboriginal peoples in Canada: First Nations people, Métis and Inuit, national household survey, 2011.* Ottawa: Ministry of Industry. Retrieved from www12.statcan.gc.ca/nhs-enm/2011/as-sa/99-011-x/99-011-x2011001-eng.pdf.

———. (2013b). *Canadian survey on disability, 2012.* Retrieved from www.statcan.gc.ca/daily-quotidien/131203/dq131203a-eng.pdf.

———. (2013c). *Disability in Canada: Initial findings from the Canadian survey on disability.* Retrieved from www.statcan.gc.ca/daily-quotidien/131203/dq131203a-eng.pdf.

———. (2013d). Generation status: Canadian-born children of immigrants. *National Household Survey (NHS), 2011.* Ottawa: Ministry of Industry.

———. (2013e). HRSDC (2014). *Financial security: Low income incidence.* Employment and Social Development Canada. Retrieved from www4.hrsdc.gc.ca/.3ndic.1t.4r@-eng.jsp?iid=23.

———. (2013f). Immigration and ethnocultural diversity in Canada. *National Household Survey, 2011.* Ottawa: Ministry of Industry. Retrieved from www.statscan.gc.ca.

———. (2013g). Women in Canada: A gender-based Statistical Profile. Retrieved from www.statcan.gc.ca/pub/89-503-x/2010001/article/11543-eng.htm#a29.

———. (2014a). CANSIM, Table 102-0551. Deaths and mortality rate, by selected grouped causes, age group and sex, Canada annual from 2007 to 2011. Retrieved from www.statcan.gc.ca/tables-tableaux/sum-som/l01/cst01/hlth66b-eng.htm.

———. (2014b). *The Daily* at www.statcan.gc.ca/daily-quotidien/140225/dq140225b-eng.htm.

————. (2014c). Study: The long-term labour market premiums associated with a postsecondary education, 1991 to 2010. *The Daily*, February 27. Retrieved from www.statcan.gc.ca/daily-quotidien/140227/dq140227c-eng.htm.

————. (2014d). *.Survey of financial security, 2012,* Table 3. Distribution and median net worth by quintile. Retrieved from www.statcan.gc.ca/daily-quotidien/140225/t140225b003-eng.htm.

————. (2014e). *The ten leading causes of death, 2011.* Retrieved from statcan.gc.ca/pub/82-625-x/2014001/article/11896-eng.htm.

Steele, L., Ross, L., Dobinson, C., Veldhuizen, S., & Tinmouth,, J. (2009). Women's sexual orientation and health: Results for a Canadian population-based survey. *Women & Health, 49*(5), 353–67.

Stein, L. (1967). The doctor/nurse game. *Archives of General Psychiatry, 16*, 699–703.

Steingraber, S. (1998). *Living downstream: A scientist's personal investigation of cancer and the environment.* New York, NY: Vintage Books.

————. (2010). *Living downstream: An ecologist's personal investigation of cancer and the environment* (2nd ed.). Philadelphia, PA: Da Capo Press.

Stienstra, D. (2002). *Disability and race/ethnicity/heritage languages/religion.* Winnipeg: Canadian Centre on Disability Studies.

Stolberg, H.O. (2004, September). Canadian health care system: Past, present, and future. *Journal of the American College of Radiology, 1*(9).

Stone, S. (2008). Resisting an illness label: Disability, impairment, and illness. In P. Moss & Teghtsoonian (Eds.), *Contesting illness: Processes and practices* (pp. 201–17). Toronto: University of Toronto Press.

Storch, J., Rodney, P., & Starzomski, R. (2013). *Toward a new horizon: Nursing ethics for leadership and practice* (2nd ed.). Toronto: Pearson Canada.

Strasser, R.D. (1992). The gatekeeper role of general practice. *Medical Journal of Australia, 156*, 108–10.

Strauss, A., & Corbin, J. (1990). *Basics of qualitative research.* London, UK: Sage.

Strauss, A., & Glaser, B. (1975). *Chronic illness and the quality of life.* St. Louis, MO: Mosby.

Strauss, J. (2005, October 31). Running from the shadows of despair. Retrieved from www.theglobeandmail.com/news/national/running-from-the-shadows-of-despair/article1109028/?page=all.

Strong, P.M. (1979). Sociological imperialism and the profession of medicine: A critical examination of the thesis of medical imperialism. *Social Science & Medicine, 13A*(2), 199–215.

Subedi, R.P., & Rosenberg, M.W. (2014). Determinants of the variations in self-reported health status among recent and more established immigrants in Canada. *Social Science & Medicine, 115*, 103–10.

Sugaring the Pill. (1996, January 27). *New Scientist*, 27–9.

Suicide in Canada: Facts and Figures. (2013, September 10). Retrieved from http://www.med.uottawa.ca/sim/data/Suicide_e.htm.

Sulik, G. (2011). "Our diagnoses, our selves": The rise of the technoscientific illness identity. *Sociology Compass*, 5/6, 463–477.

Supreme Court of Canada. (2015). Carter v. Canada (Attorney General), 2015 SCC 5. Retrieved from https://scc-csc.lexum.com/scc-csc/scc-csc/en/item/14637/index.do.

Sutherns, R. (2009, Spring). Human resources and the environment of birth in Canada. *Women and Environments, 80/81*, 19–21.

Sutton, J.R. (1991). The political economy of madness: The expansion of the asylum in progressive America. *American Sociological Review, 56*, 665–78.

Suzack, C., Huhndorf, S., Perreault, J., & Barman, J. (Eds.). (2010). *Indigenous Women and Feminism: Politics, Activism, Culture.* Vancouver: UBC Press.

Svensson, R. (1996). The interplay between doctors and nurses: A negotiated order perspective. *Sociology of Health and Illness, 18*(3), 379–98.

Swan, S.H., Main, K.M., Fan, L., Stewart, S.L., Kruse, R.L., Calafat, A.M.,...Teague, J.L. (2005). Decrease in anogenital distance among male infants with prenatal phthalate exposure. *Environmental Health Perspectives, 113*(8), 1056–61.

Swoboda, D. (2008). Listening to the body: Women with chronic fatigue syndrome, fibromyalgia, and multiple chemical sensitivities talk about illness and the body. In D. Driedger & M. Owen (Eds.), *Dissonant disabilities: Women with chronic illnesses explore their lives* (pp. 87–97). Toronto: Canadian Scholars' Press/Women's Press.

Sydie, R.A. (1987). *Natural women, cultured men: A feminist perspective on sociological theory.* Toronto, ON: Methuen Publications.

Szasz, T.S. (1960). The myth of mental illness. *The American Psychologist, 15*, 113–18.

————. (1961). *The myth of mental illness: Foundation of a theory of personal conduct.* New York, NY: Holber-Harper.

————. (1973). *Ideology and insanity: Essays on the psychiatric dehumanization of man.* London, UK: Colder & Boyars.

————. (2007). *The medicalization of everyday life.* Syracuse, NY: Syracuse University Press.

Szreter, S. (1988). The importance of social intervention in Britain's mortality decline c. 1850–1914: A re-interpretation of the role of public health. *Society for the Social History of Medicine, 1*(1), 1–37.

Talking points re: media reports. Dr. Holbrook and AstraZeneca. (2002). Retrieved March 1, 2003 from www.canadapharma.org/Media_Centre/Backgrounders/Holbrook99_e.html.

Tang, S., & Browne, A. (2008, April). "Race" matters: Racialization and egalitarian discourses involving Aboriginal people in the Canadian health care context. *Ethnicity & Health, 13*(2), 108–27.

Tarasuk, V. (2009). Health implications of food insecurity. In D. Raphael (Ed.), *Social Determinants of Health Canadian Perspectives* (2nd ed.). Toronto: Canadian Scholars' Press, Inc.

Tarasuk, V., Mitchell, A., & Dachner, N. (2013). *Household food insecurity in Canada 2012.* Retrieved from www.feednovascotia.ca/images/Household_Food_Insecurity_in_Canada.pdf.

Targeting doctors. Graph: top 50 drugs by promotion dollars. (2002). *CBC-TV Disclosure.*

Taube, G. (2009). An interview with Ana Soto. *Science Watch.com*: Tracking trends & performance in basic research. Retrieved from http://sciencewatch.com/ana/st/bis/09sepBisSoto/.

Taylor, E., Jantzen, A., & Clow, B. (2012). *Rethinking LGBTQ health.* Atlantic Centre of Excellence for Women's Health. Halifax, NS. Retrieved from www.dal.ca/content/dam/dalhousie/pdf/ace-women-health/3/ACEWH_rethinking_LGBTQ_health.pdf.

Taylor, K.M. (1991). The impact of the pharmaceutical industry's clinical research programs on medical education, practice and researchers in Canada: A discussion paper. *Canadian pharmaceutical research and development: Four short-term studies.* Ottawa, ON: Industry, Science & Technology Canada.

Teelucksingh, C. (2007). Environmental racialization: Linking racialization to the environment in Canada. *Local Environment, 12*(6), 645–61.

Templeman, K., & Robinson, A. (2011). Integrative medicine models in contemporary primary health care. *Complementary Therapies in Medicine, 19,* 84–92.

The battle over a drug ad. (2001). CBC-TV. *Undercurrents.*

The Doctors versus the Nurses. (1962, June 15). *Nursing Times,* 783–4.

The Henry J. Kaiser Family Foundation. (2009). Profitability of pharmaceutical manufacturers, 1995–2009.

The New York Times. (2009, March 3). *Harvard medical school in ethics quandary.* Retrieved from www.nytimes.com/2009/03/03/business/03medschool.html.

The Perfect Potato. (2002, October 25). CTV. *W5.* Retrieved from http://healthcoalition.ca/archive/W5.pdf.

The Source: Women's Health Data Directory. (2009). Maternal mortality. Retrieved from www.womenshealthdata.ca/category -aspx'catid.

Theorell T., Ahlberg-Hulten, G., Jodko, M., Sigala, F., & de la Torre, B. (1993). Influence of job strain and emotion on blood pressure in female hospital personnel during work hours. *Scandinavian Journal of Work, Environment and Health, 19,* 313–18.

Therapeutic Products Directorate. (2004). *Business transformation progress report.* Ottawa, ON: Health Canada.

Tholl, B., & Bujold, G. (2012). *Functional federalism and the future of Medicare in Canada: A report to the health action lobby (HEAL).* Retrieved from www.healthactionlobby.ca/images/stories/publications/2012/ThollBujoldFinalReportJanuary2012.pdf.

Thomson, P., Jones, J., Browne, M., & Leslie, S.J. (2014). Why people seek complementary and alternative medicine before conventional medical treatment: A population based study. *Complementary Therapies in Clinical Practice, 20,* 339–46.

Thorpe, K., & Chénier, L. (2011). *Building mentally healthy workplaces: Perspectives of Canadian workers and front-line managers.* Ottawa: The Conference Board of Canada. Retrieved from www.e-library.ca.

Titchkosky, T., & Michalko, R. (2012). The body as the problem of individuality: A phenomenological disability studies approach. In D. Goodley, B. Hughes, & L. Davis (Eds.), *Disability and social theory: New development and directions* (pp. 127–42). London, England: Palgrave Macmillan.

Titchkosky, T., & Michalko, R. (Eds.). (2009). *Rethinking normalcy.* Toronto: Canadian Scholars' Press, Inc.

Tjepkema, M. (2002). The health of the off-reserve Aboriginal population. Supplement to *Health Reports,* 13. Ottawa, ON: Statistics Canada.

———. (2008). Heath care use among gay, lesbian and bisexual Canadians. *Health Reports.* Statistics Canada, *19*(1), March. Retrieved from www.glhv.org.au/files/canada_glb_health_use_0.pdf.

Tjepkema, M., Wilkins, R., & Long, A. (2013). Socio-economic inequalities in cause-specific mortality: A 16-year follow-up study. *Canadian Journal of Public Health, 104*(7), November/December, e472–78.

Tomczak, J. (n.d.). A short history of hospice and palliative care. Retrieved from www.myseniorsite.ca/eldercare-tomczak27.htm.

Tommy Douglas Research Institute. (n.d.). Tommy's life story. Retrieved from www.tommydouglas.ca/?page_id=21.

Tompa, E., Polanyi, K., & Foley, J. (2009). Labour market flexibility and worker insecurity. In D. Raphael (Ed.), *Social determinants of health: Canadian perspectives* (2nd ed.) (pp. 88–98). Toronto: Canadian Scholars' Press Inc.

Toronto Star. (2009, October 5). Canada 4th in UN ranking. Retrieved from www.thestar.com/news/world/article/705518--canada-4th -in-un-ranking.

Torrance, G. (1998). Socio-historical overview: The development of the Canadian health system. In D. Coburn, C. D'Arcy, & G. Torrance (Eds.), *Health and Canadian society* (3rd ed.). Toronto, ON: University of Toronto Press.

Torrance, G., & Kaufert, J. (1983). Medical dominance in Canada in historical perspective: The rise and fall of medicine. *International Journal of Health Services.*

Toupin April, K., & Gaboury, I. (2013). A survey of Canadian regulated complementary and alternative medicine schools about research, evidence-based health care and interprofessional training, as well as continuing education. *BMC Complementary and Alternative Medicine, 13*(374), 1–7. Retrieved from www.biomedcentral.com/1472-6882/13/374.

Towards increasing research and development in Canada: a new innovative pharmaceutical strategy. (2004). Ottawa: Rx&D.

Townsend, P., Davidson, N., & Whitehead, M. (Eds.). (1992). *Inequalities in health: The Black report and the health divide.* London, UK: Penguin.

Townsend, P., Davidson, N., & Whitehead, M. (2009). *Women's poverty and the recession.* Ottawa, ON: Canadian Centre for Policy Alternatives.

Trautmann, N.M., Porter, K.S., & Wagenet, R.J. (n.d). Modern agriculture: Its effects on the environment. Pesticide Safety Education Program, Cornell University Cooperative Extension. Retrieved from http://pmep.cals.cornell.edu/facts-slides-self/facts/mod-ag-grw85.aspx.

Travers, A. (2009). The health and well-being of sexual and gender minority women: Still struggling with silence and invisibility. In P. Armstrong & J. Deadman (Eds.), *Women's health. Intersections of policy, research and practice* (pp. 151–63). Toronto, ON: Women's Press.

Travers, A. (2015). The health of sexual and gender minority women. In P. Armstrong & A. Pederson (Eds.), *Ontario Perspectives and Invisibility.*

Travers, K. (1996). The social organization of nutritional inequities. *Social Sciences and Medicine, 43,* 543–53.

Tremblay, M., Shields, M., Laviolette, M., Craig, C., Janssen, I., & Gorber, S. (2010, March 1). Fitness of Canadian children and youth: Results from the 2007–2009. Canadian health measures survey. *Health Reports, 21,* 7–20.

Truth and Reconciliation Commission (TRC). (2015). *Honouring the truth, reconciling for the future: Summary of the final report of the truth and reconciliation commission of Canada.* Retrieved from www.trc.ca/websites/trcinstitution/File/2015/Findings/Exec_Summary_2015_05_31_web_o.pdf.

Tulandi, T., Martin, J., Al-Fadhi, R., Kabli, N., Forman, R., Hitkari, J., ... Casper, R.F. (2006). Congenital malformation among 911 newborns conceived after infertility treatment with letrozole or clamiphene citrate. *Fertility and Sterility 85*(6), 1761–5.

Turcotte, M., & Schellenberg. (2007). A portrait of seniors 2006. Ottawa, ON: Statistics Canada. Retrieved from www.statcan.gc.ca/pub/89-519-x/89-519-x2006001-eng.pdf.

Turner, B.S. (1986a). *Citizenship and capitalism: The debate over reformism.* London, UK: Allen & Unwin.

——. (1986b). The vocabulary of complaints: Nursing professionalism and job context. *Australian and New Zealand Journal of Sociology, 22*(3), 368–86.

——. (1987). *Medical power and social knowledge.* London, UK: Sage.

——. (1992). *Regulating bodies: Essays in medical sociology.* London, UK: Routledge.

——. (2004). *The new medical sociology.* New York, NY: W.W. Norton.

Turner, B.S., & Samson, C. (1995). *Medical power and social knowledge* (2nd ed.). London, UK: Sage.

Turner, J., & Grieco, M. (2000). Gender and time poverty: The neglected social policy implications of gendered time, transport and travel. *Time and Society 9*(1), 129–36.

United States Senate, J.E.C. (2000). The benefits of medical research and the role of the NIH. Washington, DC: Author.

United Nations Environmental Program. (2014, September 10). Retrieved from www.unep.org/newscentre/default.aspx?DocumentID=2796&ArticleID=10978.

Unruh, A.M., Ritchie, J., & Merskey, H. (1999). Does gender affect appraisal of pain and pain coping strategies. *The Clinical Journal of Pain, 15*(1), 31–40.

Urmetzer, P., & Guppy, N. (2009). Changing income inequality in Canada. In E. Grabb & N. Guppy (Eds.), *Social inequality in Canada: Patterns, problems and policies* (5th ed.) (pp. 82–91). Toronto, ON: Pearson Prentice Hall.

Usdin, S. (2007). *The no-nonsense guide to world health.* Toronto, ON: Between the Lines.

UToday. (2011, October 4). *More male nursing students.* Retrieved from www.ucalgary.ca/news/utoday/october4-2011/nursing.

Vachon, D. (2005, May & June). Doctor John Snow blames water pollution for cholera epidemic. *Old News 16*(8), 8–10. Retrieved from www.ph.ucla.edu/epi/snow/fatherofepidemiology.html.

Valverde, M., & White-Mair, K. (1999). "One day at a time" and other slogans for everyday life: The ethical practices of Alcoholics Anonymous. *Sociology, 33*, 393–410.

Varcoe, C. (2009). Inequality, violence, and women's health. In S. Bolaria & H. Dickinson (Eds.), *Health, illness, and health care in Canada* (4th ed.) (pp. 259–82). Toronto, ON: Nelson Educational Ltd.

Varcoe, C., Doane, G., Pauly, B., Rodney, P., Storch, J.L.,Mahoney, K., et al. (2004). Ethical practice in nursing: Working the in-betweens. *Journal of Advanced Nursing, 45*(3), 316–25.

Vares. T., & Braun, V. (2006). Spreading the word, but what word is that? Viagra and male sexuality in popular culture. *Sexualities, 9*(3), 315–32.

Veenstra, G. (2009a). Racialized identity and health in Canada: Results from a nationally representative survey. *Social Science & Medicine, 69*, 538–42.

——. (2009b). Social inequality and health. In E. Grabb & N. Guppy (Eds.), *Social inequality in Canada: Patterns, problems, and policies* (5th ed.) (pp. 353–66). Toronto, ON: Pearson Prentice Hall.

——. (2011). Race, gender, class, and sexual orientation: Intersecting axes of inequality and self-rated health in Canada. *International Journal for Equity in Health, 10*(3).

Verhoef, M., Boon, H., & Mutasingwa, D. (2006). The scope of naturopathic medicine in Canada: An emerging profession. *Social Science & Medicine, 63*, 409–17.

Video: Dr. Donald Low. Retrieved from www.youtube.com/watch?v=q3jgSkxV1rw.

Vijoen, M., Panzer, A., Roos, J.L., & Bodemer, W. (2003). Psychoneuroimmunology: From philosophy, intuition and folklore to a recognized science. *South African Journal of Science, 99*(7–8), 332–6.

Waitzkin, H. (1983). *The second sickness: Contradictions of capitalist health care.* New York, NY: Free Press.

——. (2000). *The second sickness: Contradictions of capitalist health care* (2nd ed.). Lanham, MD: Rowman & Littlefield.

Walby, S. (1990). *Theorising patriarchy.* Oxford, UK: Blackwell.

——. (1992). Post-post-modernism? Theorizing social complexity. In M. Barrett & A. Phillips (Eds.), *Destabilizing theory: Contemporary feminist debates* (pp. 31–52). Cambridge, UK: Polity Press.

Waldfogel, J. (2002). Child care, women's employment and child outcomes. *Journal of Population Economics, 15*, 527–48.

Waldram, J., Herring, D.A., & Young, T.K. (1995). *Aboriginal health in Canada. Historical, cultural and epidemiological perspectives.* Toronto: University of Toronto Press.

Walji, R., Weeks, L., Cooley, K., & Seely, D. (2010). Naturopathic medicine and Aboriginal health: An exploratory study at Anishnawbe health Toronto. *Canadian Journal of Public Health, 101*(6), 475–80.

Walker, A. (1990). The economic "burden" of ageing and the prospect of intergenerational conflict. *Ageing and Society, 10*, 377–96.

Walker, D., & Myrick, F. (2006). Grounded theory: An exploration of process and procedure. *Qualitative Health Research, 16*(4), 547–559.

Wall, S. (2006). An autoethnography on learning autoethnography. *International Journal of Qualitative Methods, 5*(2), June, 1–12.

Walters, V. (1992). Women's views of their main health problem. *Canadian Journal of Public Health, 83*(5), 371–4.

——. (1994). Women's perceptions regarding health and illness. In S. Bolaria & H. Dickinson (Eds.), *Health, illness and health care in Canada.* Scarborough, ON: Nelson Thomson Learning.

Ware, N. (1992). Suffering and the social construction of illness: The delegitimation of illness experience in chronic fatigue syndrome. *Medical Anthropology Quarterly, 6*(4), 347–61.

Wargo, J. (1996). *Our children's toxic legacy: How science and law fail to protect us from pesticides.* New Haven, CT: Yale University Press.

Wathen, C.N., & Harris, R.M. (2006, July 4). An examination of the health information seeking experiences of women in rural Ontario, Canada. *Information Research, 11.* Retrieved from http://informationr.net/ir/11-4/paper267.html.

Waxler-Morrison, N., Hislop, T.G., Mears, B., & Kan, L. (1991). Effects of social relationships on survival for women with breast cancer: A prospective study. *Social Science & Medicine, 33*(2), 177–83.

Weber, M. (1968/1921). *Economy and society.* New York, NY: Bedminster.

Weedon, C. (1997). *Feminist practice and poststructuralist theory* (2nd ed.). Cambridge, MA: Blackwell.

Weinberg, D.B. (2006). When little things are big things: The importance of relationships for nurses' professional practice. In S. Nelson

& S. Gordon (Eds.), *Complexities of care: Nursing reconsidered* (pp. 30–43). New York: Cornell University Press.

Weiss, G., & Lonnquist, L. (2006). *The sociology of health, healing, and illness* (5th ed.). New Jersey: Pearson Education Inc.

——— & ———. (2009). *The sociology of health, healing, and illness* (6th ed.). New Jersey: Pearson Education Inc.

Wendell, S. (1989). Toward a feminist theory of disability. *Hypatia, 4*(2), 104–24.

———. (1996). *The rejected body: Feminist philosophical reflections on disability.* New York, NY: Routledge.

———. (2001). Unhealthy disabled: Treating chronic illnesses as disability. *Hypatia, 16*(4), 17–33.

———. (2010). Toward a feminist theory of disability. In L. Davis (Ed.), *The disability studies reader* (3rd ed.) (pp. 336–52). New York: Routledge.

Westra, L., & Lawson, B.E. (Eds.). (2001). *Faces of environmental racism: Confronting issues of global justice.* Lanham, MD: Rowman & Littlefield Publishers.

What are Oil Sands? Canadian Association of Petroleum Product. Retrieved December 22, 2015, www.capp.ca/canadian-oil-and -natural-gas/oil-sands/what-are-oil-sands.

What is homeopathy? (2009). Ontario College of Homeopathic Medicine. Retrieved from www.ochm.ca/what-is-homeopathy.html.

White, K. (2000). The state, the market, and general practice: The Australian case. *International Journal of Health Services, 30*(2), 285–308.

———. (Ed.). (2001). *The early sociology of health and illness,* 6 vols. London, UK: Routledge.

Whitehead, M. (1998). Diffusion of ideas on social inequalities in health: A European perspective. *Milbank Quarterly, 76*, 469–92.

Whitley, R., Kirmayer, L.J., & Groleau, D. (2006). Understanding immigrants' reluctance to use mental health services: A qualitative study from Montreal. *Canadian Journal of Psychiatry, 51*(4).

Whittington, L. (2013). Conservatives dismantling social programs built over generations. Thestar.com. Retrieved from www.thestar.com/news/canada/2013/12/09/conservatives_dismantling_social_programs_built_over_generations.html.

Whittington, L. (2014, June 2). Energy wars: First Nations group says process to expand oilsands "like an environmental horror story." Retrieved from www.thestar.com/news/canada/2014/06/02/energy_wars_first_nations_group_says_process_to_expand_oilsands_like_an_environmental_horror_story.html.

WHO. (n.d.). Definition of health. Retrieved from https://apps.who.int/aboutwho/en/definition.html.

———. (1946). Constitution of the World Health Organization. WHO, Geneva.

———. (1978, September 6–12). Alma-Ata declaration. Declaration of Alma-Ata International Conference on Primary Health Care. Alma-Ata, USSR. Retrieved from www.who.int/hpr/NPH/docs/declaration_almaata.pdf.

———. (2004). *Suicide rates.* Retrieved from www.who.int/mental_health/media/cana.pdf.

———. (2008). *Closing the gap in a generation. Health equity through action on the social determinants of health.* Commission on the Social Determinants of Health. Retrieved from www.who.int/social_determinants/final_report/csdh_finalreport_2008.pdf.

———. (2011). *All for Equity. World Conference on Social Determinants of Health.* Meeting Report. Rio De Janeiro. Brazil. October. Retrieved from www.who.int/sdhconference/resources/wcsdh_report/en/.

———. (2014). *Noncommunicable diseases country profiles 2014.* Retrieved from www.who.int/nmh/countries/can_en.pdf?ua=1.

Wicks, D. (1995a). Contested femininity: Gender and work at the Sydney infirmary 1868–1875. *Journal of Interdisciplinary Gender Studies, 1*, 89–99.

———. (1995b). Nurses and doctors and discourses of healing. *Australian and New Zealand Journal of Sociology, 31*(2), 122–39.

———. (1999). *Nurses and doctors at work: Rethinking professional boundaries.* Sydney: Allen & Unwin.

Wienke, C. (2005). Male sexuality, medicalization, and the marketing of Cialis and Levitra. *Sexuality & Culture, 9*(4), 29–57.

Wiktorowicz, M.E., Lexchin, J., Moscou, K., Silversides, A., & Eggertson, L. (2010). *Keeping an eye on prescripiton drugs . . . Keeping Canadians safe: active monitoring systems for drug safety and effectiveness in Canada and internationally.* Toronto: Health Council of Canada.

Wilkins, R.J., Berthelot, J-M., & Ng, E. (2002). Trends in mortality by neighbourhood income in urban Canada from 1971–1996. *Health Reports, 13*, (supplement), 1–28. Ottawa, ON: Statistics Canada.

Wilkins, R.J., Tjepkema, M., Mustard, C., & Choini're, R. (2008, September). The Canadian census mortality follow-up study, 1991 through 2001. *Health Reports, 19*, 3. Ottawa, ON: Statistics Canada.

Wilkins, R.J., Uppal, S., Fines, P., Senecal, S., Guimond, E., & Dion, R. (2008, March). Life expectancy in the Inuit-inhabited areas of Canada, 1989 to 2003. *Health Reports, 19*(1). Ottawa, ON: Statistics Canada.

Wilkinson, R. (1996). *Unhealthy societies: The afflictions of inequality.* London, UK: Routledge.

Wilkinson, R., & Pickett, K. (2009). *The spirit level: Why more equal societies almost always do better.* London, UK: Allen Lane.

——— & ———. (2010). *The spirit level: Why equality is better for everyone.* London: Penguin Books.

Williams, A.P., Deber, R., Baranek, P., & Gildiner, A. (2001). From Medicare to home care: Globalization, state retrenchment, and the profitization of Canada's health-care system. In P. Armstrong, H. Armstrong, & D. Coburn (Eds.), *Unhealthy times: Political economy perspectives on health and care in Canada* (pp. 7–30). Toronto, ON: Oxford University Press.

Williams, A.P., Domnick-Pierre, K., Vayda, E., Stevenson, H.M., & Burke, M. (1990). Women in medicine: Practice patterns and attitudes. *Canadian Medical Association Journal, 143*(3), 194–201.

Williams, G. (2000). The genesis of chronic illness: Narrative reconstruction. In P. Brown, *Perspectives in medical sociology* (3rd ed.). Illinois: Waveland Press Inc.

Williams, G. (2004). The genesis of chronic illness. In M. Bury & J. Gabe (Eds.), *The sociology of health and illness* (pp. 247–55). London, UK: Routledge Press.

Williams, L., & Germov, J. (2004). The thin ideal: Women, food and dieting. In J. Germov & L. Williams (Eds.), *A sociology of food and nutrition: The social appetite* (2nd ed.). Melbourne: Oxford University Press.

Williams, S., Martin, P., & Gabe, J. (2011). The pharmaceuticalisation of society? A framework for analysis. *Sociology of Health & Illness, 33*(5), 710–25.

Williams-Piehota, P., Sirois, F., Bann, C., Isenberg, K., & Walsh, E. (2011). Agents of change: How do complementary and alternative medicine providers play a role in health behavior change?. *Alternative Therapies in Health and Medicine, 17*(1), 22–30.

Willis, E. (1983). *Medical dominance*. Sydney: Allen & Unwin.

———. (1989a). Complementary healers. In G.M. Lupton & J. Najman (Eds.), *Sociology of health and illness: Australian readings* (pp. 259–79). Melbourne: Macmillan.

———. (1989b). *Medical dominance* (Rev. ed.). Sydney: Allen & Unwin.

———. (2004). *The sociological quest* (4th ed.). Sydney: Allen & Unwin.

Willman, D. (2000, June 4). The rise and fall of the killer drug Rezulin. *Los Angeles Times*.

Wilson, D., & Macdonald, D. (2010). *The income gap between Aboriginal peoples and the rest of Canada*. Ottawa: Canadian Centre for Policy Alternatives.

Wingrove, J. (2014, January 22). Refugee claims hit "histsoric low" as Ottawa's policy faces fresh criticism. Retrieved from www .theglobeandmail.com/news/politics/refugee-claims-hit-historic-low-as-ottawas-policy-faces-fresh-criticism/article16461486/.

Winter, I. (Ed.). (2000a). Social capital and public policy in Australia. Melbourne: Australian Institute of Family Studies.

———. (2000b). Major themes and debates in the social capital literature: The Australian connection. In I. Winter (Ed.), *Social capital and public policy in Australia* (pp. 7–42). Melbourne: Australian Institute of Family Studies.

Witz, A. (1992). *Professions and patriarchy*. London, UK: Routledge.

Witzig, R. (1996). The medicalization of race: Scientific legitimizatiion of a flawed social construct. *Annals of Internal Medicine, 125*(8), 675–9.

Wolf, N. (1991). *The beauty myth*. Toronto, ON: Vintage Books.

Wolpe, P.R. (1985). The maintenance of professional authority: Acupuncture and the American physician. *Social Problems, 32*(5), 409–24.

Women and Health Care Reform. (2008). Women and private health insurance. Retrieved from www.womenandhealthcarereform.ca/en/publications.html#insurance.

Women's Health in Women's Hands Community Health Centre. (2003). Racial discrimination as a health risk for female youth: Implications for policy and healthcare delivery in Canada. Toronto, ON: The Canadian Race Relations Foundation.

Wordsworth, A., & Armstrong, L. (2009, Spring). Risks of exposure to environmental contaminants during pregnancy. *Women and Environments, 80/81*, 26–8.

World Bank. (n.d.). *Health*. Retrieved from http://data.worldbank.org/topic/health.

———. (2004). *World development report 2004: Making services work for poor people*. New York, NY: World Bank and Oxford University Press.

———. (2013). Lifetime risk of maternal death (1 in: rates varies by country). Retrieved from http://data.worldbank.org/indicator/SH.MMR.RISK.

———. (2014). *World health statistics*. Retrieved from http://apps.who.int/iris/bitstream/10665/112738/1/9789240692671_eng.pdf.

World Nuclear Association. (2009). Retrieved from www.world-nuclear.org/info/inf32.html.

Wotherspoon, T. (2009). Transformation in Canadian nursing and nurse education. In S. Bolaria & H. Dickinson (Eds.), *Health, illness and health care in Canada* (4th ed.) (pp. 99–121). Toronto, ON: Nelson Education Ltd.

Wright, E.O. (1997). *Class counts: Comparative studies in class analysis*. Cambridge, UK: Cambridge University Press.

Wright, K. (2011). *The rise of the therapeutic society: Psychological knowledge and the contradictions of cultural change*. Washington, D.C.: New Academic Publishing.

Wuest, J., Hodgins, M.J., Malcolm, J., Merritt-Gray, M., & Seaman, P. (2007). The effects of past relationship and obligation on health and health promotion in women caregivers of adult family members. *Advances in Nursing Science, 30*(3), 206–20.

Yakabuski, K. (2014, July 13). Does doc's religion trump your prescription? *The Globe and Mail*, p. A 9.

Yalnizyan, A. (2005). *Getting better health care: Lessons from (and for) Canada*. Ottawa, ON: Canadian Centre for Policy Alternatives.

———. (2007). *The rich and the rest of us*. Ottawa: ON, Canadian Centre for Policy Alternatives, March.

———. (2010). *The rise of Canada's richest 1%*. Ottawa: Canada Centre for Policy Alternatives. Retrieved from www.growinggap.ca.

Yassi, A., & Hancock, T. (2005, October). Patient safety-worker safety: Building a culture of safety to improve healthcare worker and patient well-being. *Healthcare Quarterly, 8* (Special Issue), 32–8.

York University Centre for Health Studies. (1999). *Complementary and alternative health practices and therapies: A Canadian overview*. Toronto, ON: Prepared for Health Promotion and Programs Branch, Health Canada.

Zamora, Miguel. (2013, July 17). Farmworkers left behind: The human cost of coffee production. *Roast Magazine*. Retrieved from http://dailycoffeenews.com/2013/07/17/farmworkers-left-behind-the-human-cost-of-coffee-production/.

Zazzera, L.D. (2007, Winter). Marginalization and its connection to stroke in women. *OWHN e-Bulletin*. Retrieved from www.owhn.on.ca/ebulletin,spring2007 .htm#a.

Zborowski, M. (1952). Cultural components in responses to pain. *Journal of Social Issues, 8*(4), 16–30.

Zhao, J., Xue, L., & Gilkinson, T. (2010). *Research and evaluation health status and social capital of recent immigrants in canada evidence from the longitudinal survey of immigrants to Canada*. Retrieved from http://www.cic.gc.ca/english/pdf/research-stats/immigrant-survey.pdf.

Znaimer, M. (2010). Who's zooming who? CARP Health. Retrieved from http://imakesnews.com/ca/carppromotions/e.

Zola, I.K. (1972). Medicine as an institution of social control. *Sociological Review, 20*, 407–584.

———. (2000). Pathways to the doctor: From person to patient. In P. Brown (Ed.), *Perspectives in medical sociology* (3rd ed.) (pp. 198–214). Illinois: Waveland Press.

Zusevics, K.L. (2013). Public health genomics: A new space for a dialogue on racism through Community Based Participatory Research. *Public Health, 127*, 981–3.

Index